INSTRUCTOR'S SOLUTIONS MANUAL

BOB DAVIS
Taylor University

J. ERIK HENDRICKSON
University of Wisconsin - Eau Claire

Volume 1

Sixth Edition

PHYSICS

Principles with Applications

GIANCOLI

PEARSON

Prentice
Hall

Upper Saddle River, NJ 07458

Associate Editor: Christian Botting
Senior Editor: Erik Fahlgren
Editor-in-Chief, Science: John Challice
Vice President of Production & Manufacturing: David W. Riccardi
Executive Managing Editor: Kathleen Schiaparelli
Assistant Managing Editor: Becca Richter
Production Editor: Dana Dunn
Supplement Cover Manager: Paul Gourhan
Supplement Cover Designer: Joanne Alexandris
Manufacturing Buyer: Ilene Kahn
Editorial Assistant: Andrew Sobel
Marketing Assistant: Larry Grodsky

© 2005 Pearson Education, Inc.
Pearson Prentice Hall
Pearson Education, Inc.
Upper Saddle River, NJ 07458

Printed in the United States of America

10 9 8 7 6 5 4 3 2 1

ISBN 0-13-035237-3

Vol II
013/A1545X

Pearson Education Ltd., *London*
Pearson Education Australia Pty. Ltd., *Sydney*
Pearson Education Singapore, Pte. Ltd.
Pearson Education North Asia Ltd., *Hong Kong*
Pearson Education Canada, Inc., *Toronto*
Pearson Educación de Mexico, S.A. de C.V.
Pearson Education—Japan, *Tokyo*
Pearson Education Malaysia, Pte. Ltd.

PREFACE

This *Instructor's Solutions Manual* provides answers and worked-out solutions to all end of chapter questions and problems from chapters 1 – 15 of *Physics: Principles with Applications, 6th Edition*, by Douglas C. Giancoli. At the end of the manual are grids that correlate the 5th edition questions and problems to the 6th edition questions and problems.

We formulated the solutions so that they are, in most cases, useful both for the student and the instructor. Accordingly, some solutions may seem to have more algebra than necessary for the instructor. Other solutions may seem to take bigger steps than a student would normally take: e.g. simply quoting the solutions from a quadratic equation instead of explicitly solving for them. There has been an emphasis on algebraic solutions, with the substitution of values given as a very last step in most cases. We feel that this helps to keep the physics of the problem foremost in the solution, rather than the numeric evaluation.

Much effort has been put into having clear problem statements, reasonable values, pedagogically sound solutions, and accurate answers/solutions for all of the questions and problems. Working with us was a team of three additional solvers – David Curott (University of North Alabama), Bryan Long (Columbia State Community College), and Rich Louie (Pacific Lutheran University). Between the five solvers we had either 3 or 4 complete solutions for every question and problem. From those solutions we uncovered questions about the wording of the problems, style of the possible solutions, reasonableness of the values and framework of the questions and problems, and then consulted with one another and Doug Giancoli until we reached what we feel is both a good statement and a good solution for each question and problem from the text.

Many people have been involved in the production of this manual. We especially thank Doug Giancoli for his helpful conversations. Christian Botting and Karen Karlin at Prentice Hall have been helpful, encouraging, and patient as we have turned our thoughts into a manual. And the solutions from David Curott, Bryan Long, and Rich Louie were often thought-provoking and always appreciated. We also acknowledge the benefit of having solutions from the previous edition, prepared by Irv Miller.

Even with all the assistance we have had, the final responsibility for the content of this manual is ours. We would appreciate being notified via e-mail of any errors that are discovered. We hope that you will find this presentation of answers and solutions useful.

Bob Davis (rbdavis@taylor.edu)
Upland, IN

J. Erik Hendrickson (hendrije@uwec.edu)
Eau Claire, WI

CONTENTS

CHAPTER 1: Introduction, Measurement, Estimating

Answers to Questions

1. (a) Fundamental standards should be accessible, invariable, indestructible, and reproducible. A particular person's foot would not be very accessible, since the person could not be at more than one place at a time. The standard would be somewhat invariable if the person were an adult, but even then, due to swelling or injury, the length of the standard foot could change. The standard would not be indestructible – the foot would not last forever. The standard could be reproducible – tracings or plaster casts could be made as secondary standards.

   (b) If any person's foot were to be used as a standard, "standard" would vary significantly depending on the person whose foot happened to be used most recently for a measurement. The standard would be very accessible, because wherever a measurement was needed, it would be very easy to find someone with feet. The standard would be extremely variable – perhaps by a factor of 2. That also renders the standard as not reproducible, because there could be many reproductions that were quite different from each other. The standard would be almost indestructible in that there is essentially a limitless supply of feet to be used.

2. There are various ways to alter the signs. The number of meters could be expressed in one significant figure, as "900 m (3000 ft)". Or, the number of feet could be expressed with the same precision as the number of meters, as "914 m (2999 ft)". The signs could also be moved to different locations, where the number of meters was more exact. For example, if a sign was placed where the elevation was really 1000 m to the nearest meter, then the sign could read "1000 m (3280 ft)".

3. Including more digits in an answer does not necessarily increase its accuracy. The accuracy of an answer is determined by the accuracy of the physical measurement on which the answer is based. If you draw a circle, measure its diameter to be 168 mm and its circumference to be 527 mm, their quotient, representing π, is 3.136904762. The last seven digits are meaningless – they imply a greater accuracy than is possible with the measurements.

4. The problem is that the precision of the two measurements are quite different. It would be more appropriate to give the metric distance as 11 km, so that the numbers are given to about the same precision (nearest mile or nearest km).

5. A measurement must be measured against a scale, and the units provide that scale. Units must be specified or the answer is meaningless – the answer could mean a variety of quantities, and could be interpreted in a variety of ways. Some units are understood, such as when you ask someone how old they are. You assume their answer is in years. But if you ask someone how long it will be until they are done with their task, and they answer "five", does that mean five minutes or five hours or five days? If you are in an international airport, and you ask the price of some object, what does the answer "ten" mean? Ten dollars, or ten pounds, or ten marks, or ten euros?

6. If the jar is rectangular, for example, you could count the number of marbles along each dimension, and then multiply those three numbers together for an estimate of the total number of marbles. If the jar is cylindrical, you could count the marbles in one cross section, and then multiply by the number of layers of marbles. Another approach would be to estimate the volume of one marble. If we assume that the marbles are stacked such that their centers are all on vertical and horizontal lines, then each marble would require a cube of edge 2R, or a volume of $8R^3$, where R is the radius of a marble. The number of marbles would then be the volume of the container divided by $8R^3$.

7. The result should be written as 8.32 cm. The factor of 2 used to convert radius to diameter is exact – it has no uncertainty, and so does not change the number of significant figures.

8. $\sin 30.0° = 0.500$

9. Since the size of large eggs can vary by 10%, the random large egg used in a recipe has a size with an uncertainty of about $\pm 5\%$. Thus the amount of the other ingredients can also vary by about $\pm 5\%$ and not adversely affect the recipe.

10. In estimating the number of car mechanics, the assumptions and estimates needed are:
    the population of the city
    the number of cars per person in the city
    the number of cars that a mechanic can repair in a day
    the number of days that a mechanic works in a year
    the number of times that a car is taken to a mechanic, per year
    We estimate that there is 1 car for every 2 people, that a mechanic can repair 3 cars per day, that a mechanic works 250 days a year, and that a car needs to be repaired twice per year.

    (*a*) For San Francisco, we estimate the population at one million people. The number of mechanics is found by the following calculation.

    $$\left(1\times10^6\,\text{people}\right)\left(\frac{1\,\text{car}}{2\,\text{people}}\right)\left(\frac{2\,\dfrac{\text{repairs}}{\text{year}}}{1\,\text{car}}\right)\left(\frac{1\,\text{yr}}{250\,\text{workdays}}\right)\left(\frac{1\,\text{mechanic}}{3\,\dfrac{\text{repairs}}{\text{workday}}}\right) = \boxed{1300\,\text{mechanics}}$$

    (*b*) For Upland, Indiana, the population is about 4000. The number of mechanics is found by a similar calculation, and would be $\boxed{5\,\text{mechanics}}$. There are actually two repair shops in Upland, employing a total of 6 mechanics.

Solutions to Problems

1. (*a*) 14 billion years $= \boxed{1.4\times10^{10}\,\text{years}}$

    (*b*) $\left(1.4\times10^{10}\,\text{y}\right)\left(3.156\times10^7\,\text{s}/1\,\text{y}\right) = \boxed{4.4\times10^{17}\,\text{s}}$

2. (*a*) 214 $\boxed{\text{3 significant figures}}$

    (*b*) 81.60 $\boxed{\text{4 significant figures}}$

    (*c*) 7.03 $\boxed{\text{3 significant figures}}$

    (*d*) 0.03 $\boxed{\text{1 significant figure}}$

    (*e*) 0.0086 $\boxed{\text{2 significant figures}}$

    (*f*) 3236 $\boxed{\text{4 significant figures}}$

    (*g*) 8700 $\boxed{\text{2 significant figures}}$

3.   (a) $1.156 = \boxed{1.156 \times 10^0}$

    (b) $21.8 = \boxed{2.18 \times 10^1}$

    (c) $0.0068 = \boxed{6.8 \times 10^{-3}}$

    (d) $27.635 = \boxed{2.7635 \times 10^1}$

    (e) $0.219 = \boxed{2.19 \times 10^{-1}}$

    (f) $444 = \boxed{4.44 \times 10^2}$

4.   (a) $8.69 \times 10^4 = \boxed{86,900}$

    (b) $9.1 \times 10^3 = \boxed{9,100}$

    (c) $8.8 \times 10^{-1} = \boxed{0.88}$

    (d) $4.76 \times 10^2 = \boxed{476}$

    (e) $3.62 \times 10^{-5} = \boxed{0.0000362}$

5.   The uncertainty is taken to be 0.01 m.

$$\% \text{ uncertainty} = \frac{0.01 \text{ m}}{1.57 \text{ m}} \times 100\% = \boxed{1\%}$$

6. $\% \text{ uncertainty} = \dfrac{0.25 \text{ m}}{3.76 \text{ m}} \times 100\% = \boxed{6.6\%}$

7.   (a) $\% \text{ uncertainty} = \dfrac{0.2 \text{ s}}{5 \text{ s}} \times 100\% = \boxed{4\%}$

    (b) $\% \text{ uncertainty} = \dfrac{0.2 \text{ s}}{50 \text{ s}} \times 100\% = \boxed{0.4\%}$

    (c) $\% \text{ uncertainty} = \dfrac{0.2 \text{ s}}{300 \text{ s}} \times 100\% = \boxed{0.07\%}$

8.   To add values with significant figures, adjust all values to be added so that their exponents are all the same.

$$9.2 \times 10^3 \text{ s} + 8.3 \times 10^4 \text{ s} + 0.008 \times 10^6 \text{ s} = 9.2 \times 10^3 \text{ s} + 83 \times 10^3 \text{ s} + 8 \times 10^3 \text{ s} = (9.2 + 83 + 8) \times 10^3 \text{ s}$$

$$= 100 \times 10^3 \text{ s} = \boxed{1.00 \times 10^5 \text{ s}}$$

When adding, keep the least accurate value, and so keep to the "ones" place in the parentheses.

9. $(2.079 \times 10^2 \text{ m})(0.082 \times 10^{-1}) = \boxed{1.7 \text{ m}}$. When multiplying, the result should have as many digits as the number with the least number of significant digits used in the calculation.

10. To find the approximate uncertainty in the area, calculate the area for the specified radius, the minimum radius, and the maximum radius. Subtract the extreme areas. The uncertainty in the area is then half this variation in area. The uncertainty in the radius is assumed to be $0.1 \times 10^4 \text{ cm}$.

$$A_{specified} = \pi r_{specified}^2 = \pi \left(3.8 \times 10^4 \, cm\right)^2 = 4.5 \times 10^9 \, cm^2$$

$$A_{min} = \pi r_{min}^2 = \pi \left(3.7 \times 10^4 \, cm\right)^2 = 4.30 \times 10^9 \, cm^2$$

$$A_{max} = \pi r_{max}^2 = \pi \left(3.9 \times 10^4 \, cm\right)^2 = 4.78 \times 10^9 \, cm^2$$

$$\Delta A = \tfrac{1}{2}\left(A_{max} - A_{min}\right) = \tfrac{1}{2}\left(4.78 \times 10^9 \, cm^2 - 4.30 \times 10^9 \, cm^2\right) = 0.24 \times 10^9 \, cm^2$$

Thus the area should be quoted as $\boxed{A = (4.5 \pm 0.2) \times 10^9 \, cm^2}$

11. To find the approximate uncertainty in the volume, calculate the volume for the specified radius, the minimum radius, and the maximum radius. Subtract the extreme volumes. The uncertainty in the volume is then half this variation in volume.

$$V_{specified} = \tfrac{4}{3}\pi r_{specified}^3 = \tfrac{4}{3}\pi \left(2.86 \, m\right)^3 = 9.80 \times 10^1 \, m^3$$

$$V_{min} = \tfrac{4}{3}\pi r_{min}^3 = \tfrac{4}{3}\pi \left(2.77 \, m\right)^3 = 8.903 \times 10^1 \, m^3$$

$$V_{max} = \tfrac{4}{3}\pi r_{max}^3 = \tfrac{4}{3}\pi \left(2.95 \, m\right)^3 = 10.754 \times 10^1 \, m^3$$

$$\Delta V = \tfrac{1}{2}\left(V_{max} - V_{min}\right) = \tfrac{1}{2}\left(10.754 \times 10^1 \, m^3 - 8.903 \times 10^1 \, m^3\right) = 0.926 \times 10^1 \, m^3$$

The percent uncertainty is $\dfrac{\Delta V}{V_{specified}} = \dfrac{0.923 \times 10^1 \, m^3}{9.80 \times 10^1 \, m^3} \times 100 = 0.09444 = \boxed{9\%}$

12. (a) 286.6 mm $\qquad$ $286.6 \times 10^{-3} \, m$ $\qquad$ $\boxed{0.286\ 6 \, m}$

   (b) 85 μV $\qquad$ $85 \times 10^{-6} \, V$ $\qquad$ $\boxed{0.000\ 085 \, V}$

   (c) 760 mg $\qquad$ $760 \times 10^{-6} \, kg$ $\qquad$ $\boxed{0.000\ 760 \, kg}$ (if last zero is significant)

   (d) 60.0 ps $\qquad$ $60.0 \times 10^{-12} \, s$ $\qquad$ $\boxed{0.000\ 000\ 000\ 0600 \, s}$

   (e) 22.5 fm $\qquad$ $22.5 \times 10^{-15} \, m$ $\qquad$ $\boxed{0.000\ 000\ 000\ 000\ 022\ 5 \, m}$

   (f) 2.50 gigavolts $\qquad$ $2.5 \times 10^9 \, volts$ $\qquad$ $\boxed{2,500,000,000 \, volts}$

13. (a) $1 \times 10^6 \, volts$ $\qquad$ $\boxed{1 \, megavolt} = 1 \, Mvolt$

   (b) $2 \times 10^{-6} \, meters$ $\qquad$ $\boxed{2 \, micrometers} = 2 \mu m$

   (c) $6 \times 10^3 \, days$ $\qquad$ $\boxed{6 \, kilodays} = 6 \, kdays$

   (d) $18 \times 10^2 \, bucks$ $\qquad$ $\boxed{18 \, hectobucks} = 18 \, hbucks$

   (e) $8 \times 10^{-9} \, pieces$ $\qquad$ $\boxed{8 \, nanopieces} = 8 \, npieces$

14. (a) Assuming a height of 5 feet 10 inches, then $5'10'' = (70 \, in)(1 \, m/39.37 \, in) = \boxed{1.8 \, m}$

   (b) Assuming a weight of 165 lbs, then $(165 \, lbs)(0.456 \, kg/1 \, lb) = \boxed{75.2 \, kg}$

   Technically, pounds and mass measure two separate properties. To make this conversion, we have to assume that we are at a location where the acceleration due to gravity is 9.8 m/s^2.

15. (a)   93 million miles $= \left(93 \times 10^6 \text{ miles}\right)\left(1610 \text{ m}/1 \text{ mile}\right) = \boxed{1.5 \times 10^{11} \text{ m}}$

    (b) $1.5 \times 10^{11} \text{ m} = 150 \times 10^9 \text{ m} = \boxed{150 \text{ gigameters}}$ or $1.5 \times 10^{11} \text{ m} = 0.15 \times 10^{12} \text{ m} = \boxed{0.15 \text{ terameters}}$

16. (a) $1 \text{ ft}^2 = \left(1 \text{ ft}^2\right)\left(1 \text{ yd}/3 \text{ ft}\right)^2 = \boxed{0.111 \text{ yd}^2}$

    (b) $1 \text{ m}^2 = \left(1 \text{ m}^2\right)\left(3.28 \text{ ft}/1 \text{ m}\right)^2 = \boxed{10.8 \text{ ft}^2}$

17. Use the speed of the airplane to convert the travel distance into a time.

$$1.00 \text{ km}\left(\frac{1 \text{ h}}{950 \text{ km}}\right)\left(\frac{3600 \text{ s}}{1 \text{ h}}\right) = \boxed{3.8 \text{ s}}$$

18. (a) $1.0 \times 10^{-10} \text{ m} = \left(1.0 \times 10^{-10} \text{ m}\right)\left(39.37 \text{ in}/1 \text{ m}\right) = \boxed{3.9 \times 10^{-9} \text{ in}}$

    (b) $\left(1.0 \text{ cm}\right)\left(\dfrac{1 \text{ m}}{100 \text{ cm}}\right)\left(\dfrac{1 \text{ atom}}{1.0 \times 10^{-10} \text{ m}}\right) = \boxed{1.0 \times 10^8 \text{ atoms}}$

19. To add values with significant figures, adjust all values to be added so that their units are all the same.

$$1.80 \text{ m} + 142.5 \text{ cm} + 5.34 \times 10^5 \ \mu\text{m} = 1.80 \text{ m} + 1.425 \text{ m} + 0.534 \text{ m} = 3.759 \text{ m} = \boxed{3.76 \text{ m}}$$

When adding, the final result is to be no more accurate than the least accurate number used. In this case, that is the first measurement, which is accurate to the hundredths place.

20. (a) $\left(1 \text{k}/\text{h}\right)\left(\dfrac{0.621 \text{ mi}}{1 \text{ km}}\right) = \boxed{0.621 \text{ mi}/\text{h}}$

    (b) $\left(1 \text{m}/\text{s}\right)\left(\dfrac{3.28 \text{ ft}}{1 \text{ m}}\right) = \boxed{3.28 \text{ ft}/\text{s}}$

    (c) $\left(1 \text{km}/\text{h}\right)\left(\dfrac{1000 \text{ m}}{1 \text{ km}}\right)\left(\dfrac{1 \text{ h}}{3600 \text{ s}}\right) = \boxed{0.278 \text{ m}/\text{s}}$

21. One mile is $1.61 \times 10^3 \text{ m}$. It is 110 m longer than a 1500-m race. The percentage difference is

$$\frac{110 \text{ m}}{1500 \text{ m}} \times 100\% = \boxed{7.3\%}$$

22. (a) $1.00 \text{ ly} = \left(2.998 \times 10^8 \text{ m}/\text{s}\right)\left(3.156 \times 10^7 \text{ s}\right) = \boxed{9.46 \times 10^{15} \text{ m}}$

    (b) $\left(1.00 \text{ ly}\right)\left(\dfrac{9.462 \times 10^{15} \text{ m}}{1.00 \text{ ly}}\right)\left(\dfrac{1 \text{ AU}}{1.50 \times 10^{11} \text{ m}}\right) = \boxed{6.31 \times 10^4 \text{ AU}}$

    (c) $\left(2.998 \times 10^8 \text{ m}/\text{s}\right)\left(\dfrac{1 \text{ AU}}{1.50 \times 10^{11} \text{ m}}\right)\left(\dfrac{3600 \text{ s}}{1 \text{ hr}}\right) = \boxed{7.20 \text{ AU}/\text{h}}$

23. The surface area of a sphere is found by $A = 4\pi r^2 = 4\pi (d/2)^2 = \pi d^2$.

(a) $A_{Moon} = \pi D_{Moon}^2 = \pi (3.48 \times 10^6 \, m)^2 = \boxed{3.80 \times 10^{13} \, m^2}$

(b) $\dfrac{A_{Earth}}{A_{Moon}} = \dfrac{\pi D_{Earth}^2}{\pi D_{Moon}^2} = \left(\dfrac{D_{Earth}}{D_{Moon}}\right)^2 = \left(\dfrac{R_{Earth}}{R_{Moon}}\right)^2 = \left(\dfrac{6.38 \times 10^6 \, m}{1.74 \times 10^6 \, m}\right)^2 = \boxed{13.4}$

24. (a) $2800 = 2.8 \times 10^3 \approx 1 \times 10^3 = \boxed{10^3}$

(b) $86.30 \times 10^2 = 8.630 \times 10^3 \approx 10 \times 10^3 = \boxed{10^4}$

(c) $0.0076 = 7.6 \times 10^{-3} \approx 10 \times 10^{-3} = \boxed{10^{-2}}$

(d) $15.0 \times 10^8 = 1.5 \times 10^9 \approx 1 \times 10^9 = \boxed{10^9}$

25. The textbook is approximately 20 cm deep and 4 cm wide. With books on both sides of a shelf, with a little extra space, the shelf would need to be about 50 cm deep. If the aisle is 1.5 meter wide, then about 1/4 of the floor space is covered by shelving. The number of books on a single shelf level is

then $\frac{1}{4}(3500 \, m^2)\left(\dfrac{1 \, book}{(0.25 \, m)(0.04 \, m)}\right) = 8.75 \times 10^4 \, books$. With 8 shelves of books, the total number

of books stored is as follows.

$$\left(8.75 \times 10^4 \, \dfrac{books}{shelf \, level}\right)(8 \, shelves) \approx \boxed{7 \times 10^5 \, books}.$$

26. The distance across the United States is about 3000 miles.

$$(3000 \, mi)(1 \, km/0.621 \, mi)(1 \, hr/10 \, km) \approx \boxed{500 \, hr}$$

Of course, it would take more time on the clock for the runner to run across the U.S. The runner could obviously not run for 500 hours non-stop. If they could run for 5 hours a day, then it would take about 100 days for them to cross the country.

27. An NCAA-regulation football field is 360 feet long (including the end zones) and 160 feet wide, which is about 110 meters by 50 meters, or 5,500 m². The mower has a cutting width of 0.5 meters. Thus the distance to be walked is

$$d = \dfrac{Area}{width} = \dfrac{5500 \, m^2}{0.5 \, m} = 11000 \, m = 11 \, km$$

At a speed of 1 km/hr, then it will take about $\boxed{11 \, h}$ to mow the field.

28. A commonly accepted measure is that a person should drink eight 8-oz. glasses of water each day. That is about 2 quarts, or 2 liters of water per day. Then approximate the lifetime as 70 years.

$$(70 \, y)(365 \, d/1 \, y)(2 \, L/1 \, d) \approx \boxed{5 \times 10^4 \, L}$$

29. Consider the body to be a cylinder, about 170 cm tall, and about 12 cm in cross-sectional radius (a 30-inch waist). The volume of a cylinder is given by the area of the cross section times the height.

$$V = \pi r^2 h = \pi (12 \, cm)^2 (170 \, cm) = 9 \times 10^4 \, cm^3 \approx \boxed{8 \times 10^4 \, cm^3}$$

30. Estimate one side of a house to be about 40 feet long, and about 10 feet high. Then the wall area of that particular wall is 400 ft^2. There would perhaps be 4 windows in that wall, each about 3 ft wide and 4 feet tall, so 12 ft^2 per window, or about 50 ft^2 of window per wall. Thus the percentage of wall area that is window area is $\dfrac{50\ \text{ft}^2}{400\ \text{ft}^2} \times 100 = 12.5\%$. Thus a rough estimate would be $\boxed{10\% - 15\%}$ of the house's outside wall area.

31. Assume that the tires last for 5 years, and so there is a tread wearing of 0.2 cm/year. Assume the average tire has a radius of 40 cm, and a width of 10 cm. Thus the volume of rubber that is becoming pollution each year from one tire is the surface area of the tire, times the thickness per year that is wearing. Also assume that there are 150,000,000 automobiles in the country – approximately one automobile for every two people. So the mass wear per year is given by

$$\left(\frac{\text{Mass}}{\text{year}}\right) = \left(\frac{\text{Surface area}}{\text{tire}}\right)\left(\frac{\text{Thickness wear}}{\text{year}}\right)(\text{density of rubber})(\#\ \text{of tires})$$

$$= \left[2\pi\,(0.4\ \text{m})(0.1\ \text{m})\right](0.002\ \text{m/y})(1200\,\text{kg/m}^3)(600,000,000\ \text{tires})$$

$$= \boxed{4 \times 10^8\ \text{kg/y}}$$

32. For the equation $v = At^3 - Bt$, the units of At^3 must be the same as the units of v. So the units of A must be the same as the units of v/t^3, which would be $\boxed{\text{distance}/\text{time}^4}$. Also, the units of Bt must be the same as the units of v. So the units of B must be the same as the units of v/t, which would be $\boxed{\text{distance}/\text{time}^2}$.

33. (a) The quantity vt^2 has units of $(\text{m/s})(\text{s}^2) = \text{m} \cdot \text{s}$, which do not match with the units of meters for x. The quantity $2at$ has units $(\text{m/s}^2)(\text{s}) = \text{m/s}$, which also do not match with the units of meters for x. Thus this equation $\boxed{\text{cannot be correct}}$.

   (b) The quantity $v_0 t$ has units of $(\text{m/s})(\text{s}) = \text{m}$, and $\frac{1}{2}at^2$ has units of $(\text{m/s}^2)(\text{s}^2) = \text{m}$. Thus, since each term has units of meters, this equation $\boxed{\text{can be correct}}$.

   (c) The quantity $v_0 t$ has units of $(\text{m/s})(\text{s}) = \text{m}$, and $2at^2$ has units of $(\text{m/s}^2)(\text{s}^2) = \text{m}$. Thus, since each term has units of meters, this equation $\boxed{\text{can be correct}}$.

34. The percentage accuracy is $\dfrac{2\ \text{m}}{2 \times 10^7\ \text{m}} \times 100\% = \boxed{1 \times 10^{-5}\%}$. The distance of 20,000,000 m needs to be distinguishable from 20,000,002 m, which means that $\boxed{8\ \text{significant figures}}$ are needed in the distance measurements.

35. Multiply the number of chips per wafer times the number of wafers that can be made fro a cylinder.

$$\left(100\frac{\text{chips}}{\text{wafer}}\right)\left(\frac{1\ \text{wafer}}{0.60\ \text{mm}}\right)\left(\frac{300\ \text{mm}}{1\ \text{cylinder}}\right) = \boxed{50,000\frac{\text{chips}}{\text{cylinder}}}$$

36. (*a*) # of seconds in 1.00 y: $1.00 \text{ y} = (1.00 \text{ y}) \left(\dfrac{3.156 \times 10^7 \text{s}}{1 \text{ y}} \right) = \boxed{3.16 \times 10^7 \text{s}}$

    (*b*) # of nanoseconds in 1.00 y: $1.00 \text{ y} = (1.00 \text{ y}) \left(\dfrac{3.156 \times 10^7 \text{s}}{1 \text{ y}} \right) \left(\dfrac{1 \times 10^9 \text{ ns}}{1 \text{ s}} \right) = \boxed{3.16 \times 10^{16} \text{ns}}$

    (*c*) # of years in 1.00 s: $1.00 \text{ s} = (1.00 \text{ s}) \left(\dfrac{1 \text{ y}}{3.156 \times 10^7 \text{s}} \right) = \boxed{3.17 \times 10^{-8} \text{y}}$

37. Assume that the alveoli are spherical, and that the volume of a typical human lung is about 2 liters, which is .002 m³. The diameter can be found from the volume of a sphere, $\frac{4}{3}\pi r^3$.

$$\tfrac{4}{3}\pi r^3 = \tfrac{4}{3}\pi (d/2)^3 = \frac{\pi d^3}{6}$$

$$(3 \times 10^8)\pi \frac{d^3}{6} = 2 \times 10^{-3} \text{m}^3 \quad \rightarrow \quad d = \left[\frac{6(2 \times 10^{-3})}{3 \times 10^8 \pi} \text{m}^3 \right]^{1/3} = \boxed{2 \times 10^{-4} \text{m}}$$

38. $1 \text{ hectare} = (1 \text{ hectare}) \left(\dfrac{10^4 \text{ m}^2}{1 \text{ hectare}} \right) \left(\dfrac{3.28 \text{ ft}}{1 \text{ m}} \right)^2 \left(\dfrac{1 \text{ acre}}{4 \times 10^4 \text{ ft}^2} \right) = \boxed{2.69 \text{ acres}}$

39. (*a*) $\left(\dfrac{10^{-15} \text{kg}}{1 \text{ bacterium}} \right) \left(\dfrac{1 \text{ proton or neutron}}{10^{-27} \text{kg}} \right) = \boxed{10^{12} \text{ protons or neutrons}}$

    (*b*) $\left(\dfrac{10^{-17} \text{kg}}{1 \text{ DNA molecule}} \right) \left(\dfrac{1 \text{ proton or neutron}}{10^{-27} \text{kg}} \right) = \boxed{10^{10} \text{ protons or neutrons}}$

    (*c*) $\left(\dfrac{10^2 \text{kg}}{1 \text{ human}} \right) \left(\dfrac{1 \text{ proton or neutron}}{10^{-27} \text{kg}} \right) = \boxed{10^{29} \text{ protons or neutrons}}$

    (*d*) $\left(\dfrac{10^{41} \text{kg}}{1 \text{ galaxy}} \right) \left(\dfrac{1 \text{ proton or neutron}}{10^{-27} \text{kg}} \right) = \boxed{10^{68} \text{ protons or neutrons}}$

40. There are about 300,000,000 people in the United States. Assume that half of them have cars, that they each drive 12,000 miles per year, and their cars get 20 miles per gallon of gasoline.

$$(3 \times 10^8 \text{ people}) \left(\frac{1 \text{ automobile}}{2 \text{ people}} \right) \left(\frac{12{,}000 \text{ mi}}{1 \text{ y}} \right) \left(\frac{1 \text{ gallon}}{20 \text{ mi}} \right) \approx \boxed{1 \times 10^{11} \text{ gallons}/\text{y}}$$

41. Approximate the gumball machine as a rectangular box with a square cross-sectional area. In counting gumballs across the bottom, there are about 10 in a row. Thus we estimate that one layer contains about 100 gumballs. In counting vertically, we see that there are bout 15 rows. Thus we estimate that there are about $\boxed{1500 \text{ gumballs}}$ in the machine.

42. The volume of water used by the people can be calculated as follows:

$$(4 \times 10^4 \text{ people}) \left(\frac{1200 \text{ L}/\text{day}}{4 \text{ people}} \right) \left(\frac{365 \text{ day}}{1 \text{ y}} \right) \left(\frac{1000 \text{ cm}^3}{1 \text{ L}} \right) \left(\frac{1 \text{ km}}{10^5 \text{ cm}} \right)^3 = 4.4 \times 10^{-3} \text{ km}^3/\text{y}$$

The depth of water is found by dividing the volume by the area.

$$d = \frac{V}{A} = \frac{4.4 \times 10^{-3} \text{ km}^3/\text{y}}{50 \text{ km}^2} = \left(8.76 \times 10^{-5} \frac{\text{km}}{\text{y}}\right)\left(\frac{10^5 \text{ cm}}{1 \text{ km}}\right) = 8.76 \text{ cm}/\text{y} \approx \boxed{9 \text{ cm}/\text{y}}$$

43. The volume of a sphere is given by $V = \frac{4}{3}\pi r^3$. For our 1-ton rock, we can calculate the volume to be

$$V = (1 \text{ T})\left(\frac{2000 \text{ lb}}{1 \text{ T}}\right)\left(\frac{1 \text{ ft}^3}{186 \text{ lb}}\right) = 10.8 \text{ ft}^3 .$$

Then the radius is found by

$$d = 2r = 2\left(\frac{3V}{4\pi}\right)^{1/3} = 2\left[\frac{3(10.8 \text{ ft}^3)}{4\pi}\right]^{1/3} = 2.74 \text{ ft} \approx \boxed{3 \text{ ft}}$$

44. To calculate the mass of water, we need to find the volume of water, and then convert the volume to mass.

$$\left[\left(4 \times 10^1 \text{ km}^2\right)\left(\frac{10^5 \text{cm}}{1 \text{ km}}\right)^2\right](1.0 \text{ cm})\left(\frac{10^{-3} \text{ kg}}{1 \text{ cm}^3}\right)\left(\frac{1 \text{ ton}}{10^3 \text{ kg}}\right) = \boxed{4 \times 10^5 \text{ ton}}$$

To find the number of gallons, convert the volume to gallons.

$$\left[\left(4 \times 10^1 \text{ km}^2\right)\left(\frac{10^5 \text{cm}}{1 \text{ km}}\right)^2\right](1.0 \text{ cm})\left(\frac{1 \text{ L}}{1 \times 10^3 \text{ cm}^3}\right)\left(\frac{1 \text{ gal}}{3.78 \text{ L}}\right) = \boxed{1 \times 10^8 \text{ gal}}$$

45. A pencil has a diameter of about 0.7 cm. If held about 0.75 m from the eye, it can just block out the Moon. The ratio of pencil diameter to arm length is the same as the ratio of Moon diameter to Moon distance. From the diagram, we have the following ratios.

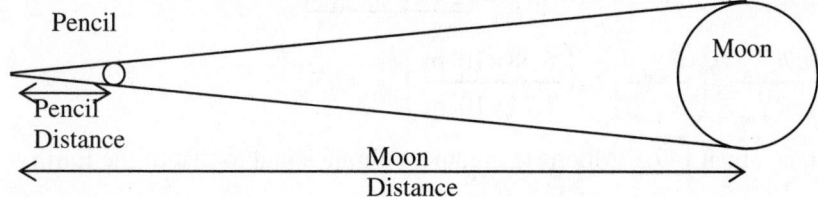

$$\frac{\text{Pencil diameter}}{\text{Pencil distance}} = \frac{\text{Moon diameter}}{\text{Moon distance}} \rightarrow$$

$$\text{Moon diameter} = \frac{\text{pencil diameter}}{\text{pencil distance}}(\text{Moon distance}) = \frac{7 \times 10^{-3} \text{ m}}{0.75 \text{ m}}(3.8 \times 10^5 \text{ km}) \approx \boxed{3500 \text{ km}}$$

46. The person walks $4 \text{ km}/\text{h}$, 10 hours each day. The radius of the Earth is about 6380 km, and the distance around the world at the equator is the circumference, $2\pi R_{\text{Earth}}$. We assume that the person can "walk on water", and so ignore the existence of the oceans.

$$2\pi (6380 \text{ km})\left(\frac{1 \text{ h}}{4 \text{ km}}\right)\left(\frac{1 \text{ d}}{10 \text{ h}}\right) = \boxed{1 \times 10^3 \text{ d}}$$

47. A cubit is about a half of a meter, by measuring several people's forearms. Thus the dimensions of Noah's ark would be $\boxed{150 \text{ m long} , 25 \text{ m wide}, 15 \text{ m high}}$. The volume of the ark is found by multiplying the three dimensions.

$$V = (150 \text{ m})(25 \text{ m})(15 \text{ m}) = 5.625 \times 10^4 \text{ m}^3 \approx \boxed{6 \times 10^4 \text{ m}^3}$$

48. The volume of the oil will be the area times the thickness. The area is $\pi r^2 = \pi (d/2)^2$, and so

$$V = \pi (d/2)^2 t \;\rightarrow\; d = 2\sqrt{\frac{V}{\pi t}} = 2\sqrt{\frac{1000 \text{cm}^3 \left(\dfrac{1 \text{ m}}{100 \text{ cm}}\right)^3}{\pi \left(2 \times 10^{-10} \text{ m}\right)}} = \boxed{3 \times 10^3 \text{ m}} .$$

49. Consider the diagram shown. L is the distance she walks upstream, which is about 120 yards. Find the distance across the river from the diagram.

$$\tan 60^\circ = \frac{d}{L} \;\rightarrow\; d = L \tan 60^\circ = (120 \text{ yd}) \tan 60^\circ = \boxed{210 \text{ yd}}$$

$$(210 \text{ yd}) \left(\frac{3 \text{ ft}}{1 \text{ yd}}\right) \left(\frac{0.305 \text{ m}}{1 \text{ ft}}\right) = \boxed{190 \text{ m}}$$

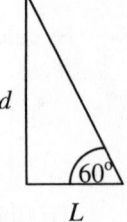

50. $\left(\dfrac{8 \text{ s}}{1 \text{ y}}\right) \left(\dfrac{1 \text{ y}}{3.156 \times 10^7 \text{s}}\right) \times 100\% = \boxed{3 \times 10^{-5} \%}$

$\boxed{51.}$ The volume of a sphere is found by $V = \frac{4}{3}\pi r^3$.

$$V_{\text{Moon}} = \tfrac{4}{3}\pi R_{\text{Moon}}^3 = \tfrac{4}{3}\pi \left(1.74 \times 10^6 \text{ m}\right)^3 = \boxed{2.21 \times 10^{19} \text{ m}^3}$$

$$\frac{V_{\text{Earth}}}{V_{\text{Moon}}} = \frac{\tfrac{4}{3}\pi R_{\text{Earth}}^3}{\tfrac{4}{3}\pi R_{\text{Moon}}^3} = \left(\frac{R_{\text{Earth}}}{R_{\text{Moon}}}\right)^3 = \left(\frac{6.38 \times 10^6 \text{ m}}{1.74 \times 10^6 \text{ m}}\right)^3 = 49.3 .$$

Thus it would take about $\boxed{49.3}$ Moons to create a volume equal to that of the Earth.

52. (a) $1.0 \, \overset{\circ}{\text{A}} = \left(1.0 \, \overset{\circ}{\text{A}}\right) \left(\dfrac{10^{-10} \text{ m}}{1 \overset{\circ}{\text{A}}}\right) \left(\dfrac{1 \text{ nm}}{10^{-9} \text{ m}}\right) = \boxed{0.10 \text{ nm}}$

(b) $1.0 \, \overset{\circ}{\text{A}} = \left(1.0 \, \overset{\circ}{\text{A}}\right) \left(\dfrac{10^{-10} \text{ m}}{1 \overset{\circ}{\text{A}}}\right) \left(\dfrac{1 \text{ fm}}{10^{-15} \text{ m}}\right) = \boxed{1.0 \times 10^5 \text{ fm}}$

(c) $1.0 \text{ m} = (1.0 \text{ m}) \left(\dfrac{1 \overset{\circ}{\text{A}}}{10^{-10} \text{ m}}\right) = \boxed{1.0 \times 10^{10} \, \overset{\circ}{\text{A}}}$

(d) $1.0 \text{ ly} = (1.0 \text{ ly}) \left(\dfrac{9.46 \times 10^{15} \text{ m}}{1 \text{ ly}}\right) \left(\dfrac{1 \overset{\circ}{\text{A}}}{10^{-10} \text{ m}}\right) = \boxed{9.5 \times 10^{25} \, \overset{\circ}{\text{A}}}$

53. (*a*) Note that $\sin 15.0° = 0.259$ and $\sin 15.5° = 0.267$.

$$\left(\frac{\Delta\theta}{\theta}\right)100 = \left(\frac{0.5°}{15.0°}\right)100 = \boxed{3\%} \qquad\qquad \left(\frac{\Delta\sin\theta}{\sin\theta}\right)100 = \left(\frac{8\times10^{-3}}{0.259}\right)100 = \boxed{3\%}$$

(*b*) Note that $\sin 75.0° = 0.966$ and $\sin 75.5° = 0.968$.

$$\left(\frac{\Delta\theta}{\theta}\right)100 = \left(\frac{0.5°}{75.0°}\right)100 = \boxed{0.7\%} \qquad\qquad \left(\frac{\Delta\sin\theta}{\sin\theta}\right)100 = \left(\frac{2\times10^{-3}}{0.966}\right)100 = \boxed{0.2\%}$$

A consequence of this result is that when using a protractor, and you have a fixed uncertainty in the angle ($\pm0.5°$ in this case), you should measure the angles from a reference line that gives a large angle measurement rather than a small one. Note above that the angles around 75° had only a 0.2% error in $\sin\theta$, while the angles around 15° had a 3% error in $\sin\theta$.

54. Utilize the fact that walking totally around the Earth along the meridian would trace out a circle whose full 360° would equal the circumference of the Earth.

$$(1\text{ minute})\left(\frac{1°}{60\text{ minute}}\right)\left(\frac{2\pi\left(6.38\times10^3\text{km}\right)}{360°}\right)\left(\frac{0.621\text{ m}}{1\text{ km}}\right) = \boxed{1.15\text{ mi}}$$

CHAPTER 2: Describing Motion: Kinematics in One Dimension

Answers to Questions

1. A car speedometer measures only speed. It does not give any information about the direction, and so does not measure velocity.

2. By definition, if an object has a constant velocity, then both the object's speed and its direction of motion are constant. Therefore the object CANNOT have a varying speed if its velocity is constant.

3. When an object moves with constant velocity, its average velocity over any time interval is exactly equal to its instantaneous velocity at all times

4. For both cars, the time elapsed is the distance traveled divided by the average velocity. Since both cars travel the same distance, the car with the larger average velocity will have the smaller elapsed time. Consider this scenario. Assume that one car has a constant acceleration down the track. Then a graph of its speed versus time would look like line "A" on the first graph. The shaded area of the graph represents the distance traveled, and the graph is plotted to such a time that the shaded area represents the length of the track. The time for this car to finish the race is labeled "t_1".

   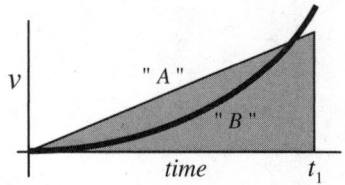

   Now let the second car have a much smaller acceleration initially, but with an increasing acceleration. A graph of its velocity, superimposed on the above graph and labeled "B", might look like the second diagram.

   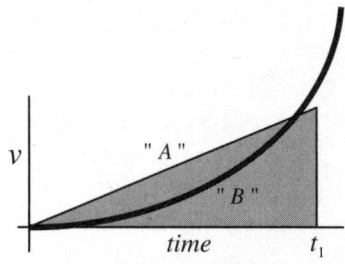

   It is seen that at the time t_1 when the first car finished the race, the second car is going faster than the first car, because the heavy line is "higher" on the graph than the line representing the first car. However, the area under the "B" line (the distance that the second car has traveled) is smaller than the shaded area, and so is less than the full track length. For the area under the "B" line to be the same as the area under the "A" line, the graph would need to look like the third diagram, indicating a longer time for the second car to finish the race.

5. There is no general relationship between the magnitude of speed and the magnitude of acceleration. For example, one object may have a large but constant speed. The acceleration of that object is then 0. Another object may have a small speed but be gaining speed, and therefore have a positive acceleration. So in this case the object with the greater speed has the lesser acceleration.

   Or consider two objects that are dropped from rest at different times. If we ignore air resistance, then the object dropped first will always have a greater speed than the object dropped second, but both will have the same acceleration of 9.80 m/s^2.

6. The acceleration of both the motorcycle and the bicycle are the same, since the same change in velocity occurred during the same time interval.

   If you do a further calculation, you will find that the distance traveled by the motorcycle during the acceleration is 17 times the distance traveled by the bicycle.

7. If an object is traveling to the north but slowing down, it has a northward velocity and a southward acceleration.

8. The velocity of an object can be negative when its acceleration is positive. If we define the positive direction to be to the right, then an object traveling to the left that is having a reduction in speed will have a negative velocity with a positive acceleration.

   If again we define the positive direction to be to the right, then an object traveling to the right that is having a reduction in speed will have a positive velocity and a negative acceleration.

9. If north is defined as the positive direction, then an object traveling to the south and increasing in speed has both a negative velocity and a negative acceleration. Or, if up is defined as the positive direction, then an object falling due to gravity has both a negative velocity and a negative acceleration.

10. If the two cars emerge side by side, then the one moving faster is passing the other one. Thus car A is passing car B. With the acceleration data given for the problem, the ensuing motion would be that car A would pull away from car B for a time, but eventually car B would catch up to and pass car A.

11. Assume that north is the positive direction. If a car is moving south and gaining speed at an increasing rate, then the acceleration will be getting larger in magnitude. However, since the acceleration is directed southwards, the acceleration is negative, and is getting more negative. That is a decreasing acceleration as the speed increases.

   Another example would be an object falling WITH air resistance. As the object falls, it gains speed, the air resistance increases. As the air resistance increases, the acceleration of the falling object decreases, and it gains speed less quickly the longer it falls.

12. Assuming that the catcher catches the ball at the same height at which it left the bat, then the ball will be traveling with a speed of 120 km/h when caught. This is proven in problem 41.

13. As a freely falling object speeds up, its acceleration due to gravity stays the same. If air resistance is considered, then the acceleration of the object is due to both gravity and air resistance. The total acceleration gets smaller as the object speeds up, until the object reaches a terminal velocity, at which time its total acceleration is zero. Thereafter its speed remains constant.

14. To estimate the height, throw the ball upward and time the flight from throwing to catching. Then, ignoring air resistance, the time of rising would be half of the time of flight. With that "half" time, assuming that the origin is at the top of the path and that downward is positive, knowing that the ball started from the top of the path with a speed of 0, use the equation $y = \frac{1}{2}gt^2$ with that time and the acceleration due to gravity to find the distance that the ball fell. With the same "half" time, we know that at the top of the path, the speed is 0. Taking the upward direction as positive, use the equation $v = v_0 + at \rightarrow 0 = v_0 - gt \rightarrow v_0 = gt$ to find the throwing speed.

15. The average speed is NOT 80 km/h. Since the two distances traveled were the same, the times of travel were unequal. The time to travel from A to B at 70 km/h is longer than the time to travel from B to C at 90 km/h. Thus we cannot simply average the speed numbers. To find the average speed, we need to calculate (total distance) / (total time). We assume the distance from A to B and the distance from B to C are both d km. The time to travel a distance d with a speed v is $t = d / v$.

$$\overline{v} = \frac{d_{AB} + d_{BC}}{t_{AB} + t_{BC}} = \frac{(d \text{ km}) + (d \text{ km})}{\dfrac{d \text{ km}}{70 \text{ km/h}} + \dfrac{d \text{ km}}{90 \text{ km/h}}} = 78.75 \text{ km/h} . \text{ The average speed is } 78.75 \text{ km/h.}$$

16. The sounds will not occur at equal time intervals because the longer any particular nut falls, the faster it will be going. With equal distances between nuts, each successive nut, having fallen a longer time when its predecessor reaches the plate, will have a higher average velocity and thus travel the inter-nut distance in shorter periods of time. Thus the sounds will occur with smaller and smaller intervals between sounds.

    To hear the sounds at equal intervals, the nuts would have to be tied at distances corresponding to equal time intervals. Since for each nut the distance of fall and time of fall are related by $d_i = \frac{1}{2} g t_i^2$, assume that $d_1 = \frac{1}{2} g t_1^2$. If we want $t_2 = 2t_1$, $t_3 = 3t_1$, $t_4 = 4t_1$, $\cdots$, then $d_2 = \frac{1}{2} g \left(2t_1\right)^2 = 4 d_1$, $d_3 = \frac{1}{2} g \left(3t_1\right)^2 = 9 d_1$, $d_4 = \frac{1}{2} g \left(4t_1\right)^2 = 16 d_1$, etc.

17. The elevator moving from the second floor to the fifth floor is NOT an example of constant acceleration. The elevator accelerates upward each time it starts to move, and it accelerates downward each time it stops.

    Ignoring air resistance, a rock falling from a cliff would have a constant acceleration. (If air resistance is included, then the acceleration will be decreasing as the rock falls.) A dish resting on a table has an acceleration of 0, so the acceleration is constant.

18. As an object rises WITH air resistance, the acceleration is larger in magnitude than g, because both gravity and air resistance will be causing a downward acceleration. As the object FALLS with air resistance, the acceleration will be smaller in magnitude than g, because gravity and resistance will be opposing each other. Because of the smaller acceleration being applied over the same distance, the return speed will be slower than the launch speed.

19. If an object is at the instant of reversing direction (like an object thrown upward, at the top of its path), it instantaneously has a zero velocity and a non-zero acceleration at the same time. A person at the exact bottom of a "bungee" cord plunge also has an instantaneous velocity of zero but a non-zero (upward) acceleration at the same time.

20. An object moving with a constant velocity has a non-zero velocity and a zero acceleration at the same time. So a car driving at constant speed on a straight, level roadway would meet this condition.

21. The object starts with a constant velocity in the positive direction. At about $t = 17$ s, when the object is at the 5 meter position, it begins to gain speed – it has a positive acceleration. At about $t = 27$ s, when the object is at about the 12 m position, it begins to slow down – it has a negative acceleration. The object instantaneously stops at about $t = 37$ s, reaching its maximum distance from the origin of 20 m. The object then reverses direction, gaining speed while moving backwards. At about $t = 47$ s, when the object is again at about the 12 m position, the object starts to slow down, and appears to stop at $t = 50$ s, 10 m from the starting point.

22. Initially, the object moves in the positive direction with a constant acceleration, until about $t = 45$ s, when it has a velocity of about 37 m/s in the positive direction. The acceleration then decreases, reaching an instantaneous acceleration of 0 at about $t = 50$ s, when the object has its maximum speed of about 38 m/s. The object then begins to slow down, but continues to move in the positive

direction. The object stops moving at $t = 90$ s and stays at rest until about $t = 108$ s. Then the object begins to move to the right again, at first with a large acceleration, and then a lesser acceleration. At the end of the recorded motion, the object is still moving to the right and gaining speed.

Solutions to Problems

1. The average speed is given by:
    $$\bar{v} = d/\Delta t = 235 \text{ km}/3.25 \text{ h} = \boxed{72.3 \text{ km/h}}.$$

2. The time of travel can be found by rearranging the average speed equation.
    $$\bar{v} = d/\Delta t \rightarrow \Delta t = d/\bar{v} = (15 \text{ km})/(25 \text{ km/h}) = \boxed{0.60 \text{ h}} = 36 \text{ min}$$

3. The distance of travel (displacement) can be found by rearranging the average speed equation. Also note that the units of the velocity and the time are not the same, so the speed units will be converted.
    $$\bar{v} = \frac{d}{\Delta t} \rightarrow d = \bar{v}\Delta t = (110 \text{ km/h})\left(\frac{1 \text{ h}}{3600 \text{ s}}\right)(2.0 \text{ s}) = 0.061 \text{ km} = \boxed{61 \text{ m}}$$

4. (a) $35 \text{ mi/h} = (35 \text{ mi/h})(1.61 \text{ km/mi}) = \boxed{56 \text{ km/h}}$

    (b) $35 \text{ mi/h} = (35 \text{ mi/h})(1610 \text{ m/mi})(1 \text{ h}/3600 \text{ s}) = \boxed{16 \text{ m/s}}$

    (c) $35 \text{ mi/h} = (35 \text{ mi/h})(5280 \text{ ft/mi})(1 \text{ h}/3600 \text{ s}) = \boxed{51 \text{ ft/s}}$

5. The average velocity is given by $\bar{v} = \frac{\Delta x}{\Delta t} = \frac{-4.2 \text{ cm} - 3.4 \text{ cm}}{6.1 \text{ s} - 3.0 \text{ s}} = \frac{-7.6 \text{ cm}}{3.1 \text{ s}} = \boxed{-2.5 \text{ cm/s}}.$

6. The average velocity is given by $\bar{v} = \frac{\Delta x}{\Delta t} = \frac{8.5 \text{ cm} - 3.4 \text{ cm}}{4.5 \text{ s} - (-2.0 \text{ s})} = \frac{5.1 \text{ cm}}{6.5 \text{ s}} = \boxed{0.78 \text{ cm/s}}.$

    $\boxed{\text{The average speed cannot be calculated.}}$ To calculate the average speed, we would need to know the actual distance traveled, and it is not given.

7. The time for the first part of the trip is calculated from the initial speed and the first distance.
    $$\text{ave speed}_1 = v_1 = \frac{d_1}{\Delta t_1} \rightarrow \Delta t_1 = \frac{d_1}{v_1} = \frac{130 \text{ km}}{95 \text{ km/h}} = 1.37 \text{ h} = 82 \text{ min}$$
    The time for the second part of the trip is therefore
    $$\Delta t_2 = \Delta t_{tot} - \Delta t_1 = 3.33 \text{ h} - 1.37 \text{ h} = 1.96 \text{ h} = 118 \text{ min}$$
    The distance for the second part of the trip is calculated from the average speed for that part of the trip and the time for that part of the trip.
    $$\text{ave speed}_2 = v_2 = \frac{d_2}{\Delta t_2} \rightarrow d_2 = v_2\Delta t_2 = (65 \text{ km/h})(1.96 \text{ h}) = 127.5 \text{ km} = 1.3 \times 10^2 \text{ km}$$

    (a) The total distance is then $d_{total} = d_1 + d_2 = 130 \text{ km} + 127.5 \text{ km} = 257.5 \text{ km} \approx \boxed{2.6 \times 10^2 \text{ km}}$

    (b) The average speed is NOT the average of the two speeds. Use the definition of average speed.

$$\text{ave speed} = \frac{d_{total}}{\Delta t_{total}} = \frac{257.5 \text{ km}}{3.33 \text{ h}} = \boxed{77 \text{ km/h}}$$

8. The speed of sound is intimated in the problem as 1 mile per 5 seconds. The speed is calculated by:

$$\text{speed} = \frac{\text{distance}}{\text{time}} = \left(\frac{1 \text{ mi}}{5 \text{ s}}\right)\left(\frac{1610 \text{ m}}{1 \text{ mi}}\right) = \boxed{300 \text{ m/s}} .$$

Note that only 1 significant figure is given, (5 sec), and so only 1 significant figure is justified in the result.

9. The distance traveled is 2.0 miles $(8 \text{ laps} \times 0.25 \text{ mi/lap})$. The displacement is 0 because the ending point is the same as the starting point.

(a) Average speed $= \dfrac{d}{\Delta t} = \dfrac{2.0 \text{ mi}}{12.5 \text{ min}} = \left(\dfrac{2 \text{ mi}}{12.5 \text{ min}}\right)\left(\dfrac{1610 \text{ m}}{1 \text{ mi}}\right)\left(\dfrac{1 \text{ min}}{60 \text{ s}}\right) = \boxed{4.3 \text{ m/s}}$

(b) Average velocity $= \overline{v} = \Delta x/\Delta t = \boxed{0 \text{ m/s}}$

10. The distance traveled is $116 \text{ km} + \frac{1}{2}(116 \text{ km}) = 174 \text{ km}$, and the displacement is $116 \text{ km} - \frac{1}{2}(116 \text{ km}) = 58 \text{ km}$. The total time is $14.0 \text{ s} + 4.8 \text{ s} = 18.8 \text{ s}$.

(a) Average speed $= \dfrac{d}{\Delta t} = \dfrac{174 \text{ m}}{18.8 \text{ s}} = \boxed{9.26 \text{ m/s}}$

(b) Average velocity $= \overline{v} = \dfrac{\Delta x}{\Delta t} = \dfrac{58 \text{ m}}{18.8 \text{ s}} = \boxed{3.1 \text{ m/s}}$

11. Since the locomotives have the same speed, they each travel half the distance, 4.25 km. Find the time of travel from the average speed.

$$\text{ave speed} = v = \frac{d}{\Delta t} \rightarrow \Delta t = \frac{d}{v} = \frac{4.25 \text{ km}}{95 \text{ km/h}} = 0.0447 \text{ h}\left(\frac{60 \text{ min}}{1 \text{ h}}\right) = 2.68 \text{ min} \cong \boxed{2.7 \text{ min}}$$

12. Both objects will have the same time of travel. If the truck travels a distance d_{truck}, then the distance the car travels will be $d_{car} = d_{truck} + 110 \text{ m}$. Using the equation for average speed, $\overline{v} = d/\Delta t$, solve for time, and equate the two times.

$$\Delta t = \frac{d_{truck}}{\overline{v}_{truck}} = \frac{d_{car}}{\overline{v}_{car}} \qquad \frac{d_{truck}}{75 \text{ km/h}} = \frac{d_{truck} + 110 \text{ m}}{88 \text{ km/h}}$$

Solving for d_{truck} gives $d_{truck} = (110 \text{ m})\dfrac{(75 \text{ km/h})}{(88 \text{ km/h} - 75 \text{ km/h})} = 634.6 \text{ m}$.

The time of travel is

$$\Delta t = \frac{d_{truck}}{\overline{v}_{truck}} = \left(\frac{634.6 \text{ m}}{75000 \text{ m/h}}\right)\left(\frac{60 \text{ min}}{1 \text{ h}}\right) = 0.5077 \text{ min} = 30.46 \text{ s} = \boxed{3.0 \times 10^1 \text{ s}} .$$

Also note that $\Delta t = \dfrac{d_{car}}{\overline{v}_{car}} = \left(\dfrac{634.6 \text{ m} + 110 \text{ m}}{88000 \text{ m/h}}\right)\left(\dfrac{60 \text{ min}}{1 \text{ h}}\right) = 0.5077 \text{ min} = 30.46 \text{ s}$.

ALTERNATE SOLUTION:

The speed of the car relative to the truck is $88 \text{ km/h} - 75 \text{ km/h} = 13 \text{ km/h}$. In the reference frame of the truck, the car must travel 110 m to catch it.

$$\Delta t = \frac{0.11 \text{ km}}{13 \text{ km/h}} \left(\frac{3600 \text{ s}}{1 \text{ h}} \right) = 30.46 \text{ s}$$

13. The average speed for each segment of the trip is given by $\bar{v} = \dfrac{d}{\Delta t}$, so $\Delta t = \dfrac{d}{\bar{v}}$ for each segment.

   For the first segment, $\Delta t_1 = \dfrac{d_1}{\bar{v}_1} = \dfrac{3100 \text{ km}}{790 \text{ km/h}} = 3.924 \text{ h}$.

   For the second segment, $\Delta t_2 = \dfrac{d_2}{\bar{v}_2} = \dfrac{2800 \text{ km}}{990 \text{ km/h}} = 2.828 \text{ h}$.

   Thus the total time is $\Delta t_{tot} = \Delta t_1 + \Delta t_2 = 3.924 \text{ h} + 2.828 \text{ h} = 6.752 \text{ h} \approx \boxed{6.8 \text{ h}}$.

   The average speed of the plane for the entire trip is

   $$\bar{v} = \frac{d_{tot}}{\Delta t_{tot}} = \frac{3100 \text{ km} + 2800 \text{ km}}{6.752 \text{ h}} = 873.8 \approx \boxed{8.7 \times 10^2 \text{ km/h}}.$$

14. The distance traveled is 500 km (250 km outgoing, 250 km return, keep 2 significant figures). The displacement (Δx) is 0 because the ending point is the same as the starting point.

   (*a*) To find the average speed, we need the distance traveled (500 km) and the total time elapsed.

   During the outgoing portion, $\bar{v}_1 = \dfrac{d_1}{\Delta t_1}$ and so $\Delta t_1 = \dfrac{d_1}{\bar{v}_1} = \dfrac{250 \text{ km}}{95 \text{ km/h}} = 2.632 \text{ h}$. During the return

   portion, $\bar{v}_2 = \dfrac{d_2}{\Delta t_2}$, and so $\Delta t_2 = \dfrac{d_2}{\bar{v}_2} = \dfrac{250 \text{ km}}{55 \text{ km/h}} = 4.545 \text{ h}$. Thus the total time, including lunch, is

   $\Delta t_{total} = \Delta t_1 + \Delta t_{lunch} + \Delta t_2 = 8.177 \text{ h}$. Average speed $= \dfrac{d_{total}}{\Delta t_{total}} = \dfrac{500 \text{ km}}{8.177 \text{ h}} = \boxed{61 \text{ km/h}}$.

   (*b*) Average velocity $= \boxed{\bar{v} = \Delta x / \Delta t = 0}$

15. The average speed of sound is given by $\bar{v} = d / \Delta t$, and so the time for the sound to travel from the

   end of the lane back to the bowler is $\Delta t_{sound} = \dfrac{d}{\bar{v}_{sound}} = \dfrac{16.5 \text{ m}}{340 \text{ m/s}} = 4.85 \times 10^{-2} \text{ s}$. Thus the time for the

   ball to travel from the bowler to the end of the lane is given by

   $\Delta t_{ball} = \Delta t_{total} - \Delta t_{sound} = 2.50 \text{ s} - 4.85 \times 10^{-2} \text{ s} = 2.4515 \text{ s}$. And so the speed of the ball is:

   $$\bar{v}_{ball} = \frac{d}{\Delta t_{ball}} = \frac{16.5 \text{ m}}{2.4515 \text{ s}} = \boxed{6.73 \text{ m/s}}.$$

16. The average acceleration is given by

   $$\bar{a} = \frac{\Delta v}{\Delta t} = \frac{95 \text{ km/h} - 0 \text{ km/h}}{6.2 \text{ s}} = \frac{(95 \text{ km/h}) \left(\dfrac{1 \text{ m/s}}{3.6 \text{ km/h}} \right)}{6.2 \text{ s}} = \boxed{4.3 \text{ m/s}^2}.$$

17. (*a*)   The average acceleration of the sprinter is $\overline{a} = \dfrac{\Delta v}{\Delta t} = \dfrac{10.0 \, \text{m/s} - 0.0 \, \text{m/s}}{1.35 \, \text{s}} = \boxed{7.41 \, \text{m/s}^2}$.

(*b*) $\overline{a} = \left(7.41 \, \text{m/s}^2\right)\left(\dfrac{1 \, \text{km}}{1000 \, \text{m}}\right)\left(\dfrac{3600 \, \text{s}}{1 \, \text{h}}\right)^2 = \boxed{9.60 \times 10^4 \, \text{km/h}^2}$

18. The time can be found from the average acceleration, $\overline{a} = \dfrac{\Delta v}{\Delta t}$.

$$\Delta t = \dfrac{\Delta v}{\overline{a}} = \dfrac{110 \, \text{km/h} - 80 \, \text{km/h}}{1.6 \, \text{m/s}^2} = \dfrac{\left(30 \, \text{km/h}\right)\left(\dfrac{1 \, \text{m/s}}{3.6 \, \text{km/h}}\right)}{1.6 \, \text{m/s}^2} = \boxed{5.2 \, \text{s}}$$

19. The initial velocity of the car is the average speed of the car before it accelerates.

$$\overline{v} = \dfrac{d}{\Delta t} = \dfrac{110 \, \text{m}}{5.0 \, \text{s}} = 22 \, \text{m/s} = v_0$$

The final speed is $v = 0$, and the time to stop is 4.0 s. Use Eq. 2-11a to find the acceleration.

$v = v_0 + at \quad \rightarrow$

$$a = \dfrac{v - v_0}{t} = \dfrac{0 - 22 \, \text{m/s}}{4.0 \, \text{s}} = \boxed{-5.5 \, \text{m/s}^2} = \left(-5.5 \, \text{m/s}^2\right)\left(\dfrac{1 \, g}{9.80 \, \text{m/s}^2}\right) = \boxed{-0.56 \, g \text{'s}}$$

20. To estimate the velocity, find the average velocity over each time interval, and assume that the car had that velocity at the midpoint of the time interval. To estimate the acceleration, find the average acceleration over each time interval, and assume that the car had that acceleration at the midpoint of the time interval. A sample of each calculation is shown.

From 2.00 s to 2.50 s, for average velocity:

$$t_{\text{mid}} = \dfrac{2.50 \, \text{s} + 2.00 \, \text{s}}{2} = 2.25 \, \text{s}$$

$$\overline{v} = \dfrac{\Delta x}{\Delta t} = \dfrac{13.79 \, \text{m} - 8.55 \, \text{m}}{2.50 \, \text{s} - 2.00 \, \text{s}} = \dfrac{5.24 \, \text{m}}{0.50 \, \text{s}} = 10.48 \, \text{m/s}$$

From 2.25 s to 2.75 s, for average acceleration:

$$t_{\text{mid}} = \dfrac{2.25 \, \text{s} + 2.75 \, \text{s}}{2} = 2.50 \, \text{s}$$

$$\overline{a} = \dfrac{\Delta v}{\Delta t} = \dfrac{13.14 \, \text{m/s} - 10.48 \, \text{m/s}}{2.75 \, \text{s} - 2.25 \, \text{s}} = \dfrac{2.66 \, \text{m/s}}{0.50 \, \text{s}} = 5.32 \, \text{m/s}^2$$

Table of Calculations

t (s)	x (m)	t (s)	v (m/s)	t (s)	a (m/s^2)
0.00	0.00	0.00	0.00		
		0.125	0.44	0.063	3.52
0.25	0.11			0.25	3.84
		0.375	1.40		
0.50	0.46			0.50	4.00
		0.625	2.40		
0.75	1.06			0.75	4.48
		0.875	3.52		
1.00	1.94			1.06	4.91
		1.25	5.36		
1.50	4.62			1.50	5.00
		1.75	7.86		
2.00	8.55			2.00	5.24
		2.25	10.48		
2.50	13.79			2.50	5.32
		2.75	13.14		
3.00	20.36			3.00	5.52
		3.25	15.90		
3.50	28.31			3.50	5.56
		3.75	18.68		
4.00	37.65			4.00	5.52
		4.25	21.44		
4.50	48.37			4.50	4.84
		4.75	23.86		
5.00	60.30			5.00	4.12
		5.25	25.92		
5.50	73.26			5.50	3.76
		5.75	27.80		
6.00	87.16				

Graph of the velocity

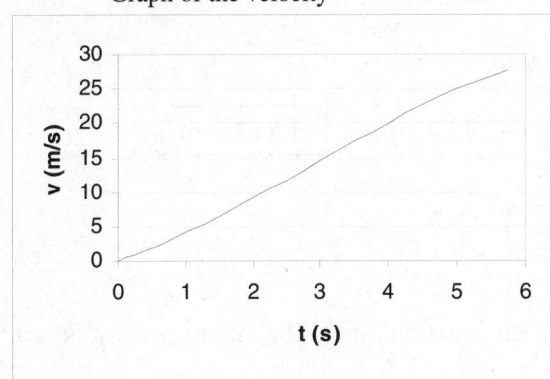

Graph of the acceleration

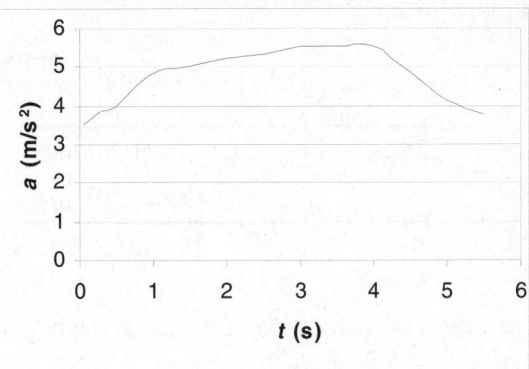

21. By definition, the acceleration is $a = \dfrac{v - v_0}{t} = \dfrac{25\,\text{m/s} - 13\,\text{m/s}}{6.0\,\text{s}} = \boxed{2.0\,\text{m/s}^2}$.

The distance of travel can be found from Eq. 2-11b.

$$x - x_0 = v_0 t + \tfrac{1}{2} a t^2 = (13\,\text{m/s})(6.0\,\text{s}) + \tfrac{1}{2}(2.0\,\text{m/s}^2)(6.0\,\text{s})^2 = \boxed{114\,\text{m}}$$

22. The acceleration can be found from Eq. (2-11c).

$$v^2 = v_0^2 + 2a(x - x_0) \rightarrow a = \frac{v^2 - v_0^2}{2(x - x_0)} = \frac{0 - (23\,\text{m/s})^2}{2(85\,\text{m})} = \boxed{-3.1\,\text{m/s}^2}.$$

23. Assume that the plane starts from rest. The runway distance is found by solving Eq. 2-11c for $x - x_0$.

$$v^2 = v_0^2 + 2a(x - x_0) \rightarrow x - x_0 = \frac{v^2 - v_0^2}{2a} = \frac{(33\,\text{m/s})^2 - 0}{2(3.0\,\text{m/s}^2)} = \boxed{1.8 \times 10^2\,\text{m}}$$

24. The sprinter starts from rest. The average acceleration is found from Eq. 2-11c.

$$v^2 = v_0^2 + 2a(x - x_0) \rightarrow a = \frac{v^2 - v_0^2}{2(x - x_0)} = \frac{(11.5\,\text{m/s})^2 - 0}{2(15.0\,\text{m})} = 4.408\,\text{m/s}^2 \approx \boxed{4.41\,\text{m/s}^2}.$$

The elapsed time is found by solving Eq. 2-11a for time.

$$v = v_0 + at \rightarrow t = \frac{v - v_0}{a} = \frac{11.5\,\text{m/s} - 0}{4.408\,\text{m/s}^2} = \boxed{2.61\,\text{s}}$$

25. The words "slowing down uniformly" implies that the car has a constant acceleration. The distance of travel is found form combining Eqs. 2-7 and 2-8.

$$x - x_0 = \frac{v_0 + v}{2} t = \left(\frac{21.0\,\text{m/s} + 0\,\text{m/s}}{2}\right)(6.00\,\text{sec}) = \boxed{63.0\,\text{m}}.$$

26. The final velocity of the car is zero. The initial velocity is found from Eq. 2-11c with $v = 0$ and solving for v_0.

$$v^2 = v_0^2 + 2a(x - x_0) \rightarrow v_0 = \sqrt{v^2 - 2a(x - x_0)} = \sqrt{0 - 2(-7.00\,\text{m/s}^2)(92\,\text{m})} = \boxed{36\,\text{m/s}}$$

27. The final velocity of the driver is zero. The acceleration is found from Eq. 2-11c with $v = 0$ and solving for a.

$$a = \frac{v^2 - v_0^2}{2(x - x_0)} = \frac{0 - \left[(85 \,\text{km/h}) \left(\frac{1 \,\text{m/s}}{3.6 \,\text{km/h}} \right) \right]^2}{2(0.80 \,\text{m})} = -348.4 \,\text{m/s}^2 \approx \boxed{-3.5 \times 10^2 \,\text{m/s}^2}$$

Converting to "g's": $a = \dfrac{-3.484 \times 10^2 \,\text{m/s}^2}{(9.8 \,\text{m/s}^2)/g} = \boxed{-36 \, g\text{'s}}$.

28. The origin is the location of the car at the beginning of the reaction time. The initial speed of the car is $(95 \,\text{km/h}) \left(\dfrac{1 \,\text{m/s}}{3.6 \,\text{km/h}} \right) = 26.39 \,\text{m/s}$. The location where the brakes are applied is found from the equation for motion at constant velocity: $x_0 = v_0 t_R = (26.39 \,\text{m/s})(1.0 \,\text{s}) = 26.39 \,\text{m}$. This is now the starting location for the application of the brakes. In each case, the final speed is 0.
    (*a*) Solve Eq. 2-11c for the final location.

$$v^2 = v_0^2 + 2a(x - x_0) \quad \rightarrow \quad x = x_0 + \frac{v^2 - v_0^2}{2a} = 26.39 \,\text{m} + \frac{0 - (26.39 \,\text{m/s})^2}{2(-4.0 \,\text{m/s}^2)} = \boxed{113 \,\text{m}}$$

    (*b*) Solve Eq. 2-11c for the final location with the second acceleration.

$$x = x_0 + \frac{v^2 - v_0^2}{2a} = 26.39 \,\text{m} + \frac{0 - (26.39 \,\text{m/s})^2}{2(-8.0 \,\text{m/s}^2)} = \boxed{70 \,\text{m}}$$

29. The origin is the location of the car at the beginning of the reaction time. The location where the brakes are applied is found from the equation for motion at constant velocity: $x_0 = v_0 t_R$
    This is the starting location for the application of the brakes. Solve Eq. 2-11c for the final location of the car, with $v = 0$.

$$x = x_0 + \frac{v^2 - v_0^2}{2a} = v_0 t_R - \frac{v_0^2}{2a}$$

30. The critical condition is that the total distance covered by the passing car and the approaching car must be less than 400 m so that they do not collide. The passing car has a total displacement composed of several individual parts. These are: i) the 10 m of clear room at the rear of the truck, ii) the 20 m length of the truck, iii) the 10 m of clear room at the front of the truck, and iv) the distance the truck travels. Since the truck travels at a speed of $\overline{v} = 25 \,\text{m/s}$, the truck will have a displacement of $\Delta x_{\text{truck}} = (25 \,\text{m/s}) t$. Thus the total displacement of the car during passing is
    $\Delta x_{\substack{\text{passing} \\ \text{car}}} = 40 \,\text{m} + (25 \,\text{m/s}) t$.

    To express the motion of the car, we choose the origin to be at the location of the passing car when the decision to pass is made. For the passing car, we have an initial velocity of $v_0 = 25 \,\text{m/s}$ and an acceleration of $a = 1.0 \,\text{m/s}^2$. Find $\Delta x_{\substack{\text{passing} \\ \text{car}}}$ from Eq. 2-11b.

$$\Delta x_{\substack{\text{passing} \\ \text{car}}} = x_c - x_0 = v_0 t + \tfrac{1}{2} a t^2 = (25 \,\text{m/s}) t + \tfrac{1}{2} (1.0 \,\text{m/s}^2) t^2$$

Set the two expressions for $\Delta x_{\substack{passing \\ car}}$ equal to each other in order to find the time required to pass.

$$40\,\text{m} + (25\,\text{m/s})t_{pass} = (25\,\text{m/s})t_{pass} + \tfrac{1}{2}(1.0\,\text{m/s}^2)t_{pass}^2 \rightarrow 40\,\text{m} = \tfrac{1}{2}(1.0\,\text{m/s}^2)t_{pass}^2 \rightarrow$$

$$t_{pass} = \sqrt{80\text{s}^2} = 8.94\ \text{s}$$

Calculate the displacements of the two cars during this time.

$$\Delta x_{\substack{passing \\ car}} = 40\,\text{m} + (25\,\text{m/s})(8.94\ \text{s}) = 264\ \text{m}$$

$$\Delta x_{\substack{approaching \\ car}} = v_{\substack{approaching \\ car}}t = (25\,\text{m/s})(8.94\ \text{s}) = 224\ \text{m}$$

Thus the two cars together have covered a total distance of 488 m, which is more than allowed.

$\boxed{\text{The car should not pass.}}$

31. During the final part of the race, the runner must have a displacement of 1100 m in a time of 180 s (3 min). Assume that the starting speed for the final part is the same as the average speed thus far.

$$\text{Average speed} = \frac{d}{\Delta t} = \frac{8900\ \text{m}}{(27 \times 60)\ \text{s}} = 5.494\,\text{m/s} = v_0$$

The runner will accomplish this by accelerating from speed v_0 to speed v for t seconds, covering a distance d_1, and then running at a constant speed of v for $(180-t)$ seconds, covering a distance d_2. We have these relationships:

$$v = v_o + at \qquad d_1 = v_o t + \tfrac{1}{2}at^2 \qquad d_2 = v(180-t) = (v_0 + at)(180-t)$$

$$1100\ \text{m} = d_1 + d_2 = v_o t + \tfrac{1}{2}at^2 + (v_0 + at)(180-t) \rightarrow 1100\ \text{m} = 180v_0 + 180at - \tfrac{1}{2}at^2 \rightarrow$$

$$1100\ \text{m} = (180\ \text{s})(5.494\,\text{m/s}) + (180\ \text{s})(0.2\,\text{m/s}^2)t - \tfrac{1}{2}(0.2\,\text{m/s}^2)t^2$$

$$0.1t^2 - 36t + 111 = 0 \qquad t = 357\ \text{s}\,,\ 3.11\ \text{s}$$

Since we must have $t < 180$ s, the solution is $t = 3.1$ s.

$\boxed{32.}$ The car's initial speed is $v_o = (45\,\text{km/h})\left(\dfrac{1\,\text{m/s}}{3.6\,\text{km/h}}\right) = 12.5\,\text{m/s}$.

Case I: trying to stop. The constraint is, with the braking deceleration of the car $(a = -5.8\,\text{m/s}^2)$, can the car stop in a 28 m displacement? The 2.0 seconds has no relation to this part of the problem. Using equation (2-11c), the distance traveled during braking is

$$(x - x_0) = \frac{v^2 - v_0^2}{2a} = \frac{0 - (12.5\,\text{m/s})^2}{2(-5.8\,\text{m/s}^2)} = 13.5\ \text{m}\quad \boxed{\text{She can stop the car in time.}}$$

Case II: crossing the intersection. The constraint is, with the acceleration of the car

$$\boxed{a = \left(\frac{65\,\text{km/h} - 45\,\text{km/h}}{6.0\ \text{s}}\right)\left(\frac{1\,\text{m/s}}{3.6\,\text{km/h}}\right) = 0.9259\,\text{m/s}^2}\,, \text{can she get through the intersection}$$

(travel 43 meters) in the 2.0 seconds before the light turns red? Using equation (2.11b), the distance traveled during the 2.0 sec is

$$(x - x_0) = v_0 t + \tfrac{1}{2}at^2 = (12.5\,\text{m/s})(2.0\ \text{s}) + \tfrac{1}{2}(0.927\,\text{m/s}^2)(2.0\ \text{s})^2 = 26.9\ \text{m}.$$

$\boxed{\text{She should stop.}}$

33. Choose downward to be the positive direction, and take $y_0 = 0$ at the top of the cliff. The initial velocity is $v_0 = 0$, and the acceleration is $a = 9.80 \, \text{m/s}^2$. The displacement is found from equation (2-11b), with x replaced by y.

$$y = y_0 + v_0 t + \tfrac{1}{2} a t^2 \quad \rightarrow \quad y - 0 = 0 + \tfrac{1}{2}\left(9.80 \, \text{m/s}^2\right)(3.25 \, \text{s})^2 \quad \rightarrow \quad y = \boxed{51.8 \, \text{m}}$$

34. Choose downward to be the positive direction. The initial velocity is $v_0 = 0$, the final velocity is

$$v = \left(85 \, \text{km/h}\right)\left(\frac{1 \, \text{m/s}}{3.6 \, \text{km/h}}\right) = 23.61 \, \text{m/s}, \text{ and the acceleration is } a = 9.80 \, \text{m/s}^2. \text{ The time can be}$$

found by solving Eq. 2-11a for the time.

$$v = v_0 + at \quad \rightarrow \quad t = \frac{v - v_0}{a} = \frac{23.61 \, \text{m/s} - 0}{9.80 \, \text{m/s}^2} = \boxed{2.4 \, \text{s}}$$

35. Choose downward to be the positive direction, and take $y_0 = 0$ to be at the top of the Empire State Building. The initial velocity is $v_0 = 0$, and the acceleration is $a = 9.80 \, \text{m/s}^2$.

    (a) The elapsed time can be found from Eq. 2-11b, with x replaced by y.

$$y - y_0 = v_0 t + \tfrac{1}{2} a t^2 \quad \rightarrow \quad t = \sqrt{\frac{2y}{a}} = \sqrt{\frac{2(380 \, \text{m})}{9.80 \, \text{m/s}^2}} = 8.806 \, \text{s} \approx \boxed{8.8 \, \text{s}}.$$

    (b) The final velocity can be found from equation (2-11a).

$$v = v_0 + at = 0 + \left(9.80 \, \text{m/s}^2\right)(8.806 \, \text{s}) = \boxed{86 \, \text{m/s}}$$

36. Choose upward to be the positive direction, and take $y_0 = 0$ to be at the height where the ball was hit. For the upward path, $v_0 = 22 \, \text{m/s}$, $v = 0$ at the top of the path, and $a = -9.80 \, \text{m/s}^2$.

    (a) The displacement can be found from Eq. 2-11c, with x replaced by y.

$$v^2 = v_0^2 + 2a\left(y - y_0\right) \quad \rightarrow \quad y = y_0 + \frac{v^2 - v_0^2}{2a} = 0 + \frac{0 - (22 \, \text{m/s})^2}{2\left(-9.80 \, \text{m/s}^2\right)} = \boxed{25 \, \text{m}}$$

    (b) The time of flight can be found from Eq. 2-11b, with x replaced by y, using a displacement of 0 for the displacement of the ball returning to the height from which it was hit.

$$y = y_0 + v_0 t + \tfrac{1}{2} a t^2 = 0 \quad \rightarrow \quad t\left(v_0 + \tfrac{1}{2} a t\right) = 0 \quad \rightarrow \quad t = 0 \, , \, t = \frac{2 v_0}{-a} = \frac{2(22 \, \text{m/s})}{-9.80 \, \text{m/s}^2} = \boxed{4.5 \, \text{s}}$$

    The result of $t = 0$ s is the time for the original displacement of zero (when the ball was hit), and the result of $t = 4.5$ s is the time to return to the original displacement. Thus the answer is $t = 4.5$ seconds.

37. Choose upward to be the positive direction, and take $y_0 = 0$ to be the height from which the ball was thrown. The acceleration is $a = -9.80 \, \text{m/s}^2$. The displacement upon catching the ball is 0, assuming it was caught at the same height from which it was thrown. The starting speed can be found from Eq. 2-11b, with x replaced by y.

$$y = y_0 + v_0 t + \tfrac{1}{2} a t^2 = 0 \quad \rightarrow$$

$$v_0 = \frac{y - y_0 - \tfrac{1}{2} a t^2}{t} = -\tfrac{1}{2} a t = -\tfrac{1}{2}\left(-9.80 \, \text{m/s}^2\right)(3.0 \, \text{s}) = 14.7 \, \text{m/s} \approx \boxed{15 \, \text{m/s}}$$

The height can be calculated from Eq. 2-11c, with a final velocity of $v = 0$ at the top of the path.

$$v^2 = v_0^2 + 2a(y - y_0) \quad \rightarrow \quad y = y_0 + \frac{v^2 - v_0^2}{2a} = 0 + \frac{0 - (14.7\,\text{m/s})^2}{2(-9.8\,\text{m/s}^2)} = \boxed{11\,\text{m}}$$

38. Choose downward to be the positive direction, and take $y_0 = 0$ to be at the height where the object was released. The initial velocity is $v_0 = 0$, and the acceleration is $a = 9.80\,\text{m/s}^2$.

    (a) The speed of the object will be given by Eq. 2-11a with $v_0 = 0$, and so $v = at = (9.80\,\text{m/s}^2)t$.

    This is the equation of a straight line passing through the origin with a slope of $9.80\,\text{m/s}^2$.

    (b) The distance fallen will be given by equation (2-11b) with $v_0 = 0$, and so

    $y = y_0 + v_0 t + \frac{1}{2}at^2 = 0 + 0 + (4.90\,\text{m/s}^2)t^2$. This is the equation of a parabola, centered on the t-axis, opening upward.

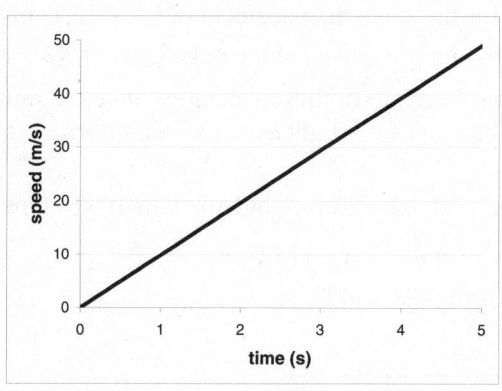 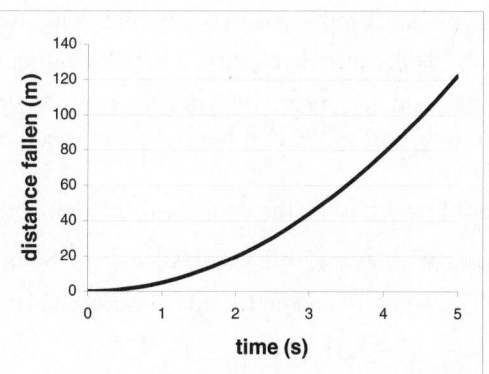

39. Choose downward to be the positive direction, and take $y_0 = 0$ to be the height where the object was released. The initial velocity is $v_0 = -5.20\,\text{m/s}^2$, the acceleration is $a = 9.80\,\text{m/s}^2$, and the displacement of the package will be $y = 125\,\text{m}$. The time to reach the ground can be found from Eq. 2-11b, with x replaced by y.

$$y = y_0 + v_0 t + \frac{1}{2}at^2 \quad \rightarrow \quad t^2 + \frac{2v_0}{a}t - \frac{2y}{a} = 0 \quad \rightarrow \quad t^2 + \frac{2(-5.2\,\text{m/s})}{9.80\,\text{m/s}^2}t - \frac{2(125\,\text{m})}{9.80\,\text{m/s}^2} = 0 \quad \rightarrow$$

$t = 5.61\,\text{s}, \ -4.55\,\text{s}$

The correct time is the positive answer, $\boxed{t = 5.61\,\text{s}}$.

40. Choose downward to be the positive direction, and take $y_0 = 0$ to be the height from which the object is released. The initial velocity is $v_0 = 0$, the acceleration is $a = g$. Then we can calculate the position as a function of time from Eq. 2-11b, with x replaced by y, as $y(t) = \frac{1}{2}gt^2$. At the end of each second, the position would be as follows:

$$y(0) = 0 \; ; \quad y(1) = \tfrac{1}{2}g \; ; \quad y(2) = \tfrac{1}{2}g(2)^2 = 4y(1) \; ; \quad y(3) = \tfrac{1}{2}g(3)^2 = 9y(1)$$

The distance traveled during each second can be found by subtracting two adjacent position values from the above list.

$$d(1) = y(1) - y(0) = y(1) \; ; \quad d(2) = y(2) - y(1) = 3y(1) \; ; \quad d(3) = y(3) - y(2) = 5y(1)$$

We could do this in general.

$$y(n) = \tfrac{1}{2} g n^2 \qquad y(n+1) = \tfrac{1}{2} g (n+1)^2$$

$$d(n+1) = y(n+1) - y(n) = \tfrac{1}{2} g (n+1)^2 - \tfrac{1}{2} g n^2 = \tfrac{1}{2} g \left((n+1)^2 - n^2 \right)$$

$$= \tfrac{1}{2} g \left(n^2 + 2n + 1 - n^2 \right) = \tfrac{1}{2} g (2n+1)$$

The value of $(2n+1)$ is always odd, in the sequence $\boxed{1, 3, 5, 7, \ldots}$

41. Choose upward to be the positive direction, and take $y_0 = 0$ to be the height from which the ball is thrown. The initial velocity is v_0, the acceleration is $a = -g$, and the final location for the round trip is $y = 0$. The velocity under those conditions can be found from Eq. 2-11c, with x replaced by y.

$$v^2 - v_0^2 = 2ay = 0 \quad \rightarrow \quad v^2 = v_0^2 \quad \rightarrow \quad \boxed{v = \pm v_0}$$

The two results represent two different velocities for the same displacement of 0. The positive sign $(v = v_0)$ is the initial velocity, when the ball is moving upwards, and the negative sign $(v = -v_0)$ is the final velocity, when the ball is moving downwards. Both of these velocities have the same magnitude, and so the ball has the same speed at the end of its flight as at the beginning.

42. Choose upward to be the positive direction, and $y_0 = 0$ to be the height from which the stone is thrown. We have $v_0 = 18.0 \, \text{m/s}$, $a = -9.80 \, \text{m/s}^2$, and $y - y_0 = 11.0 \, \text{m}$.

    (a) The velocity can be found from Eq, 2-11c, with x replaced by y.

    $$v^2 = v_0^2 + 2a(y - y_0) = 0 \quad \rightarrow$$

    $$v = \pm\sqrt{v_0^2 + 2ay} = \pm\sqrt{(18.0 \, \text{m/s})^2 + 2(-9.80 \, \text{m/s}^2)(11.0 \, \text{m})} = \pm 10.4 \, \text{m/s}$$

    Thus the speed is $\boxed{|v| = 10.4 \, \text{m/s}}$

    (b) The time to reach that height can be found from equation (2-11b).

    $$y = y_0 + v_0 t + \tfrac{1}{2} a t^2 \quad \rightarrow \quad t^2 + \frac{2(18.0 \, \text{m/s})}{-9.80 \, \text{m/s}^2} t + \frac{2(-11.0 \, \text{m})}{-9.80 \, \text{m/s}^2} = 0 \quad \rightarrow$$

    $$t^2 - 3.673t + 2.245 = 0 \quad \rightarrow \quad \boxed{t = 2.90 \, \text{s} \,, \, 0.775 \, \text{s}}$$

    (c) $\boxed{\text{There are two times at which the object reaches that height}}$ – once on the way up $(t = 0.775 \, \text{s})$, and once on the way down $(t = 2.90 \, \text{s})$.

43. The 10-cm (100 mm) apple has a diameter of about 6 mm as measured in the photograph. Thus any distances measured from the picture need to be multiplied by 100 / 6. Choose the downward direction to be positive. Choose $y_0 = 0$ to be stem of the apple on the THIRD image from the top of the picture. It is the first picture in which the stem of the apple is visible. The velocity of the apple at that position is not 0, but it is not known either. Call it v_0. We will choose that the time at that point is $t = 0$, and we call the time interval from one picture to the next to be T. The acceleration of the apple is $a = g = 9.8 \, \text{m/s}^2$.

Giancoli   *Physics: Principles with Applications, 6th Edition*

The 3rd picture after the $t = 0$ picture (the first one that is not overlapping with another image) has the stem 16.5 mm from the origin of coordinates, at a time of $t = 3T$. The actual position would be found by

$$y_1 = (16.5 \text{ mm})(100/6) = 275 \text{ mm} = 0.275 \text{ m} .$$

The 6th picture after the $t = 0$ picture (the next to last one in the picture) has the stem 42 mm from the origin of coordinates, at a time of $t = 6T$. The actual position would be found by

$$y_2 = (42 \text{ mm})(100/6) = 700 \text{ mm} = 0.70 \text{ m} .$$

Now we have two sets of position-time data, relative to the origin. Both of those sets of position-time data must satisfy equation Eq. 2-11b.

$$y_1 = y_0 + v_0 t_1 + \tfrac{1}{2} a t_1^2 \quad \rightarrow \quad 0.275 = 3v_0 T + \tfrac{1}{2} g (3T)^2$$

$$y_2 = y_0 + v_0 t_2 + \tfrac{1}{2} a t_2^2 \quad \rightarrow \quad 0.70 = 6v_0 T + \tfrac{1}{2} g (6T)^2$$

Multiply the first equation by 2, and then subtract it from the second equation to eliminate the dependence on v_0. The resulting equation can be solved for T.

$$\left. \begin{array}{l} 0.55 \text{ m} = 6v_0 T + 9gT^2 \\ 0.70 \text{ m} = 6v_0 T + 18gT^2 \end{array} \right\} \quad \rightarrow \quad 0.15 \text{ m} = 9gT^2 \quad \rightarrow \quad T = \sqrt{\frac{0.15 \text{ m}}{9 (9.8 \text{ m/s}^2)}} = \boxed{4.1 \times 10^{-2} \text{ s}}$$

This is equivalent to $\dfrac{1 \text{ flash}}{T} = \dfrac{1 \text{ flash}}{4.1 \times 10^{-2} \text{ s}} = \boxed{24 \text{ flashes per second}}$.

44. Choose downward to be the positive direction, and $y_0 = 0$ to be the height from which the stone is dropped. Call the location of the top of the window y_w, and the time for the stone to fall from release to the top of the window is t_w. Since the stone is dropped from rest, using Eq. 2-11b with y substituting for x, we have $y_w = y_0 + v_0 t + \tfrac{1}{2} a t^2 = 0 + 0 + \tfrac{1}{2} g t_w^2$. The location of the bottom of the window is $y_w + 2.2 \text{ m}$, and the time for the stone to fall from release to the bottom of the window is $t_w + 0.28 \text{ s}$. Since the stone is dropped from rest, using Eq. 2-11b, we have

$y_w + 2.2 \text{ m} = y_0 + v_0 + \tfrac{1}{2} a t^2 = 0 + 0 + \tfrac{1}{2} g (t_w + 0.28 \text{ s})^2$. Substituting the first expression for y_w into the second one.

$$\tfrac{1}{2} g t_w^2 + 2.2 \text{ m} = \tfrac{1}{2} g (t_w + 0.28 \text{ s})^2 \quad \rightarrow \quad t_w = 0.662 \text{ s}$$

Use this time in the first equation.

$$y_w = \tfrac{1}{2} g t_w^2 = \tfrac{1}{2} (9.8 \text{ m/s}^2)(0.662 \text{ s})^2 = \boxed{2.1 \text{ m}} .$$

45. For the falling rock, choose downward to be the positive direction, and $y_0 = 0$ to be the height from which the stone is dropped. The initial velocity is $v_0 = 0 \text{ m/s}$, the acceleration is $a = g$, the displacement is $y = H$, and the time of fall is t_1. Using Eq. 2-11b with y substituting for x, we have $H = y_0 + v_0 t + \tfrac{1}{2} t^2 = 0 + 0 + \tfrac{1}{2} g t_1^2$.

For the sound wave, use the constant speed equation that $v_s = \dfrac{d}{\Delta t} = \dfrac{H}{T - t_1}$, which can be rearranged

© 2005 Pearson Education, Inc., Upper Saddle River, NJ. All rights reserved. This material is protected under all copyright laws as they currently exist. No portion of this material may be reproduced, in any form or by any means, without permission in writing from the publisher.

25

to give $t_1 = T - \dfrac{H}{v_s}$, where $T = 3.2$ s is the total time elapsed from dropping the rock to hearing the

sound. Insert this expression for t_1 into the equation for H, and solve for H.

$$H = \tfrac{1}{2}g\left(T - \frac{H}{v_s}\right)^2 \quad \rightarrow \quad \frac{g}{2v_s^2}H^2 - \left(\frac{gT}{v_s} + 1\right)H + \tfrac{1}{2}gT^2 = 0 \quad \rightarrow$$

$$4.239 \times 10^{-5} H^2 - 1.092H + 50.18 = 0 \quad \rightarrow \quad H = 46.0 \text{ m}, \ 2.57 \times 10^4 \text{ m}$$

If the larger answer is used in $t_1 = T - \dfrac{H}{v_s}$, a negative time of fall results, and so the physically

correct answer is $\boxed{H = 46 \text{ m}}$.

46. Choose upward to be the positive direction, and $y_0 = 0$ to be the location of the nozzle. The
    initial velocity is v_0, the acceleration is $a = -9.8 \text{ m/s}^2$, the final location is $y = -1.5 \text{ m}$, and
    the time of flight is $t = 2.0$ s. Using Eq. 2-11b and substituting y for x gives the following.

$$y = y_0 + v_0 t + \tfrac{1}{2}at^2 \quad \rightarrow \quad v_0 = \frac{y - \tfrac{1}{2}at^2}{t} = \frac{-1.5 \text{ m} - \tfrac{1}{2}\left(-9.8 \text{ m/s}^2\right)\left(2.0 \text{ s}\right)^2}{2.0 \text{ s}} = \boxed{9.1 \text{ m/s}}$$

$\boxed{47.}$ Choose downward to be the positive direction, and $y_0 = 0$ to be at the top of the cliff. The initial
    velocity is $v_0 = -12.0 \text{ m/s}$, the acceleration is $a = 9.80 \text{ m/s}^2$, and the final location is $y = 70.0 \text{ m}$.
    (a) Using Eq. 2-11b and substituting y for x, we have

$$y = y_0 + v_0 t + \tfrac{1}{2}at^2 \quad \rightarrow \quad \left(4.9 \text{ m/s}^2\right)t^2 - \left(12.0 \text{ m/s}\right)t - 70 \text{ m} = 0 \quad \rightarrow \quad t = -2.749 \text{ s}, \ 5.198 \text{ s}.$$

The positive answer is the physical answer: $\boxed{t = 5.20 \text{ s}}$.

(b) Using Eq. 2-11a, we have $v = v_0 + at = -12.0 \text{ m/s} + \left(9.80 \text{ m/s}^2\right)\left(5.198 \text{ s}\right) = \boxed{38.9 \text{ m/s}}$.

(c) The total distance traveled will be the distance up plus the distance down. The distance down
    will be 70 m more than the distance up. To find the distance up, use the fact that the speed at
    the top of the path will be 0. Then using Eq. 2-11c:

$$v^2 = v_0^2 + 2a\left(y - y_0\right) \quad \rightarrow \quad y = y_0 + \frac{v^2 - v_0^2}{2a} = 0 + \frac{0 - \left(-12.0 \text{ m/s}\right)^2}{2\left(9.80 \text{ m/s}^2\right)} = -7.35 \text{ m}.$$

Thus the distance up is 7.35 m, the distance down is 77.35 m, and the total distance traveled is
$\boxed{84.7 \text{ m}}$.

48. Choose upward to be the positive direction, and $y_0 = 0$ to be the level from which the ball was
    thrown. The initial velocity is v_0, the instantaneous velocity is $v = 13 \text{ m/s}$, the acceleration is
    $a = -9.80 \text{ m/s}^2$, and the location of the window is $y = 28 \text{ m}$.
    (a) Using Eq. 2-11c and substituting y for x, we have

$$v^2 = v_0^2 + 2a\left(y - y_0\right) \quad \rightarrow$$

$$v_0 = \pm\sqrt{v^2 - 2a\left(y - y_0\right)} = \pm\sqrt{\left(13 \text{ m/s}\right)^2 - 2\left(-9.8 \text{ m/s}^2\right)\left(28 \text{ m}\right)} = \boxed{27 \text{ m/s}}$$

Choose the positive value because the initial direction is upward.

(b)   At the top of its path, the velocity will be 0, and so we can use the initial velocity as found above, along with Eq. 2-11c.

$$v^2 = v_0^2 + 2a(y - y_0) \quad \rightarrow \quad y = y_0 + \frac{v^2 - v_0^2}{2a} = 0 + \frac{0 - (27\,\text{m/s})^2}{2(-9.8\,\text{m/s}^2)} = \boxed{37\,\text{m}}$$

(c)   We want the time elapsed from throwing (speed $v_0 = 27\,\text{m/s}$) to reaching the window (speed $v = 13\,\text{m/s}$). Using Eq. 2-11a, we have:

$$v = v_0 + at \quad \rightarrow \quad t = \frac{v - v_0}{a} = \frac{13\,\text{m/s} - 27\,\text{m/s}}{-9.80\,\text{m/s}^2} = \boxed{1.4\,\text{s}}.$$

(d)   We want the time elapsed from the window (speed $v_0 = 13\,\text{m/s}$) to reaching the street (speed $v = -27\,\text{m/s}$). Using Eq. 2-11a, we have:

$$v = v_0 + at \quad \rightarrow \quad t = \frac{v - v_0}{a} = \frac{-27\,\text{m/s} - 13\,\text{m/s}}{-9.80\,\text{m/s}^2} = \boxed{4.1\,\text{s}}.$$

49.   Slightly different answers may be obtained since the data comes from reading the graph.
  (a)   The greatest velocity is found at the highest point on the graph, which is at $\boxed{t \approx 48\,\text{s}}$.
  (b)   The indication of a constant velocity on a velocity-time graph is a slope of 0, which occurs from $\boxed{t = 90\,\text{s} \text{ to } t \approx 108\,\text{s}}$.
  (c)   The indication of a constant acceleration on a velocity-time graph is a constant slope, which occurs from $\boxed{t = 0\,\text{s} \text{ to } t \approx 38\,\text{s}}$, again from $\boxed{t \approx 65\,\text{s} \text{ to } t \approx 83\,\text{s}}$, and again from $\boxed{t = 90\,\text{s} \text{ to } t \approx 108\,\text{s}}$.
  (d)   The magnitude of the acceleration is greatest when the magnitude of the slope is greatest, which occurs from $\boxed{t \approx 65\,\text{s} \text{ to } t \approx 83\,\text{s}}$.

50.   Slightly different answers may be obtained since the data comes from reading the graph.
  (a)   The instantaneous velocity is given by the slope of the tangent line to the curve. At $t = 10.0\,\text{s}$, the slope is approximately $v(10) \approx \dfrac{3\,\text{m} - 0}{10.0\,\text{s} - 0} = \boxed{0.3\,\text{m/s}}$.
  (b)   At $t = 30.0\,\text{s}$, the slope of the tangent line to the curve, and thus the instantaneous velocity, is approximately $v(30) \approx \dfrac{22\,\text{m} - 8\,\text{m}}{35\,\text{s} - 25\,\text{s}} = \boxed{1.4\,\text{m/s}}$.
  (c)   The average velocity is given by $\overline{v} = \dfrac{x(5)\,\text{m} - x(0)\,\text{m}}{5.0\,\text{s} - 0\,\text{s}} = \dfrac{1.5\,\text{m} - 0}{5.0\,\text{s}} = \boxed{.30\,\text{m/s}}$.
  (d)   The average velocity is given by $\overline{v} = \dfrac{x(30)\,\text{m} - x(25)\,\text{m}}{30.0\,\text{s} - 25.0\,\text{s}} = \dfrac{16\,\text{m} - 9\,\text{m}}{5.0\,\text{s}} = \boxed{1.4\,\text{m/s}}$.
  (e)   The average velocity is given by $\overline{v} = \dfrac{x(50)\,\text{m} - x(40)\,\text{m}}{50.0\,\text{s} - 40.0\,\text{s}} = \dfrac{10\,\text{m} - 19.5\,\text{m}}{10.0\,\text{s}} = \boxed{-0.95\,\text{m/s}}$.

51.   Slightly different answers may be obtained since the data comes from reading the graph.
  (a)   The indication of a constant velocity on a position-time graph is a constant slope, which occurs from $\boxed{t = 0\,\text{s} \text{ to } t \approx 18\,\text{s}}$.
  (b)   The greatest velocity will occur when the slope is the highest positive value, which occurs at

about $\boxed{t = 27 \text{ s}}$.

(c)   The indication of a 0 velocity on a position-time graph is a slope of 0, which occurs at about
      from $\boxed{t = 38 \text{ s}}$.

(d) $\boxed{\text{The object moves in both directions.}}$ When the slope is positive, from $t = 0$ s to $t = 38$ s,
      the object is moving in the positive direction. When the slope is negative, from $t = 38$ s to
      $t = 50$ s, the object is moving in the negative direction.

52. Slightly different answers may be obtained since the data comes from reading the graph. We assume
     that the short, nearly horizontal portions of the graph are the times that shifting is occurring, and
     those times are not counted as being "in" a certain gear.

(a)   The average acceleration in 2nd gear is given by $\bar{a}_2 = \dfrac{\Delta v_2}{\Delta t_2} = \dfrac{24 \text{ m/s} - 14 \text{ m/s}}{8 \text{ s} - 4 \text{ s}} = \boxed{2.5 \text{ m/s}^2}$.

      The average acceleration in 4th gear is given by $\bar{a}_4 = \dfrac{\Delta v_4}{\Delta t_4} = \dfrac{44 \text{ m/s} - 37 \text{ m/s}}{27 \text{ s} - 16 \text{ s}} = \boxed{0.64 \text{ m/s}^2}$.

(b)   The distance traveled can be determined from a velocity-time graph by calculating the area
      between the graph and the $v = 0$ axis, bounded by the times under consideration. For this case,
      we will approximate the area as a rectangle.

$$\text{height} = \bar{v} = \dfrac{v_f + v_0}{2} = \dfrac{44 \text{ m/s} + 37 \text{ m/s}}{2} = 40.5 \text{ m/s} \quad \text{width} = \Delta t = 27 \text{ s} - 16 \text{ s} = 11 \text{ s}$$

      Thus the distance traveled is $d = \bar{v}\Delta t = (40.5 \text{ m/s})(11 \text{ s}) = \boxed{450 \text{ m}}$.

53. Slightly different answers may be obtained since the data comes from reading the graph. We assume
     that the short, nearly horizontal portions of the graph are the times that shifting is occurring, and
     those times are not counted as being "in" a certain gear.

(a)   The average acceleration in first gear is given by $\bar{a} = \dfrac{\Delta v}{\Delta t} = \dfrac{14 \text{ m/s} - 0 \text{ m/s}}{4 \text{ s} - 0 \text{ s}} = \boxed{4 \text{ m/s}^2}$.

(b)   The average acceleration in third gear is given by $\bar{a} = \dfrac{\Delta v}{\Delta t} = \dfrac{37 \text{ m/s} - 24 \text{ m/s}}{14 \text{ s} - 9 \text{ s}} = \boxed{3 \text{ m/s}^2}$.

(c)   The average acceleration in fifth gear is given by $\bar{a} = \dfrac{\Delta v}{\Delta t} = \dfrac{52 \text{ m/s} - 44 \text{ m/s}}{50 \text{ s} - 27 \text{ s}} = \boxed{0.35 \text{ m/s}^2}$.

(d)   The average acceleration through the first four gears is given by

$$\bar{a} = \dfrac{\Delta v}{\Delta t} = \dfrac{44 \text{ m/s} - 0 \text{ m/s}}{27 \text{ s} - 0 \text{ s}} = \boxed{1.6 \text{ m/s}^2}.$$

54. Slightly different answers may be obtained since the data comes from reading the graph.

(a)   To estimate the distance the object traveled during the first minute, we need to find the area
      under the graph, from $t = 0$ s to $t = 60$ s. Each "block" of the graph represents an "area" of
      $\Delta x = (10 \text{ m/s})(10 \text{ s}) = 100$ m. By counting and estimating, there are about 17.5 blocks under
      the 1st minute of the graph, and so the distance traveled during the 1st minute is about $\boxed{1750 \text{ m}}$.

(b)   For the second minute, there are about 5 blocks under the graph, and so the distance traveled
      during the second minute is about $\boxed{500 \text{ m}}$.

     Alternatively, average accelerations can be estimated for various portions of the graph, and then the
     uniform acceleration equations may be applied. For instance, for part (a), break the motion up into

two segments, from 0 to 50 seconds and then from 50 to 60 seconds.

(a) t = 0 to 50: $\bar{a}_1 = \dfrac{\Delta v}{\Delta t} = \dfrac{38\,\text{m/s} - 14\,\text{m/s}}{50\,\text{s} - 0\,\text{s}} = 0.48\,\text{m/s}^2$

$d_1 = v_{o1}t_1 + \tfrac{1}{2}\bar{a}_1 t_1^2 = \left(14\,\text{m/s}\right)\left(50\,\text{s}\right) + \tfrac{1}{2}\left(0.48\,\text{m/s}^2\right)\left(50\,\text{s}\right)^2 = 1300\,\text{m}$

$\bar{a}_2 = \dfrac{\Delta v}{\Delta t} = \dfrac{31\,\text{m/s} - 38\,\text{m/s}}{60\,\text{s} - 50\,\text{s}} = -0.70\,\text{m/s}^2$

$d_2 = v_{o2}t_2 + \tfrac{1}{2}\bar{a}_2 t_2^2 = \left(38\,\text{m/s}\right)\left(10\,\text{s}\right) + \tfrac{1}{2}\left(-0.70\,\text{m/s}^2\right)\left(10\,\text{s}\right)^2 = 345\,\text{m}$

$d_1 + d_2 = 1645\,\text{m}$

55. The v vs. t graph is found by taking the slope of the x vs. t graph. Both graphs are shown here.

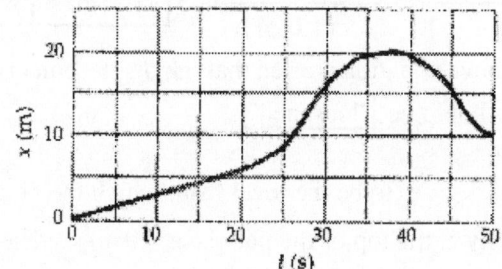
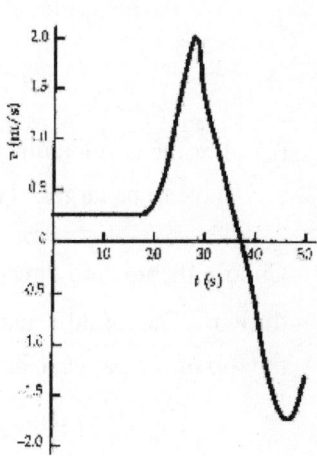

56. (a) During the interval from A to B, it is $\boxed{\text{moving in the negative direction}}$, because its displacement is negative.

(b) During the interval from A to B, it is $\boxed{\text{speeding up}}$, because the magnitude of its slope is increasing (changing from less steep to more steep).

(c) During the interval from A to B, $\boxed{\text{the acceleration is negative}}$, because the graph is concave downward, indicating that the slope is getting more negative, and thus the acceleration is negative.

(d) During the interval from D to E, it is $\boxed{\text{moving in the positive direction}}$, because the displacement is positive.

(e) During the interval from D to E, it is $\boxed{\text{speeding up}}$, because the magnitude of its slope is increasing (changing from less steep to more steep).

(f) During the interval from D to E, $\boxed{\text{the acceleration is positive}}$, because the graph is concave upward, indicating the slope is getting more positive, and thus the acceleration is positive.

(g) During the interval from C to D, $\boxed{\text{the object is not moving in either direction}}$.

$\boxed{\text{The velocity and acceleration are both 0.}}$

57. (*a*) For the free-falling part of the motion, choose downward to be the positive direction, and
$y_0 = 0$ to be the height from which the person jumped. The initial velocity is $v_0 = 0$,
acceleration is $a = 9.80 \text{ m/s}^2$, and the location of the net is $y = 15.0 \text{ m}$. Find the speed upon
reaching the net from Eq. (2-11c) with x replaced by y.

$$v^2 = v_0^2 + 2a\left(y - y_{()}\right) \rightarrow v = \pm\sqrt{0 + 2a(y - 0)} = \pm\sqrt{2(9.80 \text{ m/s}^2)(15.0 \text{ m})} = 17.1 \text{ m/s}$$

The positive root is selected since the person is moving downward.
For the net-stretching part of the motion, choose downward to be the positive direction, and
$y_0 = 15.0 \text{ m}$ to be the height at which the person first contacts the net. The initial velocity is
$v_0 = 17.1 \text{ m/s}$, the final velocity is $v = 0$, and the location at the stretched position is
$y = 16.0 \text{ m}$. Find the acceleration from Eq. (2-11c) with x replaced by y.

$$v^2 = v_0^2 + 2a(y - y_0) \rightarrow a = \frac{v^2 - v_0^2}{2(y - y_0)} = \frac{0^2 - (17.1 \text{ m/s})^2}{2(1.0 \text{ m})} = \boxed{-150 \text{ m/s}^2}$$

(*b*) For the acceleration to be smaller, in the above equation we see that the displacement would
have to be larger. This means that the net should be $\boxed{\text{"loosened"}}$.

58. Choose the upward direction to be positive, and $y_0 = 0$ to be the level from which the object was
thrown. The initial velocity is v_0 and the velocity at the top of the path is $v = 0 \text{ m/s}$. The height at
the top of the path can be found from Eq. (2-11c) with x replaced by y.

$$v^2 = v_0^2 + 2a(y - y_0) \rightarrow y - y_0 = \frac{-v_0^2}{2a}.$$

From this we see that the displacement is inversely proportional to the acceleration, and so if the
acceleration is reduced by a factor of 6 by going to the Moon, and the initial velocity is unchanged,
the $\boxed{\text{displacement increases by a factor of 6}}$.

59. The initial velocity of the car is $v_0 = (100 \text{ km/h})\left(\dfrac{1 \text{ m/s}}{3.6 \text{ km/h}}\right) = 27.8 \text{ m/s}$. Choose $x_0 = 0$ to be

location at which the deceleration begins. We have $v = 0 \text{ m/s}$ and $a = -30g = -294 \text{ m/s}^2$. Find
the displacement from Eq. (2-11c).

$$v^2 = v_0^2 + 2a(x - x_0) \rightarrow x = x_0 + \frac{v^2 - v_0^2}{2a} = 0 + \frac{0 - (27.8 \text{ m/s})^2}{2(-2.94 \times 10^2 \text{ m/s}^2)} = 1.31 \text{ m} \approx \boxed{1.3 \text{ m}}$$

60. Choose downward to be the positive direction, and $y_0 = 0$ to be at the height of the bridge. Agent
Bond has an initial velocity of $v_0 = 0$, an acceleration of $a = g$, and will have a displacement of
$y = 12 \text{ m} - 1.5 \text{ m} = 11.5 \text{ m}$. Find the time of fall from Eq. 2-11b with x replaced by y.

$$y = y_0 + v_0 t + \tfrac{1}{2}at^2 \rightarrow t = \sqrt{\frac{2y}{a}} = \sqrt{\frac{2(11.5 \text{ m})}{9.80 \text{ m/s}^2}} = 1.532 \text{ s}$$

If the truck is approaching with $v = 25 \text{ m/s}$, then he needs to jump when the truck is a distance away
given by $d = vt = (25 \text{ m/s})(1.532 \text{ s}) = 38.30 \text{ m}$. Convert this distance into "poles".

$$d = (38.30 \text{ m})(1 \text{ pole}/25 \text{ m}) = 1.53 \text{ poles}$$

So he should jump when the truck is about $\boxed{1.5 \text{ poles}}$ away from the bridge.

61. (a) Choose downward to be the positive direction, and $y_0 = 0$ to be the level from which the car was dropped. The initial velocity is $v_0 = 0$, the final location is $y = H$, and the acceleration is $a = g$. Find the final velocity from Eq. 2-11c, replacing x with y.

$$v^2 = v_0^2 + 2a(y - y_0) \rightarrow v = \pm\sqrt{v_0^2 + 2a(y - y_0)} = \pm\sqrt{2gH}.$$

The speed is the magnitude of the velocity, $\boxed{v = \sqrt{2gH}}$.

(b) Solving the above equation for the height, we have that $H = \dfrac{v^2}{2g}$. Thus for a collision of

$$v = (60\,\text{km/h})\left(\frac{1\,\text{m/s}}{3.6\,\text{km/h}}\right) = 16.67\,\text{m/s}, \text{ the corresponding height is:}$$

$$H = \frac{v^2}{2g} = \frac{(16.67\,\text{m/s})^2}{2(9.80\,\text{m/s}^2)} = 14.17\,\text{m} \approx \boxed{14\,\text{m}}.$$

(c) For a collision of $v = (100\,\text{km/h})\left(\dfrac{1\,\text{m/s}}{3.6\,\text{km/h}}\right) = 27.78\,\text{m/s}$, the corresponding height is:

$$H = \frac{v^2}{2g} = \frac{(27.78\,\text{m/s})^2}{2(9.80\,\text{m/s}^2)} = 39.37\,\text{m} \approx \boxed{39\,\text{m}}.$$

62. The average speed is the distance divided by the time.

$$\overline{v} = \frac{d}{t} = \left(\frac{1 \times 10^9\,\text{km}}{1\,\text{y}}\right)\left(\frac{1\,\text{y}}{365\,\text{d}}\right)\left(\frac{1\,\text{d}}{24\,\text{h}}\right) = 1.142 \times 10^5\,\text{km/h} \approx \boxed{1 \times 10^5\,\text{km/h}}$$

63. Use the information for the first 180 m to find the acceleration, and the information for the full motion to find the final velocity. For the first segment, the train has $v_0 = 0\,\text{m/s}$, $v_1 = 25\,\text{m/s}$, and a displacement of $x_1 - x_0 = 180\,\text{m}$. Find the acceleration from Eq. 2-11c.

$$v_1^2 = v_0^2 + 2a(x_1 - x_0) \rightarrow a = \frac{v_1^2 - v_0^2}{2(x_1 - x_0)} = \frac{(25\,\text{m/s})^2 - 0}{2(180\,\text{m})} = 1.736\,\text{m/s}^2$$

Find the speed of the train after it has traveled the total distance (total displacement of $x_2 - x_0 = 275\,\text{m}$) using Eq. 2-11c.

$$v_2^2 = v_0^2 + 2a(x_2 - x_0) \rightarrow v_2 = \sqrt{v_0^2 + 2a(x_2 - x_0)} = \sqrt{2(1.736\,\text{m/s}^2)(275\,\text{m})} = \boxed{31\,\text{m/s}}.$$

64. For the motion in the air, choose downward to be the positive direction, and $y_0 = 0$ to be at the height of the diving board. Then diver has $v_0 = 0$, (assuming the diver does not jump upward or downward), $a = g = 9.8\,\text{m/s}^2$, and $y = 4.0\,\text{m}$ when reaching the surface of the water. Find the diver's speed at the water's surface from Eq. 2-11c, with x replaced by y.

$$v^2 = v_0^2 + 2a(y - y_0)x \rightarrow v = \pm\sqrt{v_0^2 + 2a(y - y_0)} = \sqrt{0 + 2(9.8\,\text{m/s}^2)(4.0\,\text{m})} = 8.85\,\text{m/s}$$

For the motion in the water, again choose down to be positive, but redefine $y_0 = 0$ to be at the surface of the water. For this motion, $v_0 = 8.85 \, \text{m/s}$, $v = 0$, and $y - y_0 = 2.0 \, \text{m}$. Find the acceleration from Eq. 2-11c, with x replaced by y.

$$v^2 = v_0^2 + 2a(y - y_0) \quad \rightarrow \quad a = \frac{v^2 - v_0^2}{2(y - y_0)x} = \frac{0 - (8.85 \, \text{m/s})^2}{2(2.0 \, \text{m})} = -19.6 \, \text{m/s}^2 \approx \boxed{-20 \, \text{m/s}^2}$$

The negative sign indicates that the acceleration is directed upwards.

65. This problem can be analyzed as a series of three one-dimensional motions: the acceleration phase, the constant speed phase, and the deceleration phase. The maximum speed of the train is:

$$(90 \, \text{km/h})\left(\frac{1 \, \text{m/s}}{3.6 \, \text{km/h}}\right) = 25 \, \text{m/s} \, .$$

In the acceleration phase, the initial velocity is $v_0 = 0 \, \text{m/s}$, the acceleration is $a = 1.1 \, \text{m/s}^2$, and the final velocity is $v = 25 \, \text{m/s}$. Find the elapsed time for the acceleration phase from Eq. 2-11a.

$$v = v_0 + at \quad \rightarrow \quad t_{acc} = \frac{v - v_0}{a} = \frac{25 \, \text{m/s} - 0}{1.1 \, \text{m/s}^2} = 22.73 \, \text{s} \, .$$

Find the displacement during the acceleration phase from Eq. 2-11b.

$$(x - x_0)_{acc} = v_0 t + \tfrac{1}{2}at^2 = 0 + \tfrac{1}{2}(1.1 \, \text{m/s}^2)(22.73 \, \text{s})^2 = 284 \, \text{m} \, .$$

In the deceleration phase, the initial velocity is $v_0 = 25 \, \text{m/s}$, the acceleration is $a = -2.0 \, \text{m/s}^2$, and the final velocity is $v = 0 \, \text{m/s}$. Find the elapsed time for the deceleration phase from equation Eq. 2-11a.

$$v = v_0 + at \quad \rightarrow \quad t_{dec} = \frac{v - v_0}{a} = \frac{0 - 25 \, \text{m/s}}{-2.0 \, \text{m/s}^2} = 12.5 \, \text{s} \, .$$

Find the distance traveled during the deceleration phase from Eq. 2-11b.

$$(x - x_0)_{dec} = v_0 t + \tfrac{1}{2}at^2 = (25 \, \text{m/s})(12.5 \, \text{s}) + \tfrac{1}{2}(-2.0 \, \text{m/s}^2)(12.5 \, \text{s})^2 = 156 \, \text{m} \, .$$

The total elapsed time and distance traveled for the acceleration / deceleration phases are:

$$t_{acc} + t_{dec} = 22.7 \, \text{s} + 12.5 \, \text{s} = 35.2 \, \text{s}$$

$$(x - x_0)_{acc} + (x - x_0)_{dec} = 284 \, \text{m} + 156 \, \text{m} = 440 \, \text{m} \, .$$

(a) If the stations are spaced 1.80 km = 1800 m apart, then there is a total of $\dfrac{9000 \, \text{m}}{1800 \, \text{m}} = 5$ inter-station segments. A train making the entire trip would thus have a total of 5 inter-station segments and 4 stops of 20 s each at the intermediate stations. Since 440 m is traveled during acceleration and deceleration, 1360 m of each segment is traveled at an average speed of $\overline{v} = 25 \, \text{m/s}$. The time for that 1360 m is given by

$$d = \overline{v}t \quad \rightarrow \quad t_{\substack{constant \\ speed}} = \frac{d}{\overline{v}} = \frac{1360 \, \text{m}}{25 \, \text{m/s}} = 54.4 \, \text{s} \, . \text{ Thus a total inter-station segment will take 35.2 s}$$

+ 54.4 s = 89.6 s. With 5 inter-station segments of 89.6 s each, and 4 stops of 20 s each, the total time is given by:

$$t_{0.8 \, \text{km}} = 5(89.6 \, \text{s}) + 4(20 \, \text{s}) = 528 \, \text{s} = \boxed{8.8 \, \text{min}} \, .$$

(*b*) If the stations are spaced 3.0 km =3000 m apart, then there is a total of $\dfrac{9000 \text{ m}}{3000 \text{ m}} = 3$ inter-station segments. A train making the entire trip would thus have a total of 3 inter-station segments and 2 stops of 20 s each at the intermediate stations. Since 440 m is traveled during acceleration and deceleration, 2560 m of each segment is traveled at an average speed of

$\overline{v} = 25 \text{ m/s}$. The time for that 2560 m is given by $d = \overline{v}t \rightarrow t = \dfrac{d}{\overline{v}} = \dfrac{2560 \text{ m}}{25 \text{ m/s}} = 102.4 \text{ s}$.

Thus a total inter-station segment will take 35.2 s + 102.4 s = 137.6 s. With 3 inter-station segments of 137.6 s each, and 2 stops of 20 s each, the total time is

$$t_{3.0 \text{ km}} = 3(137.6 \text{ s}) + 2(20 \text{ s}) = 453 \text{ s} = \boxed{7.5 \text{ min}}.$$

66. Choose downward to be the positive direction, and $y_0 = 0$ to be at the start of the pelican's dive. The pelican has an initial velocity is $v_0 = 0$ and an acceleration of $a = g$, and a final location of $y = 16.0 \text{ m}$. Find the total time of the pelican's dive from Eq. 2-11b, with *x* replaced by *y*.

$$y = y_0 + v_0 t + \tfrac{1}{2}at^2 \rightarrow y = 0 + 0 + \tfrac{1}{2}at^2 \rightarrow t_{\text{dive}} = \sqrt{\frac{2y}{a}} = \sqrt{\frac{2(16.0 \text{ m})}{9.80 \text{ m/s}^2}} = 1.81 \text{ s}.$$

The fish can take evasive action if he sees the pelican at a time of 1.81 s – 0.20 s = 1.61 s into the dive. Find the location of the pelican at that time from Eq. 2-11b.

$$y = y_0 + v_0 t + \tfrac{1}{2}at = 0 + 0 + \tfrac{1}{2}\left(9.80 \text{ m/s}^2\right)(1.61 \text{ s})^2 = 12.7 \text{ m}$$

Thus the fish must spot the pelican at a minimum height from the surface of the water of

16.0 m – 12.7 m = $\boxed{3.3 \text{ m}}$.

67. First consider the "uphill lie", in which the ball is being putted down the hill. Choose $x_0 = 0$ to be the ball's original location, and the direction of the ball's travel as the positive direction. The final velocity of the ball is $v = 0 \text{ m/s}$, the acceleration of the ball is $a = -2.0 \text{ m/s}^2$, and the displacement of the ball will be $x - x_0 = 6.0 \text{ m}$ for the first case, and $x - x_0 = 8.0 \text{ m}$ for the second case. Find the initial velocity of the ball from Eq. 2-11c.

$$v^2 = v_0^2 + 2a(x - x_0) \rightarrow v_0 = \sqrt{v^2 - 2a(x - x_0)} = \begin{cases} \sqrt{0 - 2(-2.0 \text{ m/s}^2)(6.0 \text{ m})} = 4.9 \text{ m/s} \\ \sqrt{0 - 2(-2.0 \text{ m/s}^2)(8.0 \text{ m})} = 5.7 \text{ m/s} \end{cases}$$

The range of acceptable velocities for the uphill lie is $\boxed{4.9 \text{ m/s to } 5.7 \text{ m/s}}$, with a spread of 0.8 m/s.

Now consider the "downhill lie", in which the ball is being putted up the hill. Use a very similar set-up for the problem, with the basic difference being that the acceleration of the ball is now $a = -3.0 \text{ m/s}^2$. Find the initial velocity of the ball from Eq. 2-11c.

$$v^2 = v_0^2 + 2a(x - x_0) \rightarrow v_0 = \sqrt{v^2 - 2a(x - x_0)} = \begin{cases} \sqrt{0 - 2(-3.0 \text{ m/s}^2)(6.0 \text{ m})} = 6.0 \text{ m/s} \\ \sqrt{0 - 2(-3.0 \text{ m/s}^2)(8.0 \text{ m})} = 6.9 \text{ m/s} \end{cases}$$

The range of acceptable velocities for the downhill lie is $\boxed{6.0 \text{ m/s to } 6.9 \text{ m/s}}$, with a spread of 0.9 m/s.

Because the range of acceptable velocities is smaller for putting down the hill, more control in putting is necessary, and so the downhill putt is more difficult.

68. (a) The train's constant speed is $v_{train} = 6.0\,\text{m/s}$, and the location of the empty box car as a function of time is given by $x_{train} = v_{train}t = (6.0\,\text{m/s})t$. The fugitive has $v_0 = 0\,\text{m/s}$ and $a = 4.0\,\text{m/s}^2$ until his final speed is $8.0\,\text{m/s}$. The elapsed time during acceleration is

$$t_{acc} = \frac{v - v_0}{a} = \frac{8.0\,\text{m/s}}{4.0\,\text{m/s}^2} = 2.0\,\text{s}.$$ Let the origin be the location of the fugitive when he starts to

run. The first possibility to consider is, "Can the fugitive catch the train before he reaches his maximum speed?" During the fugitive's acceleration, his location as a function of time is given by $x_{fugitive} = x_0 + v_0 t + \frac{1}{2}at^2 = 0 + 0 + \frac{1}{2}(4.0\,\text{m/s}^2)t^2$. For him to catch the train, we must have

$x_{train} = x_{fugitive} \rightarrow (6.0\,\text{m/s})t = \frac{1}{2}(4.0\,\text{m/s}^2)t^2$. The solutions of this are $t = 0\,\text{s}, 3\,\text{s}$. Thus the fugitive cannot catch the car during his 2.0 s of acceleration.

Now the equation of motion of the fugitive changes. After the 2.0 s acceleration, he runs with a constant speed of $8.0\,\text{m/s}$. Thus his location is now given (for times $t > 2\,\text{s}$) by the following.

$$x_{fugitive} = \frac{1}{2}(4.0\,\text{m/s}^2)(2.0\,\text{s})^2 + (8.0\,\text{m/s})(t - 2.0\,\text{s}) = (8.0\,\text{m/s})t - 8.0\,\text{m}.$$

So now, for the fugitive to catch the train, we again set the locations equal.

$$x_{train} = x_{fugitive} \rightarrow (6.0\,\text{m/s})t = (8.0\,\text{m/s})t - 8.0\,\text{m} \rightarrow t = \boxed{4.0\,\text{s}}$$

(b) The distance traveled to reach the box car is given by

$$x_{fugitive}(t = 4.0\,\text{s}) = (8.0\,\text{m/s})(4.0\,\text{s}) - 8.0\,\text{m} = \boxed{24\,\text{m}}.$$

69. Choose downward to be the positive direction, and $y_0 = 0$ to be at the roof from which the stones are dropped. The first stone has an initial velocity of $v_0 = 0$ and an acceleration of $a = g$. Eqs. 2-11a and 2-11b (with x replaced by y) give the velocity and location, respectively, of the first stone as a function of time.

$$v = v_0 + at \rightarrow v_1 = gt_1 \qquad y = y_0 + v_0 t + \frac{1}{2}at^2 \rightarrow y_1 = \frac{1}{2}gt_1^2.$$

The second stone has the same initial conditions, but its elapsed time $t - 1.50\,\text{s}$, and so has velocity and location equations as follows.

$$v_2 = g(t_1 - 1.50\,\text{s}) \qquad y_2 = \frac{1}{2}g(t_1 - 1.50\,\text{s})^2$$

The second stone reaches a speed of $v_2 = 12.0\,\text{m/s}$ at a time given by

$$t_1 = 1.50\,\text{s} + \frac{v_2}{g} = 1.50\,\text{s} + \frac{12.0\,\text{m/s}}{9.80\,\text{m/s}^2} = 2.72\,\text{s}.$$

The location of the first stone at that time is

$$y_1 = \frac{1}{2}gt_1^2 = \frac{1}{2}(9.80\,\text{m/s}^2)(2.72\,\text{s})^2 = 36.4\,\text{m}.$$

The location of the second stone at that time is

$$y_2 = \frac{1}{2}g(t_1 - 1.50\,\text{s})^2 = \frac{1}{2}(9.80\,\text{m/s}^2)(2.72 - 1.50\,\text{s})^2 = 7.35\,\text{m}.$$

Thus the distance between the two stones is $y_1 - y_2 = 36.4\,\text{m} - 7.35\,\text{m} = \boxed{29.0\,\text{m}}$.

70. To find the average speed for the entire race, we must take the total distance divided by the total time. If one lap is a distance of L, then the total distance will be $10L$. The time elapsed at a given constant speed is given by $t = d/v$, so the time for the first 9 laps would be $t_1 = \dfrac{9L}{198.0\,\text{km/h}}$, and the time for the last lap would be $t_2 = L/v_2$, where v_2 is the average speed for the last lap. Write an expression for the average speed for the entire race, and then solve for v_2.

$$\overline{v} = \frac{d_{\text{total}}}{t_1 + t_2} = \frac{10L}{\dfrac{9L}{198.0\,\text{km/h}} + \dfrac{L}{v_2}} = 200.0\,\text{km/h} \quad \rightarrow$$

$$v_2 = \frac{1}{\dfrac{10}{200.0\,\text{km/h}} - \dfrac{9}{198.0\,\text{km/h}}} = \boxed{220.0\,\text{km/h}}$$

71. The initial velocity is $v_0 = (18\,\text{km/h})\left(\dfrac{1\,\text{m/s}}{3.6\,\text{km/h}}\right) = 5.0\,\text{m/s}$. The final velocity is

$v_0 = (75\,\text{km/h})\left(\dfrac{1\,\text{m/s}}{3.6\,\text{km/h}}\right) = 20.83\,\text{m/s}$. The displacement is $x - x_0 = 4.0\,\text{km} = 4000\,\text{m}$. Find the average acceleration from Eq. 2-11c.

$$v^2 = v_0^2 + 2a(x - x_0) \quad \rightarrow \quad a = \frac{v^2 - v_0^2}{2(x - x_0)} = \frac{(20.83\,\text{m/s})^2 - (5.0\,\text{m/s})^2}{2(4000\ \text{m})} = \boxed{5.1 \times 10^{-2}\ \text{m/s}^2}$$

72. Assume that $y_0 = 0$ for each child is the level at which the child loses contact with the trampoline surface. Choose upward to be the positive direction.

   (*a*) The second child has $v_{02} = 5.0\,\text{m/s}$, $a = -g = -9.8\,\text{m/s}^2$, and $v = 0\,\text{m/s}$ at the maximum height position. Find the child's maximum height from Eq. 2-11c, with x replaced by y.

$$v^2 = v_{02}^2 + 2a(y_2 - y_0) \quad \rightarrow \quad y_2 = y_0 + \frac{v^2 - v_{02}^2}{2a} = 0 + \frac{0 - (5.0\,\text{m/s})^2}{2(-9.8\,\text{m/s}^2)} = 1.276\,\text{m} \approx \boxed{1.3\ \text{m}}$$

   (*b*) Since the first child can bounce up to one-and-a-half times higher than the second child, the first child can bounce up to a height of $1.5(1.276\,\text{m}) = 1.913\,\text{m} = y_1 - y_0$. Eq. 2-11c is again used to find the initial speed of the first child.

$$v^2 = v_{01}^2 + 2a(y_1 - y_0) \quad \rightarrow$$

$$v_{01} = \pm\sqrt{v^2 - 2a(y_1 - y_0)} = \sqrt{0 - 2(-9.8\,\text{m/s}^2)(1.913\ \text{m})} = 6.124\,\text{m/s} \approx \boxed{6.1\,\text{m/s}}$$

   The positive root was chosen since the child was initially moving upward.

   (*c*) To find the time that the first child was in the air, use Eq. 2-11b with a total displacement of 0, since the child returns to the original position.

$$y = y_0 + v_{01}t_1 + \tfrac{1}{2}at_1^2 \quad \rightarrow \quad 0 = (6.124\,\text{m/s})t_1 + \tfrac{1}{2}(-9.8\,\text{m/s}^2)t_1^2 \quad \rightarrow \quad t_1 = 0\ \text{s},\ 1.2497\ \text{s}$$

   The time of 0 s corresponds to the time the child started the jump, so the correct answer is $\boxed{1.2\ \text{s}}$.

73. For the car to pass the train, the car must travel the length of the train AND the distance the train travels. The distance the car travels can thus be written as either $d_{car} = v_{car}t = (95 \text{ km/h})t$ or $d_{car} = L_{train} + v_{train}t = 1.10 \text{ km} + (75 \text{ km/h})t$. To solve for the time, equate these two expressions for the distance the car travels.

$$(95 \text{ km/h})t = 1.10 \text{ km} + (75 \text{ km/h})t \rightarrow t = \frac{1.10 \text{ km}}{20 \text{ km/h}} = 0.055 \text{ h} = \boxed{3.3 \text{ min}}$$

The distance the car travels during this time is $d = (95 \text{ km/h})(0.055 \text{ h}) = 5.225 \text{ km} \approx \boxed{5.2 \text{ km}}$.

If the train is traveling the opposite direction from the car, then the car must travel the length of the train MINUS the distance the train travels. Thus the distance the car travels can be written as either $d_{car} = (95 \text{ km/h})t$ or $d_{car} = 1.10 \text{ km} - (75 \text{ km/h})t$. To solve for the time, equate these two expressions for the distance the car travels.

$$(95 \text{ km/h})t = 1.10 \text{ km} - (75 \text{ km/h})t \rightarrow t = \frac{1.10 \text{ km}}{170 \text{ km/h}} = 6.47 \times 10^{-3} \text{ h} = \boxed{23.3 \text{ s}}$$

The distance the car travels during this time is $d = (95 \text{ km/h})(6.47 \times 10^{-3} \text{ h}) = \boxed{0.61 \text{ km}}$.

74. For the baseball, $v_0 = 0$, $x - x_0 = 3.5 \text{ m}$, and the final speed of the baseball (during the throwing motion) is $v = 44 \text{ m/s}$. The acceleration is found from Eq. 2-11c.

$$v^2 = v_0^2 + 2a(x - x_0) \rightarrow a = \frac{v^2 - v_0^2}{2(x - x_0)} = \frac{(44 \text{ m/s})^2 - 0}{2(3.5 \text{ m})} = \boxed{280 \text{ m/s}^2}$$

75. (a) Choose upward to be the positive direction, and $y_0 = 0$ at the ground. The rocket has $v_0 = 0$, $a = 3.2 \text{ m/s}^2$, and $y = 1200 \text{ m}$ when it runs out of fuel. Find the velocity of the rocket when it runs out of fuel from Eq 2-11c, with x replaced by y.

$$v_{1200 \text{ m}}^2 = v_0^2 + 2a(y - y_0) \rightarrow$$

$$v_{1200 \text{ m}} = \pm\sqrt{v_0^2 + 2a(y - y_0)} = \pm\sqrt{0 + 2(3.2 \text{ m/s}^2)(1200 \text{ m})} = 87.64 \text{ m/s} \approx \boxed{88 \text{ m/s}}$$

The positive root is chosen since the rocket is moving upwards when it runs out of fuel.

(b) The time to reach the 1200 m location can be found from equation (2-11a).

$$v_{1200 \text{ m}} = v_0 + at_{1200 \text{ m}} \rightarrow t_{1200 \text{ m}} = \frac{v_{1200 \text{ m}} - v_0}{a} = \frac{87.64 \text{ m/s} - 0}{3.2 \text{ m/s}^2} = 27.39 \text{ s} \approx \boxed{27 \text{ s}}$$

(c) For this part of the problem, the rocket will have an initial velocity $v_0 = 87.64 \text{ m/s}$, an acceleration of $a = -9.8 \text{ m/s}^2$, and a final velocity of $v = 0$ at its maximum altitude. The altitude reached from the out-of-fuel point can be found from equation (2-11c).

$$v^2 = v_{1200 \text{ m}}^2 + 2a(y - 1200 \text{ m}) \rightarrow$$

$$y_{max} = 1200 \text{ m} + \frac{0 - v_{1200 \text{ m}}^2}{2a} = 1200 \text{ m} + \frac{-(87.64 \text{ m/s})^2}{2(-9.8 \text{ m/s}^2)} = 1200 \text{ m} + 390 \text{ m} = \boxed{1590 \text{ m}}$$

(d) The time for the "coasting" portion of the flight can be found from Eq. 2-11a.

$$v = v_{1200 \text{ m}} + at_{coast} \rightarrow t_{coast} = \frac{v - v_0}{a} = \frac{0 - 87.64 \text{ m/s}}{-9.8 \text{ m/s}^2} = 8.94 \text{ s}$$

Thus the total time to reach the maximum altitude is $t = 27\text{ s} + 8.94\text{ s} \approx \boxed{36\text{ s}}$.

(e) For this part of the problem, the rocket has $v_0 = 0\text{ m/s}$, $a = -9.8\text{ m/s}^2$, and a displacement of -1600 m (it falls from a height of 1600 m to the ground). Find the velocity upon reaching the Earth from Eq. 2-11c.

$$v^2 = v_0^2 + 2a(y - y_0) \quad \rightarrow$$

$$v = \pm\sqrt{v_0^2 + 2a(y - y_0)} = \pm\sqrt{0 + 2(-9.80\text{ m/s}^2)(-1600\text{ m})} = \boxed{-177\text{ m/s}}$$

The negative root was chosen because the rocket is moving downward, which is the negative direction.

(f) The time for the rocket to fall back to the Earth is found from Eq. 2-11a.

$$v = v_0 + at \quad \rightarrow \quad t_{\text{fall}} = \frac{v - v_0}{a} = \frac{-177\text{ m/s} - 0}{-9.80\text{ m/s}^2} = 18.1\text{ s}$$

Thus the total time for the entire flight is $t = 36\text{ s} + 18.1\text{ s} = \boxed{54\text{ s}}$.

76. The speed limit is $50\text{ km/h}\left(\dfrac{1\text{ m/s}}{3.6\text{ km/h}}\right) = 13.89\text{ m/s}$.

(a) For your motion, you would need to travel $(10 + 15 + 50 + 15 + 70)\text{ m} = 160\text{ m}$ to get through the third light. The time to travel the 160 m is found using the distance and the constant speed.

$$d = \overline{v}\,t \quad \rightarrow \quad t = \frac{d}{\overline{v}} = \frac{160\text{ m}}{13.89\text{ m/s}} = 11.52\text{ s}$$

$\boxed{\text{Yes}}$, you can make it through all three lights without stopping.

(b) The second car needs to travel 150 m before the third light turns red. This car accelerates from $v_0 = 0\text{ m/s}$ to a maximum of $v = 13.89\text{ m/s}$ with $a = 2.0\text{ m/s}^2$. Use Eq. 2-11a to determine the duration of that acceleration.

$$v = v_0 + at \quad \rightarrow \quad t_{\text{acc}} = \frac{v - v_0}{a} = \frac{13.89\text{ m/s} - 0\text{ m/s}}{2.0\text{ m/s}^2} = 6.94\text{ s}$$

The distance traveled during that time is found from Eq. 2-11b.

$$(x - x_0)_{\text{acc}} = v_0 t_{\text{acc}} + \tfrac{1}{2}at_{\text{acc}}^2 = 0 + \tfrac{1}{2}(2.0\text{ m/s}^2)(6.94\text{ s})^2 = 48.2\text{ m}.$$

Since 6.94 sec have elapsed, there are $13 - 6.94 = 6.06$ sec remaining to clear the intersection. The car travels another 6 seconds at a speed of 13.89 m/s, covering a distance of

$$d_{\substack{\text{constant}\\\text{speed}}} = \overline{v}\,t = (13.89\text{ m/s})(6.06\text{ s}) = 84.2\text{ m}. \text{ Thus the total distance is 48.2 m} + 84.2\text{ m} =$$

132.4 m. $\boxed{\text{No}}$, the car cannot make it through all three lights without stopping.

77. Take the origin to be the location where the speeder passes the police car. The speeder's constant speed is $v_{\text{speeder}} = (120\text{ km/h})\left(\dfrac{1\text{ m/s}}{3.6\text{ km/h}}\right) = 33.3\text{ m/s}$, and the location of the speeder as a function of time is given by $x_{\text{speeder}} = v_{\text{speeder}}t_{\text{speeder}} = (33.3\text{ m/s})t_{\text{speeder}}$. The police car has an initial velocity of $v_0 = 0\text{ m/s}$ and a constant acceleration of a_{police}. The location of the police car as a function of time is given by Eq. 2-11b.

$$x_{\text{police}} = v_0 t + \tfrac{1}{2}at^2 = \tfrac{1}{2}a_{\text{police}}t_{\text{police}}^2.$$

(*a*)   The position vs. time graphs would qualitatively look
        like the graph shown here.

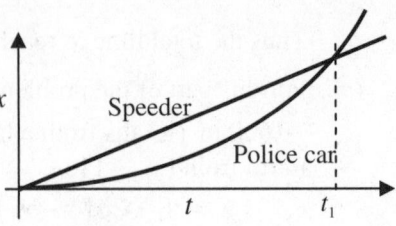

(*b*)   The time to overtake the speeder occurs when the speeder
        has gone a distance of 750 m. The time is found using the
        speeder's equation from above.

$$750 \text{ m} = (33.3 \text{ m/s}) t_{speeder} \quad \rightarrow \quad t_{speeder} = \frac{750 \text{ m}}{33.3 \text{ m/s}} = 22.5 \text{ s} \approx \boxed{23 \text{ s}}$$

(*c*)   The police car's acceleration can be calculated knowing that the police car also had gone a
        distance of 750 m in a time of 22.5 s.

$$750 \text{ m} = \tfrac{1}{2} a_p (22.5 \text{ s})^2 \quad \rightarrow \quad a_p = \frac{2(750 \text{ m})}{(22.5 \text{ s})^2} = 2.96 \text{ m/s}^2 \approx \boxed{3.0 \text{ m/s}^2}$$

(*d*)   The speed of the police car at the overtaking point can be found from Eq. 2-11a.

$$v = v_0 + at = 0 + (2.96 \text{ m/s}^2)(22.5 \text{ s}) = 66.67 \text{ m/s} \approx \boxed{67 \text{ m/s}}$$

        Note that this is exactly twice the speed of the speeder.

78.   Choose downward to be the positive direction, and the origin to be at the roof of the building from
      which the stones were dropped. The first stone has $y_0 = 0$, $v_0 = 0$, a final location of $y = H$ (as yet
      unknown), and $a = g$. If the time for the first stone to reach the ground is t_1, then Eq. 2-11c gives
      the following, replacing *x* with *y*:

$$y = y_0 + v_0 t + \tfrac{1}{2} at^2 \quad \rightarrow \quad H = \tfrac{1}{2} (9.80 \text{ m/s}^2) t_1^2 .$$

      The second stone has $v_0 = 25.0 \text{ m/s}$, $y_0 = 0$, a final location of $y = H$, and $a = g$. The time for
      the second stone to reach the ground is $t_1 - 2.00 \text{ s}$, and so Eq. 2-11c for the second stone is

$$H = (25.0 \text{ m/s})(t_1 - 2.00) + \tfrac{1}{2} (9.80 \text{ m/s}^2)(t_1 - 2.00)^2 .$$

(*a*)   Set the two expressions for *H* equal to each other, and solve for t_1.

$$\tfrac{1}{2} (9.80 \text{ m/s}^2) t_1^2 = (25.0 \text{ m/s})(t_1 - 2) + \tfrac{1}{2} (9.80 \text{ m/s}^2)(t_1 - 2)^2 \quad \rightarrow \quad t_1 = \boxed{5.63 \text{ s}}$$

(*b*)   The building height is given by $H = \tfrac{1}{2} g t_1^2 = \tfrac{1}{2} (9.80 \text{ m/s}^2)(5.63 \text{ s})^2 = \boxed{155 \text{ m}}$.

(*c*)   The speed of the stones is found using Eq. 2-11a.

        #1: $v = v_0 + at = g t_1 = (9.80 \text{ m/s}^2)(5.63 \text{ s}) = \boxed{55.2 \text{ m/s}}$

        #2: $v = v_0 + at = v_0 + g(t_1 - 2) = 25.0 \text{ m/s} + (9.80 \text{ m/s}^2)(3.63 \text{ s}) = \boxed{60.6 \text{ m/s}}$

79.   Choose upward to be the positive direction, and the origin to be at ground level. The initial velocity
      of the first stone is $v_{0A} = 11.0 \text{ m/s}$, and the acceleration of both stones is $a = -9.80 \text{ m/s}^2$. The
      starting location is $y_{0A} = H_A$, and it takes 4.5 s for the stone to reach the final location $y = 0$. Use
      Eq. 2-11b (with *x* replaced by *y*) to find a value for H_A.

$$y = y_0 + v_0 t + \tfrac{1}{2} at^2 \quad \rightarrow \quad 0 = H_A + (11.0 \text{ m/s})(4.5 \text{ s}) - \tfrac{1}{2} (9.80 \text{ m/s}^2)(4.5 \text{ s})^2 \quad \rightarrow$$

$$H_A = 49.7 \text{ m}$$

      Assume that the 12th floor balcony is three times higher above the ground than the 4th floor balcony.
      Thus the height of 4th floor balcony is $\tfrac{1}{3}(49.7 \text{ m}) = 16.6 \text{ m}$. So for the second stone, $y_{0B} = 16.6 \text{ m}$,

and it takes 4.5 s for the stone to reach the final location $y = 0$. Use Eq. 2-11b to find the starting velocity, v_{0B}.

$$y = y_0 + v_0 t + \tfrac{1}{2} a t^2 \quad \rightarrow \quad 0 = 16.6 \text{ m} + v_{0B}(4.5 \text{ s}) - \tfrac{1}{2}(9.80 \text{ m/s}^2)(4.5 \text{ s})^2 \quad \rightarrow$$

$$v_{0B} = \boxed{18 \text{ m/s}}$$

80. Choose downward to be the positive direction, and the origin to be at the location of the plane. The parachutist has $v_0 = 0$, $a = g = 9.8 \text{ m/s}^2$, and will have $y - y_0 = 2850 \text{ m}$ when she pulls the ripcord. Eq. 2-11b, with x replaced by y, is used to find the time when she pulls the ripcord.

$$y = y_0 + v_0 t + \tfrac{1}{2} a t^2 \quad \rightarrow \quad t = \sqrt{2(y - y_0)/a} = \sqrt{2(2850 \text{ m})/(9.80 \text{ m/s}^2)} = \boxed{24.1 \text{ s}}$$

The speed is found from Eq. 2-11a.

$$v = v_0 + at = 0 + (9.80 \text{ m/s}^2)(24.1 \text{ s}) = 236 \text{ m/s} \cong \boxed{2.3 \times 10^2 \text{ m/s}} = 850 \text{ km/h}$$

81. The speed of the conveyor belt is given by $d = \overline{v} \Delta t \rightarrow \overline{v} = \dfrac{d}{\Delta t} = \dfrac{1.1 \text{ m}}{2.5 \text{ min}} = \boxed{0.44 \text{ m/min}}$. The rate of burger production, assuming the spacing given is center to center, can be found as

$$\left(\frac{1 \text{ burger}}{0.15 \text{ m}} \right) \left(\frac{0.44 \text{ m}}{1 \text{ min}} \right) = \boxed{2.9 \frac{\text{burgers}}{\text{min}}}.$$

82. Choose upward to be the positive direction, and the origin to be at the level where the ball was thrown. The velocity at the top of the ball's path will be $v = 0$, and the ball will have an acceleration of $a = -g$. If the maximum height that the ball reaches is $y = H$, then the relationship between the initial velocity and the maximum height can be found from Eq. 2-11c, with x replaced by y.

$$v^2 = v_0^2 + 2a(y - y_0) \quad \rightarrow \quad 0 = v_0^2 + 2(-g)H \quad \rightarrow \quad H = v_0^2/2g.$$

We are told that $v_{0 \text{ Bill}} = 1.5 v_{0 \text{ Joe}}$, so $\dfrac{H_{\text{Bill}}}{H_{\text{Joe}}} = \dfrac{(v_{0 \text{ Bill}})^2/2g}{(v_{0 \text{ Joe}})^2/2g} = \dfrac{(v_{0 \text{ Bill}})^2}{(v_{0 \text{ Joe}})^2} = 1.5^2 = 2.25 \approx \boxed{2.3}$.

83. As shown in problem 41, the speed with which the ball was thrown upward is the same as its speed on returning to the ground. From the symmetry of the two motions (both motions have speed = 0 at top, have same distance traveled and have same acceleration), the time for the ball to rise is 1.2 s. Choose upward to be the positive direction, and the origin to be at the level where the ball was thrown. For the ball, $v = 0$ at the top of the motion, and $a = -g$. Find the initial velocity from Eq. 2-11a.

$$v = v_0 + at \quad \rightarrow \quad v_0 = v - at = 0 - (-9.80 \text{ m/s}^2)(1.2 \text{ s}) = \boxed{12 \text{ m/s}}$$

84. Choose downward to be the positive direction, and the origin to be at the top of the building. The barometer has $y_0 = 0$, $v_0 = 0$, and $a = g = 9.8 \text{ m/s}^2$. Use Eq. 2-11b to find the height of the building, with x replaced by y.

$$y = y_0 + v_0 t + \tfrac{1}{2} a t^2 = 0 + 0 + \tfrac{1}{2}(9.8 \text{ m/s}^2)t^2$$

$$y_{t=2.0} = \tfrac{1}{2}(9.8 \text{ m/s}^2)(2.0 \text{ s})^2 = 20 \text{ m} \qquad y_{t=2.3} = \tfrac{1}{2}(9.8 \text{ m/s}^2)(2.3 \text{ s})^2 = 26 \text{ m}$$

The difference in the estimates is $\boxed{6 \text{ m}}$.

The intent of the method was probably to use the change in air pressure between the ground level and the top of the building to find the height of the building. The very small difference in time measurements, which could be due to human reaction time, makes a 6 m difference in the height. This could be as much as 2 floors in error.

85. (a) The two bicycles will have the same velocity at any
          time when the instantaneous slopes of their x vs. t
          graphs are the same. That occurs near the time t_1 as
          marked on the graph.

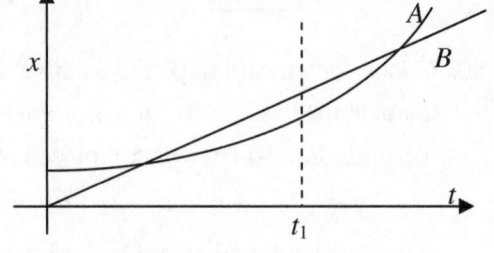

     (b) Bicycle A has the larger acceleration, because
          its graph is concave upward, indicating a positive
          acceleration. Bicycle B has no acceleration because
          its graph has a constant slope.
     (c) The bicycles are passing each other at the times
          when the two graphs cross, because they both have the same position at that time. The graph
          with the steepest slope is the faster bicycle, and so is the one that is passing at that instant. So at
          the first crossing, bicycle B is passing bicycle A. At the second crossing, bicycle A is passing
          bicycle B.
     (d) Bicycle B has the highest instantaneous velocity at all times until the time t_1, where both graphs
          have the same slope. For all times after t_1, bicycle A has the highest instantaneous velocity.
          The largest instantaneous velocity is for bicycle A at the latest time shown on the graph.
     (e) The bicycles appear to have the same average velocity. If the starting point of the graph for a
          particular bicycle is connected to the ending point with a straight line, the slope of that line is
          the average velocity. Both appear to have the same slope for that "average" line.

CHAPTER 3: Kinematics in Two Dimensions; Vectors

Answers to Questions

1. Their velocities are NOT equal, because the two velocities have different directions.

2. (a) During one year, the Earth travels a distance equal to the circumference of its orbit, but has a displacement of 0 relative to the Sun.
   (b) The space shuttle travels a large distance during any flight, but the displacement from one launch to the next is 0.
   (c) Any kind of cross country "round trip" air travel would result in a large distance traveled, but a displacement of 0.
   (d) The displacement for a race car from the start to the finish of the Indy 500 auto race is 0.

3. The displacement can be thought of as the "straight line" path from the initial location to the final location. The length of path will always be greater than or equal to the displacement, because the displacement is the shortest distance between the two locations. Thus the displacement can never be longer than the length of path, but it can be less. For any path that is not a single straight line segment, the length of path will be longer than the displacement.

4. Since both the batter and the ball started their motion at the same location (where the ball was hit) and ended their motion at the same location (where the ball was caught), the displacement of both was the same.

5. The magnitude of the vector sum need not be larger than the magnitude of either contributing vector. For example, if the two vectors being added are the exact opposite of each other, the vector sum will have a magnitude of 0. The magnitude of the sum is determined by the angle between the two contributing vectors.

6. If the two vectors are in the same direction, the magnitude of their sum will be a maximum, and will be 7.5 km. If the two vectors are in the opposite direction, the magnitude of their sum will be a minimum, and will be 0.5 km. If the two vectors are oriented in any other configuration, the magnitude of their sum will be between 0.5 km and 7.5 km.

7. Two vectors of unequal magnitude can never add to give the zero vector. However, three vectors of unequal magnitude can add to give the zero vector. If their geometric sum using the tail-to-tip method gives a closed triangle, then the vector sum will be zero. See the diagram, in which $\vec{A} + \vec{B} + \vec{C} = 0$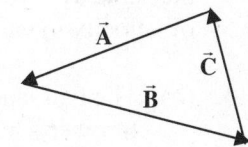

8. (a) The magnitude of a vector can equal the length of one of its components if the other components of the vector are all 0; i.e. if the vector lies along one of the coordinate axes.
   (b) The magnitude of a vector can never be less than one of its components, because each component contributes a positive amount to the overall magnitude, through the Pythagorean relationship. The square root of a sum of squares is never less than the absolute value of any individual term.

9. A particle with constant speed can be accelerating, if its direction is changing. Driving on a curved roadway at constant speed would be an example. However, a particle with constant velocity cannot be accelerating – its acceleration must be zero. It has both constant speed and constant direction.

10. To find the initial speed, use the slingshot to shoot the rock directly horizontally (no initial vertical speed) from a height of 1 meter. The vertical displacement of the rock can be related to the time of flight by Eq. 2-11b. Take downward to be positive.

$$y = y_0 + v_{y0}t + \tfrac{1}{2}at^2 \quad \rightarrow \quad 1\,\text{m} = \tfrac{1}{2}gt^2 \quad \rightarrow \quad t = \sqrt{2(1\,\text{m})/(9.8\,\text{m/s}^2)} = 0.45\,\text{s}\,.$$

Measure the horizontal range R of the rock with the meter stick. Then, if we measure the horizontal range R, we know that $R = v_x t = v_x(0.45\,\text{s})$, and so $v_x = R/0.45\,\text{s}$. The only measurements are the height of fall and the range, both of which can be measured by a meter stick.

11. Assume that the bullet was fired from behind and below the airplane. As the bullet rose in the air, its vertical speed would be slowed by both gravity and air resistance, and its horizontal speed would be slowed by air resistance. If the altitude of the airplane was slightly below the maximum height of the bullet, then at the altitude of the airplane, the bullet would be moving quite slowly in the vertical direction. If the bullet's horizontal speed had also slowed enough to approximately match the speed of the airplane, then the bullet's velocity relative to the airplane would be small. With the bullet moving slowly, it could safely be caught by hand.

12. The moving walkway will be moving at the same speed as the "car". Thus, if you are on the walkway, you are moving the same speed as the car. Your velocity relative to the car is 0, and it is easy to get into the car. But it is very difficult to keep your balance while trying to sit down into a moving car from a stationary platform. It is easier to keep your balance by stepping on to the moving platform while walking, and then getting into the car with a velocity of 0 relative to the car.

13. Your reference frame is that of the train you are riding. If you are traveling with a relatively constant velocity (not over a hill or around a curve or drastically changing speed), then you will interpret your reference frame as being at rest. Since you are moving forward faster than the other train, the other train is moving backwards relative to you. Seeing the other train go past your window from front to rear makes it look like the other train is going backwards. This is similar to passing a semi truck on the interstate – out of a passenger window, it looks like the truck is going backwards.

14. When you stand still under the umbrella in a vertical rain, you are in a cylinder-shaped volume in which there is no rain. The rain has no horizontal component of velocity, and so the rain cannot move from outside that cylinder into it. You stay dry. But as you run, you have a forward horizontal velocity relative to the rain, and so the rain has a backwards horizontal velocity relative to you. It is the same as if you were standing still under the umbrella but the rain had some horizontal component of velocity towards you. The perfectly vertical umbrella would not completely shield you.

15. (a) The ball lands at the same point from which it was thrown inside the train car – back in the thrower's hand.
    (b) If the car accelerates, the ball will land behind the point from which it was thrown.
    (c) If the car decelerates, the ball will land in front of the point from which it was thrown.
    (d) If the car rounds a curve (assume it curves to the right), then the ball will land to the left of the point from which it was thrown.
    (e) The ball will be slowed by air resistance, and so will land behind the point from which it was thrown.

16. Both rowers need to cover the same "cross river" distance. The rower with the greatest speed in the "cross river" direction will be the one that reaches the other side first. The current has no bearing on the problem because the current doesn't help either of the boats move across the river. Thus the rower heading straight across will reach the other side first. All of his rowing effort has gone into

crossing the river. For the upstream rower, some of his rowing effort goes into battling the current, and so his "cross river" speed will be only a fraction of his rowing speed.

17. The baseball is hit and caught at approximately the same height, and so the range formula of $R = v_0^2 \sin 2\theta_0 / g$ is particularly applicable. Thus the baseball player is judging the initial speed of the ball and the initial angle at which the ball was hit.

18. The arrow should be aimed above the target, because gravity will deflect the arrow downward from a horizontal flight path. The angle of aim (above the horizontal) should increase as the distance from the target increases, because gravity will have more time to act in deflecting the arrow from a straight-line path. If we assume that the arrow when shot is at the same height as the target, then the range formula is applicable: $R = v_0^2 \sin 2\theta_0 / g \;\rightarrow\; \theta = \frac{1}{2}\sin^{-1}\left(Rg / v_0^2\right)$. As the range and hence the argument of the inverse sine function increases, the angle increases.

19. The horizontal component of the velocity stays constant in projectile motion, assuming that air resistance is negligible. Thus the horizontal component of velocity 1.0 seconds after launch will be the same as the horizontal component of velocity 2.0 seconds after launch. In both cases the horizontal velocity will be given by $v_x = v_0 \cos\theta = (30\,\text{m/s})(\cos 30^\circ) = 26\,\text{m/s}$.

20. (a) Cannonball A, with the larger angle, will reach a higher elevation. It has a larger initial vertical velocity, and so by Eq. 2-11c, will rise higher before the vertical component of velocity is 0.
    (b) Cannonball A, with the larger angle, will stay in the air longer. It has a larger initial vertical velocity, and so takes more time to decelerate to 0 and start to fall.
    (c) The cannonball with a launch angle closest to 45° will travel the farthest. The range is a maximum for a launch angle of 45°, and decreases for angles either larger or smaller than 45°.

Solutions to Problems

1. The resultant vector displacement of the car is given by $\vec{\mathbf{D}}_R = \vec{\mathbf{D}}_{west} + \vec{\mathbf{D}}_{south-west}$. The westward displacement is 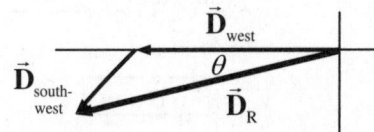 $215 + 85\cos 45^\circ = 275.1\,\text{km}$ and the south displacement is $85\sin 45^\circ = 60.1\,\text{km}$. The resultant displacement has a magnitude of $\sqrt{275.1^2 + 60.1^2} = 281.6\,\text{km}$ $\approx \boxed{282\,\text{km}}$. The direction is $\theta = \tan^{-1} 60.1/275.1 = 12.3^\circ \approx \boxed{12^\circ\ \text{south of west}}$.

2. The truck has a displacement of $18 + (-16) = 2$ blocks north and 10 blocks east. The resultant has a magnitude of $\sqrt{2^2 + 10^2} = \boxed{10\ \text{blocks}}$ and a direction of $\tan^{-1} 2/10 = \boxed{11^\circ\ \text{north of east}}$.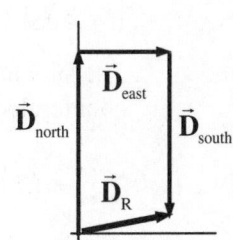

3. Label the "INCORRECT" vector as vector $\vec{\mathbf{X}}$. Then Fig. 3-6 (c) illustrates the relationship $\vec{\mathbf{V}}_1 + \vec{\mathbf{X}} = \vec{\mathbf{V}}_2$ via the tail-to-tip method. Thus $\vec{\mathbf{X}} = \boxed{\vec{\mathbf{V}}_2 - \vec{\mathbf{V}}_1}$.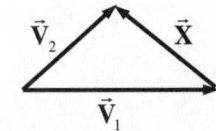

4. Given that $V_x = 6.80$ units and $V_y = -7.40$ units, the magnitude of $\vec{V}$ is

given by $V = \sqrt{V_x^2 + V_y^2} = \sqrt{6.80^2 + (-7.40)^2} = \boxed{10.0 \text{ units}}$. The direction

is given by an angle of $\theta = \tan^{-1}\dfrac{-7.40}{6.80} = \boxed{-47°}$, or $47°$ below the positive x-

axis.

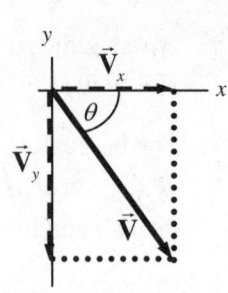

5. The vectors for the problem are drawn approximately to scale. The resultant has a length of $\boxed{58 \text{ m}}$ and a direction $\boxed{48°}$ north of east. If calculations are done, the actual resultant should be 57.4 m at 47.5° north of east.

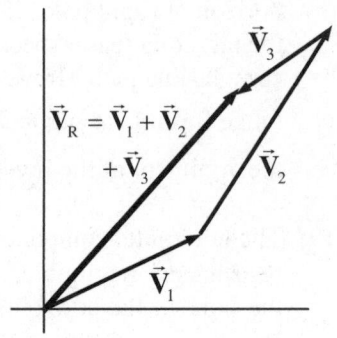

6. The sum is found by adding the components of vectors $\vec{V}_1$ and $\vec{V}_2$

$$\vec{V} = \vec{V}_1 + \vec{V}_2 = (8.0, -3.7, 0.0) + (3.9, -8.1, -4.4) = \boxed{(11.9, -11.8, -4.4)}$$

$$V = |\vec{V}| = \sqrt{(11.9)^2 + (-11.8)^2 + (-4.4)^2} = \boxed{17.3}$$

7. (a) See the accompanying diagram

   (b) $V_x = -14.3\cos 34.8° = \boxed{-11.7 \text{ units}}$ $V_y = 14.3\sin 34.8° = \boxed{8.16 \text{ units}}$

   (c) $V = \sqrt{V_x^2 + V_y^2} = \sqrt{(-11.7)^2 + (8.16)^2} = \boxed{14.3 \text{ units}}$

   $\theta = \tan^{-1}\dfrac{8.16}{11.7} = \boxed{34.8° \text{ above the } -x \text{ axis}}$

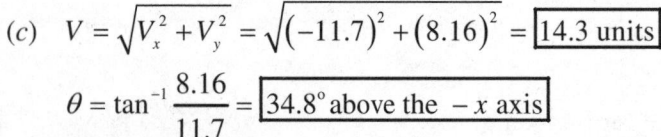
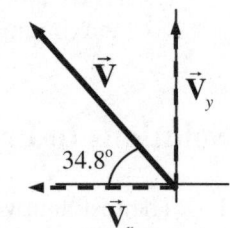

8. (a) $V_{1x} = \boxed{-6.6 \text{ units}}$ $V_{1y} = \boxed{0 \text{ units}}$

   $V_{2x} = 8.5\cos 45° = \boxed{6.0 \text{ units}}$ $V_{2y} = 8.5\sin 45° = \boxed{6.0 \text{ units}}$

   (b) $\vec{V}_1 + \vec{V}_2 = (V_{1x} + V_{2x}, V_{1y} + V_{2y}) = (-0.6, 6.0)$

   $|\vec{V}_1 + \vec{V}_2| = \sqrt{(-0.6)^2 + (6.0)^2} = 6.0 \text{ units}$ $\theta = \tan^{-1}\dfrac{6.0}{0.6} = 84°$

   The sum has a magnitude of $\boxed{6.0 \text{ units}}$, and is $\boxed{84° \text{ clockwise from the } - \text{negative } x\text{-axis}}$, or $96°$ counterclockwise from the positive x-axis.

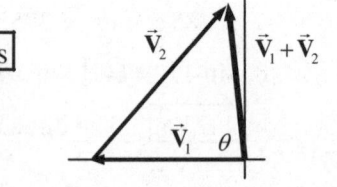

9. (a) $v_{\text{north}} = (735 \text{ km/h})(\cos 41.5°) = \boxed{550 \text{ km/h}}$ $v_{\text{west}} = (735 \text{ km/h})(\sin 41.5°) = \boxed{487 \text{ km/h}}$

   (b) $\Delta d_{\text{north}} = v_{\text{north}}t = (550 \text{ km/h})(3.00 \text{ h}) = \boxed{1650 \text{ km}}$

   $\Delta d_{\text{west}} = v_{\text{west}}t = (487 \text{ km/h})(3.00 \text{ h}) = \boxed{1460 \text{ km}}$

10. $A_x = 44.0\cos 28.0° = 38.85$ $A_y = 44.0\sin 28.0° = 20.66$

$B_x = -26.5\cos 56.0° = -14.82$ $B_y = 26.5\sin 56.0° = 21.97$

$C_x = 31.0\cos 270° = 0.0$ $C_y = 31.0\sin 270° = -31.0$

(a) $\left(\vec{A}+\vec{B}+\vec{C}\right)_x = 38.85+\left(-14.82\right)+0.0 = 24.03 = \boxed{24.0}$

$\left(\vec{A}+\vec{B}+\vec{C}\right)_y = 20.66+21.97+\left(-31.0\right) = 11.63 = \boxed{11.6}$

(b) $\left|\vec{A}+\vec{B}+\vec{C}\right| = \sqrt{\left(24.03\right)^2 + \left(11.63\right)^2} = \boxed{26.7}$ $\theta = \tan^{-1}\dfrac{11.63}{24.03} = \boxed{25.8°}$

11. $A_x = 44.0\cos 28.0° = 38.85$ $A_y = 44.0\sin 28.0° = 20.66$

$C_x = 31.0\cos 270° = 0.0$ $C_y = 31.0\sin 270° = -31.0$

$\left(\vec{A}-\vec{C}\right)_x = 38.85-0.0 = 38.85$ $\left(\vec{A}-\vec{C}\right)_y = 20.66-\left(-31.0\right) = 51.66$

$\left|\vec{A}-\vec{C}\right| = \sqrt{\left(38.85\right)^2 + \left(51.66\right)^2} = \boxed{64.6}$ $\theta = \tan^{-1}\dfrac{51.66}{38.85} = \boxed{53.1°}$

12. $A_x = 44.0\cos 28.0° = 38.85$ $A_y = 44.0\sin 28.0° = 20.66$

$B_x = -26.5\cos 56.0° = -14.82$ $B_y = 26.5\sin 56.0° = 21.97$

(a) $\left(\vec{B}-\vec{A}\right)_x = \left(-14.82\right)-38.85 = -53.67$ $\left(\vec{B}-\vec{A}\right)_y = 21.97-20.66 = 1.31$

Note that since the x component is negative and the y component is positive, the vector is in the 2nd quadrant.

$\left|\vec{B}-\vec{A}\right| = \sqrt{\left(-53.67\right)^2 + \left(1.31\right)^2} = \boxed{53.7}$ $\theta_{B-A} = \tan^{-1}\dfrac{1.31}{-53.67} = \boxed{1.4°\ \text{above}\ -x\ \text{axis}}$

(b) $\left(\vec{A}-\vec{B}\right)_x = 38.85-\left(-14.82\right) = 53.67$ $\left(\vec{A}-\vec{B}\right)_y = 20.66-21.97 = -1.31$

Note that since the x component is positive and the y component is negative, the vector is in the 4th quadrant.

$\left|\vec{A}-\vec{B}\right| = \sqrt{\left(53.67\right)^2 + \left(-1.31\right)^2} = \boxed{53.7}$ $\theta = \tan^{-1}\dfrac{-1.31}{53.7} = \boxed{1.4°\ \text{below}\ +x\ \text{axis}}$

Comparing the results shows that $\vec{B}-\vec{A}$ is the opposite of $\vec{A}-\vec{B}$.

13. $A_x = 44.0\cos 28.0° = 38.85$ $A_y = 44.0\sin 28.0° = 20.66$

$B_x = -26.5\cos 56.0° = -14.82$ $B_y = 26.5\sin 56.0° = 21.97$

$C_x = 31.0\cos 270° = 0.0$ $C_y = 31.0\sin 270° = -31.0$

(a) $\left(\vec{A}-\vec{B}+\vec{C}\right)_x = 38.85-\left(-14.82\right)+0.0 = 53.67$

$\left(\vec{A}-\vec{B}+\vec{C}\right)_y = 20.66-21.97+\left(-31.0\right) = -32.31$

Note that since the x component is positive and the y component is negative, the vector is in the 4th quadrant.

$\left|\vec{A}-\vec{B}+\vec{C}\right| = \sqrt{\left(53.67\right)^2 + \left(-32.31\right)^2} = \boxed{62.6}$ $\theta = \tan^{-1}\dfrac{-32.31}{53.67} = \boxed{31.0°\ \text{below}\ +x\ \text{axis}}$

(b) $\left(\vec{\mathbf{A}} + \vec{\mathbf{B}} - \vec{\mathbf{C}}\right)_x = 38.85 + \left(-14.82\right) - 0.0 = 24.03$

$\left(\vec{\mathbf{A}} + \vec{\mathbf{B}} - \vec{\mathbf{C}}\right)_y = 20.66 + 21.97 - \left(-31.0\right) = 73.63$

$\left|\vec{\mathbf{A}} + \vec{\mathbf{B}} - \vec{\mathbf{C}}\right| = \sqrt{\left(24.03\right)^2 + \left(73.63\right)^2} = \boxed{77.5}$ $\theta = \tan^{-1} \dfrac{73.63}{24.03} = \boxed{71.9°}$

(c) $\left(\vec{\mathbf{C}} - \vec{\mathbf{A}} - \vec{\mathbf{B}}\right)_x = 0.0 - 38.85 - \left(-14.82\right) = -24.03$

$\left(\vec{\mathbf{C}} - \vec{\mathbf{A}} - \vec{\mathbf{B}}\right)_y = -31.0 - 20.66 - 21.97 = -73.63$

Note that since both components are negative, the vector is in the 3rd quadrant.

$\left|\vec{\mathbf{C}} - \vec{\mathbf{A}} - \vec{\mathbf{B}}\right| = \sqrt{\left(-24.03\right)^2 + \left(-73.63\right)^2} = \boxed{77.5}$ $\theta = \tan^{-1} \dfrac{-73.63}{-24.03} = \boxed{71.9° \text{ below } -x \text{ axis}}$

Note that the answer to (c) is the exact opposite of the answer to (b).

14. $A_x = 44.0\cos 28.0° = 38.85$ $A_y = 44.0\sin 28.0° = 20.66$

   $B_x = -26.5\cos 56.0° = -14.82$ $B_y = 26.5\sin 56.0° = 21.97$

   $C_x = 31.0\cos 270° = 0.0$ $C_y = 31.0\sin 270° = -31.0$

   (a) $\left(\vec{\mathbf{B}} - 2\vec{\mathbf{A}}\right)_x = -14.82 - 2\left(38.85\right) = -92.52$ $\left(\vec{\mathbf{B}} - 2\vec{\mathbf{A}}\right)_y = 21.97 - 2\left(20.66\right) = -19.35$

   Note that since both components are negative, the vector is in the 3rd quadrant.

   $\left|\vec{\mathbf{B}} - 2\vec{\mathbf{A}}\right| = \sqrt{\left(-92.52\right)^2 + \left(-19.35\right)^2} = \boxed{94.5}$ $\theta = \tan^{-1} \dfrac{-19.35}{-92.52} = \boxed{11.8° \text{ below } -x \text{ axis}}$

   (b) $\left(2\vec{\mathbf{A}} - 3\vec{\mathbf{B}} + 2\vec{\mathbf{C}}\right)_x = 2\left(38.85\right) - 3\left(-14.82\right) + 2\left(0.0\right) = 122.16$

   $\left(2\vec{\mathbf{A}} - 3\vec{\mathbf{B}} + 2\vec{\mathbf{C}}\right)_y = 2\left(20.66\right) - 3\left(21.97\right) + 2\left(-31.0\right) = -86.59$

   Note that since the x component is positive and the y component is negative, the vector is in the 4th quadrant.

   $\left|2\vec{\mathbf{A}} - 3\vec{\mathbf{B}} + 2\vec{\mathbf{C}}\right| = \sqrt{\left(122.16\right)^2 + \left(-86.59\right)^2} = \boxed{149.7}$ $\theta = \tan^{-1} \dfrac{-86.59}{122.16} = \boxed{35.3° \text{ below } +x \text{ axis}}$

15. The x component is negative and the y component is positive, since the summit is to the west of north. The angle measured counterclockwise from the positive x axis would be 122.4°. Thus the components are found to be

   $x = -4580\sin 32.4° = -2454 \text{ m}$ $y = 4580\cos 32.4° = 3867 \text{ m}$ $z = 2450 \text{ m}$

   $\boxed{\vec{\mathbf{r}} = \left(-2450 \text{ m}, 3870 \text{ m}, 2450 \text{ m}\right)}$ $\boxed{\left|\vec{\mathbf{r}}\right| = \sqrt{\left(-2454\right)^2 + \left(4580\right)^2 + \left(2450\right)^2} = \boxed{5190 \text{ m}}}$

16. $70.0 = \sqrt{x^2 + \left(-55.0\right)^2}$ $\rightarrow$ $4900 = x^2 + 3025$ $\rightarrow$ $x^2 = 1875$ $\rightarrow$ $x = \boxed{\pm 43.3 \text{ units}}$

17. Choose downward to be the positive y direction. The origin will be at the point where the tiger leaps from the rock. In the horizontal direction, $v_{x0} = 3.5 \text{ m/s}$ and $a_x = 0$. In the vertical direction, $v_{y0} = 0$, $a_y = 9.80 \text{ m/s}^2$, $y_0 = 0$, and the final location $y = 6.5 \text{ m}$. The time for the tiger to reach the ground is found from applying Eq. 2-11b to the vertical motion.

$$y = y_0 + v_{y0}t + \tfrac{1}{2}a_y t^2 \quad \rightarrow \quad 6.5\text{m} = 0 + 0 + \tfrac{1}{2}\left(9.8\,\text{m/s}^2\right)t^2 \quad \rightarrow \quad t = \sqrt{\frac{2(6.5\text{m})}{9.8\,\text{m/s}^2}} = 1.15 \text{ sec}$$

The horizontal displacement is calculated from the constant horizontal velocity.

$$\Delta x = v_x t = (3.5\,\text{m/s})(1.15 \text{ sec}) = \boxed{4.0 \text{ m}}$$

18. Choose downward to be the positive y direction. The origin will be at the point where the diver dives from the cliff. In the horizontal direction, $v_{x0} = 1.8\,\text{m/s}$ and $a_x = 0$. In the vertical direction, $v_{y0} = 0$, $a_y = 9.80\,\text{m/s}^2$, $y_0 = 0$, and the time of flight is $t = 3.0$ s. The height of the cliff is found from applying Eq. 2-11b to the vertical motion.

$$y = y_0 + v_{y0}t + \tfrac{1}{2}a_y t^2 \quad \rightarrow \quad y = 0 + 0 + \tfrac{1}{2}\left(9.80\,\text{m/s}^2\right)(3.0\text{s})^2 = \boxed{44 \text{ m}}$$

The distance from the base of the cliff to where the diver hits the water is found from the horizontal motion at constant velocity:

$$\Delta x = v_x t = (1.8\,\text{m/s})(3 \text{ s}) = \boxed{5.4 \text{ m}}$$

19. Apply the range formula from Example 3-8.

$$R = \frac{v_0^2 \sin 2\theta_0}{g} \quad \rightarrow$$

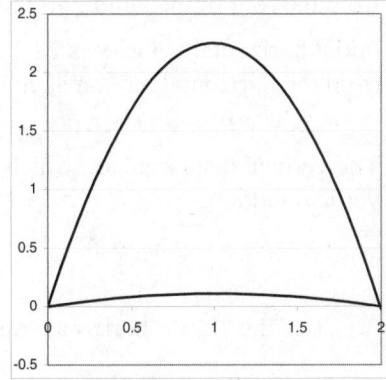

$$\sin 2\theta_0 = \frac{Rg}{v_0^2} = \frac{(2.0 \text{ m})\left(9.8\,\text{m/s}^2\right)}{(6.8\,\text{m/s})^2} = 0.4239$$

$$2\theta_0 = \sin^{-1} 0.4239 \quad \rightarrow \quad \theta_0 = \boxed{13°, 77°}$$

There are two angles because each angle gives the same range. If one angle is $\theta = 45° + \delta$, then $\theta = 45° - \delta$ is also a solution. The two paths are shown in the graph.

20. Choose upward to be the positive y direction. The origin is the point from which the pebbles are released. In the vertical direction, $a_y = -9.80\,\text{m/s}^2$, the velocity at the window is $v_y = 0$, and the vertical displacement is 4.5 m. The initial y velocity is found from Eq. 2-11c.

$$v_y^2 = v_{y0}^2 + 2a_y(y - y_0) \quad \rightarrow$$

$$v_{y0} = \sqrt{v_y^2 - 2a_y(y - y_0)} = \sqrt{0 - 2\left(-9.80\,\text{m/s}^2\right)(4.5 \text{ m})} = 9.39\,\text{m/s}$$

Find the time for the pebbles to travel to the window from Eq. 2-11a.

$$v_y = v_{y0} + at \quad \rightarrow \quad t = \frac{v_y - v_{y0}}{a} = \frac{0 - 9.4\,\text{m/s}}{-9.8\,\text{m/s}^2} = 0.958 \text{ s}$$

Find the horizontal speed from the horizontal motion at constant velocity.

$$\Delta x = v_x t \quad \rightarrow \quad v_x = \Delta x / t = 5.0 \text{ m} / 0.958 \text{ s} = \boxed{5.2\,\text{m/s}}$$

This is the speed of the pebbles when they hit the window.

21. Choose downward to be the positive y direction. The origin will be at the point where the ball is thrown from the roof of the building. In the vertical direction, $v_{y0} = 0$, $a_y = 9.80\,\text{m/s}^2$, $y_0 = 0$, and the displacement is 45.0 m. The time of flight is found from applying Eq. 2-11b to the vertical motion.

$$y = y_0 + v_{y0}t + \tfrac{1}{2}a_y t^2 \quad \rightarrow \quad 45.0 \text{ m} = \tfrac{1}{2}\left(9.80 \text{ m/s}^2\right)t^2 \quad \rightarrow \quad t = \sqrt{\frac{2\left(45.0 \text{ m}\right)}{9.80 \text{ m/s}^2}} = 3.03 \text{ sec}$$

The horizontal speed (which is the initial speed) is found from the horizontal motion at constant velocity:

$$\Delta x = v_x t \quad \rightarrow \quad v_x = \Delta x / t = 24.0 \text{ m} / 3.03 \text{ s} = \boxed{7.92 \text{ m/s}}.$$

22. Choose the point at which the football is kicked the origin, and choose upward to be the positive y direction. When the football reaches the ground again, the y displacement is 0. For the football, $v_{y0} = \left(18.0 \sin 35.0°\right) \text{m/s}$, $a_y = -9.80 \text{ m/s}^2$ and the final y velocity will be the opposite of the starting y velocity (reference problem 3-28). Use Eq. 2-11a to find the time of flight.

$$v_y = v_{y0} + at \quad \rightarrow \quad t = \frac{v_y - v_{y0}}{a} = \frac{\left(-18.0 \sin 35.0°\right) \text{m/s} - \left(18.0 \sin 35.0°\right) \text{m/s}}{-9.80 \text{ m/s}^2} = \boxed{2.11 \text{ s}}$$

23. Choose downward to be the positive y direction. The origin is the point where the ball is thrown from the roof of the building. In the vertical direction, $v_{y0} = 0$, $y_0 = 0$, and $a_y = 9.80 \text{ m/s}^2$. The initial horizontal velocity is 22.2 m/s and the horizontal range is 36.0 m. The time of flight is found from the horizontal motion at constant velocity.

$$\Delta x = v_x t \quad \rightarrow \quad t = \Delta x / v_x = 36.0 \text{ m} / 22.2 \text{ m/s} = 1.62 \text{ s}$$

The vertical displacement, which is the height of the building, is found by applying Eq. 2-11b to the vertical motion.

$$y = y_0 + v_{y0}t + \tfrac{1}{2}a_y t^2 \quad \rightarrow \quad y = 0 + 0 + \tfrac{1}{2}\left(9.80 \text{ m/s}^2\right)\left(1.62 \text{ s}\right)^2 = \boxed{12.9 \text{ m}}$$

$\boxed{24.}$ (a) Use the "Level horizontal range" formula from Example 3-8.

$$R = \frac{v_0^2 \sin 2\theta_0}{g} \quad \rightarrow \quad v_0 = \sqrt{\frac{Rg}{\sin 2\theta_0}} = \sqrt{\frac{\left(7.80 \text{ m}\right)\left(9.80 \text{ m/s}^2\right)}{\sin 2\left(28.0°\right)}} = \boxed{9.60 \text{ m/s}}$$

(b) Now increase the speed by 5.0% and calculate the new range. The new speed would be $9.60 \text{ m/s}\left(1.05\right) = 10.1 \text{ m/s}$ and the new range would be

$$R = \frac{v_0^2 \sin 2\theta_0}{g} = \frac{\left(10.1 \text{ m/s}\right)^2 \sin 2\left(28.0°\right)}{9.80 \text{ m/s}^2} = 8.60 \text{ m},$$

an increase of $\boxed{0.80 \text{ m} \left(10\% \text{ increase}\right)}$.

25. Calculate the range as derived in Example 3-8: $R = \dfrac{v_0^2 \sin 2\theta_0}{g}$. If the launching speed and angle are held constant, the range is inversely proportional to the value of g. The acceleration due to gravity on the Moon is 1/6th that on Earth.

$$R_{\text{Earth}} = \frac{v_0^2 \sin 2\theta_0}{g_{\text{Earth}}} \qquad R_{\text{Moon}} = \frac{v_0^2 \sin 2\theta_0}{g_{\text{Moon}}} \quad \rightarrow \quad R_{\text{Earth}} g_{\text{Earth}} = R_{\text{Moon}} g_{\text{Moon}}$$

$$R_{\text{Moon}} = R_{\text{Earth}} \frac{g_{\text{Earth}}}{g_{\text{Moon}}} = 6 R_{\text{Earth}}$$

Thus on the Moon, the person can jump $\boxed{\text{6 times farther}}$.

26. (a) Choose downward to be the positive y direction. The origin is the point where the bullet leaves the gun. In the vertical direction, $v_{y0} = 0$, $y_0 = 0$, and $a_y = 9.80 \, \text{m/s}^2$. In the horizontal direction, $\Delta x = 75.0 \, \text{m}$ and $v_x = 180 \, \text{m/s}$. The time of flight is found from the horizontal motion at constant velocity.
$$\Delta x = v_x t \quad \rightarrow \quad t = \Delta x / v_x = 75.0 \, \text{m}/180 \, \text{m/s} = 0.4167 \, \text{s}$$
This time can now be used in Eq. 2-11b to find the vertical drop of the bullet.
$$y = y_0 + v_{y0}t + \tfrac{1}{2}a_y t^2 \quad \rightarrow \quad y = 0 + 0 + \tfrac{1}{2}\left(9.80 \, \text{m/s}^2\right)\left(0.4167 \, \text{s}\right)^2 = \boxed{0.851 \, \text{m}}$$

(b) For the bullet to hit the target at the same level, the level horizontal range formula of Example 3-8 applies. The range is 75.0 m, and the initial velocity is 180 m/s. Solving for the angle of launch results in the following.
$$R = \frac{v_0^2 \sin 2\theta_0}{g} \quad \rightarrow \quad \sin 2\theta_0 = \frac{Rg}{v_0^2} \quad \rightarrow \quad \theta_0 = \frac{1}{2}\sin^{-1}\frac{\left(75.0 \, \text{m}\right)\left(9.80 \, \text{m/s}^2\right)}{\left(180 \, \text{m/s}\right)^2} = \boxed{0.650°}$$

Because of the symmetry of the range formula, there is also an answer of the complement of the above answer, which would be 89.35°. That is an unreasonable answer from a practical physical viewpoint – it is pointing the gun almost straight up.

27. Choose downward to be the positive y direction. The origin is the point where the supplies are dropped. In the vertical direction, $v_{y0} = 0$, $a_y = 9.80 \, \text{m/s}^2$, $y_0 = 0$, and the final position is $y = 160 \, \text{m}$. The time of flight is found from applying Eq. 2-11b to the vertical motion.
$$y = y_0 + v_{y0}t + \tfrac{1}{2}a_y t^2 \quad \rightarrow \quad 160 \, \text{m} = 0 + 0 + \tfrac{1}{2}\left(9.80 \, \text{m/s}^2\right)t^2 \quad \rightarrow$$
$$t = \sqrt{\frac{2\left(160 \, \text{m}\right)}{9.80 \, \text{m/s}^2}} = \boxed{5.71 \, \text{s}}$$

Note that the speed of the airplane does not enter into this calculation.

28. The horizontal component of the speed does not change during the course of the motion, and so $v_{xf} = v_{x0}$. The net vertical displacement is 0 if the firing level equals the landing level. Eq. 2-11c then gives $v_{yf}^2 = v_{y0}^2 + 2a_y\Delta y = v_{y0}^2$. Thus $v_{yf}^2 = v_{y0}^2$, and from the horizontal $v_{xf}^2 = v_{x0}^2$. The initial speed is $v_0 = \sqrt{v_{y0}^2 + v_{x0}^2}$. The final speed is $v_f = \sqrt{v_{yf}^2 + v_{xf}^2} = \sqrt{v_{y0}^2 + v_{x0}^2} = v_0$. Thus $\boxed{v_f = v_0}$.

29. Choose upward to be the positive y direction. The origin is point from which the football is kicked. The initial speed of the football is $v_0 = 20.0 \, \text{m/s}$. We have $v_{y0} = v_0 \sin 37.0° = 12.04 \, \text{m/s}$, $y_0 = 0$, and $a_y = -9.80 \, \text{m/s}^2$. In the horizontal direction, $v_x = v_0 \cos 37.0° = 15.97 \, \text{m/s}$, and $\Delta x = 36.0 \, \text{m}$. The time of flight to reach the goalposts is found from the horizontal motion at constant speed:
$$\Delta x = v_x t \quad \rightarrow \quad t = \Delta x / v_x = 36.0 \, \text{m}/15.97 \, \text{m/s} = 2.254 \, \text{s}.$$
Now use this time with the vertical motion data and Eq. 2-11b to find the height of the football when it reaches the horizontal location of the goalposts.
$$y = y_0 + v_{y0}t + \tfrac{1}{2}a_y t^2 = 0 + \left(12.04 \, \text{m/s}\right)\left(2.254 \, \text{s}\right) + \tfrac{1}{2}\left(-9.80 \, \text{m/s}^2\right)\left(2.254 \, \text{s}\right)^2 = 2.24 \, \text{m}$$

Since the ball's height is less than 3.00 m, the football does not clear the bar. It is 0.76 m too low when it reaches the horizontal location of the goalposts.

30. Choose the origin to be where the projectile is launched, and upwards to be the positive y direction. The initial velocity of the projectile is v_0, the launching angle is θ_0, $a_y = -g$, and $v_{y0} = v_0 \sin \theta_0$.

    (a) The maximum height is found from Eq. 2-11c, $v_y^2 = v_{y0}^2 + 2a_y (y - y_0)$, with $v_y = 0$ at the maximum height.

    $$y_{max} = 0 + \frac{v_y^2 - v_{y0}^2}{2a_y} = \frac{-v_0^2 \sin^2 \theta_0}{-2g} = \frac{v_0^2 \sin^2 \theta_0}{2g} = \frac{(65.2\,\text{m/s})^2 \sin^2 34.5°}{2(9.80\,\text{m/s}^2)} = \boxed{69.6\,\text{m}}$$

    (b) The total time in the air is found from Eq. 2-11b, with a total vertical displacement of 0 for the ball to reach the ground.

    $$y = y_0 + v_{y0}t + \tfrac{1}{2}a_y t^2 \quad \rightarrow \quad 0 = v_0 \sin \theta_0 t - \tfrac{1}{2}gt^2 \quad \rightarrow$$

    $$t = \frac{2v_0 \sin \theta_0}{g} = \frac{2(65.2\,\text{m/s})\sin 34.5°}{(9.80\,\text{m/s}^2)} = \boxed{7.54\,\text{s}} \text{ and } t = 0$$

    The time of 0 represents the launching of the ball.

    (c) The total horizontal distance covered is found from the horizontal motion at constant velocity.

    $$\Delta x = v_x t = (v_0 \cos \theta_0)t = (65.2\,\text{m/s})(\cos 34.5°)(7.54\,\text{s}) = \boxed{405\,\text{m}}$$

    (d) The velocity of the projectile 1.50 s after firing is found as the vector sum of the horizontal and vertical velocities at that time. The horizontal velocity is a constant $v_0 \cos \theta_0 = (65.2\,\text{m/s})(\cos 34.5°) = 53.7\,\text{m/s}$. The vertical velocity is found from Eq. 2-11a.

    $$v_y = v_{y0} + at = v_0 \sin \theta_0 - gt = (65.2\,\text{m/s})\sin 34.5° - (9.80\,\text{m/s}^2)(1.50\,\text{s}) = 22.2\,\text{m/s}$$

    Thus the speed of the projectile is $v = \sqrt{v_x^2 + v_y^2} = \sqrt{53.7^2 + 22.2^2} = \boxed{58.1\,\text{m/s}}$.

    The direction above the horizontal is given by $\theta = \tan^{-1}\dfrac{v_y}{v_x} = \tan^{-1}\dfrac{22.2}{53.7} = \boxed{22.5°}$.

31. Choose the origin to be at ground level, under the place where the projectile is launched, and upwards to be the positive y direction. For the projectile, $v_0 = 65.0\,\text{m/s}$, $\theta_0 = 37.0°$, $a_y = -g$, $y_0 = 125$, and $v_{y0} = v_0 \sin \theta_0$

    (a) The time taken to reach the ground is found from Eq. 2-11b, with a final height of 0.

    $$y = y_0 + v_{y0}t + \tfrac{1}{2}a_y t^2 \quad \rightarrow \quad 0 = 125 + v_0 \sin \theta_0 t - \tfrac{1}{2}gt^2 \quad \rightarrow$$

    $$t = \frac{-v_0 \sin \theta_0 \pm \sqrt{v_0^2 \sin^2 \theta_0 - 4(-\tfrac{1}{2}g)(125)}}{2(-\tfrac{1}{2}g)} = \frac{-39.1 \pm 63.1}{-9.8} = 10.4\,\text{s},\ -2.45\,\text{s} = \boxed{10.4\,\text{s}}$$

    Choose the positive sign since the projectile was launched at time $t = 0$.

    (b) The horizontal range is found from the horizontal motion at constant velocity.

    $$\Delta x = v_x t = (v_0 \cos \theta_0)t = (65.0\,\text{m/s})\cos 37.0° (10.4\,\text{s}) = \boxed{541\,\text{m}}$$

    (c) At the instant just before the particle reaches the ground, the horizontal component of its velocity is the constant $v_x = v_0 \cos \theta_0 = (65.0\,\text{m/s})\cos 37.0° = \boxed{51.9\,\text{m/s}}$. The vertical component is found from Eq. 2-11a.

$$v_y = v_{y0} + at = v_0 \sin\theta_0 - gt = (65.0\,\text{m/s})\sin 37.0° - (9.80\,\text{m/s}^2)(10.4\,\text{s})$$

$$= \boxed{-63.1\,\text{m/s}}$$

(d) The magnitude of the velocity is found from the x and y components calculated in part c) above.

$$v = \sqrt{v_x^2 + v_y^2} = \sqrt{(51.9\,\text{m/s})^2 + (-63.1\,\text{m/s})^2} = \boxed{81.7\,\text{m/s}}$$

(e) The direction of the velocity is $\theta = \tan^{-1}\dfrac{v_y}{v_x} = \tan^{-1}\dfrac{-63.1}{51.9} = -50.6°$, and so the object is

moving $\boxed{50.6°\ \text{below the horizon}}$.

(f) The maximum height above the cliff top reached by the projectile will occur when the y-velocity is 0, and is found from Eq. 2-11c.

$$v_y^2 = v_{y0}^2 + 2a_y(y - y_0) \quad \rightarrow \quad 0 = v_0^2 \sin^2\theta_0 - 2gy_{max}$$

$$y_{max} = \frac{v_0^2 \sin^2\theta_0}{2g} = \frac{(65.0\,\text{m/s})^2 \sin^2 37.0°}{2(9.80\,\text{m/s}^2)} = \boxed{78.1\,\text{m}}$$

32. Choose the origin to be the point of release of the shot put. Choose upward to be the positive y direction. Then $y_0 = 0$, $v_{y0} = (15.5\sin 34.0°)\,\text{m/s} = 8.67\,\text{m/s}$, $a_y = -9.80\,\text{m/s}^2$, and $y = -2.20$ m at the end of the motion. Use Eq. 2-11b to find the time of flight.

$$y = y_0 + v_{y0}t + \tfrac{1}{2}a_y t^2 \quad \rightarrow \quad \tfrac{1}{2}a_y t^2 + v_{y0}t - y = 0 \quad \rightarrow$$

$$t = \frac{-v_{y0} \pm \sqrt{v_{y0}^2 - 4\left(\tfrac{1}{2}a_y\right)(-y)}}{2\tfrac{1}{2}a_y} = \frac{-8.67 \pm \sqrt{(8.67)^2 - 2(-9.80)(2.20)}}{-9.80} = 1.99\,\text{s}, -0.225\,\text{s}$$

Choose the positive result since the time must be greater than 0. Now calculate the horizontal distance traveled using the horizontal motion at constant velocity.

$$\Delta x = v_x t = (15.5\cos 34°)\,\text{m/s}(1.99\,\text{s}) = \boxed{25.6\,\text{m}}$$

33. Choose the origin to be where the projectile is launched, and upwards to be the positive y direction. The initial velocity of the projectile is v_0, the launching angle is θ_0, $a_y = -g$, and $v_{y0} = v_0 \sin\theta_0$.

The range of the projectile is given by the range formula from Example 3-8, $R = \dfrac{v_0^2 \sin 2\theta_0}{g}$. The

maximum height of the projectile will occur when its vertical speed is 0. Apply Eq. 2-11c.

$$v_y^2 = v_{y0}^2 + 2a_y(y - y_0) \quad \rightarrow \quad 0 = v_0^2 \sin^2\theta_0 - 2gy_{max} \quad \rightarrow \quad y_{max} = \frac{v_0^2 \sin^2\theta_0}{2g}$$

Now find the angle for which $R = y_{max}$.

$$R = y_{max} \quad \rightarrow \quad \frac{v_0^2 \sin 2\theta_0}{g} = \frac{v_0^2 \sin^2\theta_0}{2g} \quad \rightarrow \quad \sin 2\theta_0 = \frac{\sin^2\theta_0}{2} \quad \rightarrow$$

$$2\sin\theta_0\cos\theta_0 = \frac{\sin^2\theta_0}{2} \quad \rightarrow \quad 4\cos\theta_0 = \sin\theta_0 \quad \rightarrow \quad \tan\theta_0 = 4 \quad \rightarrow \quad \theta_0 = \tan^{-1}4 = \boxed{76°}$$

34. Choose the origin to be the location from which the balloon is
    fired, and choose upward as the positive y direction. Assume
    the boy in the tree is a distance H up from the point at which
    the balloon is fired, and that the tree is a distance D horizontally
    from the point at which the balloon is fired. The equations of
    motion for the balloon and boy are as follows, using constant
    acceleration relationships.

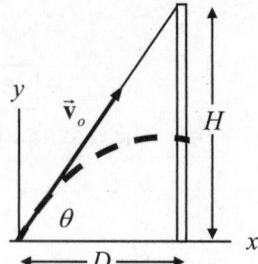

$$x_{\text{Balloon}} = v_0 \cos\theta_0 t \qquad y_{\text{Balloon}} = 0 + v_0 \sin\theta_0 t - \tfrac{1}{2}gt^2 \qquad y_{\text{Boy}} = H - \tfrac{1}{2}gt^2$$

Use the horizontal motion at constant velocity to find the elapsed time after the balloon has traveled
D to the right.

$$D = v_0 \cos\theta_0 t_D \quad\rightarrow\quad t_D = \frac{D}{v_0 \cos\theta_0}$$

Where is the balloon vertically at that time?

$$y_{\text{Balloon}} = v_0 \sin\theta_0 t_D - \tfrac{1}{2}gt_D^2 = v_0 \sin\theta_0 \frac{D}{v_0 \cos\theta_0} - \tfrac{1}{2}g\left(\frac{D}{v_0 \cos\theta_0}\right)^2 = D\tan\theta_0 - \tfrac{1}{2}g\left(\frac{D}{v_0 \cos\theta_0}\right)^2$$

Where is the boy vertically at that time? Note that $H = D\tan\theta_o$.

$$y_{\text{Boy}} = H - \tfrac{1}{2}gt_D^2 = H - \tfrac{1}{2}g\left(\frac{D}{v_0 \cos\theta_0}\right)^2 = D\tan\theta_0 - \tfrac{1}{2}g\left(\frac{D}{v_0 \cos\theta_0}\right)^2$$

The boy and the balloon are at the same height and the same horizontal location at the same time.
Thus they collide!

35. Choose the origin to be the location on the ground directly below the airplane at the time the supplies
    are dropped, and choose upward as the positive y direction. For the supplies, $y_0 = 235 \text{ m}$, $v_{y0} = 0$,
    $a_y = -g$, and the final y location is $y = 0 \text{ m}$. The initial (and constant) x velocity of the supplies is
    $v_x = 69.4 \text{ m/s}$.

    (a) The time for the supplies to reach the ground is found from Eq. 2-11b.
    $$y = y_0 + v_{y0}t + \tfrac{1}{2}a_y t^2 \quad\rightarrow\quad 0 = y_0 + 0 + \tfrac{1}{2}at^2 \quad\rightarrow$$
    $$t = \sqrt{\frac{-2y_0}{a}} = \sqrt{\frac{-2(235 \text{ m})}{(-9.80 \text{ m/s}^2)}} = 6.93 \text{ s}$$

    Then the horizontal distance of travel for the package is found from the horizontal motion at
    constant velocity.
    $$\Delta x = v_x t = (69.4 \text{ m/s})(6.93 \text{ s}) = \boxed{481 \text{ m}}$$

    (b) Now the supplies have to travel a horizontal distance of only 425 m. Thus the time of flight will
    be less, and is found from the horizontal motion at constant velocity.
    $$\Delta x = v_x t \quad\rightarrow\quad t = \Delta x / v_x = 425 \text{ m} / 69.4 \text{ m/s} = 6.124 \text{ s}.$$

    The y motion must satisfy Eq. 2-11b for this new time, but the same vertical displacement and
    acceleration.
    $$y = y_0 + v_{y0}t + \tfrac{1}{2}a_y t^2 \quad\rightarrow$$
    $$v_{y0} = \frac{y - y_0 - \tfrac{1}{2}a_y t^2}{t} = \frac{0 - 235 \text{ m} - \tfrac{1}{2}(-9.80 \text{ m/s}^2)(6.124 \text{ s})^2}{6.124 \text{ s}} = \boxed{-8.37 \text{ m/s}}$$

    Notice that since this is a negative velocity, the object must be projected DOWN.

(*c*)   The horizontal component of the speed of the supplies upon landing is the constant horizontal speed of 69.4 m/s. The vertical speed is found from Eq. 2-11a.

$$v_y = v_{y0} + a_y t = -8.37 \text{ m/s} + \left(-9.80 \text{ m/s}^2\right)\left(6.124 \text{ s}\right) = 68.4 \text{ m/s}$$

Thus the speed is given by

$$v = \sqrt{v_x^2 + v_y^2} = \sqrt{\left(69.4 \text{ m/s}\right)^2 + \left(68.4 \text{ m/s}\right)^2} = \boxed{97.4 \text{ m/s}}$$

36. Call the direction of the boat relative to the water the positive direction.

(*a*) $\vec{\mathbf{v}}_{\substack{\text{jogger} \\ \text{rel. water}}} = \vec{\mathbf{v}}_{\substack{\text{jogger} \\ \text{rel. boat}}} + \vec{\mathbf{v}}_{\substack{\text{boat rel.} \\ \text{water}}} = 2.2 \text{ m/s} + 7.5 \text{ m/s}$

$= \boxed{9.7 \text{ m/s in the direction the boat is moving}}$

(*b*) $\vec{\mathbf{v}}_{\substack{\text{jogger} \\ \text{rel. water}}} = \vec{\mathbf{v}}_{\substack{\text{jogger} \\ \text{rel. boat}}} + \vec{\mathbf{v}}_{\substack{\text{boat rel.} \\ \text{water}}} = -2.2 \text{ m/s} + 7.5 \text{ m/s}$

$= \boxed{5.3 \text{ m/s in the direction the boat is moving}}$

37. Call the direction of the flow of the river the *x* direction, and the direction of Huck walking relative to the raft the *y* direction.

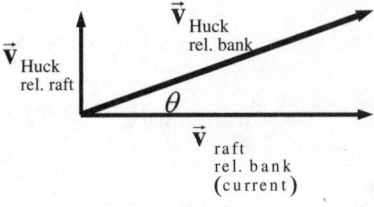

$\vec{\mathbf{v}}_{\substack{\text{Huck} \\ \text{rel. bank}}} = \vec{\mathbf{v}}_{\substack{\text{Huck} \\ \text{rel. raft}}} + \vec{\mathbf{v}}_{\substack{\text{raft rel.} \\ \text{bank}}} = (0, 0.6) \text{ m/s} + (1.7, 0) \text{ m/s}$

$= (1.7, 0.6) \text{ m/s}$

Magnitude: $v_{\substack{\text{Huck} \\ \text{rel. bank}}} = \sqrt{1.7^2 + 0.6^2} = \boxed{1.8 \text{ m/s}}$

Direction: $\theta = \tan^{-1} \dfrac{0.6}{1.7} = \boxed{19° \text{ relative to river}}$

38. We have $v_{\substack{\text{car rel.} \\ \text{ground}}} = 25 \text{ m/s}$. Use the diagram, illustrating $\vec{\mathbf{v}}_{\substack{\text{snow rel.} \\ \text{ground}}} = \vec{\mathbf{v}}_{\substack{\text{snow rel.} \\ \text{car}}} + \vec{\mathbf{v}}_{\substack{\text{car rel.} \\ \text{ground}}}$, to calculate the other speeds.

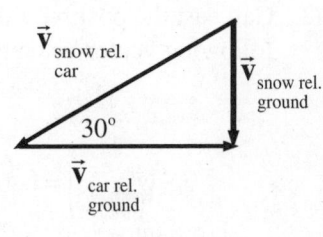

$\cos 30° = \dfrac{v_{\substack{\text{car rel.} \\ \text{ground}}}}{v_{\substack{\text{snow rel.} \\ \text{car}}}} \quad \rightarrow \quad v_{\substack{\text{snow rel.} \\ \text{car}}} = 25 \text{ m/s} / \cos 30° = \boxed{29 \text{ m/s}}$

$\tan 30° = \dfrac{v_{\substack{\text{snow rel.} \\ \text{ground}}}}{v_{\substack{\text{car rel.} \\ \text{ground}}}} \quad \rightarrow \quad v_{\substack{\text{snow rel.} \\ \text{ground}}} = (25 \text{ m/s}) \tan 30° = \boxed{14 \text{ m/s}}$

39. Call the direction of the flow of the river the *x* direction, and the direction the boat is headed the *y* direction.

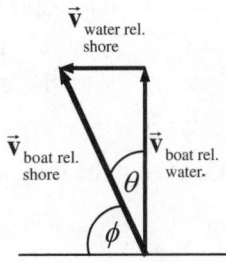

(*a*) $v_{\substack{\text{boat rel.} \\ \text{shore}}} = \sqrt{v_{\substack{\text{water rel.} \\ \text{shore}}}^2 + v_{\substack{\text{boat rel.} \\ \text{water}}}^2} = \sqrt{1.20^2 + 2.30^2} = \boxed{2.59 \text{ m/s}}$

$\theta = \tan^{-1} \dfrac{1.20}{2.30} = 27.6° \ , \ \phi = 90° - \theta = \boxed{62.4° \text{ relative to shore}}$

(b) The position of the boat after 3.00 seconds is given by

$$\Delta d = v_{\underset{\text{shore}}{\text{boat rel.}}} t = \left[(1.20, 2.30)\,\text{m/s} \right] (3.00\,\text{sec})$$

$$= \boxed{(3.60\ \text{m downstream}, 6.90\ \text{m across the river})}$$

As a magnitude and direction, it would be 7.8 m away from the starting point, at an angle of 62.4° relative to the shore.

40. If each plane has a speed of 785 km/hr, then their relative speed of approach is 1570 km/hr. If the planes are 11 km apart, then the time for evasive action is found from

$$\Delta d = vt \quad \rightarrow \quad t = \frac{\Delta d}{v} = \left(\frac{11.0\ \text{km}}{1570\ \text{km/hr}} \right) \left(\frac{3600\ \text{sec}}{1\ \text{hr}} \right) = \boxed{25.2\ \text{s}}$$

41. Call east the positive x direction and north the positive y direction. Then the following vector velocity relationship exists.

(a) $\vec{v}_{\underset{\text{ground}}{\text{plane rel.}}} = \vec{v}_{\underset{\text{rel. air}}{\text{plane}}} + \vec{v}_{\underset{\text{ground}}{\text{air rel.}}}$

$$= (0, -600)\,\text{km/h} + (100\cos 45.0°, 100\sin 45.0°)\,\text{km/h}$$

$$= (70.7, -529)\,\text{km/h}$$

$$v_{\underset{\text{ground}}{\text{plane rel.}}} = \sqrt{(70.7\ \text{km/h})^2 + (-529\ \text{km/h})^2} = \boxed{540\ \text{km/h}}$$

$$\theta = \tan^{-1}\frac{70.7}{529} = \boxed{7.6°\ \text{east of south}}$$

(b) The plane is away from its intended position by the distance the air has caused it to move. The wind speed is 100 km/h, so after 10 min (1/6 h), the plane is off course by $\Delta x = v_x t = (100\ \text{km/h})(\tfrac{1}{6}\text{h}) = \boxed{17\ \text{km}}$.

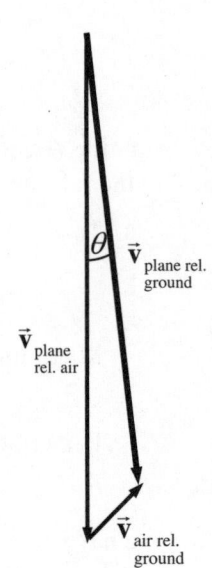

42. Call east the positive x direction and north the positive y direction. Then the following vector velocity relationship exists.

$$\vec{v}_{\underset{\text{ground}}{\text{plane rel.}}} = \vec{v}_{\underset{\text{rel. air}}{\text{plane}}} + \vec{v}_{\underset{\text{ground}}{\text{air rel.}}} \quad \rightarrow$$

$$\left(0, -v_{\underset{\text{ground}}{\text{plane rel.}}} \right) = (-600\sin\theta, 600\cos\theta)\,\text{km/h}$$

$$+ (100\cos 45.0°, 100\sin 45.0°)\,\text{km/h}$$

Equate x components in the above equation.

$$0 = -600\sin\theta + 100\cos 45.0° \quad \rightarrow$$

$$\theta = \sin^{-1}\frac{100\cos 45.0°}{600} = \boxed{6.77°,\ \text{west of south}}$$

43. From the diagram in figure 3-29, it is seen that

$$v_{\underset{\text{shore}}{\text{boat rel.}}} = v_{\underset{\text{water}}{\text{boat rel.}}} \cos\theta = (1.85\ \text{m/s})\cos 40.4° = \boxed{1.41\ \text{m/s}}.$$

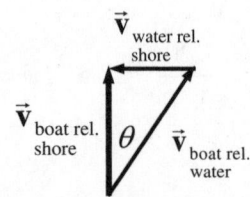

44. Call the direction of the boat relative to the water the x direction, and upward the y direction. Also see the diagram.

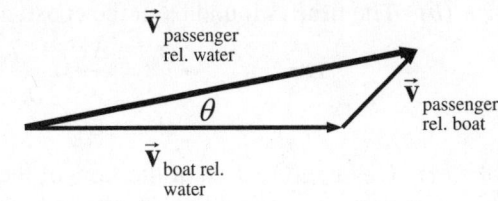

$$\vec{\mathbf{v}}_{\substack{passenger \\ rel.\ water}} = \vec{\mathbf{v}}_{\substack{passenger \\ rel.\ boat}} + \vec{\mathbf{v}}_{\substack{boat\ rel. \\ water}}$$

$$= \left(0.50\cos 45°, 0.50\sin 45°\right) m/s$$

$$+ \left(1.50, 0\right) m/s = \left(1.854, 0.354\right) m/s$$

$$v_{\substack{passenger \\ rel.\ water}} = \sqrt{1.854^2 + 0.354^2} = \boxed{1.89\ m/s}$$

45. Call the direction of the flow of the river the x direction, and the direction straight across the river the y direction. The boat is traveling straight across the river. The boat is headed at $\theta = 28.5°$ upstream, at a speed of $v_{\substack{boat\ rel. \\ water}} = 2.60\ m/s$.

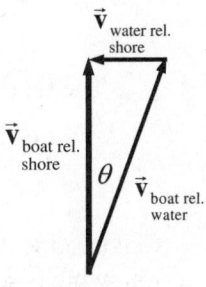

(a) $\sin\theta = v_{\substack{water\ rel. \\ shore}} / v_{\substack{boat\ rel. \\ water}}$ → $v_{\substack{water\ rel. \\ shore}} = \left(2.60\ m/s\right)\sin 28.5° = \boxed{1.24\ m/s}$

(b) $\cos\theta = v_{\substack{boat\ rel. \\ shore}} / v_{\substack{boat\ rel. \\ water}}$ → $v_{\substack{boat\ rel. \\ shore}} = \left(2.60\ m/s\right)\cos 28.5° = \boxed{2.28\ m/s}$

46. Call the direction of the flow of the river the x direction, and the direction straight across the river the y direction. From the diagram, $\theta = \tan^{-1} 110\ m/260\ m = 22.9°$. Equate the vertical components of the velocities to find the speed of the boat relative to the shore.

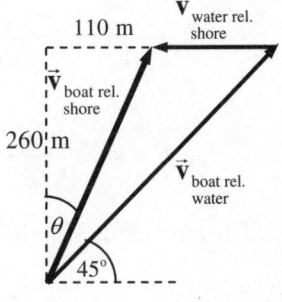

$$v_{\substack{boat\ rel. \\ shore}} \cos\theta = v_{\substack{boat\ rel. \\ water}} \sin 45° →$$

$$v_{\substack{boat\ rel. \\ shore}} = \left(1.70\ m/s\right)\frac{\sin 45°}{\cos 22.9°} = 1.305\ m/s$$

Equate the horizontal components of the velocities.

$$v_{\substack{boat\ rel. \\ shore}} \sin\theta = v_{\substack{boat\ rel. \\ water}} \cos 45° - v_{\substack{water \\ rel.\ shore}} →$$

$$v_{\substack{water \\ rel.\ shore}} = v_{\substack{boat\ rel. \\ water}} \cos 45° - v_{\substack{boat\ rel. \\ shore}} \sin\theta$$

$$= \left(1.70\ m/s\right)\cos 45° - \left(1.305\ m/s\right)\sin 22.9° = \boxed{0.69\ m/s}$$

47. Call the direction of the flow of the river the x direction, and the direction straight across the river the y direction. Call the location of the swimmer's starting point the origin.

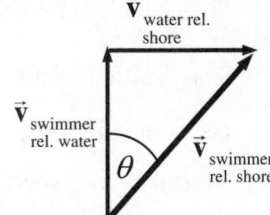

$$\vec{\mathbf{v}}_{\substack{swimmer \\ rel.\ shore}} = \vec{\mathbf{v}}_{\substack{swimmer \\ rel.\ water}} + \vec{\mathbf{v}}_{\substack{water\ rel. \\ shore}} = \left(0, 0.45\ m/s\right) + \left(0.40\ m/s, 0\right)$$

$$= \left(0.40, 0.45\right) m/s$$

(a) Since the swimmer starts from the origin, the distances covered in the x and y directions will be exactly proportional to the speeds in those directions.

$$\frac{\Delta x}{\Delta y} = \frac{v_x t}{v_y t} = \frac{v_x}{v_y} → \frac{\Delta x}{75\ m} = \frac{0.40\ m/s}{0.45\ m/s} → \Delta x = \boxed{67\ m}$$

(b)   The time is found from the constant velocity relationship for either the x or y directions.

$$\Delta y = v_y t \quad \rightarrow \quad t = \frac{\Delta y}{v_y} = \frac{75 \text{ m}}{0.45 \text{ m/s}} = \boxed{170 \text{ s}}$$

48.   (a)   Call the direction of the flow of the river the x direction, and the
direction straight across the river the y direction.

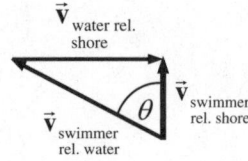

$$\sin \theta = \frac{v_{\text{water rel.} \atop \text{shore}}}{v_{\text{swimmer} \atop \text{rel. water}}} = \frac{0.40 \text{ m/s}}{0.45 \text{ m/s}} \quad \rightarrow \quad \theta = \sin^{-1} \frac{0.40}{0.45} = 62.73° = \boxed{62°}$$

(b)   From the diagram her speed with respect to the shore is

$$v_{\text{swimmer} \atop \text{rel. shore}} = v_{\text{swimmer} \atop \text{rel. water}} \cos \theta = (0.45 \text{ m/s}) \cos 62.73° = 0.206 \text{ m/s}$$

The time to cross the river can be found from the constant velocity relationship.

$$\Delta x = vt \quad \rightarrow \quad t = \frac{\Delta x}{v} = \frac{75 \text{ m}}{0.206 \text{ m/s}} = 364 \text{ s} = \boxed{3.6 \times 10^2 \text{ s} = 6.1 \text{ min}}$$

49.   Call east the positive x direction and north the positive y direction. The
following is seen from the diagram. Apply the law of sines to the triangle
formed by the three vectors.

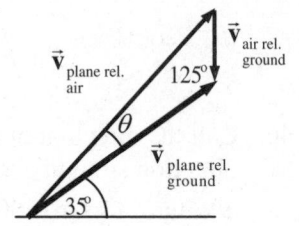

$$\frac{v_{\text{plane} \atop \text{rel. air}}}{\sin 125°} = \frac{v_{\text{air rel.} \atop \text{ground}}}{\sin \theta} \quad \rightarrow \quad \sin \theta = \frac{v_{\text{air rel.} \atop \text{ground}}}{v_{\text{plane} \atop \text{rel. air}}} \sin 125° \quad \rightarrow$$

$$\theta = \sin^{-1} \left(\frac{95}{620} \sin 125° \right) = 7.211°$$

So the plane should head in a direction of $35.0° + 7.2° = \boxed{42.2° \text{ north of east}}$.

50.   Take the origin to be the location at which the speeder passes the police car, in the reference frame of

the unaccelerated police car. The speeder is traveling at $145 \text{ km/h} \left(\dfrac{1 \text{ m/s}}{3.6 \text{ km/h}} \right) = 40.28 \text{ m/s}$

relative to the ground, and the policeman is traveling at $95 \text{ km/h} \left(\dfrac{1 \text{ m/s}}{3.6 \text{ km/h}} \right) = 26.39 \text{ m/s}$ relative

to the ground. Relative to the unaccelerated police car, the speeder is traveling at $13.89 \text{ m/s} = v_s$,
and the police car is not moving. Do all of the calculations in the frame of reference of the
unaccelerated police car.

The position of the speeder in the chosen reference frame is given by $\Delta x_s = v_s t$. The position of the

policeman in the chosen reference frame is given by $\Delta x_p = \frac{1}{2} a_p (t-1)^2, t > 1$. The police car

overtakes the speeder when these two distances are the same.; i.e., $\Delta x_s = \Delta x_p$.

$$\Delta x_s = \Delta x_p \quad \rightarrow \quad v_s t = \frac{1}{2} a_p (t-1)^2 \quad \rightarrow \quad (13.89 \text{ m/s}) t = \frac{1}{2} (2 \text{ m/s}^2)(t^2 - 2t + 1) = t^2 - 2t + 1$$

$$t^2 - 15.89t + 1 = 0 \quad \rightarrow \quad t = \frac{15.89 \pm \sqrt{15.89^2 - 4}}{2} = 0.0632 \text{ s}, 15.83 \text{ s}$$

Since the police car doesn't accelerate until $t = 1.00$ s, the correct answer is $\boxed{t = 15.8 \text{ s}}$.

51. Take the origin to be the location at which the speeder passes the police car. The speed of the speeder is v_s. The position of the speeder after the 7.00 seconds is $\Delta x_s = v_s t = v_s (7.00 \text{ s})$. The position of the police car is calculated based on the fact that the car traveled 1 second at the original velocity, and then 6 seconds under acceleration. Note that the police car's velocity must have the units changed.

$$v_p = (95 \text{ km/h}) \left(\frac{1 \text{ m/s}}{3.6 \text{ km/h}} \right) = 26.39 \text{ m/s} \qquad a_p = 2.00 \text{ m/s}^2$$

$$\Delta x_p = v_p (1.00 \text{ s}) + v_p (6.00 \text{ s}) + \tfrac{1}{2} a_p (6.00 \text{ s})^2 = 220.7 \text{ m}$$

The police car overtakes the speeder when these two distances are the same; i.e., $\Delta x_s = \Delta x_p$.

$$v_s (7 \text{ s}) = 220.7 \text{ m} \quad \rightarrow \quad v_s = \frac{220.7 \text{ m}}{7 \text{ s}} \left(\frac{3.6 \text{ km/h}}{1 \text{ m/s}} \right) = \boxed{114 \text{ km/h}}$$

52. Call east the positive x direction and north the positive y direction. From the first diagram, this relative velocity relationship is seen.

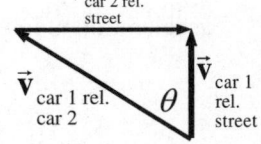

$$\vec{\mathbf{v}}_{\substack{\text{car 1 rel.} \\ \text{street}}} = \vec{\mathbf{v}}_{\substack{\text{car 1 rel.} \\ \text{car 2}}} + \vec{\mathbf{v}}_{\substack{\text{car 2 rel.} \\ \text{street}}} \quad \rightarrow \quad v_{\substack{\text{car 1 rel.} \\ \text{car 2}}} = \sqrt{(-55)^2 + (35)^2} = \boxed{65 \text{ km/h}}$$

$$\theta = \tan^{-1} 55/35 = \boxed{58° \text{ West of North}}$$

For the other relative velocity relationship:

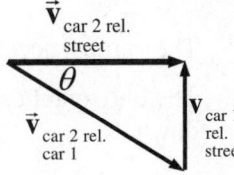

$$\vec{\mathbf{v}}_{\substack{\text{car 2 rel.} \\ \text{street}}} = \vec{\mathbf{v}}_{\substack{\text{car 2 rel.} \\ \text{car 1}}} + \vec{\mathbf{v}}_{\substack{\text{car 1 rel.} \\ \text{street}}} \quad \rightarrow \quad v_{\substack{\text{car 2 rel.} \\ \text{car 1}}} = \sqrt{(55)^2 + (-35)^2} = \boxed{65 \text{ km/h}}$$

$$\theta = \tan^{-1} 35/55 = \boxed{32° \text{ South of East}}$$

Notice that the two relative velocities are opposites of each other: $\vec{\mathbf{v}}_{\substack{\text{car 2 rel.} \\ \text{car 1}}} = -\vec{\mathbf{v}}_{\substack{\text{car 1 rel.} \\ \text{car 2}}}$

53. Since the arrow will start and end at the same height, use the range formula derived in Example 3-8. The range is 27 m, and the initial speed of the arrow is 35 m/s.

$$R = \frac{v_0^2 \sin 2\theta_0}{g} \quad \rightarrow \quad \sin 2\theta_0 = \frac{Rg}{v_0^2} = \frac{(27 \text{ m})(9.80 \text{ m/s}^2)}{(35 \text{ m/s})^2} = 0.216$$

$$\theta_0 = \tfrac{1}{2} \sin^{-1} 0.216 = 6.2°, 83.8°$$

Only the first answer is practical, so the result is $\boxed{\theta_0 = 6.2°}$.

54. The plumber's displacement in component notation is

$\boxed{\vec{\mathbf{d}} = (50 \text{ m}, -25 \text{ m}, -10 \text{ m})}$. Since this is a 3-dimensional problem, it requires 2 angles to determine his location (similar to latitude and longitude on the surface of the Earth). In the x-y plane, this follows.

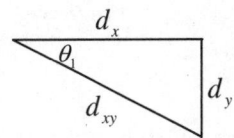

$$\theta_1 = \tan^{-1} \frac{d_y}{d_x} = \tan^{-1} \frac{25}{50} = 27° \text{ South of East}$$

$$d_{xy} = \sqrt{d_x^2 + d_y^2} = \sqrt{(50)^2 + (-25)^2} = 55.9 \text{ m}$$

For the vertical motion, consider another right triangle, made up of d_{xy} as one

leg, and the vertical displacement d_z as the other leg. See the second figure,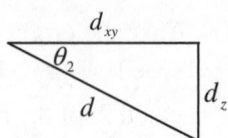

and the following calculations.

$$\theta_2 = \tan^{-1}\frac{d_z}{d_{xy}} = \tan^{-1}\frac{10 \text{ m}}{55.9 \text{ m}} = 10° \text{ Below the Horizontal}$$

$$d = \sqrt{d_{xy}^2 + d_z^2} = \sqrt{d_x^2 + d_y^2 + d_z^2} = \sqrt{(50)^2 + (-25)^2 + (-10)^2} = 57 \text{ m}$$

The result is that the displacement is $\boxed{57 \text{ m}}$, at an angle of $\boxed{27° \text{ South of East}}$, and

$\boxed{10° \text{ Below the Horizontal}}$.

55. Assume a constant upward slope, and so the deceleration is along a straight line. The starting

velocity along that line is $120 \text{ km/h}\left(\dfrac{1 \text{ m/s}}{3.6 \text{ km/h}}\right) = 33.3 \text{ m/s}$. The ending velocity is 0 m/s. The

acceleration is found from Eq. 2-11a.

$$v = v_0 + at \quad \rightarrow \quad 0 = 33.3 \text{ m/s} + a(6.0 \text{ s}) \quad \rightarrow \quad a = -\frac{33.3 \text{ m/s}}{6.0 \text{ s}} = -5.56 \text{ m/s}^2$$

The horizontal acceleration is $a_{\text{horiz}} = a\cos\theta = -5.56 \text{ m/s}^2\left(\cos 32°\right) = \boxed{-4.7 \text{ m/s}^2}$.

The vertical acceleration is $a_{\text{vert}} = a\sin\theta = -5.56 \text{ m/s}^2\left(\sin 30°\right) = \boxed{-2.8 \text{ m/s}^2}$

The horizontal acceleration is to the left in the textbook diagram, and the vertical acceleration is down.

56. Magnitude $= \sqrt{75.4^2 + y^2} = 88.5 \quad \rightarrow \quad y = \pm\sqrt{88.5^2 - 75.4^2} = \pm 46.34 = \boxed{\pm 46.3}$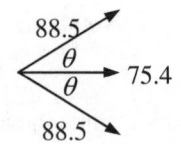

Direction $= \tan^{-1}\dfrac{46.34}{75.4} = \boxed{31.6° \text{ relative to } x \text{ axis}}$

See the diagram for the two possible answers.

57. Choose the x direction to be the direction of train travel (the direction the
passenger is facing) and choose the y direction to be up. This relationship exists
among the velocities: $\vec{v}_{\substack{\text{rain rel.} \\ \text{ground}}} = \vec{v}_{\substack{\text{rain rel.} \\ \text{train}}} + \vec{v}_{\substack{\text{train rel.} \\ \text{ground}}}$. From the diagram, find the

expression for the speed of the raindrops.

$$\tan\theta = \frac{v_{\substack{\text{train rel.} \\ \text{ground}}}}{v_{\substack{\text{rain rel.} \\ \text{ground}}}} = \frac{v_T}{v_{\substack{\text{rain rel.} \\ \text{ground}}}} \quad \rightarrow \quad \boxed{v_{\substack{\text{rain rel.} \\ \text{ground}}} = \frac{v_T}{\tan\theta}}.$$

58. Call east the positive x direction and north the positive y direction. Then this
relative velocity relationship follows (see the accompanying diagram).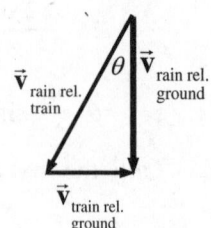

$$\vec{v}_{\substack{\text{plane rel.} \\ \text{ground}}} = \vec{v}_{\substack{\text{plane} \\ \text{rel. air}}} + \vec{v}_{\substack{\text{air rel.} \\ \text{ground}}}$$

Equate the x components of the velocity vectors.

$$\left(125\,\text{km/h}\right)\cos 45° = 0 + v_{\text{wind }x} \quad \rightarrow \quad v_{\text{wind }x} = 88.4\,\text{km/h}.$$

From the y components of the above equation:

$$-125\sin 45° = -155 + v_{\text{wind-y}} \quad \rightarrow \quad v_{\text{wind-y}} = 155 - 125\sin 45° = 66.6\,\text{km/h}$$

The magnitude of the wind velocity is

$$v_{\text{wind}} = \sqrt{v_{\text{wind-x}}^2 + v_{\text{wind-y}}^2} = \sqrt{\left(88.4\,\text{km/h}\right)^2 + \left(66.6\,\text{km/h}\right)^2} = \boxed{111\,\text{km/h}}.$$

The direction of the wind is $\theta = \tan^{-1}\dfrac{v_{\text{wind-y}}}{v_{\text{wind-x}}} = \tan^{-1}\dfrac{66.6}{88.4} = \boxed{37.0°\text{ north of east}}$.

59. Work in the frame of reference in which the train is at rest. Then, relative to the train, the car is moving at 20 km/h. The car has to travel 1 km in that frame of reference to pass the train, and so the time to pass can be found from the constant horizontal velocity relationship.

$$\Delta x = v_x t \quad \rightarrow \quad t_{\substack{\text{same} \\ \text{direction}}} = \frac{\Delta x}{\left(v_x\right)_{\substack{\text{same} \\ \text{direction}}}} = \frac{1\,\text{km}}{20\,\text{km/h}} = 0.05\,\text{h}\left(\frac{3600\,\text{s}}{1\,\text{h}}\right) = \boxed{180\,\text{s}}$$

The car travels 1 km in the frame of reference of the stationary train, but relative to the ground, the car is traveling at 95 km/hr and so relative to the ground the car travels this distance:

$$\Delta x = v_x t_{\substack{\text{same} \\ \text{direction}}} = \left(95\,\text{km/h}\right)\left(0.05\,\text{h}\right) = \boxed{4.8\,\text{km}}$$

If the car and train are traveling in opposite directions, then the velocity of the car relative to the train will be 170 km/h. Thus the time to pass will be

$$t_{\substack{\text{opposite} \\ \text{direction}}} = \frac{\Delta x}{\left(v_x\right)_{\substack{\text{opposite} \\ \text{direction}}}} = \frac{1\,\text{km}}{170\,\text{km/h}} = \left(\frac{1}{170}\,\text{h}\right)\left(\frac{3600\,\text{s}}{1\,\text{h}}\right) = \boxed{21.2\,\text{s}}.$$

The distance traveled by the car relative to the ground will be

$$\Delta x = v_x t_{\substack{\text{opposite} \\ \text{direction}}} = \left(95\,\text{km/h}\right)\left(\frac{1}{170}\,\text{h}\right) = \boxed{0.56\,\text{km}}.$$

60. The time of flight is found from the constant velocity relationship for horizontal motion.

$$\Delta x = v_x t = \quad \rightarrow \quad t = \Delta x / v_x = 8.0\,\text{m}/9.1\,\text{m/s} = \boxed{0.88\,\text{s}}$$

The y motion is symmetric in time – it takes half the time of flight to rise, and half to fall. Thus the time for the jumper to fall from his highest point to the ground is 0.44 sec. His vertical speed is zero at the highest point. From this time, starting vertical speed, and the acceleration of gravity, the maximum height can be found. Call upward the positive y direction. The point of maximum height is the starting position y_0, the ending position is $y = 0$, the starting vertical speed is 0, and $a = -g$. Use Eq. 2-11b to find the height.

$$y = y_0 + v_{y0}t + \tfrac{1}{2}a_y t^2 \quad \rightarrow \quad 0 = y_0 + 0 - \tfrac{1}{2}\left(9.8\,\text{m/s}^2\right)\left(0.44\,\text{s}\right)^2 \quad \rightarrow \quad y_0 = \boxed{0.95\,\text{m}}.$$

61. Assume that the golf ball takes off and lands at the same height, so that the range formula derived in Example 3-8 can be applied. The only variable is to be the acceleration due to gravity.

$$R_{\text{Earth}} = v_0^2 \sin 2\theta_0 / g_{\text{Earth}} \qquad R_{\text{Moon}} = v_0^2 \sin 2\theta_0 / g_{\text{Moon}}$$

$$\frac{R_{\text{Earth}}}{R_{\text{Moon}}} = \frac{v_0^2 \sin 2\theta_0 / g_{\text{Earth}}}{v_0^2 \sin 2\theta_0 / g_{\text{Moon}}} = \frac{1/g_{\text{Earth}}}{1/g_{\text{Moon}}} = \frac{g_{\text{Moon}}}{g_{\text{Earth}}} = \frac{35\,\text{m}}{180\,\text{m}} = 0.19 \quad \rightarrow$$

$$g_{\text{Moon}} = 0.19\,g_{\text{Earth}} \approx \boxed{1.9\,\text{m/s}^2}$$

62. The minimum speed will be that for which the ball just clears the fence; i.e., the ball has a height of 7.5 m when it is 95 m horizontally from home plate. The origin is at home plate, with upward as the positive y direction. For the ball, $y_0 = 1.0$ m , $y = 7.5$ m , $a_y = -g$, $v_{y0} = v_0 \sin\theta_0$, $v_x = v_0 \cos\theta_0$, and $\theta_0 = 38°$. See the diagram (not to scale). For the horizontal motion at constant velocity,

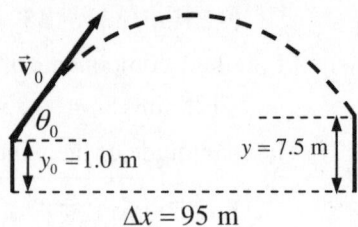

$\Delta x = v_x t = v_0 \cos\theta_0 t$, and so $t = \dfrac{\Delta x}{v_0 \cos\theta_0}$. For the vertical motion, apply Eq. 2-11b.

$$y = y_0 + v_{y0}t + \tfrac{1}{2}a_y t^2 = y_0 + v_0 \left(\sin\theta_0\right)t - \tfrac{1}{2}gt^2$$

Substitute the value of the time of flight for the first occurrence only in the above equation, and then solve for the time.

$$y = y_0 + v_0 t \sin\theta_0 - \tfrac{1}{2}gt^2 \quad \rightarrow \quad y = y_0 + v_0 \sin\theta_0 \frac{\Delta x}{v_0 \cos\theta_0} - \tfrac{1}{2}gt^2 \quad \rightarrow$$

$$t = \sqrt{2\left(\frac{y_0 - y + \Delta x \tan\theta_0}{g}\right)} = \sqrt{2\left(\frac{1.0 \text{ m} - 7.5 \text{ m} + (95 \text{ m})\tan 38°}{9.80 \text{ m/s}^2}\right)} = 3.718 \text{ s}$$

Finally, use the time with the horizontal range to find the initial speed.

$$\Delta x = v_0 \cos\theta_0 t \quad \rightarrow \quad v_0 = \frac{\Delta x}{t \cos\theta_0} = \frac{95 \text{ m}}{(3.718 \text{ s})\cos 38°} = \boxed{32 \text{ m/s}}$$

63. Choose downward to be the positive y direction. The origin is at the point from which the divers push off the cliff. In the vertical direction, the initial velocity is $v_{y0} = 0$, the acceleration is $a_y = 9.80 \text{ m/s}^2$, and the displacement is 35 m. The time of flight is found from Eq. 2-11b.

$$y = y_0 + v_{y0}t + \tfrac{1}{2}a_y t^2 \quad \rightarrow \quad 35 \text{ m} = 0 + 0 + \tfrac{1}{2}\left(9.8 \text{ m/s}^2\right)t^2 \quad \rightarrow \quad t = \sqrt{\frac{2(35 \text{ m})}{9.8 \text{ m/s}^2}} = \boxed{2.7 \text{ s}}$$

The horizontal speed (which is the initial speed) is found from the horizontal motion at constant velocity.

$$\Delta x = v_x t \quad \rightarrow \quad v_x = \Delta x / t = 5.0 \text{ m}/2.7 \text{ s} = \boxed{1.9 \text{ m/s}}$$

64. Choose the origin to be the location on the ground directly underneath the ball when served, and choose upward as the positive y direction. Then for the ball, $y_0 = 2.50$ m , $v_{y0} = 0$, $a_y = -g$, and the y location when the ball just clears the net is $y = 0.90$ m . The time for the ball to reach the net is calculated from Eq. 2-11b.

$$y = y_0 + v_{y0}t + \tfrac{1}{2}a_y t^2 \quad \rightarrow \quad 0.90 \text{ m} = 2.50 \text{ m} + 0 + \tfrac{1}{2}\left(-9.80 \text{ m/s}^2\right)t^2 \quad \rightarrow$$

$$t_{\substack{\text{to} \\ \text{net}}} = \sqrt{\frac{2(-1.60 \text{ m})}{-9.80 \text{ m/s}^2}} = 0.57143 \text{ s}$$

The x velocity is found from the horizontal motion at constant velocity.

$$\Delta x = v_x t \quad \rightarrow \quad v_x = \frac{\Delta x}{t} = \frac{15.0 \text{ m}}{0.57143 \text{ s}} = 26.25 \approx \boxed{26.3 \text{ m/s}} .$$

This is the minimum speed required to clear the net.

To find the full time of flight of the ball, set the final y location to be $y = 0$, and again use Eq. 2-11b.

$$y = y_0 + v_{y0}t + \tfrac{1}{2}a_y t^2 \;\to\; 0.0 \text{ m} = 2.50 \text{ m} + \tfrac{1}{2}\left(-9.80 \text{ m/s}^2\right)t^2 \;\to$$

$$t_{total} = \sqrt{\frac{2(-2.50 \text{ m})}{-9.80 \text{ m/s}^2}} = 0.7143 \approx \boxed{0.714 \text{ s}}$$

The horizontal position where the ball lands is found from the horizontal motion at constant velocity.

$$\Delta x = v_x t = (26.25 \text{ m/s})(0.7143 \text{ s}) = 18.75 \approx \boxed{18.8 \text{ m}}.$$

Since this is between 15.0 and 22.0 m, $\boxed{\text{the ball lands in the "good" region}}$.

65. Work in the frame of reference in which the car is at rest at ground level. In this reference frame, the helicopter is moving horizontally with a speed of

$$215 \text{ km/h} - 155 \text{ km/h} = 60 \text{ km/h}\left(\frac{1 \text{ m/s}}{3.6 \text{ km/h}}\right) = 16.67 \text{ m/s}.$$

For the vertical motion, choose the level of the helicopter to be the origin, and downward to be positive. Then the package's y displacement is $y = 78.0$ m, $v_{y0} = 0$, and $a_y = g$. The time for the package to fall is calculated from Eq. 2-11b.

$$y = y_0 + v_{y0}t + \tfrac{1}{2}a_y t^2 \;\to\; 78.0 \text{ m} = \tfrac{1}{2}\left(9.80 \text{ m/s}^2\right)t^2 \;\to\; t = \sqrt{\frac{2(78.0 \text{ m})}{9.80 \text{ m/s}^2}} = 3.99 \text{ sec}$$

The horizontal distance that the package must move, relative to the "stationary" car, is found from the horizontal motion at constant velocity.

$$\Delta x = v_x t = (16.67 \text{ m/s})(3.99 \text{ s}) = 66.5 \text{ m}$$

Thus the angle under the horizontal for the package release will be

$$\theta = \tan^{-1}\left(\frac{\Delta y}{\Delta x}\right) = \tan^{-1}\left(\frac{78.0 \text{ m}}{66.5 \text{ m}}\right) = 49.55° \approx \boxed{50°} \text{ (to 2 significant figures).}$$

66. (a) For the upstream trip, the boat will cover a distance of $D/2$ with a net speed of $v - u$, so the

time is $t_1 = \dfrac{D/2}{v-u} = \dfrac{D}{2(v-u)}$. For the downstream trip, the boat will cover a distance of $D/2$

with a net speed of $v + u$, so the time is $t_2 = \dfrac{D/2}{v+u} = \dfrac{D}{2(v+u)}$. Thus the total time for the

round trip will be $t = t_1 + t_2 = \dfrac{D}{2(v-u)} + \dfrac{D}{2(v+u)} = \boxed{\dfrac{Dv}{(v^2 - u^2)}}$.

(b) For the boat to go directly across the river, it must be angled against the current in such a way that the net velocity is straight across the river, as in the picture. This equation must be satisfied:

$$\vec{\mathbf{v}}_{\substack{\text{boat rel.} \\ \text{shore}}} = \vec{\mathbf{v}}_{\substack{\text{boat rel.} \\ \text{water}}} + \vec{\mathbf{v}}_{\substack{\text{water rel.} \\ \text{shore}}} = \vec{\mathbf{v}} + \vec{\mathbf{u}}.$$

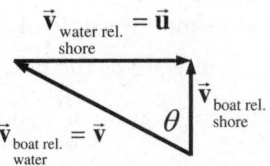

Thus $v_{\substack{\text{boat rel.} \\ \text{shore}}} = \sqrt{v^2 - u^2}$, and the time to go a distance $D/2$ across the river is $t_1 = \dfrac{D/2}{\sqrt{v^2-u^2}} = \dfrac{D}{2\sqrt{v^2-u^2}}$. The same relationship would be in effect for crossing

back, so the time to come back is given by $t_2 = t_1$ and the total time is $t = t_1 + t_2 = \boxed{\dfrac{D}{\sqrt{v^2-u^2}}}$.

The speed v must be greater than the speed u. The velocity of the boat relative to the shore when going upstream is $v-u$. If $v < u$, the boat will not move upstream at all, and so the first part of the trip would be impossible. Also, in part b, we see that v is longer than u in the triangle, since v is the hypotenuse.

67. Choose the origin to be the point from which the projectile is launched, and choose upward as the positive y direction. The y displacement of the projectile is 155 m, and the horizontal range of the projectile is 195 m. The acceleration in the y direction is $a_y = -g$, and the time of flight is 7.6 s.

The horizontal velocity is found from the horizontal motion at constant velocity.

$$\Delta x = v_x t \quad \rightarrow \quad v_x = \frac{\Delta x}{t} = \frac{195 \text{ m}}{7.6 \text{ s}} = 25.7 \text{ m/s}$$

Calculate the initial y velocity from the given data and Eq. 2-11b.

$$y = y_0 + v_{y0}t + \tfrac{1}{2}a_y t^2 \quad \rightarrow \quad 155 \text{ m} = v_{y0}(7.6 \text{ s}) + \tfrac{1}{2}\left(-9.80 \text{ m/s}^2\right)(7.6 \text{ s})^2 \quad \rightarrow \quad v_{y0} = 57.6 \text{ m/s}$$

Thus the initial velocity and direction of the projectile are:

$$v_0 = \sqrt{v_x^2 + v_{y0}^2} = \sqrt{(25.7 \text{ m/s})^2 + (57.6 \text{ m/s})^2} = \boxed{63 \text{ m/s}}$$

$$\theta = \tan^{-1}\frac{v_{y0}}{v_x} = \tan^{-1}\frac{57.6 \text{ m/s}}{25.7 \text{ m/s}} = \boxed{66^\circ}$$

68. Choose downward to be the positive y direction for this problem.
    (*a*) The vertical component of her acceleration is directed downward, and its magnitude will be given by $a_y = a\sin\theta = \left(1.80 \text{ m/s}^2\right)\sin 30.0^\circ = \boxed{0.900 \text{ m/s}^2}$.

    (*b*) The time to reach the bottom of the hill is calculated from Eq. 2-11b, with a y displacement of 335 m, $v_{y0} = 0$, and $a_y = 0.900 \text{ m/s}^2$.

$$y = y_0 + v_{y0}t + \tfrac{1}{2}a_y t^2 \quad \rightarrow \quad 335 \text{ m} = 0 + 0 + \tfrac{1}{2}\left(0.900 \text{ m/s}^2\right)(t)^2 \quad \rightarrow$$

$$t = \sqrt{\frac{2(335 \text{ m})}{\left(0.900 \text{ m/s}^2\right)}} = \boxed{27.3 \text{ s}}$$

69. The proper initial speeds will be those for which the ball has traveled a horizontal distance somewhere between 10.78 m and 11.22 m while it changes height from 2.10 m to 2.60 m with a shooting angle of 38.0°. Choose the origin to be at the shooting location of the basketball, with upward as the positive y direction. Then the vertical displacement is $y = 0.5 \text{ m}$, $a_y = -9.80 \text{ m/s}^2$, $v_{y0} = v_0 \sin\theta_0$, and the (constant) x velocity is $v_x = v_0 \cos\theta_0$. See the diagram (not to scale).

For the horizontal motion at constant velocity,

$$\Delta x = v_x t = v_0 \cos\theta_0 t \text{ and so } t = \frac{\Delta x}{v_0 \cos\theta_0}.$$

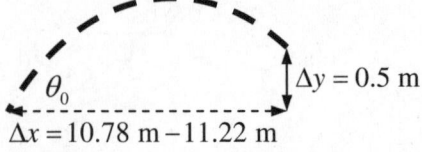
θ_0 $\Delta y = 0.5 \text{ m}$
$\Delta x = 10.78 \text{ m} - 11.22 \text{ m}$

For the vertical motion, applying Eq. 2-11b.

$$y = y_0 + v_{y0}t + \tfrac{1}{2}a_yt^2 = v_0\sin\theta t - \tfrac{1}{2}gt^2$$

Substitute the expression for the time of flight and solve for the initial velocity.

$$y = v_0\sin\theta t - \tfrac{1}{2}gt^2 = v_0\sin\theta\frac{\Delta x}{v_0\cos\theta_0} - \tfrac{1}{2}g\left(\frac{\Delta x}{v_0\cos\theta_0}\right)^2 = \Delta x\tan\theta - \frac{g(\Delta x)^2}{2v_0^2\cos^2\theta_0}$$

$$v_0 = \sqrt{\frac{g(\Delta x)^2}{2\cos^2\theta_0(-y+\Delta x\tan\theta)}}$$

For $\Delta x = 10.78$ m , the shortest shot:

$$v_0 = \sqrt{\frac{(9.80\,\text{m/s}^2)(10.78\,\text{m})^2}{2\cos^2 38.0°\left[(-0.5\,\text{m}+(10.78\,\text{m})\tan 38.0°)\right]}} = \boxed{10.8\,\text{m/s}}\,.$$

For $\Delta x = 11.22$ m , the longest shot:

$$v_0 = \sqrt{\frac{(9.80\,\text{m/s}^2)(11.22\,\text{m})^2}{2\cos^2 38.0°\left[(-0.5\,\text{m}+(11.22\,\text{m})\tan 38.0°)\right]}} = \boxed{11.0\,\text{m/s}}\,.$$

70. Choose the origin to be the location at water level directly underneath the diver when she left the board. Choose upward as the positive y direction. For the diver, $y_0 = 5.0$ m , the final y position is $y = 0.0$ m (water level), $a_y = -g$, the time of flight is $t = 1.3$ s , and the horizontal displacement is $\Delta x = 3.0$ m .

(a) The horizontal velocity is determined from the horizontal motion at constant velocity.

$$\Delta x = v_x t \quad \rightarrow \quad v_x = \frac{\Delta x}{t} = \frac{3.0\,\text{m}}{1.3\,\text{s}} = 2.31\,\text{m/s}$$

The initial y velocity is found using Eq. 2-11b.

$$y = y_0 + v_{y0}t + \tfrac{1}{2}a_yt^2 \quad \rightarrow \quad 0\,\text{m} = 5.0\,\text{m} + v_{y0}(1.3\,\text{s}) + \tfrac{1}{2}(-9.80\,\text{m/s}^2)(1.3\,\text{s})^2 \quad \rightarrow$$

$$v_{y0} = 2.52\,\text{m/s}$$

The magnitude and direction of the initial velocity is

$$v_0 = \sqrt{v_x^2 + v_{y0}^2} = \sqrt{(2.31\,\text{m/s})^2 + (2.52\,\text{m/s})^2} = \boxed{3.4\,\text{m/s}}$$

$$\theta = \tan^{-1}\frac{v_{y0}}{v_x} = \tan^{-1}\frac{2.52\,\text{m/s}}{2.31\,\text{m/s}} = \boxed{48°\,\text{above the horizontal}}$$

(b) The maximum height will be reached when the y velocity is zero. Use Eq. 2-11c.

$$v_y^2 = v_{y0}^2 + 2a\Delta y \quad \rightarrow \quad 0 = (2.52\,\text{m/s})^2 + 2(-9.80\,\text{m/s}^2)(y_{max} - 5.0\,\text{m}) \quad \rightarrow$$

$$y_{max} = \boxed{5.3\,\text{m}}$$

(c) To find the velocity when she enters the water, the horizontal velocity is the (constant) value of $v_x = 2.31\,\text{m/s}$. The vertical velocity is found from Eq. 2-11a.

$$v_y = v_{y0} + at = 2.52\,\text{m/s} + (-9.80\,\text{m/s}^2)(1.3\,\text{s}) = -10.2\,\text{m/s}\,.$$

The magnitude and direction of this velocity is given by

$$v = \sqrt{v_x^2 + v_y^2} = \sqrt{(2.31\,\text{m/s})^2 + (-10.2\,\text{m/s})^2} = 10.458\,\text{m/s} \approx \boxed{10\,\text{m/s}}$$

$$\theta = \tan^{-1}\frac{v_y}{v_x} = \tan^{-1}\frac{-10.2\,\text{m/s}}{2.31\,\text{m/s}} = \boxed{-77^\circ \ (\text{below the horizontal})}$$

71. (a) Choose the origin to be the location where the car leaves the ramp, and choose upward to be the positive y direction. At the end of its flight over the 8 cars, the car must be at $y = -1.5$ m. Also for the car, $v_{y0} = 0$, $a_y = -g$, $v_x = v_0$, and $\Delta x = 20$ m. The time of flight is found from the horizontal motion at constant velocity: $\Delta x = v_x t \ \rightarrow \ t = \Delta x/v_0$. That expression for the time is used in Eq. 2-11b for the vertical motion.

$$y = y_0 + v_{y0}t + \tfrac{1}{2}a_y t^2 \ \rightarrow \ y = 0 + 0 + \tfrac{1}{2}(-g)\left(\frac{\Delta x}{v_0}\right)^2 \ \rightarrow$$

$$v_0 = \sqrt{\frac{-g(\Delta x)^2}{2(y)}} = \sqrt{\frac{-(9.80\,\text{m/s}^2)(20\,\text{m})^2}{2(-1.5\,\text{m})}} = \boxed{36\,\text{m/s}}$$

(b) Again choose the origin to be the location where the car leaves the ramp, and choose upward to be the positive y direction. The y displacement of the car at the end of its flight over the 8 cars must again be $y = -1.5$ m. For the car, $v_{y0} = v_0 \sin\theta_0$, $a_y = -g$, $v_x = v_0 \cos\theta_0$, and $\Delta x = 20$ m. The launch angle is $\theta_0 = 10^\circ$. The time of flight is found from the horizontal motion at constant velocity.

$$\Delta x = v_x t \ \rightarrow \ t = \frac{\Delta x}{v_0 \cos\theta_0}$$

That expression for the time is used in Eq. 2-11b for the vertical motion.

$$y = y_0 + v_{y0}t + \tfrac{1}{2}a_y t^2 \ \rightarrow \ y = v_0 \sin\theta_0 \frac{\Delta x}{v_0 \cos\theta_0} + \tfrac{1}{2}(-g)\left(\frac{\Delta x}{v_0 \cos\theta_0}\right)^2 \ \rightarrow$$

$$v_0 = \sqrt{\frac{g(\Delta x)^2}{2(\Delta x \tan\theta_0 - y)\cos^2\theta_0}} = \sqrt{\frac{(9.80\,\text{m/s}^2)(20\,\text{m})^2}{2((20\,\text{m})\tan 10^\circ + 1.5\,\text{m})\cos^2 10^\circ}} = \boxed{20\,\text{m/s}}$$

72. Choose the origin to be the point at ground level directly below where the ball was hit. Call upwards the positive y direction. For the ball, we have $v_0 = 28\,\text{m/s}$, $\theta_0 = 61^\circ$, $a_y = -g$, $y_0 = 0.9$ m, and $y = 0.0$ m.

(a) To find the horizontal displacement of the ball, the horizontal velocity and the time of flight are needed. The (constant) horizontal velocity is given by $v_x = v_0 \cos\theta_0$. The time of flight is found from Eq. 2-11b.

$$y = y_0 + v_{y0}t + \tfrac{1}{2}a_y t^2 \ \rightarrow \ 0 = y_0 + v_0 \sin\theta_0 t - \tfrac{1}{2}gt^2 \ \rightarrow$$

$$t = \frac{-v_0 \sin\theta_0 \pm \sqrt{v_0^2 \sin^2\theta_0 - 4(-\tfrac{1}{2}g)y_0}}{2(-\tfrac{1}{2}g)}$$

$$= \frac{-(28\,\text{m/s})\sin 61° \pm \sqrt{(28\,\text{m/s})^2 \sin^2 61° - 4\left(-\frac{1}{2}\right)\left(9.80\,\text{m/s}^2\right)(0.9\,\text{m})}}{2\left(-\frac{1}{2}\right)\left(9.80\,\text{m/s}^2\right)}$$

$$= 5.034\,\text{s}, -0.0365\,\text{s}$$

Choose the positive time, since the ball was hit at $t = 0$. The horizontal displacement of the ball will be found by the constant velocity relationship for horizontal motion.

$$\Delta x = v_x t = v_0 \cos\theta_0 t = (28\,\text{m/s})(\cos 61°)(5.034\text{s}) = 68.34\,\text{m} \approx \boxed{68\,\text{m}}$$

(b) The center fielder catches the ball right at ground level. He ran $105\,\text{m} - 68.34\,\text{m} = 36.66\,\text{m}$ to catch the ball, so his average running speed would be

$$v_{avg} = \frac{\Delta d}{t} = \frac{36.66\,\text{m}}{5.034\,\text{s}} = 7.282\,\text{m/s} \approx \boxed{7.3\,\text{m/s}}$$

73. Since the ball is being caught at the same height from which it was struck, use the range formula to find the horizontal distance the ball travels.

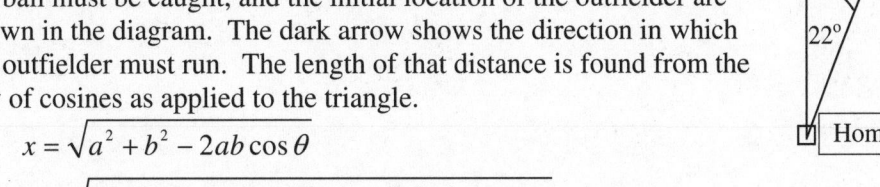

$$R = \frac{v_0^2 \sin 2\theta_0}{g} = \frac{(32\,\text{m/s})^2 \sin(2\times 55°)}{9.8\,\text{m/s}^2} = 98.188\,\text{m}$$

Then as seen from above, the location of home plate, the point where the ball must be caught, and the initial location of the outfielder are shown in the diagram. The dark arrow shows the direction in which the outfielder must run. The length of that distance is found from the law of cosines as applied to the triangle.

$$x = \sqrt{a^2 + b^2 - 2ab\cos\theta}$$

$$= \sqrt{98.188^2 + 85^2 - 2(98.188)(85)\cos 22°} = 37.27\,\text{m}$$

The angle θ at which the outfielder should run is found from the law of sines.

$$\frac{\sin 22°}{x} = \frac{\sin\theta}{98\,\text{m}} \quad \rightarrow \quad \theta = \sin^{-1}\left(\frac{98.188}{37.27}\sin 22°\right) = 81° \text{ or } 99°$$

Since $98.188^2 > 85^2 + 37.27^2$, the angle must be obtuse, so we choose $\theta = 97°$.
Assume that the outfielder's time for running is the same as the time of flight of the ball. The time of flight of the ball is found from the horizontal motion of the ball at constant velocity.

$$R = v_x t = v_0 \cos\theta_0 t \quad \rightarrow \quad t = \frac{R}{v_0 \cos\theta_0} = \frac{98.188\,\text{m}}{(32\,\text{m/s})\cos 55°} = 5.35\,\text{s}$$

Thus the average velocity of the outfielder must be $v_{avg} = \frac{\Delta d}{t} = \frac{37.27\,\text{m}}{5.35\,\text{s}} = \boxed{7.0\,\text{m/s}}$ at an angle of

$\boxed{97°}$ relative to the outfielder's line of sight to home plate.

74. Choose the origin to be the point at the top of the building from which the ball is shot, and call upwards the positive y direction. The initial velocity is $v_0 = 18\,\text{m/s}$ at an angle of $\theta_0 = 42°$. The acceleration due to gravity is $a_y = -g$.

(a) $v_x = v_0 \cos\theta_0 = (18\,\text{m/s})\cos 42° = 13.38 \approx \boxed{13\,\text{m/s}}$

$v_{y0} = v_0 \sin\theta_0 = (18\,\text{m/s})\sin 42° = 12.04 \approx \boxed{12\,\text{m/s}}$

(*b*) Since the horizontal velocity is known and the horizontal distance is known, the time of flight can be found from the constant velocity equation for horizontal motion.

$$\Delta x = v_x t \quad \rightarrow \quad t = \frac{\Delta x}{v_x} = \frac{55\ \text{m}}{13.38\ \text{m/s}} = 4.111\ \text{s}$$

With that time of flight, calculate the vertical position of the ball using Eq. 2-11b.

$$y = y_0 + v_{y0}t + \tfrac{1}{2}a_y t^2 = \left(12.04\ \text{m/s}\right)\left(4.111\ \text{s}\right) + \tfrac{1}{2}\left(-9.80\ \text{m/s}^2\right)\left(4.111\ \text{s}\right)^2$$

$$= -33.3 = \boxed{-33\ \text{m}}$$

So the ball will strike 33 m below the top of the building.

75. When shooting the gun vertically, half the time of flight is spent moving upwards. Thus the upwards flight takes two seconds. Choose upward as the positive *y* direction. Since at the top of the flight, the vertical velocity is zero, find the launching velocity from Eq. 2-11a.

$$v_y = v_{y0} + at \quad \rightarrow \quad v_{y0} = v_y - at = 0 = \left(9.8\ \text{m/s}^2\right)\left(2.0\ \text{s}\right) = 19.6\ \text{m/s}$$

Using this initial velocity and an angle of 45° in the range formula will give the maximum range for the gun.

$$R = \frac{v_0^2 \sin 2\theta_0}{g} = \frac{\left(19.6\ \text{m/s}\right)^2 \sin\left(2 \times 45°\right)}{9.80\ \text{m/s}^2} = \boxed{39\ \text{m}}$$

CHAPTER 4: Dynamics: Newton's Laws of Motion

Answers to Questions

1. The child tends to remain at rest (Newton's 1st Law), unless a force acts on her. The force is applied to the wagon, not the child, and so the wagon accelerates out from under the child, making it look like the child falls backwards relative to the wagon. If the child is standing in the wagon, the force of friction between the child and the bottom of the wagon will produce an acceleration of the feet, pulling the feet out from under the child, also making the child fall backwards.

2. (a) Mary sees the box stay stationary with respect to the ground. There is no horizontal force on the box since the truck bed is smooth, and so the box cannot accelerate. Thus Mary would describe the motion of the box in terms of Newton's 1st law – there is no force on the box, so it does not accelerate.
    (b) Chris, from his non-inertial reference frame, would say something about the box being "thrown" backwards in the truck, and perhaps use Newton's 2nd law to describe the effects of that force. But the source of that force would be impossible to specify.

3. If the acceleration of an object is zero, then by Newton's second law, the *net* force must be zero. There can be forces acting on the object as long as the vector sum of the forces is zero.

4. If only once force acts on the object, then the net force cannot be zero. Thus the object cannot have zero acceleration, by Newton's second law. The object can have zero velocity for an instant. For example, an object thrown straight up under the influence of gravity has a velocity of zero at the top of its path, but has a non-zero net force and non-zero acceleration throughout the entire flight.

5. (a) A force is needed to bounce the ball back up, because the ball changes direction, and so accelerates. If the ball accelerates, there must be a force.
    (b) The pavement exerts the force on the golf ball.

6. When you try to walk east, you push on the ground (or on the log in this case) with a westward force. When you push westward on the massive Earth, the Earth moves imperceptibly, but by Newton's 3rd law there is an eastward force on you, which propels you forward. When walking on the log, the relatively light and unrestricted log is free to move, and so when you push it westward, it moves westward as you move eastward.

7. By Newton's 3rd law, the desk or wall exerts a force on your foot equal in magnitude to the force with which you hit the desk or wall. If you hit the desk or wall with a large force, then there will be a large force on your foot, causing pain. Only a force <u>on</u> your foot causes pain.

8. (a) When you are running, the stopping force is a force of friction between your feet and the ground. You push forward with your feet on the ground, and thus the ground pushes backwards on you, slowing your speed.
    (b) A fast person can run about 10 meters per second, perhaps takes a distance of 5 meters over which to stop. Those 5 meters would be about 5 strides, of 1 meter each. The acceleration can be found from Eq. 2-11c.

$$v^2 - v_0^2 = 2a(x - x_0) \quad \rightarrow \quad a = \frac{v^2 - v_0^2}{2(x - x_0)} = \frac{0 - (10\,\text{m/s})^2}{10\,\text{m}} = -10\,\text{m/s}^2$$

9. When giving a sharp pull, the key is the suddenness of the application of the force. When a large, sudden force is applied to the bottom string, the bottom string will have a large tension in it. Because of the stone's inertia, the upper string does not immediately experience the large force. The bottom string must have more tension in it, and will break first.

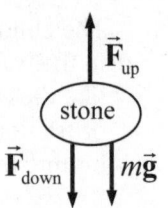

If a slow and steady pull is applied, the tension in the bottom string increases. We approximate that condition as considering the stone to be in equilibrium until the string breaks. The free-body diagram for the stone would look like this diagram. While the stone is in equilibrium, Newton's 2nd law states that $F_{up} = F_{down} + mg$.

Thus the tension in the upper string is going to be larger than the tension in the lower string because of the weight of the stone, and so the upper string will break first.

10. The acceleration of both rocks is found by dividing their weight (the force of gravity on them) by their mass. The 2-kg rock has a force of gravity on it that is twice as great as the force of gravity on the 1-kg rock, but also twice as great a mass as the 1-kg rock, so the acceleration is the same for both.

11. Only the pounds reading would be correct. The spring scale works on the fact that a certain **force** (the weight of the object being weighed) will stretch the spring a certain distance. That distance is proportional to the product of the mass and the acceleration due to gravity. Since the acceleration due to gravity is smaller by a factor of 6 on the moon, the weight of the object is smaller by a factor of 6, and the spring will be pulled to only one-sixth of the distance that it was pulled on the Earth. The mass itself doesn't change when moving to the Moon, and so a mass reading on the Moon would be incorrect.

12. When you pull the rope at an angle, only the horizontal component of the pulling force will be accelerating the box across the table. This is a smaller horizontal force than originally used, and so the horizontal acceleration of the box will decrease.

13. Let us find the acceleration of the Earth, assuming the mass of the freely falling object is $m = 1$ kg. If the mass of the Earth is M, then the acceleration of the Earth would be found using Newton's 3rd law and Newton's 2nd law.

$$F_{Earth} = F_{object} \quad \rightarrow \quad Ma_{Earth} = mg \quad \rightarrow \quad a_{Earth} = g\, m/M$$

Since the Earth has a mass that is on the order of 10^{25} kg, then the acceleration of the Earth is on the order of $10^{-25} g$, or about 10^{-24} m/s². This tiny acceleration is undetectable.

14. (a) To lift the object on the Earth requires a force the same size as its weight on Earth, $F_{Earth} = mg_{Earth} = 98$ N. To lift the object on the Moon requires a force the same size as its weight on the Moon, $F_{Moon} = mg_{Moon} = mg_{Moon}/6 = 16$ N.

   (b) The horizontal accelerating force would be the same in each case, because the mass of the object is the same on both the Earth and the Moon, and both objects would have the same acceleration to throw them with the same speed. So by Newton's second law, the forces would have to be the same.

15. In a tug of war, the team that pushes hardest against the ground wins. It is true that both teams have the same force on them due to the tension in the rope. But the winning team pushes harder against the ground and thus the ground pushes harder on the winning team, making a net unbalanced force.

The free body diagram below illustrates this. The forces are $\vec{\mathbf{F}}_{T_1G}$, the force on team 1 from the ground, $\vec{\mathbf{F}}_{T_2G}$, the force on team 2 from the ground, and $\vec{\mathbf{F}}_{TR}$, the force on each team from the rope.

Thus the net force on the winning team $\left(\vec{\mathbf{F}}_{T_1G} - \vec{\mathbf{F}}_{TR}\right)$ is in the winning direction.

	Team # 1 (winner)			Team # 2	
$\overleftarrow{\vec{\mathbf{F}}_{T_1G}}$		$\overrightarrow{\vec{\mathbf{F}}_{TR}}$	$\overleftarrow{\vec{\mathbf{F}}_{TR}}$		$\overrightarrow{\vec{\mathbf{F}}_{T_2G}}$
Large force from ground			Equal and opposite tension forces		Small force from ground

16. (*a*) The magnitude is 40 N.
    (*b*) The direction is downward.
    (*c*) It is exerted on the person.
    (*d*) It is exerted by the bag of groceries.

17. If you are at rest, the net force on you is zero. Hence the ground exerts a force on you exactly equal to your weight. The two forces acting on you sum to zero, and so you don't accelerate. If you squat down and then push with a larger force against the ground, the ground then pushes back on you with a larger force by Newton's third law, and you <u>can</u> then rise into the air.

18. In a whiplash situation, the car is violently pushed forward. Since the victim's back is against the seat of the car, the back moves forward with the car. But the head has no direct horizontal force to push it, and so it "lags behind". The victim's body is literally pushed forward, out from under their head – the head is not thrown backwards. The neck muscles must eventually pull the head forward, and that causes the whiplash. To avoid this, use the car's headrests.

19. The truck bed exerts a force of static friction on the crate, causing the crate to accelerate.

20. On the way up, there are two forces on the block that are parallel to each other causing the deceleration – the component of weight parallel to the plane, and the force of friction on the block. Since the forces are parallel to each other, both pointing down the plane, they add, causing a larger magnitude force and a larger acceleration. On the way down, those same two forces are opposite of each other, because the force of friction is now directed up the plane. With these two forces being opposite of each other, their net force is smaller, and so the acceleration is smaller.

21. Assume your weight is *W*. If you weighed yourself on an inclined plane that is inclined at angle θ, the bathroom scale would read the magnitude of the normal force between you and the plane, which would be $W\cos\theta$.

Solutions to Problems

1. Use Newton's second law to calculate the force.
$$\sum F = ma = (60.0\text{ kg})(1.25\ \text{m/s}^2) = \boxed{75.0\text{ N}}$$

2. Use Newton's second law to calculate the mass.
$$\sum F = ma \quad \rightarrow \quad m = \frac{\sum F}{a} = \frac{265\text{ N}}{2.30\,\text{m/s}^2} = \boxed{115\text{ kg}}$$

3.   Use Newton's second law to calculate the tension.

$$\sum F = F_{\text{T}} = ma = (960 \text{ kg})(1.20 \text{ m/s}^2) = \boxed{1.15 \times 10^3 \text{ N}}$$

4.   In all cases, $W = mg$, where g changes with location.

    (a) $W_{\text{Earth}} = mg_{\text{Earth}} = (76 \text{ kg})(9.8 \text{ m/s}^2) = \boxed{7.4 \times 10^2 \text{ N}}$

    (b) $W_{\text{Moon}} = mg_{\text{Moon}} = (76 \text{ kg})(1.7 \text{ m/s}^2) = \boxed{1.3 \times 10^2 \text{ N}}$

    (c) $W_{\text{Mars}} = mg_{\text{Mars}} = (76 \text{ kg})(3.7 \text{ m/s}^2) = \boxed{2.8 \times 10^2 \text{ N}}$

    (d) $W_{\text{Space}} = mg_{\text{Space}} = (76 \text{ kg})(0 \text{ m/s}^2) = \boxed{0 \text{ N}}$

5.   (a)   The 20.0 kg box resting on the table has the free-body diagram shown. Its weight
is $mg = (20.0 \text{ kg})(9.80 \text{ m/s}^2) = \boxed{196 \text{ N}}$. Since the box is at rest, the net force on

the box must be 0, and so the normal force must also be $\boxed{196 \text{ N}}$.

    (b)   Free-body diagrams are shown for both boxes. $\vec{\mathbf{F}}_{12}$ is the force on box 1 (the

top box) due to box 2 (the bottom box), and is the normal force on box 1. $\vec{\mathbf{F}}_{21}$

is the force on box 2 due to box 1, and has the same magnitude as $\vec{\mathbf{F}}_{12}$ by

Newton's 3rd law. $\vec{\mathbf{F}}_{\text{N2}}$ is the force of the table on box 2. That is the normal

force on box 2. Since both boxes are at rest, the net force on each box must
be 0. Write Newton's 2nd law in the vertical direction for each box, taking the
upward direction to be positive.

$$\sum F_1 = F_{\text{N1}} - m_1 g = 0$$

$$F_{\text{N1}} = m_1 g = (10.0 \text{ kg})(9.80 \text{ m/s}^2) = \boxed{98.0 \text{ N}} = F_{12} = F_{21}$$

$$\sum F_2 = F_{\text{N2}} - F_{21} - m_2 g = 0$$

$$F_{\text{N2}} = F_{21} + m_2 g = 98.0 \text{ N} + (20.0 \text{ kg})(9.80 \text{ m/s}^2) = \boxed{294 \text{ N}}$$

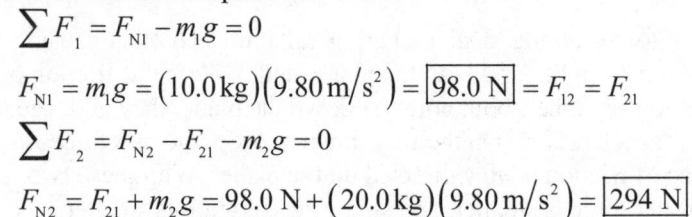

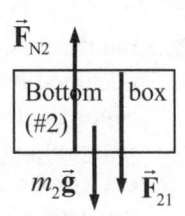

6.   Find the average acceleration from Eq. 2-2. The average force on the car is found from Newton's
second law.

$$v = 0 \quad v_0 = (95 \text{ km/h})\left(\frac{0.278 \text{ m/s}}{1 \text{ km/h}}\right) = 26.4 \text{ m/s} \quad a_{\text{avg}} = \frac{v - v_0}{t} = \frac{0 - 26.4 \text{ m/s}}{8.0 \text{ s}} = -3.30 \text{ m/s}^2$$

$$F_{\text{avg}} = ma_{\text{avg}} = (1100 \text{ kg})(-3.3 \text{ m/s}^2) = \boxed{-3.6 \times 10^3 \text{ N}}$$

The negative sign indicates the direction of the force, in the opposite direction to the initial velocity.

7.   The average force on the pellet is its mass times its average acceleration. The average acceleration is
found from Eq. 2-11c. For the pellet, $v_0 = 0$, $v = 125 \text{ m/s}$, and $x - x_0 = 0.800 \text{ m}$.

$$a_{\text{avg}} = \frac{v^2 - v_0^2}{2(x - x_0)} = \frac{(125 \text{ m/s})^2 - 0}{2(0.800 \text{ m})} = 9770 \text{ m/s}^2$$

$$F_{\text{avg}} = ma_{\text{avg}} = (7.00 \times 10^{-3} \text{ kg})(9770 \text{ m/s}^2) = \boxed{68.4 \text{ N}}$$

8. We assume that the fishline is pulling vertically on the fish, and that the fish is not jerking the line. A free-body diagram for the fish is shown. Write Newton's 2nd law for the fish in the vertical direction, assuming that up is positive. The tension is at its maximum.

$$\sum F = F_T - mg = ma \;\;\rightarrow\;\; F_T = m(g+a) \;\;\rightarrow$$

$$m = \frac{F_T}{g+a} = \frac{22\ \text{N}}{9.8\,\text{m/s}^2 + 2.5\,\text{m/s}^2} = \boxed{1.8\ \text{kg}}$$

Thus a mass of 1.8 kg is the maximum that the fishline will support with the given acceleration. Since the line broke, the fish's mass must be greater than 1.8 kg (about 4 lbs).

9. The problem asks for the average force on the glove, which in a direct calculation would require knowledge about the mass of the glove and the acceleration of the glove. But no information about the glove is given. By Newton's 3rd law, the force exerted by the ball on the glove is equal and opposite to the force exerted by the glove on the ball. So calculate the average force on the ball, and then take the opposite of that result to find the average force on the glove. The average force on the ball is its mass times its average acceleration. Use Eq. 2-11c to find the acceleration of the ball, with $v = 0$, $v_0 = 35.0\,\text{m/s}$, and $x - x_0 = 0.110\ \text{m}$. The initial direction of the ball is the positive direction.

$$a_{avg} = \frac{v^2 - v_0^2}{2(x-x_0)} = \frac{0-(35.0\,\text{m/s})^2}{2(0.110\ \text{m})} = -5568\ \text{m/s}^2$$

$$F_{avg} = ma_{avg} = (0.140\ \text{kg})(-5568\ \text{m/s}^2) = \boxed{-7.80\times10^2\,\text{N}}$$

Thus the average force on the glove was 780 N, in the direction of the initial velocity of the ball.

10. Choose up to be the positive direction. Write Newton's 2nd law for the vertical direction, and solve for the tension force.

$$\sum F = F_T - mg = ma \rightarrow F_T = m(g+a)$$

$$F_T = (1200\ \text{kg})(9.80\,\text{m/s}^2 + 0.80\,\text{m/s}^2) = \boxed{1.3\times10^4\,\text{N}}$$

11. Use Eq. 2-11b with $v_0 = 0$ to find the acceleration.

$$x - x_0 = v_0 t + \tfrac{1}{2}at^2 \;\rightarrow\; a = \frac{2(x-x_0)}{t^2} = \frac{2(402\ \text{m})}{(6.40\ \text{s})^2} = 19.6\,\text{m/s}^2 \left(\frac{1\,\text{"g"}}{9.80\,\text{m/s}^2}\right) = \boxed{2.00\ \text{g's}}$$

The accelerating force is found by Newton's 2nd law.

$$F = ma = (485\ \text{kg})(19.6\,\text{m/s}^2) = \boxed{9.51\times10^3\,\text{N}}$$

12. Choose up to be the positive direction. Write Newton's 2nd law for the vertical direction, and solve for the acceleration.

$$\sum F = F_T - mg = ma$$

$$a = \frac{F_T - mg}{m} = \frac{163\ \text{N} - (12.0\ \text{kg})(9.80\,\text{m/s}^2)}{12.0\ \text{kg}} = \boxed{3.8\,\text{m/s}^2}$$

Since the acceleration is positive, the bucket has an $\boxed{\text{upward}}$ acceleration.

13. In both cases, a free-body diagram for the elevator would look like the adjacent diagram. Choose up to be the positive direction. To find the MAXIMUM tension, assume that the acceleration is up. Write Newton's 2nd law for the elevator.

$$\sum F = ma = F_T - mg \;\; \rightarrow$$

$$F_T = ma + mg = m(a+g) = m(0.0680g + g) = (4850 \text{ kg})(1.0680)(9.80 \text{ m/s}^2)$$

$$= \boxed{5.08 \times 10^4 \text{ N}}$$

To find the MINIMUM tension, assume that the acceleration is down. Then Newton's 2nd law for the elevator becomes

$$\sum F = ma = F_T - mg \;\; \rightarrow \;\; F_T = ma + mg = m(a+g) = m(-0.0680g + g)$$

$$= (4850 \text{ kg})(0.9320)(9.80 \text{ m/s}^2) = \boxed{4.43 \times 10^4 \text{ N}}$$

14. If the thief were to hang motionless on the sheets, or descend at a constant speed, the sheets would not support him, because they would have to support the full 75 kg. But if he descends with an acceleration, the sheets will not have to support the total mass. A free-body diagram of the thief in descent is shown. If the sheets can support a mass of 58 kg, then the tension force that the sheets can exert is $F_T = (58 \text{ kg})(9.8 \text{ m/s}^2) = 570 \text{ N}$.

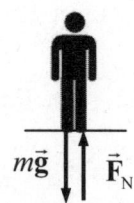

Assume that is the tension in the sheets. Then write Newton's 2nd law for the thief, taking the upward direction to be positive.

$$\sum F = F_T - mg = ma \;\; \rightarrow \;\; a = \frac{F_T - mg}{m} = \frac{570 \text{ N} - (75 \text{ kg})(9.80 \text{ m/s}^2)}{75 \text{ kg}} = -2.2 \text{ m/s}^2$$

The negative sign shows that the acceleration is downward.

If the thief descends with an acceleration of 2.2 m/s^2 or greater, the sheets will support his descent.

15. There will be two forces on the person – their weight, and the normal force of the scales pushing up on the person. A free-body diagram for the person is shown. Choose up to be the positive direction, and use Newton's 2nd law to find the acceleration.

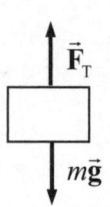

$$\sum F = F_N - mg = ma \;\; \rightarrow \;\; 0.75mg - mg = ma \;\; \rightarrow$$

$$a = -0.25g = -0.25(9.8 \text{ m/s}^2) = \boxed{-2.5 \text{ m/s}^2}$$

Due to the sign of the result, the direction of the acceleration is $\boxed{\text{down}}$. Thus the elevator must have started to move down since it had been motionless.

16. Choose UP to be the positive direction. Write Newton's 2nd law for the elevator.

$$\sum F = F_T - mg = ma \;\; \rightarrow$$

$$a = \frac{F_T - mg}{m} = \frac{21,750 \text{ N} - (2125 \text{ kg})(9.80 \text{ m/s}^2)}{2125 \text{ kg}} = 0.4353 \text{ m/s}^2 \approx \boxed{0.44 \text{ m/s}^2}$$

17. (*a*) There will be two forces on the skydivers – their combined weight, and the
upward force of air resistance, $\vec{F}_A$. Choose up to be the positive direction. Write
Newton's 2nd law for the skydivers.

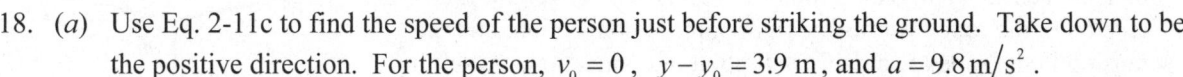

$$\sum F = F_A - mg = ma \quad \rightarrow \quad 0.25mg - mg = ma \quad \rightarrow$$

$$a = -0.75g = -0.75\left(9.8\,\text{m/s}^2\right) = \boxed{-7.4\,\text{m/s}^2}$$

Due to the sign of the result, the direction of the acceleration is down.

(*b*) If they are descending at constant speed, then the net force on them must
be zero, and so the force of air resistance must be equal to their weight.

$$F_A = mg = \left(132\ \text{kg}\right)\left(9.80\,\text{m/s}^2\right) = \boxed{1.29 \times 10^3\,\text{N}}$$

18. (*a*) Use Eq. 2-11c to find the speed of the person just before striking the ground. Take down to be
the positive direction. For the person, $v_0 = 0$, $y - y_0 = 3.9$ m, and $a = 9.8\,\text{m/s}^2$.

$$v^2 - v_0^2 = 2a\left(y - y_0\right) \quad \rightarrow \quad v = \sqrt{2a\left(y - y_0\right)} = \sqrt{2\left(9.8\,\text{m/s}^2\right)\left(3.9\ \text{m}\right)} = 8.743 = \boxed{8.7\,\text{m/s}}$$

(*b*) For the deceleration, use Eq. 2-11c to find the average deceleration, choosing down to be
positive.

$$v_0 = 8.743\,\text{m/s} \quad v = 0 \quad y - y_0 = 0.70\ \text{m} \quad v^2 - v_0^2 = 2a\left(y - y_0\right) \quad \rightarrow$$

$$a = \frac{-v_0^2}{2\Delta y} = \frac{-\left(8.743\,\text{m/s}\right)^2}{2\left(0.70\ \text{m}\right)} = -54.6\,\text{m/s}^2$$

The average force is found from Newton's 2nd law.

$$F = ma = \left(42\ \text{kg}\right)\left(-54.6\,\text{m/s}^2\right) = \boxed{-2.3 \times 10^3\,\text{N}}.$$

The negative sign shows that the force is in the negative direction, which is upward.

19. Free body diagrams for the box and the weight are shown below. The
tension exerts the same magnitude of force on both objects.

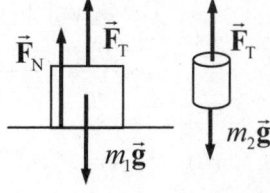

(*a*) If the weight of the hanging weight is less than the weight of the box,
the objects will not move, and the tension will be the same as the
weight of the hanging weight. The acceleration of the box will also
be zero, and so the sum of the forces on it will be zero. For the box,

$$F_N + F_T - m_1 g = 0 \quad \rightarrow \quad F_N = m_1 g - F_T = m_1 g - m_2 g = 77.0\text{N} - 30.0\ \text{N} = \boxed{47.0\ \text{N}}$$

(*b*) The same analysis as for part (*a*) applies here.

$$F_N = m_1 g - m_2 g = 77.0\ \text{N} - 60.0\ \text{N} = \boxed{17.0\ \text{N}}$$

(*c*) Since the hanging weight has more weight than the box on the table, the box on the table will be
lifted up off the table, and normal force of the table on the box will be $\boxed{0\ \text{N}}$.

20. (*a*) Just before the player leaves the ground on a jump, the forces on the player
would be his weight and the force of the floor pushing up the player. If the
player is jumping straight up, then the force of the floor pushing on the
player will be straight up – a normal force. See the first diagram. In this
case, while they are touching the floor, $F_N > mg$.

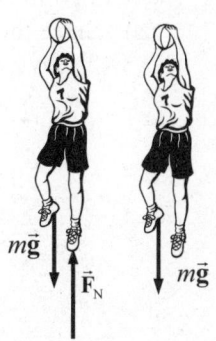

(*b*) While the player is in the air, the only force on the player is their weight.
See the second diagram.

21. (*a*) Just as the ball is being hit, if we ignore air resistance, there are two main forces on the ball – the weight of the ball, and the force of the bat on the ball.
    (*b*) As the ball flies toward the outfield, the only force on it is its weight, if air resistance is ignored.

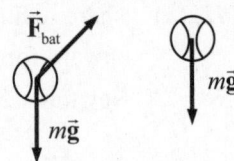

22. The two forces must be oriented so that the northerly component of the first force is exactly equal to the southerly component of the second force. Thus the second force must act southwesterly. See the diagram.

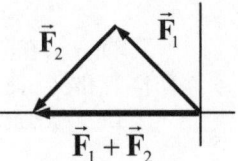

23. Consider the point in the rope directly below Arlene. That point can be analyzed as having three forces on it – Arlene's weight, the tension in the rope towards the right point of connection, and the tension in the rope towards the left point of connection. Assuming the rope is massless, those two tensions will be of the same magnitude. Since the point is not accelerating the sum of the forces must be zero. In particular, consider the sum of the vertical forces on that point, with UP as the positive direction.

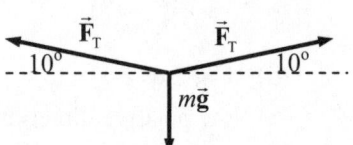

$$\sum F = F_T \sin 10.0^\circ + F_T \sin 10.0^\circ - mg = 0 \;\;\rightarrow$$

$$F_T = \frac{mg}{2\sin 10.0^\circ} = \frac{(50.0 \text{ kg})(9.80 \text{ m/s}^2)}{2\sin 10.0^\circ} = \boxed{1.41 \times 10^3 \text{ N}}$$

24. The net force in each case is found by vector addition with components.
    (*a*) $F_{\text{Net }x} = -F_1 = -10.2 \text{ N}$ $F_{\text{Net }y} = -F_2 = -16.0 \text{ N}$

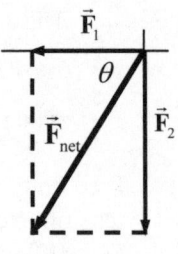

$$F_{\text{Net}} = \sqrt{(-10.2)^2 + (-16.0)^2} = \boxed{19.0 \text{ N}} \qquad \theta = \tan^{-1}\frac{-16.0}{-10.2} = 57.5^\circ$$

The actual angle from the *x*-axis is then 237.5°.

$$a = \frac{F_{\text{Net}}}{m} = \frac{19.0 \text{ N}}{27.0 \text{ kg}} = \boxed{0.703 \text{ m/s}^2} \text{ at } \boxed{237^\circ}$$

(*b*) $F_{\text{Net }x} = F_1 \cos 30^\circ = 8.83 \text{ N}$ $F_{\text{Net }y} = F_2 - F_1 \sin 30^\circ = 10.9 \text{ N}$

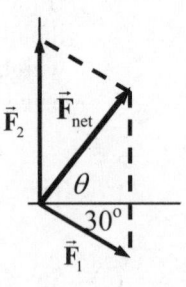

$$F_{\text{Net}} = \sqrt{(8.83 \text{ N})^2 + (10.9 \text{ N})^2} = \boxed{14.0 \text{ N}} \qquad \theta = \tan^{-1}\frac{10.9}{8.83} = \boxed{51.0^\circ}$$

$$a = \frac{F_{\text{Net}}}{m} = \frac{14.0 \text{ N}}{27.0 \text{ kg}} = \boxed{0.520 \text{ m/s}^2} \text{ at } \boxed{51.0^\circ}$$

25. We draw free-body diagrams for each bucket.
    (*a*) Since the buckets are at rest, their acceleration is 0. Write Newton's 2nd law for each bucket, calling UP the positive direction.

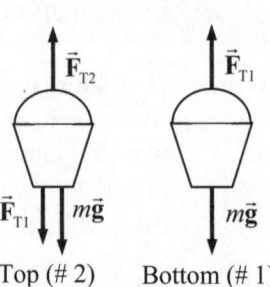

$$\sum F_1 = F_{T1} - mg = 0 \;\;\rightarrow$$

$$F_{T1} = mg = (3.2 \text{ kg})(9.8 \text{ m/s}^2) = \boxed{31 \text{ N}}$$

$$\sum F_2 = F_{T2} - F_{T1} - mg = 0 \;\;\rightarrow$$

$$F_{T2} = F_{T1} + mg = 2mg = 2(3.2 \text{ kg})(9.8 \text{ m/s}^2) = \boxed{63 \text{ N}}$$

Top (# 2)   Bottom (# 1)

(b)   Now repeat the analysis, but with a non-zero acceleration. The free-body diagrams are unchanged.

$$\sum F_1 = F_{T1} - mg = ma \ \rightarrow$$

$$F_{T1} = mg + ma = (3.2 \text{ kg})(9.80 \text{ m/s}^2 + 1.60 \text{ m/s}^2) = \boxed{36 \text{ N}}$$

$$\sum F_2 = F_{T2} - F_{T1} - mg = ma \ \rightarrow \ F_{T2} = F_{T1} + mg + ma = 2F_{T1} = \boxed{73 \text{ N}}$$

26. (a)   We assume that the mower is being pushed to the right. $\vec{\mathbf{F}}_{\text{fr}}$ is the friction force, and $\vec{\mathbf{F}}_{\text{P}}$ is the pushing force along the handle.

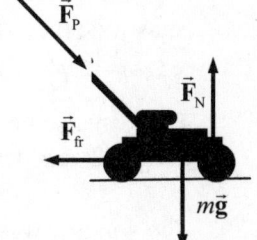

(b)   Write Newton's 2nd law for the horizontal direction. The forces must sum to 0 since the mower is not accelerating.

$$\sum F_x = F_{\text{P}} \cos 45.0° - F_{\text{fr}} = 0 \ \rightarrow$$

$$F_{\text{fr}} = F_{\text{P}} \cos 45.0° = (88.0 \text{ N}) \cos 45.0° = \boxed{62.2 \text{ N}}$$

(c)   Write Newton's 2nd law for the vertical direction. The forces must sum to 0 since the mower is not accelerating in the vertical direction.

$$\sum F_y = F_{\text{N}} - mg - F_{\text{P}} \sin 45.0° = 0 \ \rightarrow$$

$$F_{\text{N}} = mg + F_{\text{P}} \sin 45° = (14.0 \text{ kg})(9.80 \text{ m/s}^2) + (88.0 \text{ N}) \sin 45.0° = \boxed{199 \text{ N}}$$

(d)   First use Eq. 2-11a to find the acceleration.

$$v - v_0 = at \ \rightarrow \ a = \frac{v - v_0}{t} = \frac{1.5 \text{ m/s} - 0}{2.5 \text{ s}} = 0.60 \text{ m/s}^2$$

Now use Newton's 2nd law for the x direction to find the necessary pushing force.

$$\sum F_x = F_{\text{P}} \cos 45.0° - F_{\text{f}} = ma \ \rightarrow$$

$$F_{\text{P}} = \frac{F_{\text{f}} + ma}{\cos 45.0°} = \frac{62.2 \text{ N} + (14.0 \text{ kg})(0.60 \text{ m/s}^2)}{\cos 45.0°} = \boxed{99.9 \text{ N}}$$

27.   Choose the y direction to be the "forward" direction for the motion of the snowcats, and the x direction to be to the right on the diagram in the textbook. Since the housing unit moves in the forward direction on a straight line, there is no acceleration in the x direction, and so the net force in the x direction must be 0. Write Newton's 2nd law for the x direction.

$$\sum F_x = F_{Ax} + F_{Bx} = 0 \ \rightarrow \ -F_A \sin 50° + F_B \sin 30° = 0 \ \rightarrow$$

$$F_B = \frac{F_A \sin 50°}{\sin 30°} = \frac{(4500 \text{ N}) \sin 50°}{\sin 30°} = \boxed{6.9 \times 10^3 \text{ N}}$$

Since the x components add to 0, the magnitude of the vector sum of the two forces will just be the sum of their y components.

$$\sum F_y = F_{Ay} + F_{By} = F_A \cos 50° + F_B \cos 30° = (4500 \text{ N}) \cos 50° + (6900 \text{ N}) \cos 30° = \boxed{8.9 \times 10^3 \text{ N}}$$

28.   Since all forces of interest in this problem are horizontal, draw the free-body diagram showing only the horizontal forces. $\vec{\mathbf{F}}_{T1}$ is the tension in the coupling between the locomotive and the first car, and it pulls to the right on the first car. $\vec{\mathbf{F}}_{T2}$ is the tension in the coupling between the first car an the second car. It pulls to the right on car 2, labeled $\vec{\mathbf{F}}_{T2R}$ and to the left on car 1, labeled $\vec{\mathbf{F}}_{T2L}$. Both cars

have the same mass m and the same acceleration a. Note that $\left|\vec{\mathbf{F}}_{T2R}\right| = \left|\vec{\mathbf{F}}_{T2L}\right| = F_{T2}$ by Newton's 3rd law.

Write a Newton's 2nd law expression for each car.

$$\sum F_1 = F_{T1} - F_{T2} = ma \qquad \sum F_2 = F_{T2} = ma$$

Substitute the expression for ma from the second expression into the first one.

$$F_{T1} - F_{T2} = ma = F_{T2} \;\rightarrow\; F_{T1} = 2F_{T2} \;\rightarrow\; \boxed{F_{T1}/F_{T2} = 2}$$

This can also be discussed in the sense that the tension between the locomotive and the first car is pulling 2 cars, while the tension between the cars is only pulling one car.

29. The window washer pulls down on the rope with her hands with a tension force F_T, so the rope pulls up on her hands with a tension force F_T. The tension in the rope is also applied at the other end of the rope, where it attaches to the bucket. Thus there is another force F_T pulling up on the bucket. The bucket-washer combination thus has a net force of $2F_T$ upwards. See the adjacent free-body diagram, showing only forces on the bucket-washer combination, not forces exerted by the combination (the pull down on the rope by the person) or internal forces (normal force of bucket on person).

(a) Write Newton's 2nd law in the vertical direction, with up as positive. The net force must be zero if the bucket and washer have a constant speed.

$$\sum F = F_T + F_T - mg = 0 \;\rightarrow\; 2F_T = mg \;\rightarrow$$

$$F_T = \frac{mg}{2} = \frac{(65\text{ kg})(9.8\text{ m/s}^2)}{2} = \boxed{320\text{ N}}$$

(b) Now the force is increased by 15%, so $F_T = 320\text{ N}(1.15) = 368\text{ N}$. Again write Newton's 2nd law, but with a non-zero acceleration.

$$\sum F = F_T + F_T - mg = ma \;\rightarrow$$

$$a = \frac{2F_T - mg}{m} = \frac{2(368\text{ N}) - (65\text{ kg})(9.80\text{ m/s}^2)}{65\text{ kg}} = \boxed{1.5\text{ m/s}^2}$$

30. Since the sprinter exerts a force of 720 N on the ground at an angle of 22° below the horizontal, by Newton's 3rd law the ground will exert a force of 720 N on the sprinter at an angle of 22° above the horizontal. A free-body diagram for the sprinter is shown.

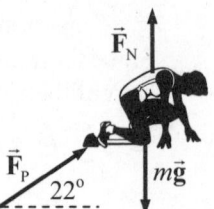

(a) The horizontal acceleration will be found from the net horizontal force. Using Newton's 2nd law, we have the following.

$$\sum F_x = F_P \cos 22° = ma_x \;\rightarrow\; a_x = \frac{F_P \cos 22°}{m} = \frac{(720\text{ N})\cos 22°}{65\text{ kg}}$$

$$= 10.27\text{ m/s}^2 \approx \boxed{1.0 \times 10^1\text{ m/s}^2}$$

(b) Eq. 2-11a is used to find the final speed. The starting speed is 0.

$$v = v_0 + at \;\rightarrow\; v = 0 + at = \left(10.27\,\text{m/s}^2\right)\left(0.32\ \text{s}\right) = 3.286\,\text{m/s} \approx \boxed{3.3\,\text{m/s}}$$

31. (a) See the free-body diagrams included.

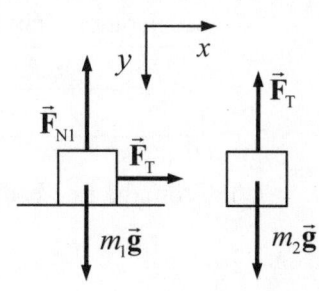

(b) For block 1, since there is no motion in the vertical direction,
     we have $F_{N1} = m_1 g$. We write Newton's 2nd law for the x
     direction: $\sum F_{1x} = F_T = m_1 a_{1x}$. For block 2, we only need to
     consider vertical forces: $\sum F_{2y} = m_2 g - F_T = m_2 a_{2y}$. Since the
     two blocks are connected, the magnitudes of their accelerations
     will be the same, and so let $a_{1x} = a_{2y} = a$. Combine the two force
     equations from above, and solve for a by substitution.

$$F_T = m_1 a \qquad m_2 g - F_T = m_2 a \;\rightarrow\; m_2 g - m_1 a = m_2 a \;\rightarrow$$

$$m_1 a + m_2 a = m_2 g \;\rightarrow\; \boxed{a = g\,\frac{m_2}{m_1 + m_2} \qquad F_T = m_1 a = g\,\frac{m_1 m_2}{m_1 + m_2}}$$

32. Consider a free-body diagram of the dice. The car is moving to the right. The
     acceleration of the dice is found from Eq. 2-11a.

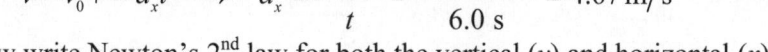

$$v = v_0 + = a_x t \;\rightarrow\; a_x = \frac{v - v_0}{t} = \frac{28\,\text{m/s} - 0}{6.0\ \text{s}} = 4.67\,\text{m/s}^2$$

Now write Newton's 2nd law for both the vertical (y) and horizontal (x) directions.

$$\sum F_y = F_T \cos\theta - mg = 0 \;\rightarrow\; F_T = \frac{mg}{\cos\theta} \qquad \sum F_x = F_T \sin\theta = ma_x$$

Substitute the expression for the tension from the y equation into the x equation.

$$ma_x = F_T \sin\theta = \frac{mg}{\cos\theta}\sin\theta = mg\tan\theta \;\rightarrow\; a_x = g\tan\theta$$

$$\theta = \tan^{-1}\frac{a_x}{g} = \tan^{-1}\frac{4.67\,\text{m/s}^2}{9.8\,\text{m/s}^2} = \boxed{25°}$$

33. (a) In the free-body diagrams below, $\vec{F}_{12}$ = force on block 1 exerted by block 2, $\vec{F}_{21}$ = force on
         block 2 exerted by block 1, $\vec{F}_{23}$ = force on block 2 exerted by block 3, and $\vec{F}_{32}$ = force on block
         3 exerted by block 2. The magnitudes of $\vec{F}_{21}$ and $\vec{F}_{12}$ are equal, and the magnitudes of $\vec{F}_{23}$ and
         $\vec{F}_{32}$ are equal, by Newton's 3rd law.

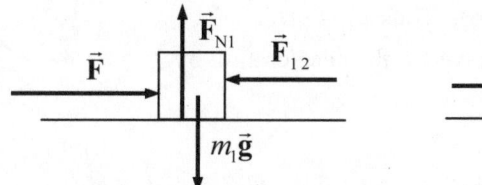
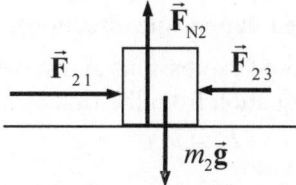
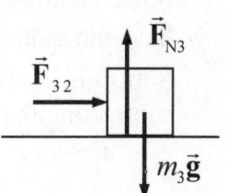

(b) All of the vertical forces on each block add up to zero, since there is no acceleration in the
     vertical direction. Thus for each block, $F_N = mg$. For the horizontal direction, we have

$$\sum F = F - F_{12} + F_{21} - F_{23} + F_{32} = F = \left(m_1 + m_2 + m_3\right)a \quad \rightarrow \quad \boxed{a = \frac{F}{m_1 + m_2 + m_3}}$$

(c) For each block, the net force must be *ma* by Newton's 2nd law. Each block has the same acceleration since they are in contact with each other.

$$\boxed{F_{1net} = \frac{m_1 F}{m_1 + m_2 + m_3}} \qquad \boxed{F_{2net} = \frac{m_2 F}{m_1 + m_2 + m_3}} \qquad \boxed{F_{3net} = \frac{m_3 F}{m_1 + m_2 + m_3}}$$

(d) From the free-body diagram, we see that for m_3, $F_{32} = F_{3net} = \boxed{\dfrac{m_3 F}{m_1 + m_2 + m_3}}$. And by Newton's

3rd law, $F_{32} = F_{23} = F_{3net} = \boxed{\dfrac{m_3 F}{m_1 + m_2 + m_3}}$. Of course, $\vec{\mathbf{F}}_{23}$ and $\vec{\mathbf{F}}_{32}$ are in opposite directions.

Also from the free-body diagram, we see that for m_1,

$$F - F_{12} = F_{1net} = \frac{m_1 F}{m_1 + m_2 + m_3} \quad \rightarrow \quad F_{12} = F - \frac{m_1 F}{m_1 + m_2 + m_3} \quad \rightarrow \quad \boxed{F_{12} = \frac{\left(m_2 + m_3\right)F}{m_1 + m_2 + m_3}}. \text{ By}$$

Newton's 3rd law, $F_{12} = F_{21} = \boxed{\dfrac{\left(m_2 + m_3\right)F}{m_1 + m_2 + m_3}}$.

(e) Using the given values, $a = \dfrac{F}{m_1 + m_2 + m_3} = \dfrac{96.0 \text{ N}}{36.0 \text{ kg}} = \boxed{2.67 \text{ m/s}^2}$. Since all three masses

are the same value, the net force on each mass is $F_{net} = ma = \left(12.0 \text{ kg}\right)\left(2.67 \text{ m/s}^2\right) = 32.0 \text{ N}$.

This is also the value of F_{32} and F_{23}. The value of F_{12} and F_{21} is

$$F_{12} = F_{21} = \left(m_2 + m_3\right)a = \left(24 \text{ kg}\right)\left(2.67 \text{ m/s}^2\right) = 64.0 \text{ N}.$$

To summarize:

$$F_{net\,1} = F_{net\,2} = F_{net\,3} = \boxed{32.0 \text{ N}} \qquad F_{12} = F_{21} = \boxed{64.0 \text{ N}} \qquad F_{23} = F_{32} = \boxed{32.0 \text{ N}}$$

The values make sense in that in order of magnitude, we should have $F > F_{21} > F_{32}$, since F is the net force pushing the entire set of blocks, F_{12} is the net force pushing the right two blocks, and F_{23} is the net force pushing the right block only.

34. First, draw a free-body diagram for each mass. Notice that the same tension force is applied to each mass. Choose UP to be the positive direction. Write Newton's 2nd law for each of the masses.

$$F_T - m_2 g = m_2 a_2 \qquad F_T - m_1 g = m_1 a_1$$

Since the masses are joined together by the cord, their accelerations will have the same magnitude but opposite directions. Thus $a_1 = -a_2$.

Substitute this into the force expressions and solve for the acceleration by subtracting the second equation from the first.

$$F_T - m_1 g = -m_1 a_2 \quad \rightarrow \quad F_T = m_1 g - m_1 a_2$$

$$F_T - m_2 g = m_2 a_2 \quad \rightarrow \quad m_1 g - m_1 a_2 - m_2 g = m_2 a_2 \quad \rightarrow \quad m_1 g - m_2 g = m_1 a_2 + m_2 a_2$$

$$a_2 = \frac{m_1 - m_2}{m_1 + m_2} g = \frac{3.2 \text{ kg} - 2.2 \text{ kg}}{3.2 \text{ kg} + 2.2 \text{ kg}} \left(9.8 \text{ m/s}^2\right) = 1.815 \text{ m/s}^2$$

The lighter block starts with a speed of 0, and moves a distance of 1.80 meters with the acceleration found above. Using Eq. 2-11c, the velocity of the lighter block at the end of this accelerated motion can be found.

$$v^2 - v_0^2 = 2a(y - y_0) \rightarrow v = \sqrt{v_0^2 + 2a(y - y_0)} = \sqrt{0 + 2(1.815 \text{ m/s}^2)(1.80 \text{ m})} = 2.556 \text{ m/s}$$

Now the lighter block has different conditions of motion. Once the heavier block hits the ground, the tension force disappears, and the lighter block is in free fall. It has an initial speed of 2.556 m/s upward as found above, with an acceleration of –9.8 m/s² due to gravity. At its highest point, its speed will be 0. Eq. 2-11c can again be used to find the height to which it rises.

$$v^2 - v_0^2 = 2a(y - y_0) \rightarrow (y - y_0) = \frac{v^2 - v_0^2}{2a} = \frac{0 - (2.556 \text{ m/s})^2}{2(-9.8 \text{ m/s}^2)} = 0.33 \text{ m}$$

Thus the total height above the ground is 1.80 m + 1.80 m + 0.33 m = $\boxed{3.93 \text{ m}}$.

35. Please refer to the free-body diagrams given in the textbook for this problem. Initially, treat the two boxes and the rope as a single system. Then the only accelerating force on the system is $\vec{F}_P$. The mass of the system is 23.0 kg, and so using Newton's 2nd law, the acceleration of the system is

$a = \dfrac{F_P}{m} = \dfrac{40.0 \text{ N}}{23.0 \text{ kg}} = \boxed{1.74 \text{ m/s}^2}$. This is the acceleration of each piece of the system.

Now consider the left box alone. The only force on it is $\vec{F}_{BT}$, and it has the acceleration found above. Thus F_{BT} can be found from Newton's 2nd law.

$$F_{BT} = m_B a = (12.0 \text{ kg})(1.74 \text{ m/s}^2) = \boxed{20.9 \text{ N}} .$$

Now consider the rope alone. The net force on it is $\vec{F}_{TA} - \vec{F}_{TB}$, and it also has the acceleration found above. Thus F_{TA} can be found from Newton's 2nd law.

$$F_{TA} - F_{TB} = m_C a \rightarrow F_{TA} = F_{TB} + m_C a = 20.9 \text{ N} + (1.0 \text{ kg})(1.74 \text{ m/s}^2) = \boxed{22.6 \text{ N}}$$

36. A free-body diagram for the crate is shown. The crate does not accelerate vertically, and so $F_N = mg$. The crate does not accelerate horizontally, and so $F_P = F_{fr}$. Putting this together, we have

$$F_P = F_{fr} = \mu_k F_N = \mu_k mg = (0.30)(35 \text{ kg})(9.8 \text{ m/s}^2) = 103 = \boxed{1.0 \times 10^2 \text{ N}}$$

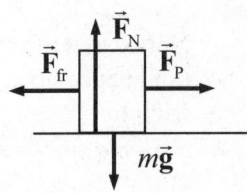

If the coefficient of kinetic friction is zero, then the horizontal force required is $\boxed{0 \text{ N}}$, since there is no friction to counteract. Of course, it would take a force to START the crate moving, but once it was moving, no further horizontal force would be necessary to maintain the motion.

37. A free-body diagram for the box is shown. Since the box does not accelerate vertically, $F_N = mg$

   (a) To start the box moving, the pulling force must just overcome the force of static friction, and that means the force of static friction will reach its maximum value of $F_{fr} = \mu_s F_N$. Thus we have for the starting motion,

$$F_{\rm P} = F_{\rm fr} = \mu_s F_{\rm N} = \mu_s mg \;\rightarrow\; \mu_s = \frac{F_{\rm P}}{mg} = \frac{48.0\ {\rm N}}{(5.0\ {\rm kg})(9.8\ {\rm m/s}^2)} = \boxed{0.98}$$

(*b*) The same force diagram applies, but now the friction is kinetic friction, and the pulling force is NOT equal to the frictional force, since the box is accelerating to the right.

$$\sum F = F_{\rm P} - F_{\rm fr} = ma \;\rightarrow\; F_{\rm P} - \mu_k F_{\rm N} = ma \;\rightarrow\; F_{\rm P} - \mu_k mg = ma \;\rightarrow$$

$$\mu_k = \frac{F_{\rm P} - ma}{mg} = \frac{48.0\ {\rm N} - (5.0\ {\rm kg})(0.70\ {\rm m/s}^2)}{(5.0\ {\rm kg})(9.8\ {\rm m/s}^2)} = \boxed{0.91}$$

38. A free-body diagram for you as you stand on the train is shown. You do not accelerate vertically, and so $F_{\rm N} = mg$. The maximum static frictional force is $\mu_s F_{\rm N}$, and that must be greater than or equal to the force needed to accelerate you.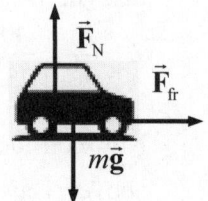

$$F_{\rm fr} \ge ma \;\rightarrow\; \mu_s F_{\rm N} \ge ma \;\rightarrow\; \mu_s mg \ge ma \;\rightarrow\; \mu_s \ge a/g = 0.20g/g = \boxed{0.20}$$

The static coefficient of friction must be at least 0.20 for you to not slide.

39. A free-body diagram for the accelerating car is shown. The car does not accelerate vertically, and so $F_{\rm N} = mg$. The static frictional force is the accelerating force, and so $F_{\rm fr} = ma$. If we assume the maximum acceleration, then we need the maximum force, and so the static frictional force would be its maximum value of $\mu_s F_{\rm N}$. Thus we have

$$F_{\rm fr} = ma \;\rightarrow\; \mu_s F_{\rm N} = ma \;\rightarrow\; \mu_s mg = ma \;\rightarrow$$

$$a = \mu_s g = 0.80(9.8\ {\rm m/s}^2) = \boxed{7.8\ {\rm m/s}^2}$$

40. See the included free-body diagram. To find the maximum angle, assume that the car is just ready to slide, so that the force of static friction is a maximum. Write Newton's 2$^{\rm nd}$ law for both directions. Note that for both directions, the net force must be zero since the car is not accelerating.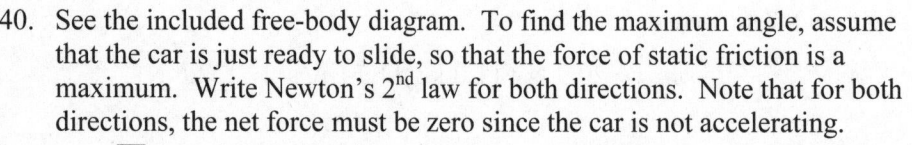

$$\sum F_y = F_{\rm N} - mg\cos\theta = 0 \;\rightarrow\; F_{\rm N} = mg\cos\theta$$

$$\sum F_x = mg\sin\theta - F_{\rm fr} = 0 \;\rightarrow\; mg\sin\theta = F_{\rm fr} = \mu_s F_{\rm N} = \mu_s mg\cos\theta$$

$$\mu_s = \frac{mg\sin\theta}{mg\cos\theta} = \tan\theta = 0.8 \;\rightarrow\; \theta = \tan^{-1} 0.8 = 39^\circ = \boxed{40^\circ} \;\;(1\ {\rm sig\ fig})$$

41. Start with a free-body diagram. Write Newton's 2$^{\rm nd}$ law for each direction.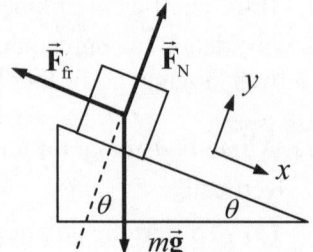

$$\sum F_x = mg\sin\theta - F_{\rm fr} = ma_x$$

$$\sum F_y = F_{\rm N} - mg\cos\theta = ma_y = 0$$

Notice that the sum in the y direction is 0, since there is no motion (and hence no acceleration) in the y direction. Solve for the force of friction.

$$mg\sin\theta - F_{\rm fr} = ma_x \;\rightarrow$$

$$F_{\rm fr} = mg\sin\theta - ma_x = (15.0\ {\rm kg})\left[(9.80\ {\rm m/s}^2)(\sin 32^\circ) - 0.30\ {\rm m/s}^2\right] = 73.40\ {\rm N} \approx \boxed{73\ {\rm N}}$$

Now solve for the coefficient of kinetic friction. Note that the expression for the normal force comes from the y direction force equation above.

$$F_{fr} = \mu_k F_N = \mu_k mg \cos\theta \;\rightarrow\; \mu_k = \frac{F_{fr}}{mg\cos\theta} = \frac{73.40\text{ N}}{(15.0\text{ kg})(9.80\text{ m/s}^2)(\cos 32°)} = \boxed{0.59}$$

42. The direction of travel for the car is to the right, and that is also the positive horizontal direction. Using the free-body diagram, write Newton's 2nd law in the x direction for the car on the level road. We assume that the car is just on the verge of skidding, so that the magnitude of the friction force is $F_{fr} = \mu_s F_N$.

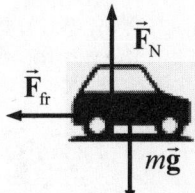

$$\sum F_x = -F_{fr} = ma \qquad F_{fr} = -ma = -\mu_s mg \;\rightarrow\; \mu_s = \frac{a}{g} = \frac{4.80\text{ m/s}^2}{9.80\text{ m/s}^2} = 0.4898$$

Now put the car on an inclined plane. Newton's 2nd law in the x-direction for the car on the plane is used to find the acceleration. We again assume the car is on the verge of slipping, so the static frictional force is at its maximum.

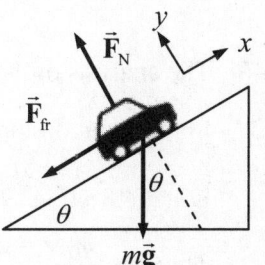

$$\sum F_x = -F_{fr} - mg\sin\theta = ma \;\rightarrow$$

$$a = \frac{-F_{fr} - mg\sin\theta}{m} = \frac{-\mu_s mg\cos\theta - mg\sin\theta}{m} = -g(\mu_s\cos\theta + \sin\theta)$$

$$= -(9.80\text{ m/s}^2)(0.4898\cos 13° + \sin 13°) = \boxed{-6.9\text{ m/s}^2}$$

43. (a) Here is a free-body diagram for the box at rest on the plane. The force of friction is a STATIC frictional force, since the box is at rest.
   (b) If the box were sliding down the plane, the only change is that the force of friction would be a KINETIC frictional force.
   (c) If the box were sliding up the plane, the force of friction would be a KINETIC frictional force, and it would point down the plane, in the opposite direction to that shown in the diagram.

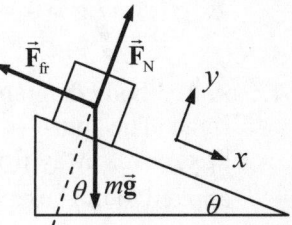

44. Assume that the static frictional force is the only force accelerating the racer. Then consider the free-body diagram for the racer as shown. It is apparent that the normal is equal to the weight, since there is no vertical acceleration. It is also assumed that the static frictional force is at its maximum. Thus

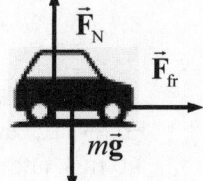

$$F_f = ma \;\rightarrow\; \mu_s mg = ma \;\rightarrow\; \mu_s = a/g$$

The acceleration of the racer can be calculated from Eq. 2-11b, with an initial speed of 0.

$$x - x_0 = v_0 t + \tfrac{1}{2}at^2 \;\rightarrow\; a = 2(x - x_0)/t^2$$

$$\mu_s = \frac{a}{g} = \frac{2(x - x_0)}{gt^2} = \frac{2(1000\text{ m})}{(9.8\text{ m/s}^2)(12\text{ sec})^2} = \boxed{1.4}$$

45. A free-body diagram for the bobsled is shown. The acceleration of the sled is found from Eq. 2-11c. The final velocity also needs to be converted to m/s.

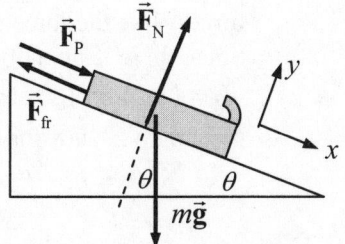

$$v = (60\text{ km/h})\left(\frac{1\text{ m/s}}{3.6\text{ km/h}}\right) = 16.667\text{ m/s}$$

$$v^2 - v_0^2 = 2a_x(x - x_0) \rightarrow$$

$$a_x = \frac{v^2 - v_0^2}{2(x - x_0)} = \frac{(16.667\,\text{m/s})^2 - 0}{2(75\,\text{m})} = 1.852\,\text{m/s}^2$$

Now write Newton's 2nd law for both directions. Since the sled does not accelerate in the y direction, the net force on the y direction must be 0. Then solve for the pushing force.

$$\sum F_y = F_N - mg\cos\theta = 0 \rightarrow F_N = mg\cos\theta$$

$$\sum F_x = mg\sin\theta + F_P - F_{fr} = ma_x$$

$$F_P = ma_x - mg\sin\theta + F_{fr} = ma_x - mg\sin\theta + \mu_k F_N$$

$$= ma_x - mg\sin\theta + \mu_k mg\cos\theta = m[a_x + g(\mu_k\cos\theta - \sin\theta)]$$

$$= (22\,\text{kg})[1.852\,\text{m/s}^2 + (9.8\,\text{m/s}^2)(0.10\cos 6.0° - \sin 6.0°)] = 39.6\,\text{N} \approx \boxed{40\,\text{N}}$$

46. The analysis of the blocks at rest can be done exactly the same as that presented in Example 4-20, up to the equation for the acceleration, $a = \dfrac{m_{II}g - F_{fr}}{m_I + m_{II}}$. Now, for the stationary case, the force of friction is static friction. To find the minimum value of m_I, we assume the maximum static frictional force.

Thus $a = \dfrac{m_{II}g - \mu_s m_I g}{m_I + m_{II}}$. Finally, for the system to stay at rest, the acceleration must be zero. Thus

$$m_{II}g - \mu_s m_I g = 0 \rightarrow m_I = m_{II}/\mu_s = 2.0\,\text{kg}/0.30 = \boxed{6.7\,\text{kg}}$$

47. A free-body diagram for the box is shown, assuming that it is moving to the right. The "push" is not shown on the free-body diagram because as soon as the box moves away from the source of the pushing force, the push is no longer applied to the box. It is apparent from the diagram that $F_N = mg$ for the vertical direction. We write Newton's 2nd law for the horizontal direction, with positive to the right, to find the acceleration of the box.

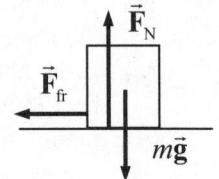

$$\sum F_x = -F_{fr} = ma \rightarrow ma = -\mu_k F_N = -\mu_k mg \rightarrow$$

$$a = -\mu_k g = -0.2(9.8\,\text{m/s}^2) = -1.96\,\text{m/s}^2$$

Eq. 2-11c can be used to find the distance that the box moves before stopping. The initial speed is 4.0 m/s, and the final speed will be 0.

$$v^2 - v_0^2 = 2a(x - x_0) \rightarrow x - x_0 = \frac{v^2 - v_0^2}{2a} = \frac{0 - (4.0\,\text{m/s})^2}{2(-1.96\,\text{m/s}^2)} = \boxed{4.1\,\text{m}}$$

48. (a) Since the two blocks are in contact, they can be treated as a single object as long as no information is needed about internal forces (like the force of one block pushing on the other block). Since there is no motion in the vertical direction, it is apparent that $F_N = (m_1 + m_2)g$, and so $F_{fr} = \mu_k F_N = \mu_k(m_1 + m_2)g$. Write Newton's 2nd law for the horizontal direction.

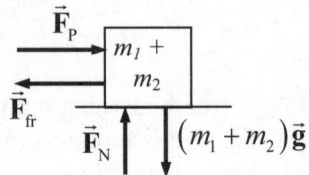

$$\sum F_x = F_P - F_{fr} = (m_1 + m_2)a \rightarrow$$

$$a = \frac{F_{\mathrm{P}} - F_{\mathrm{fr}}}{m_1 + m_2} = \frac{F_{\mathrm{P}} - \mu_k\left(m_1 + m_2\right)g}{m_1 + m_2} = \frac{620\,\mathrm{N} - (0.15)(185\,\mathrm{kg})\left(9.8\,\mathrm{m/s^2}\right)}{185\,\mathrm{kg}} = \boxed{1.9\,\mathrm{m/s^2}}$$

(*b*) To solve for the contact forces between the blocks, an individual block must be analyzed. Look at the free-body diagram for the second block. $\vec{F}_{21}$ is the force of the first block pushing on the second block. Again, it is apparent that $F_{\mathrm{N2}} = m_2 g$ and so $F_{\mathrm{fr2}} = \mu_k F_{\mathrm{N2}} = \mu_k m_2 g$. Write Newton's 2nd law for the horizontal direction.

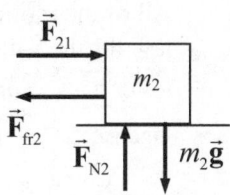

$$\sum F_x = F_{21} - F_{\mathrm{fr2}} = m_2 a \quad \rightarrow$$

$$F_{21} = \mu_k m_2 g + m_2 a = (0.15)(110\,\mathrm{kg})\left(9.8\,\mathrm{m/s^2}\right) + (110\,\mathrm{kg})\left(1.9\,\mathrm{m/s^2}\right) = \boxed{3.7\times10^2\,\mathrm{N}}$$

By Netwon's 3rd law, there will also be a 370 N force to the left on block # 1 due to block # 2.

(*c*) If the crates are reversed, the acceleration of the system will remain the same – the analysis from part (a) still applies. We can also repeat the analysis from part (b) to find the force of one block on the other, if we simply change m_1 to m_2 in the free-body diagram and the resulting equations. The result would be

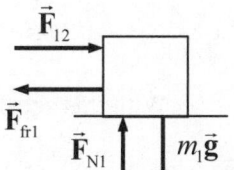

$$\sum F_x = F_{12} - F_{\mathrm{fr1}} = m_1 a \quad \rightarrow$$

$$F_{12} = \mu_k m_1 g + m_1 a = (0.15)(75\,\mathrm{kg})\left(9.8\,\mathrm{m/s^2}\right) + (75\,\mathrm{kg})\left(1.9\,\mathrm{m/s^2}\right) = \boxed{2.5\times10^2\,\mathrm{N}}$$

49. The force of static friction is what decelerates the crate if it is not sliding on the truck bed. If the crate is not to slide, but the maximum deceleration is desired, then the maximum static frictional force must be exerted, and so $F_{\mathrm{fr}} = \mu_s F_{\mathrm{N}}$.

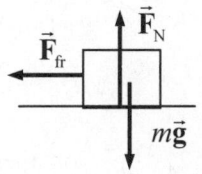

The direction of travel is to the right. It is apparent that $F_{\mathrm{N}} = mg$ since there is no acceleration in the y direction. Write Newton's 2nd law for the truck in the horizontal direction.

$$\sum F_x = -F_{\mathrm{fr}} = ma \quad \rightarrow \quad -\mu_s mg = ma \quad \rightarrow \quad a = -\mu_s g = -(0.75)\left(9.8\,\mathrm{m/s^2}\right) = \boxed{-7.4\,\mathrm{m/s^2}}$$

The negative sign indicates the direction of the acceleration – opposite to the direction of motion.

50. Consider a free-body diagram of the car on the icy inclined driveway. Assume that the car is not moving, but just ready to slip, so that the static frictional force has its maximum value of $F_{\mathrm{fr}} = \mu_s F_{\mathrm{N}}$. Write Newton's 2nd law in each direction for the car, with a net force of 0 in each case.

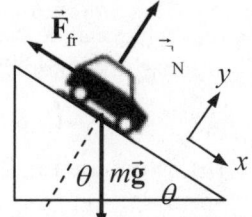

$$\sum F_y = F_{\mathrm{N}} - mg\cos\theta = 0 \quad \rightarrow \quad F_{\mathrm{N}} = mg\cos\theta$$

$$\sum F_x = mg\sin\theta - F_{\mathrm{fr}} = 0 \quad \rightarrow \quad mg\sin\theta = \mu_s mg\cos\theta$$

$$\mu_s = \sin\theta/\cos\theta = \tan\theta \quad \rightarrow \quad \theta = \tan^{-1}\mu_s = \tan^{-1}0.15 = 8.5^\circ$$

The car will not be able to stay at rest on any slope steeper than 8.5°.

$\boxed{\text{Only the driveway across the street is safe for parking.}}$

51. We assume that the child starts from rest at the top of the slide, and then slides
a distance $x - x_0$ along the slide. A force diagram is shown for the child on
the slide. First, ignore the frictional force and so consider the no-friction case.
All of the motion is in the x direction, so we will only consider Newton's 2nd
law for the x direction.

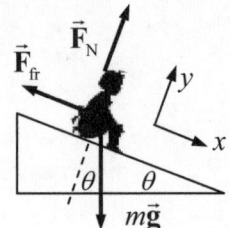

$$\sum F_x = mg\sin\theta = ma \;\rightarrow\; a = g\sin\theta$$

Use Eq. 2-11c to calculate the speed at the bottom of the slide.

$$v^2 - v_0^2 = 2a(x-x_0) \;\rightarrow\; v_{\text{(No friction)}} = \sqrt{v_0^2 + 2a(x-x_0)} = \sqrt{2g\sin\theta(x-x_0)}$$

Now include kinetic friction. We must consider Newton's 2nd law in both the x and y directions now.
The net force in the y direction must be 0 since there is no acceleration in the y direction.

$$\sum F_y = F_N - mg\cos\theta = 0 \;\rightarrow\; F_N = mg\cos\theta$$

$$\sum F_x = ma = mg\sin\theta - F_{\text{fr}} = mg\sin\theta - \mu_k F_N = mg\sin\theta - \mu_k mg\cos\theta$$

$$a = \frac{mg\sin\theta - \mu_k mg\cos\theta}{m} = g(\sin\theta - \mu_k\cos\theta)$$

With this acceleration, we can again use Eq. 2-11c to find the speed after sliding a certain distance.

$$v^2 - v_0^2 = 2a(x-x_0) \;\rightarrow\; v_{\text{(friction)}} = \sqrt{v_0^2 + 2a(x-x_0)} = \sqrt{2g(\sin\theta - \mu_k\cos\theta)(x-x_0)}$$

Now let the speed with friction be half the speed without friction, and solve for the coefficient of
friction. Square the resulting equation and divide by $g\cos\theta$ to get the result.

$$v_{\text{(friction)}} = \tfrac{1}{2}v_{\text{(No friction)}} \;\rightarrow\; \sqrt{2g(\sin\theta - \mu_k\cos\theta)(x-x_0)} = \tfrac{1}{2}\sqrt{2g(\sin\theta)(x-x_0)}$$

$$2g(\sin\theta - \mu_k\cos\theta)(x-x_0) = \tfrac{1}{4}2g(\sin\theta)(x-x_0)$$

$$\mu_k = \tfrac{3}{4}\tan\theta = \tfrac{3}{4}\tan 28° = \boxed{0.40}$$

52. (a) Consider the free-body diagram for the carton on the surface. There
is no motion in the y direction and thus no acceleration in the y
direction. Write Newton's 2nd law for both directions.

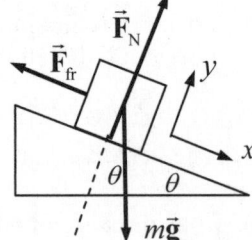

$$\sum F_y = F_N - mg\cos\theta = 0 \;\rightarrow\; F_N = mg\cos\theta$$

$$\sum F_x = mg\sin\theta - F_{\text{fr}} = ma$$

$$ma = mg\sin\theta - \mu_k F_N = mg\sin\theta - \mu_k mg\cos\theta$$

$$a = g(\sin\theta - \mu_k\cos\theta)$$

$$= (9.80\,\text{m/s}^2)(\sin 22.0° - 0.12\cos 22.0°) = 2.58 = \boxed{2.6\,\text{m/s}^2}$$

(b) Now use Eq. 2-11c, with an initial velocity of 0, to find the final velocity.

$$v^2 - v_0^2 = 2a(x-x_0) \;\rightarrow\; v = \sqrt{2a(x-x_0)} = \sqrt{2(2.58\,\text{m/s}^2)(9.30\,\text{m})} = \boxed{6.9\,\text{m/s}}$$

53. (a) Consider the free-body diagram for the carton on the frictionless
surface. There is no acceleration in the y direction. Write Newton's
2nd law for the x direction.

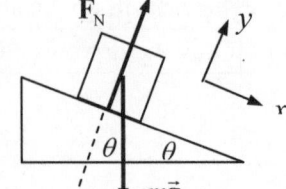

$$\sum F_x = mg\sin\theta = ma \;\rightarrow\; a = g\sin\theta$$

Use Eq. 2-11c with $v_0 = -3.0\,\text{m/s}$ and $v = 0\,\text{m/s}$ to find the distance
that it slides before stopping.

$$v^2 - v_0^2 = 2a(x - x_0) \rightarrow$$

$$(x - x_0) = \frac{v^2 - v_0^2}{2a} = \frac{0 - (-3.0\,\text{m/s})^2}{2(9.8\,\text{m/s}^2)\sin 22.0°} = \boxed{-1.2\,\text{m}}$$

The negative sign means that the block is displaced up the plane, which is the negative direction.

(b) The time for a round trip can be found from Eq. 2-11a. The free-body diagram (and thus the acceleration) is the same whether the block is rising or falling. For the entire trip, $v_0 = -3.0\,\text{m/s}$ and $v = +3.0\,\text{m/s}$.

$$v = v_0 + at \rightarrow t = \frac{v - v_0}{a} = \frac{(3.0\,\text{m/s}) - (-3.0\,\text{m/s})}{(9.8\,\text{m/s}^2)\sin 22°} = \boxed{1.6\,\text{s}}$$

54. See the free-body diagram for the descending roller coaster. It starts its

    descent with $v_0 = (6.0\,\text{km/h})\left(\dfrac{1\,\text{m/s}}{3.6\,\text{km/h}}\right) = 1.667\,\text{m/s}$. The total

    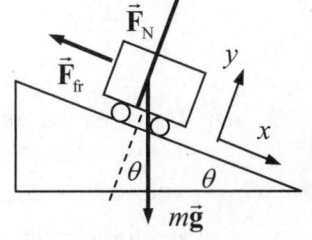

    displacement in the x direction is $x - x_0 = 45.0$ m. Write Newton's second law for both the x and y directions.

    $$\sum F_y = F_N - mg\cos\theta = 0 \rightarrow F_N = mg\cos\theta$$

    $$\sum F_x = ma = mg\sin\theta - F_{\text{fr}} = mg\sin\theta - \mu_k F_N = mg\sin\theta - \mu_k mg\cos\theta$$

    $$a = \frac{mg\sin\theta - \mu_k mg\cos\theta}{m} = g(\sin\theta - \mu_k\cos\theta)$$

    Now use Eq. 2-11c to solve for the final velocity.

    $$v^2 - v_0^2 = 2a(x - x_0) \rightarrow$$

    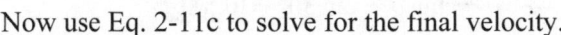

    $$v = \sqrt{v_0^2 + 2a(x - x_0)} = \sqrt{v_0^2 + 2g(\sin\theta - \mu_k\cos\theta)(x - x_0)}$$

    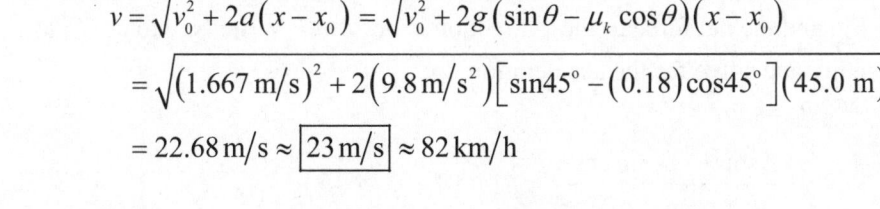

    $$= \sqrt{(1.667\,\text{m/s})^2 + 2(9.8\,\text{m/s}^2)\left[\sin 45° - (0.18)\cos 45°\right](45.0\,\text{m})}$$

    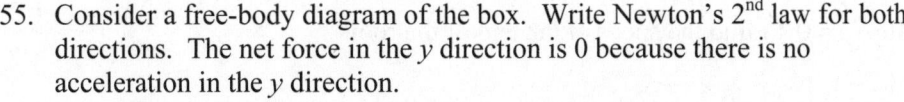

    $$= 22.68\,\text{m/s} \approx \boxed{23\,\text{m/s}} \approx 82\,\text{km/h}$$

55. Consider a free-body diagram of the box. Write Newton's 2nd law for both directions. The net force in the y direction is 0 because there is no acceleration in the y direction.

    $$\sum F_y = F_N - mg\cos\theta = 0 \rightarrow F_N = mg\cos\theta$$

    $$\sum F_x = mg\sin\theta - F_{\text{fr}} = ma$$

    Now solve for the force of friction and the coefficient of friction.

    $$\sum F_y = F_N - mg\cos\theta = 0 \rightarrow F_N = mg\cos\theta$$

    $$\sum F_x = mg\sin\theta - F_{\text{fr}} = ma$$

    $$F_{\text{fr}} = mg\sin\theta - ma = m(g\sin\theta - a) = (18.0\,\text{kg})\left[(9.80\,\text{m/s}^2)(\sin 37.0°) - 0.270\,\text{m/s}^2\right]$$

    $$= 101.3\,\text{N} \approx \boxed{101\,\text{N}}$$

$$F_{fr} = \mu_k F_N = \mu_k mg \cos\theta \rightarrow \mu_k = \frac{F_{fr}}{mg\cos\theta} = \frac{101.3\ N}{(18.0\ kg)(9.80\ m/s^2)\cos 37.0°} = \boxed{0.719}$$

56. Consider a free-body diagram for the box, showing force on the box. When
$F_P = 13\ N$, the block does not move. Thus in that case, the force of friction
is static friction, and must be at its maximum value, given by $F_{fr} = \mu_s F_N$.
Write Newton's 2nd law in both the x and y directions. The net force in each
case must be 0, since the block is at rest.

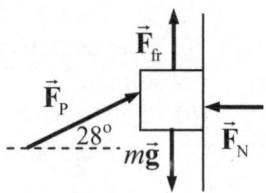

$$\sum F_x = F_P \cos\theta - F_N = 0 \rightarrow F_N = F_P \cos\theta$$

$$\sum F_y = F_{fr} + F_P \sin\theta - mg = 0 \rightarrow F_{fr} + F_P \sin\theta = mg$$

$$\mu_s F_N + F_P \sin\theta = mg \rightarrow \mu_s F_P \cos\theta + F_P \sin\theta = mg$$

$$m = \frac{F_P}{g}(\mu_s \cos\theta + \sin\theta) = \frac{13\ N}{9.80\ m/s^2}(0.40\cos 28° + \sin 28°) = \boxed{1.1\ kg}$$

57. (a) Consider the free-body diagram for the snow on the roof. If the snow
is just ready to slip, then the static frictional force is at its maximum
value, $F_{fr} = \mu_s F_N$. Write Newton's 2nd law in both directions, with the
net force equal to zero since the snow is not accelerating.

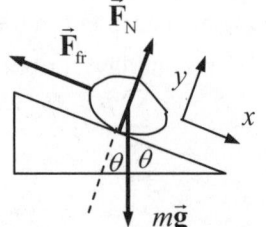

$$\sum F_y = F_N - mg\cos\theta = 0 \rightarrow F_N = mg\cos\theta$$

$$\sum F_x = mg\sin\theta - F_{fr} = 0 \rightarrow$$

$$mg\sin\theta = F_{fr} = \mu_s F_N = \mu_s mg\cos\theta \rightarrow \mu_s = \tan\theta = \tan 30° = \boxed{0.58}$$

If $\mu_s > 0.58$, then the snow would not be on the verge of slipping.

(b) The same free-body diagram applies for the sliding snow. But now the force of friction is
kinetic, so $F_{fr} = \mu_k F_N$, and the net force in the x direction is not zero. Write Newton's 2nd law
for the x direction again, and solve for the acceleration.

$$\sum F_x = mg\sin\theta - F_{fr} = ma$$

$$a = \frac{mg\sin\theta - F_{fr}}{m} = \frac{mg\sin\theta - \mu_k mg\cos\theta}{m} = g(\sin\theta - \mu_k \cos\theta)$$

Use Eq. 2-11c with $v_i = 0$ to find the speed at the end of the roof.

$$v^2 - v_0^2 = 2a(x - x_0)$$

$$v = \sqrt{v_0 + 2a(x-x_0)} = \sqrt{2g(\sin\theta - \mu_k \cos\theta)(x-x_0)}$$

$$= \sqrt{2(9.8\ m/s^2)(\sin 30° - (0.20)\cos 30°)(5.0\ m)} = 5.66 = \boxed{5.7\ m/s}$$

(c) Now the problem becomes a projectile motion problem. The projectile
has an initial speed of 5.7 m/s, directed at an angle of 30° below the
horizontal. The horizontal component of the speed, (5.66 m/s) cos 30° =
4.90 m/s, will stay constant. The vertical component will change due to
gravity. Define the positive direction to be downward. Then the starting
vertical velocity is (5.66 m/s) sin 30° = 2.83 m/s, the vertical acceleration is 9.8 m/s², and the
vertical displacement is 10.0 m. Use Eq. 2-11c to find the final vertical speed.

$$v_y^2 - v_{y0y}^2 = 2a(y - y_0)$$

$$v_y = \sqrt{v_{y0}^2 + 2a(y - y_0)} = \sqrt{(2.83 \, \text{m/s})^2 + 2(9.8 \, \text{m/s}^2)(10.0 \, \text{m})} = 14.3 \, \text{m/s}$$

To find the speed when it hits the ground, the horizontal and vertical components of velocity must again be combined, according to the Pythagorean theorem.

$$v = \sqrt{v_x^2 + v_y^2} = \sqrt{(4.90 \, \text{m/s})^2 + (14.3 \, \text{m/s})^2} = \boxed{15 \, \text{m/s}}$$

58. (a) A free-body diagram for the car is shown, assuming that it is moving to the right. It is apparent from the diagram that $F_N = mg$ for the vertical direction. Write Newton's 2nd law for the horizontal direction, with positive to the right, to find the acceleration of the car. Since the car is assumed to NOT be sliding, use the maximum force of static friction.

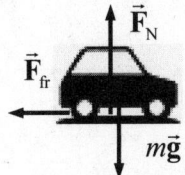

$$\sum F_x = -F_{fr} = ma \;\rightarrow\; ma = -\mu_s F_N = -\mu_s mg \;\rightarrow\; a = -\mu_s g$$

Eq. 2-11c can be used to find the distance that the car moves before stopping. The initial speed is given as v, and the final speed will be 0.

$$v^2 - v_0^2 = 2a(x - x_0) \;\rightarrow\; (x - x_0) = \frac{v^2 - v_0^2}{2a} = \frac{0 - v^2}{2(-\mu_s g)} = \boxed{\frac{v^2}{2\mu_s g}}$$

(b) Using the given values:

$$v = (95 \, \text{km/h})\left(\frac{1 \, \text{m/s}}{3.6 \, \text{km/h}}\right) = 26.38 \, \text{m/s} \qquad (x - x_0) = \frac{v^2}{2\mu_s g} = \frac{(26.38 \, \text{m/s})^2}{2(0.75)(9.8 \, \text{m/s}^2)} = \boxed{47 \, \text{m}}$$

59. A free-body diagram for the coffee cup is shown. Assume that the car is moving to the right, and so the acceleration of the car (and cup) will be to the left. The deceleration of the cup is caused by friction between the cup and the dashboard. For the cup to not slide on the dash, and to have the minimum deceleration time means the largest possible static frictional force is acting, so $F_{fr} = \mu_s F_N$. The normal force on the cup is equal to its weight, since there is no vertical acceleration. The horizontal acceleration of the cup is found from Eq. 2-11a, with a final velocity of zero.

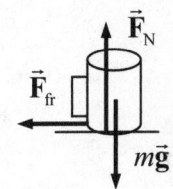

$$v_0 = (45 \, \text{km/h})\left(\frac{1 \, \text{m/s}}{3.6 \, \text{km/h}}\right) = 12.5 \, \text{m/s}$$

$$v - v_0 = at \;\rightarrow\; a = \frac{v - v_0}{t} = \frac{0 - 12.5 \, \text{m/s}}{3.5 \, \text{s}} = -3.57 \, \text{m/s}^2$$

Write Newton's 2nd law for the horizontal forces, considering to the right to be positive.

$$\sum F_x = -F_{fr} = ma \;\rightarrow\; ma = -\mu_s F_N = -\mu_s mg \;\rightarrow\; \mu_s = -\frac{a}{g} = -\frac{(-3.57 \, \text{m/s}^2)}{9.80 \, \text{m/s}^2} = \boxed{0.36}$$

60. We derive two expressions for acceleration – one from the kinematics, and one from the dynamics. From Eq. 2-11c with a starting speed of v_o up the plane and a final speed of zero, we have

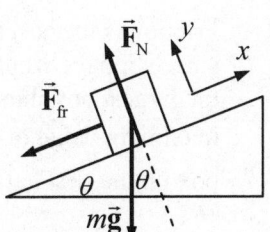

$$v^2 - v_o^2 = 2a(x - x_0) \;\rightarrow\; a = \frac{-v_o^2}{2(x - x_0)} = \frac{-v_o^2}{2d}$$

Write Newton's 2nd law for both the x and y directions. Note that the net force in the y direction is zero, since the block does not accelerate in the y direction.

$$\sum F_y = F_N - mg\cos\theta = 0 \quad \rightarrow \quad F_N = mg\cos\theta$$

$$\sum F_x = -mg\sin\theta - F_{fr} = ma \quad \rightarrow \quad a = \frac{-mg\sin\theta - F_{fr}}{m}$$

Now equate the two expressions for the acceleration, substitute in the relationship between the frictional force and the normal force, and solve for the coefficient of friction.

$$a = \frac{-mg\sin\theta - F_{fr}}{m} = \frac{-v_o^2}{2d} \quad \rightarrow \quad \frac{mg\sin\theta + \mu_k mg\cos\theta}{m} = \frac{v_o^2}{2d} \quad \rightarrow$$

$$\boxed{\mu_k = \frac{v_o^2}{2gd\cos\theta} - \tan\theta}$$

61. Since the walls are vertical, the normal forces are horizontal, away from the wall faces. We assume that the frictional forces are at their maximum values, so $F_{fr} = \mu_s F_N$ applies at each wall. We assume that the rope in the diagram is not under any tension and so does not exert any forces. Consider the free-body diagram for the climber. F_{NR} is the normal force on the climber from the right wall, and F_{NL} is the normal force on the climber from the left wall. The static frictional forces are

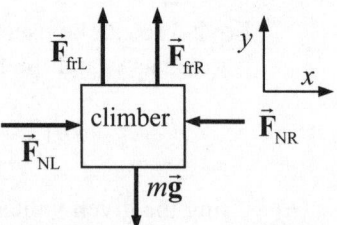

$F_{frL} = \mu_{sL}F_{NL}$ and $F_{frR} = \mu_{sR}F_{NR}$. Write Newton's 2nd law for both the x and y directions. The net force in each direction must be zero if the climber is stationary.

$$\sum F_x = F_{NL} - F_{NR} = 0 \quad \rightarrow \quad F_{NL} = F_{NR} \qquad \sum F_y = F_{frL} + F_{frR} - mg = 0$$

Substitute the information from the x equation into the y equation.

$$F_{frL} + F_{frR} = mg \quad \rightarrow \quad \mu_{sL}F_{NL} + \mu_{sR}F_{NR} = mg \quad \rightarrow \quad (\mu_{sL} + \mu_{sR})F_{NL} = mg$$

$$F_{NL} = \frac{mg}{(\mu_{sL} + \mu_{sR})} = \frac{(75\text{ kg})(9.80\text{ m/s}^2)}{1.4} = 525\text{ N}$$

And so $F_{NL} = F_{NR} = 525\text{ N}$. These normal forces arise as Newton's 3rd law reaction forces to the climber pushing on the walls. Thus the climber must exert a force of at least $5.3\times10^2\text{ N}$ against each wall.

62. Notice the symmetry of this problem – in the first half of the motion, the object accelerates with a constant acceleration to a certain speed, and then in the second half of the motion, the object decelerates with the same magnitude of acceleration back to a speed of 0. Half the time elapses during the first segment of the motion, and half the distance is traveled during the first segment of the motion. Thus we analyze half of the motion, and then double the time found to get the total time.

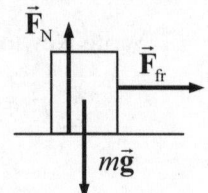

Friction is the accelerating and decelerating force. We assume that the boxes do not slip on the belt since slippage would increase the travel time. To have the largest possible acceleration, and hence the largest possible force, so that the travel time can be a minimum, the box must be moved by the maximum value of the static frictional force, and so $F_{fr} = \mu_s F_N$. See the free-body diagram for the box on the first half of the trip, assuming that the conveyor belt is level. Since there is no vertical acceleration of the box, it is apparent that $F_N = mg$, and so $F_{fr} = \mu_s mg$. Use Newton's 2nd law in the horizontal direction to find the acceleration.

$$\sum F = F_{fr} = \mu_s mg = ma \quad \rightarrow \quad a = \mu_s g = (0.60)(9.8\,\text{m/s}^2) = 5.88\,\text{m/s}^2$$

Now use Eq. 2-11b to determine the time taken to move <u>half</u> the distance with the calculated acceleration, starting from rest.

$$d/2 = x - x_0 = v_0 t + \tfrac{1}{2}at^2 \quad \rightarrow \quad t = \sqrt{d/a}\,.$$

Thus the total time for the trip will be $t_{total} = 2\sqrt{d/a} = 2\sqrt{(11.0\ \text{m})/(5.88\,\text{m/s}^2)} = \boxed{2.7\ \text{s}}$

63. (a) Draw a free-body diagram for each block. Write Newton's 2nd law for each block. Notice that the acceleration of block #1 in the y_1 direction will be zero, since it has no motion in the y_1 direction.

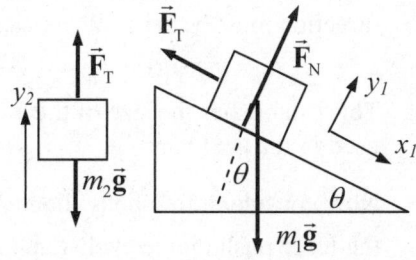

$$\sum F_{y1} = F_N - m_1 g \cos\theta = 0 \quad \rightarrow \quad F_N = m_1 g \cos\theta$$

$$\sum F_{x1} = m_1 g \sin\theta - F_T = m_1 a_{x1}$$

$$\sum F_{y2} = F_T - m_2 g = m_2 a_{y2} \quad \rightarrow \quad F_T = m_2\left(g + a_{y2}\right)$$

Since the blocks are connected by the cord, $a_{y2} = a_{x1} = a$. Substitute the expression for the tension force from the last equation into the x direction equation for block 1, and solve for the acceleration.

$$m_1 g \sin\theta - m_2\left(g + a\right) = m_1 a \quad \rightarrow \quad m_1 g \sin\theta - m_2 g = m_1 a + m_2 a$$

$$\boxed{a = g\frac{\left(m_1 \sin\theta - m_2\right)}{\left(m_1 + m_2\right)}}$$

(b) If the acceleration is to be down the plane, it must be positive. That will happen if $\boxed{m_1 \sin\theta > m_2 \ \ (\text{down the plane})}$. The acceleration will be up the plane (negative) if

$\boxed{m_1 \sin\theta < m_2 \ \ (\text{up the plane})}$. If $m_1 \sin\theta = m_2$, then the system will not accelerate. It will move with a constant speed if set in motion by a push.

64. (a) Given that m_2 is moving down, m_1 must be moving up the incline, and so the force of kinetic friction on m_1 will be directed down the incline. Since the blocks are tied together, they will both have the same acceleration, and so $a_{y2} = a_{x1} = a$. Write Newton's 2nd law for each mass.

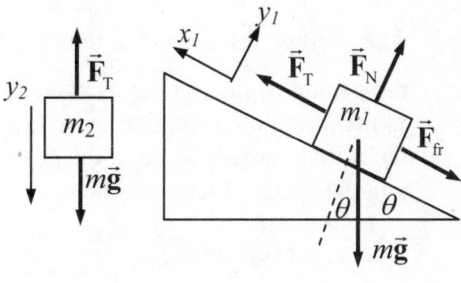

$$\sum F_{y2} = mg - F_T = ma \quad \rightarrow \quad F_T = mg - ma$$

$$\sum F_{x1} = F_T - mg \sin\theta - F_{fr} = ma$$

$$\sum F_{y1} = F_N - mg \cos\theta = 0 \quad \rightarrow \quad F_N = mg \cos\theta$$

Take the information from the two y equations and substitute into the x equation to solve for the acceleration.

$$mg - ma - mg \sin\theta - \mu_k mg \cos\theta = ma$$

$$a = g \frac{(1 - \sin\theta - \mu_k \cos\theta)}{2} = (9.8\,\text{m/s}^2) \frac{(1 - \sin 25° - 0.15\cos 25°)}{2} = \boxed{2.2\,\text{m/s}^2}$$

(*b*) To have an acceleration of zero, the expression for the acceleration must be zero.

$$a = g \frac{(1 - \sin\theta - \mu_k \cos\theta)}{2} = 0 \;\;\rightarrow\;\; 1 - \sin\theta - \mu_k \cos\theta = 0 \;\;\rightarrow$$

$$\mu_k = \frac{1 - \sin\theta}{\cos\theta} = \frac{1 - \sin 25°}{\cos 25°} = \boxed{0.64}$$

65. Consider a free-body diagram for the cyclist coasting downhill at a
constant speed. Since there is no acceleration, the net force in each
direction must be zero. Write Newton's 2nd law for the *x* direction.

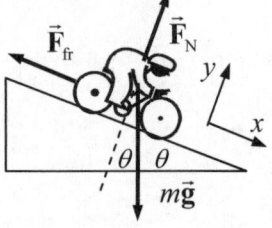

$$\sum F_x = mg\sin\theta - F_{\text{fr}} = 0 \;\;\rightarrow\;\; F_{\text{fr}} = mg\sin\theta$$

This establishes the size of the air friction force at 6.0 km/h, and so can be
used in the next part.

Now consider a free-body diagram for the cyclist climbing the hill. F_P is
the force pushing the cyclist uphill. Again, write Newton's 2nd law for the *x*
direction, with a net force of 0.

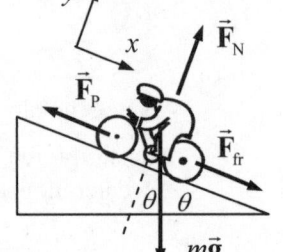

$$\sum F_x = F_{\text{fr}} + mg\sin\theta - F_P = 0 \;\;\rightarrow$$

$$F_P = F_{\text{fr}} + mg\sin\theta = 2mg\sin\theta$$

$$= 2(65\,\text{kg})(9.8\,\text{m/s}^2)(\sin 6.0°) = \boxed{1.3 \times 10^2\,\text{N}}$$

66. The average acceleration of the blood is given by $a = \dfrac{v - v_0}{t} = \dfrac{0.35\,\text{m/s} - 0.25\,\text{m/s}}{0.10\,\text{s}} = 1.0\,\text{m/s}^2$.

Thus the net force on the blood, exerted by the heart, would be

$$F = ma = (20 \times 10^{-3}\,\text{kg})(1.0\,\text{m/s}^2) = \boxed{0.020\,\text{N}}.$$

67. The acceleration of a person having a 30 "*g*" deceleration is $a = (30" g") \left(\dfrac{9.8\,\text{m/s}^2}{"g"} \right) = 290\,\text{m/s}^2$.

The average force causing that acceleration is $F = ma = (70\,\text{kg})(290\,\text{m/s}^2) = \boxed{2.1 \times 10^4\,\text{N}}$. Since

the person is undergoing a deceleration, the acceleration and force would both be directed opposite
to the direction of motion. Use Eq. 2-11c to find the distance traveled during the deceleration. Take
the initial velocity to be in the positive direction, so that the acceleration will have a negative value,
and the final velocity will be 0.

$$v_0 = (100\,\text{km/h}) \left(\frac{1\,\text{m/s}}{3.6\,\text{km/h}} \right) = 27.78\,\text{m/s}$$

$$v^2 - v_0^2 = 2a(x - x_0) \;\;\rightarrow\;\; (x - x_0) = \frac{v^2 - v_0^2}{2a} = \frac{0 - (27.78\,\text{m/s})^2}{2(-290\,\text{m/s}^2)} = \boxed{1.3\,\text{m}}$$

68. (*a*) Assume that the earthquake is moving the Earth to the right. If an object is to "hold its place", then the object must also be accelerating to the right with the Earth. The force that will accelerate that object will be the static frictional force, which would also have to be to the right. If the force were not large enough, the Earth would move out from under the chair somewhat, giving the appearance that the chair were being "thrown" to the left. Consider the free-body diagram shown for a chair on the floor. It is apparent that the normal force is equal to the weight since there is no motion in the vertical direction. Newton's 2nd law says that $F_{fr} = ma$.

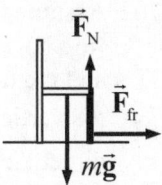

We also assume that the chair is just on the verge of slipping, which means that the static frictional force has its maximum value of $F_{fr} = \mu_s F_N = \mu_s mg$. Equate the two expressions for the frictional force to find the coefficient of friction.

$$ma = \mu_s mg \quad \rightarrow \quad \boxed{\mu_s = a/g}$$

If the static coefficient is larger than this, then there will be a larger maximum frictional force, and the static frictional force will be more than sufficient to hold the chair in place on the floor.

(*b*) For the 1989 quake, $\dfrac{a}{g} = \dfrac{4.0\,\text{m/s}^2}{9.8\,\text{m/s}^2} = 0.41$. Since $\mu_s = 0.25$, $\boxed{\text{the chair would slide}}$.

69. We draw three free-body diagrams – one for the car, one for the trailer, and then "add" them for the combination of car and trailer. Note that since the car pushes against the ground, the ground will push against the car with an equal but oppositely directed force. $\vec{\mathbf{F}}_{CG}$ is the force on the car due to the ground, $\vec{\mathbf{F}}_{TC}$ is the force on the trailer due to the car, and $\vec{\mathbf{F}}_{CT}$ is the force on the car due to the trailer. Note that by Newton's 3rd law, $\left|\vec{\mathbf{F}}_{CT}\right| = \left|\vec{\mathbf{F}}_{TC}\right|$.

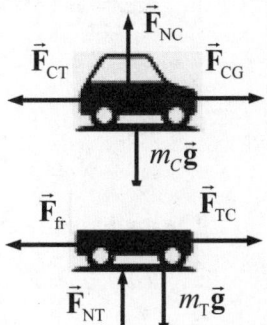

From consideration of the vertical forces in the individual free-body diagrams, it is apparent that the normal force on each object is equal to its weight. This leads to the conclusion that

$$F_{fr} = \mu_k F_{NT} = \mu_k m_T g = (0.15)(450\,\text{kg})(9.8\,\text{m/s}^2) = 660\,\text{N}\,.$$

Now consider the combined free-body diagram. Write Newton's 2nd law for the horizontal direction, This allows the calculation of the acceleration of the system.

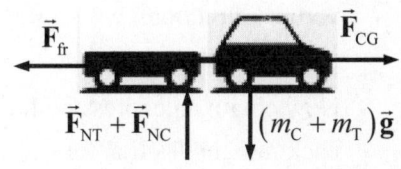

$$\sum F = F_{CG} - F_{fr} = (m_C + m_T)a \quad \rightarrow$$

$$a = \frac{F_{CG} - F_{fr}}{m_C + m_T} = \frac{3800\,\text{N} - 660\,\text{N}}{1600\,\text{kg}} = 1.9625\,\text{m/s}^2$$

Finally, consider the free-body diagram for the trailer alone. Again write Newton's 2nd law for the horizontal direction, and solve for F_{TC}.

$$\sum F = F_{TC} - F_{fr} = m_T a \quad \rightarrow$$

$$F_{TC} = F_{fr} + m_T a = 660\,\text{N} + (450\,\text{kg})(1.9625\,\text{m/s}^2) = \boxed{1.54 \times 10^3\,\text{N}}$$

70. Assume that kinetic friction is the net force causing the deceleration. See the free-body diagram for the car, assuming that the right is the positive direction, and the direction of motion of the skidding car. Since there is no acceleration in the vertical direction, and so $F_N = mg$. Applying Newton's 2nd law to the x direction gives

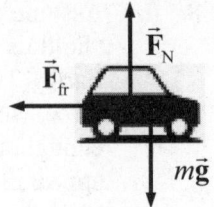

$$\sum F = -F_f = ma \;\;\rightarrow\;\; -\mu_k F_N = -\mu_k mg = ma \;\;\rightarrow\;\; a = -\mu_k g.$$

Use Eq. 2-11c to determine the initial speed of the car, with the final speed of the car being zero.
$$v^2 - v_0^2 = 2a(x - x_0) \;\;\rightarrow$$
$$v_0 = \sqrt{v^2 - 2a(x - x_0)} = \sqrt{0 - 2(-\mu_k g)(x - x_0)} = \sqrt{2(0.8)(9.8\,\text{m/s}^2)(72\text{ m})} = \boxed{34\,\text{m/s}}$$

71. We include friction from the start, and then for the no-friction result, set the coefficient of friction equal to 0. Consider a free-body diagram for the car on the hill. Write Newton's 2nd law for both directions. Note that the net force on the y direction will be zero, since there is no acceleration in the y direction.

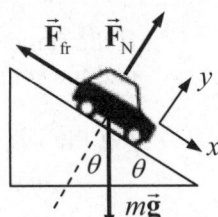

$$\sum F_y = F_N - mg\cos\theta = 0 \;\;\rightarrow\;\; F_N = mg\cos\theta$$
$$\sum F_x = mg\sin\theta - F_{fr} = ma \;\;\rightarrow$$
$$a = g\sin\theta - \frac{F_{fr}}{m} = g\sin\theta - \frac{\mu_k mg\cos\theta}{m} = g(\sin\theta - \mu_k\cos\theta)$$

Use Eq. 2-11c to determine the final velocity, assuming that the car starts from rest.
$$v^2 - v_0^2 = 2a(x - x_0) \;\;\rightarrow\;\; v = \sqrt{0 + 2a(x - x_0)} = \sqrt{2g(x - x_0)(\sin\theta - \mu_k\cos\theta)}$$

The angle is given by $\sin\theta = 1/4 \;\;\rightarrow\;\; \theta = \sin^{-1} 0.25 = 14.5°$

    (a) $\mu_k = 0 \;\;\rightarrow\;\; v = \sqrt{2g(x - x_0)x\sin\theta} = \sqrt{2(9.8\,\text{m/s}^2)(55\text{ m})\sin 14.5°} = \boxed{16\,\text{m/s}}$

    (b) $\mu_k = 0.10 \;\;\rightarrow\;\; v = \sqrt{2(9.8\,\text{m/s}^2)(55\text{ m})(\sin 14.5° - 0.10\cos 14.5°)} = \boxed{13\,\text{m/s}}$

72. See the free-body diagram for the falling purse. Assume that down is the positive direction, and that the air resistance force $\vec{F}_{fr}$ is constant. Write Newton's 2nd law for the vertical direction.

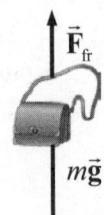

$$\sum F = mg - F_{fr} = ma \;\;\rightarrow\;\; F_{fr} = m(g - a)$$

Now obtain an expression for the acceleration from Eq. 2-11c with $v_0 = 0$, and substitute back into the friction force.

$$v^2 - v_0^2 = 2a(x - x_0) \;\;\rightarrow\;\; a = \frac{v^2}{2(x - x_0)}$$

$$F_f = m\left(g - \frac{v^2}{2(x - x_0)}\right) = (2.0\text{ kg})\left(9.8\,\text{m/s}^2 - \frac{(29\,\text{m/s})^2}{2(55\text{ m})}\right) = \boxed{4.3\text{ N}}$$

73. Consider the free-body diagram for the cyclist in the mud, assuming that the cyclist is traveling to the right. It is apparent that $F_N = mg$ since there is no vertical acceleration. Write Newton's 2nd law for the horizontal direction, positive to the right.

$$\sum F_x = -F_{fr} = ma \rightarrow -\mu_k mg = ma \rightarrow a = -\mu_k g$$

Use Eq. 2-11c to determine the distance the cyclist could travel in the mud before coming to rest.

$$v^2 - v_0^2 = 2a(x - x_0) \rightarrow (x - x_0) = \frac{v^2 - v_0^2}{2a} = \frac{-v_0^2}{-2\mu_k g} = \frac{(12\,\text{m/s})^2}{2(0.60)(9.8\,\text{m/s}^2)} = 12\,\text{m}$$

Since there is only 11 m of mud, $\boxed{\text{the cyclist will emerge from the mud.}}$ The speed upon emerging is found from Eq. 2-11c.

$$v^2 - v_0^2 = 2a(x - x_0) \rightarrow$$

$$v = \sqrt{v_0^2 + 2a(x - x_0)} = \sqrt{v_i^2 - 2\mu_k g(x - x_0)} = \sqrt{(12\,\text{m/s})^2 - 2(0.60)(9.8\,\text{m/s}^2)(11\,\text{m})}$$

$$= \boxed{3.8\,\text{m/s}}$$

74. The given data can be used to calculate the force with which the road pushes against the car, which in turn is equal in magnitude to the force the car pushes against the road. The acceleration of the car on level ground is found from Eq. 2-11a.

$$v - v_0 = at \rightarrow a = \frac{v - v_0}{t} = \frac{21\,\text{m/s} - 0}{14.0\,\text{s}} = 1.50\,\text{m/s}^2$$

The force pushing the car in order to have this acceleration is found from Newton's 2nd law.

$$F_P = ma = (1100\,\text{kg})(1.50\,\text{m/s}^2) = 1650\,\text{N}$$

We assume that this is the force pushing the car on the incline as well. Consider a free-body diagram for the car climbing the hill. We assume that the car will have a constant speed on the maximum incline. Write Newton's 2nd law for the x direction, with a net force of zero since the car is not accelerating.

$$\sum F_x = F_P - mg\sin\theta = 0 \rightarrow \sin\theta = \frac{F_P}{mg}$$

$$\theta = \sin^{-1}\frac{F_P}{mg} = \sin^{-1}\frac{1650\,\text{N}}{(1100\,\text{kg})(9.8\,\text{m/s}^2)} = \boxed{8.8°}$$

75. Consider the free-body diagram for the watch. Write Newton's 2nd law for both the x and y directions. Note that the net force in the y direction is 0 because there is no acceleration in the y direction.

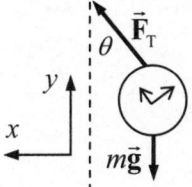

$$\sum F_y = F_T\cos\theta - mg = 0 \rightarrow F_T = \frac{mg}{\cos\theta}$$

$$\sum F_x = F_T\sin\theta = ma \rightarrow \frac{mg}{\cos\theta}\sin\theta = ma$$

$$a = g\tan\theta = (9.8\,\text{m/s}^2)\tan 25° = 4.6\,\text{m/s}^2$$

Use Eq. 2-11a with $v_0 = 0$ to find the final velocity (takeoff speed).

$$v - v_0 = at \quad \rightarrow \quad v = v_0 + at = 0 + \left(4.6\,\text{m/s}^2\right)\left(18\,\text{s}\right) = \boxed{82\,\text{m/s}}$$

76. (a) Consider the free-body diagrams for both objects, initially stationary. As sand is added, the tension will increase, and the force of static friction on the block will increase until it reaches its maximum of $F_{\text{fr}} = \mu_s F_N$. Then the system will start to move. Write Newton's 2nd law for each object, when the static frictional force is at its maximum, but the objects are still stationary.

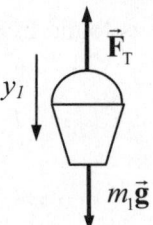

$$\sum F_{y\,\text{bucket}} = m_1 g - F_T = 0 \quad \rightarrow \quad F_T = m_1 g$$

$$\sum F_{y\,\text{block}} = F_N - m_2 g = 0 \quad \rightarrow \quad F_N = m_2 g$$

$$\sum F_{x\,\text{block}} = F_T - F_{\text{fr}} = 0 \quad \rightarrow \quad F_T = F_{\text{fr}}$$

Equate the two expressions for tension, and substitute in the expression for the normal force to find the masses.

$$m_1 g = F_{\text{fr}} \quad \rightarrow \quad m_1 g = \mu_s F_N = \mu_s m_2 g \quad \rightarrow$$

$$m_1 = \mu_s m_2 = \left(0.450\right)\left(28.0\,\text{kg}\right) = 12.6\,\text{kg}$$

Thus $12.6\,\text{kg} - 1.35\,\text{kg} = 11.25 = \boxed{11.3\,\text{kg}}$ of sand was added.

(b) The same free-body diagrams can be used, but now the objects will accelerate. Since they are tied together, $a_{y1} = a_{x2} = a$. The frictional force is now kinetic friction, given by

$F_{\text{fr}} = \mu_k F_N = \mu_k m_2 g$. Write Newton's 2nd laws for the objects in the direction of their acceleration.

$$\sum F_{y\,\text{bucket}} = m_1 g - F_T = m_1 a \quad \rightarrow \quad F_T = m_1 g - m_1 a$$

$$\sum F_{x\,\text{block}} = F_T - F_{\text{fr}} = m_2 a \quad \rightarrow \quad F_T = F_{\text{fr}} + m_2 a$$

Equate the two expressions for tension, and solve for the acceleration.

$$m_1 g - m_1 a = \mu_k m_2 g + m_2 a$$

$$a = g \frac{\left(m_1 - \mu_k m_2\right)}{\left(m_1 + m_2\right)} = \left(9.80\,\text{m/s}^2\right) \frac{\left(12.6\,\text{kg} - \left(0.320\right)\left(28.0\,\text{kg}\right)\right)}{\left(12.6\,\text{kg} + 28.0\,\text{kg}\right)} = \boxed{0.88\,\text{m/s}^2}$$

77. Consider a free-body diagram for a grocery cart being pushed up an incline. Assuming that the cart is not accelerating, we write Newton's 2nd law for the x direction.

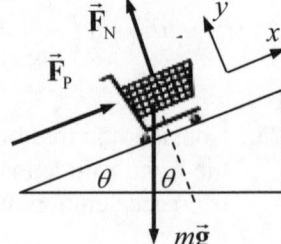

$$\sum F_x = F_P - mg \sin\theta = 0 \quad \rightarrow \quad \sin\theta = \frac{F_P}{mg}$$

$$\theta = \sin^{-1} \frac{F_P}{mg} = \sin^{-1} \frac{20\,\text{N}}{\left(20\,\text{kg}\right)\left(9.8\,\text{m/s}^2\right)} = \boxed{5.9^\circ}$$

78. (a) To find the minimum force, assume that the piano is moving with a constant velocity. Since the piano is not accelerating, $F_{T4} = Mg$. For the lower pulley, since the tension in a rope is the same throughout, and since the pulley is not accelerating, it is seen that

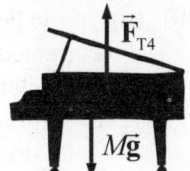

$$F_{T1} + F_{T2} = 2F_{T1} = Mg \quad \rightarrow \quad F_{T1} = F_{T2} = Mg/2.$$

It also can be seen that since $F = F_{T2}$, that $\boxed{F = Mg/2}$.

(b) Draw a free-body diagram for the upper pulley. From that diagram, we see that

$$F_{T3} = F_{T1} + F_{T2} + F = \frac{3Mg}{2}$$

To summarize:

$$\boxed{F_{T1} = F_{T2} = Mg/2 \qquad F_{T3} = 3Mg/2 \qquad F_{T4} = Mg}$$

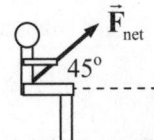

79. The acceleration of the pilot will be the same as that of the plane, since the pilot is at rest with respect to the plane. Consider first a free-body diagram of the pilot, showing only the net force. By Newton's 2nd law, the net force MUST point in the direction of the acceleration, and its magnitude is ma. That net force is the sum of ALL forces on the pilot. If we assume that the force of gravity and the force of the cockpit seat on the pilot are the only forces on the pilot, then in terms of vectors, $\vec{F}_{net} = m\vec{g} + \vec{F}_{seat} = m\vec{a}$. Solve this equation for the force of the seat to find $\vec{F}_{seat} = \vec{F}_{net} - m\vec{g} = m\vec{a} - m\vec{g}$. A vector diagram of that equation is as shown. Solve for the force of the seat on the pilot using components.

$$F_{x\,seat} = F_{x\,net} = ma\cos 45° = (75\text{ kg})(3.5\text{ m/s}^2)\cos 45° = 180\text{ N}$$

$$F_{y\,seat} = mg + F_{y\,net} = mg + ma\sin 45°$$

$$= (75\text{ kg})(9.8\text{ m/s}^2) + (75\text{ kg})(3.5\text{ m/s}^2)\cos 45° = 920\text{ N}$$

The magnitude of the cockpit seat force is

$$F = \sqrt{F_{x\,seat}^2 + F_{y\,seat}^2} = \sqrt{(180\text{ N})^2 + (920\text{ N})^2} = \boxed{940\text{ N}}$$

The angle of the cockpit seat force is

$$\theta = \tan^{-1}\frac{F_{y\,seat}}{F_{x\,seat}} = \tan^{-1}\frac{920\text{ N}}{180\text{ N}} = \boxed{79°}\text{ above the horizontal.}$$

80. The initial speed is $v_i = (45\text{ km/h})\left(\dfrac{1\text{ m/s}}{3.6\text{ km/h}}\right) = 12.5\text{ m/s}$. Use Eq. 2-11a to find the deceleration of the child.

$$v - v_0 = at \quad \rightarrow \quad a = \frac{v - v_0}{t} = \frac{0 - 12.5\text{ m/s}}{0.20\text{ s}} = -62.5\text{ m/s}^2.$$

The net force on the child is given by Newton's 2nd law.

$$F_{net} = ma = (12\text{ kg})(-62.5\text{ m/s}^2) = \boxed{-7.5\times10^2\text{ N}}\text{, opposite to the velocity}$$

We also assumed that friction between the seat and child is zero, and we assumed that the bottom of the seat is horizontal. If friction existed or if the seat was tilted back, then the force that the straps would have to apply would be less.

81 (a) The helicopter and frame will both have the same acceleration, and so can be treated as one object if no information about internal forces (like the cable tension) is needed. A free-body diagram for the helicopter-frame combination is shown. Write Newton's 2nd law for the combination, calling UP the positive direction.

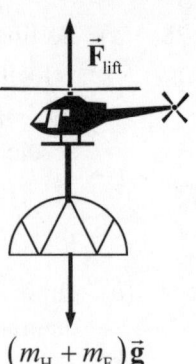

$$\sum F = F_{lift} - \left(m_H + m_F\right)g = \left(m_H + m_F\right)a \;\rightarrow$$

$$F_{lift} = \left(m_H + m_F\right)\left(g + a\right) = \left(7650\ \text{kg} + 1250\ \text{kg}\right)\left(9.80\ \text{m/s}^2 + 0.80\ \text{m/s}^2\right)$$

$$= \boxed{9.43 \times 10^4\ \text{N}}$$

$$\left(m_H + m_F\right)\vec{\mathbf{g}}$$

(b) Now draw a free-body diagram for the frame alone, in order to find the tension in the cable. Again use Newton's 2nd law.

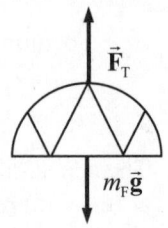

$$\sum F = F_T - m_F g = m_F a \;\rightarrow$$

$$F_T = m_F\left(g + a\right) = \left(1250\ \text{kg}\right)\left(9.80\ \text{m/s}^2 + 0.80\ \text{m/s}^2\right) = \boxed{1.33 \times 10^4\ \text{N}}$$

$$m_F\vec{\mathbf{g}}$$

(c) The tension in the cable is the same at both ends, and so the cable exerts a force of $\boxed{1.33 \times 10^4\ \text{N}}$ downward on the helicopter.

82. (a) We assume that the maximum horizontal force occurs when the train is moving very slowly, and so the air resistance is negligible. Thus the maximum acceleration is given by

$$a_{max} = \frac{F_{max}}{m} = \frac{4.0 \times 10^5\ \text{N}}{6.6 \times 10^5\ \text{kg}} = \boxed{0.61\ \text{m/s}^2}\ .$$

(b) At top speed, we assume that the train is moving at constant velocity. Therefore the net force on the train is 0, and so the air resistance must be of the same magnitude as the horizontal pushing force, which is $\boxed{1.5 \times 10^5\ \text{N}}$.

83. Consider the free-body diagram for the decelerating skater, moving to the right. It is apparent that $F_N = mg$ since there is no acceleration in the vertical direction. From Newton's 2nd law in the horizontal direction, we have

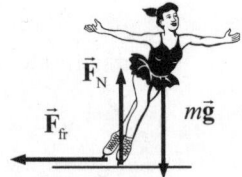

$$\sum F = F_{fr} = ma \;\rightarrow\; -\mu_k mg = ma \;\rightarrow\; a = -\mu_k g$$

Now use Eq. 2-11c to find the starting speed.

$$v^2 - v_0^2 = 2a\left(x - x_0\right) \;\rightarrow$$

$$v_0 = \sqrt{v^2 - 2a\left(x - x_0\right)} = \sqrt{0 + 2\mu_k g\left(x - x_0\right)} = \sqrt{2\left(0.10\right)\left(9.8\ \text{m/s}^2\right)\left(75\ \text{m}\right)} = \boxed{12\ \text{m/s}}$$

84. First calculate Karen's speed from falling. Let the downward direction be positive, and use Eq. 2-11c with $v_0 = 0$.

$$v^2 - v_0^2 = 2a\left(y - y_0\right) \;\rightarrow\; v = \sqrt{0 + 2a\left(y - y_0\right)} = \sqrt{2\left(9.8\ \text{m/s}^2\right)\left(2.0\ \text{m}\right)} = 6.26\ \text{m/s}$$

Now calculate the average acceleration as the rope stops Karen, again using Eq. 2-11c, with down as positive.

$$v^2 - v_0^2 = 2a\left(y - y_0\right) \;\rightarrow\; a = \frac{v^2 - v_0^2}{2\left(y - y_0\right)} = \frac{0 - \left(6.26\ \text{m/s}\right)^2}{2\left(1.0\ \text{m}\right)} = -19.6\ \text{m/s}^2$$

The negative sign indicates that the acceleration is upward. Since this is her acceleration, the net force on Karen is given by Newton's 2nd law, $F_{net} = ma$. That net force will also be upward. Now consider the free-body diagram shown of Karen as she decelerates. Call DOWN the positive direction, and Newton's 2nd law says that $F_{net} = ma = mg - F_{rope} \;\rightarrow\; F_{rope} = mg - ma$. The ratio of

this force to Karen's weight would be $\dfrac{F_{rope}}{mg} = \dfrac{mg - ma}{g} = 1.0 - \dfrac{a}{g} = 1.0 - \dfrac{-19.6\,\text{m/s}^2}{9.8\,\text{m/s}^2} = 3.0$. Thus the

rope pulls upward on Karen with an average force of $\boxed{3.0 \text{ times her weight}}$.

A completely analogous calculation for Bill gives the same speed after the 2.0 m fall, but since he stops over a distance of 0.30 m, his acceleration is –65 m/s², and the rope pulls upward on Bill with an average force of $\boxed{7.7 \text{ times his weight}}$. Thus $\boxed{\text{Bill is more likely to get hurt}}$ in the fall.

85. See the free-body diagram for the fish being pulled upward vertically. From Newton's 2nd law, calling the upward direction positive, we have

$$\sum F_y = F_T - mg = ma \;\rightarrow\; F_T = m(g + a)$$

 (*a*) If the fish has a constant speed, then its acceleration is zero, and so $F_T = mg$. Thus

  the heaviest fish that could be pulled from the water in this case is $\boxed{45\text{ N }(10\text{ lb})}$.

 (*b*) If the fish has an acceleration of 2.0 m/s², and F_T is at its maximum of 45 N, then solve the equation for the mass of the fish.

$$m = \frac{F_T}{g+a} = \frac{45\text{ N}}{9.8\,\text{m/s}^2 + 2.0\,\text{m/s}^2} = 3.8\text{ kg} \;\rightarrow$$

$$mg = (3.8\text{ kg})(9.8\,\text{m/s}^2) = \boxed{37\text{ N }(\approx 8.4\text{ lb})}$$

 (*c*) It is not possible to land a 15-lb fish using 10-lb line, if you have to lift the fish vertically. If the fish were reeled in while still in the water, and then a net used to remove the fish from the water, it might still be caught with the 10-lb line.

86. Choose downward to be positive. The elevator's acceleration is calculated by Eq. 2-11c.

$$v^2 - v_0^2 = 2a(y - y_0) \;\rightarrow\; a = \frac{v^2 - v_0^2}{2(y - y_0)} = \frac{0 - (3.5\,\text{m/s})^2}{2(2.6\text{ m})} = -2.356\,\text{m/s}^2$$

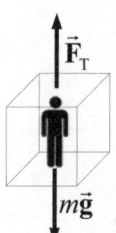

See the free-body diagram of the elevator. Write Newton's 2nd law for the elevator.

$$\sum F_y = mg - F_T = ma$$

$$F_T = m(g - a) = (1300\text{ kg})(9.80\,\text{m/s}^2 - -2.356\,\text{m/s}^2) = \boxed{1.58 \times 10^4\text{ N}}$$

87. (*a*) Draw a free-body diagram for each block, with no connecting tension. Because of the similarity of the free-body diagrams, we shall just analyze block 1. Write Newton's 2nd law in both the *x* and *y* directions. The net force in the *y* direction is zero, because there is no acceleration in the *y* direction.

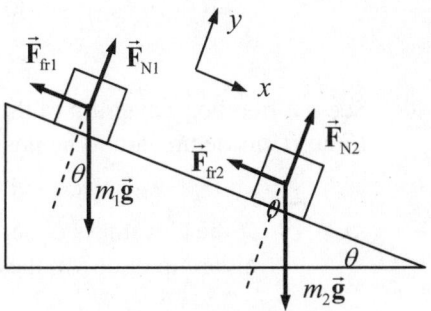

$$\sum F_{y1} = F_{N1} - m_1 g \cos\theta = 0 \;\rightarrow\; F_{N1} = m_1 g \cos\theta$$

$$\sum F_{x1} = m_1 g \sin\theta - F_{fr1} = m_1 a_1 \;\rightarrow$$

$$a_1 = \frac{m_1 g \sin\theta - F_{fr1}}{m_1} = \frac{m_1 g \sin\theta - \mu_k m_1 g \cos\theta}{m_1} = g(\sin\theta - \mu_1 \cos\theta)$$

$$= (9.8\,\text{m/s}^2)(\sin 30^\circ - 0.10\cos 30^\circ) = \boxed{4.1\,\text{m/s}^2}$$

The same analysis for block 2 would give

$$a_2 = g(\sin\theta - \mu_2 \cos\theta) = (9.8\,\text{m/s}^2)(\sin 30^\circ - 0.20\cos 30^\circ) = \boxed{3.2\,\text{m/s}^2}$$

Since $a_2 < a_1$, if both blocks were released from rest, block # 1 would "gain" on block 2.

(*b*)   Now let the rope tension be present. Before writing equations, consider that without the tension, $a_1 > a_2$. In the free-body diagram shown, m_1 now has even more force accelerating down the plane because of the addition of the tension force, which means m_1 has an even larger acceleration than before. And m_2 has less force accelerating it down the plane because of the addition of the tension force. Thus m_2 has a smaller acceleration than before. And so in any amount of time

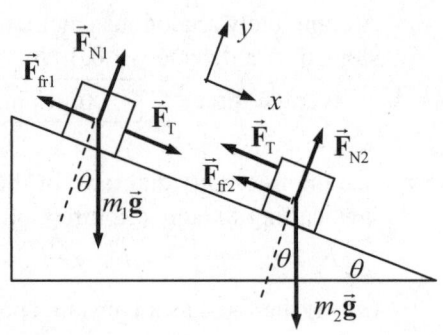

considered, m_1 will move more distance down the plane upon release than block m_2. The cord will go slack almost immediately after the blocks are released, and the blocks revert to the original free-body diagram. The conclusion is that the accelerations in this part of the problem are the same as they would be in part (*a*):

$$\boxed{a_1 = 4.1\,\text{m/s}^2 \;;\; a_2 = 3.2\,\text{m/s}^2}$$

(*c*)   Now reverse the position of the masses. Write Newton's 2nd law for each block, and assume that they have the same acceleration. The y equations and frictional forces are unchanged from the analysis in part (*a*), so we only write the x equations. After writing them, add them together (to eliminate the tension) and solve for the acceleration.

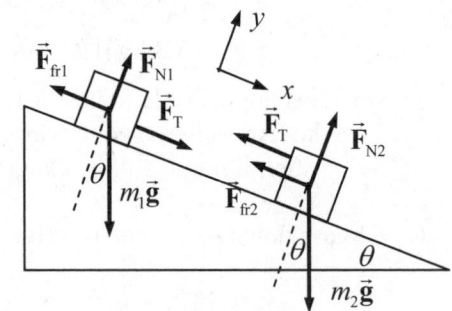

$$\sum F_{x1} = m_1 g \sin\theta - F_{fr1} - F_T = m_1 a$$

$$\sum F_{x2} = m_2 g \sin\theta - F_{fr2} + F_T = m_2 a$$

$$(m_1 + m_2) g \sin\theta - F_{fr1} - F_{fr2} = (m_1 + m_2) a$$

$$a = \frac{(m_1 + m_2) g \sin\theta - \mu_1 m_1 g \cos\theta - \mu_2 m_2 g \cos\theta}{(m_1 + m_2)} = g\left[\sin\theta - \frac{\mu_1 m_1 + \mu_2 m_2}{m_1 + m_2}\cos\theta\right]$$

$$= (9.8\,\text{m/s}^2)\left[\sin 30^\circ - \frac{(0.10)(1.0\,\text{kg}) + (0.20)(2.0\,\text{kg})}{3.0\,\text{kg}}\cos 30^\circ\right] = \boxed{3.5\,\text{m/s}^2}$$

88.   See the free-body diagram of the person in the elevator. The scale will read the normal force. Choose upward to be positive. From Newton's 2nd law,

$$\sum F = F_N - mg = ma \;\rightarrow\; F_N = m(g + a)$$

(*a, b, c*)   If the elevator is either at rest or moving with a constant vertical speed, either up or down, the acceleration is zero, and so

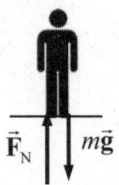

$$F_N = mg = (75.0 \text{ kg})(9.80 \text{ m/s}^2) = \boxed{7.35 \times 10^2 \text{ N}} \quad m = \frac{F_N}{g} = \boxed{75.0 \text{ kg}}$$

(*d*) When accelerating upward, the acceleration is $+3.0 \text{ m/s}^2$, and so

$$F_N = m(g+a) = (75.0 \text{ kg})(12.8 \text{ m/s}^2) = \boxed{9.60 \times 10^2 \text{ N}} \quad m = \frac{F_N}{g} = \boxed{98.0 \text{ kg}}$$

(*e*) When accelerating downward, the acceleration is -3.0 m/s^2, and so

$$F_N = m(g+a) = (75.0 \text{ kg})(6.80 \text{ m/s}^2) = \boxed{5.10 \times 10^2 \text{ N}} \quad m = \frac{F_N}{g} = \boxed{52.0 \text{ kg}}$$

89. Since the climbers are on ice, the frictional force for the lower two climbers is negligible. Consider the free-body diagram as shown. Note that all the masses are the same. Write Newton's 2nd law in the *x* direction for the lowest climber, assuming he is at rest.

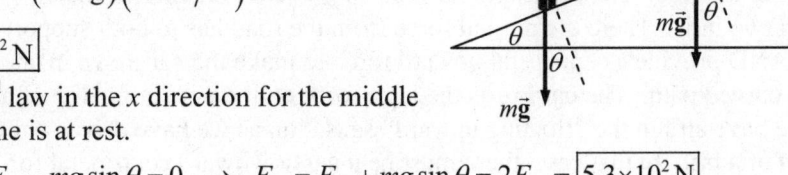

$$\sum F_x = F_{T2} - mg \sin \theta = 0$$

$$F_{T2} = mg \sin \theta = (75 \text{ kg})(9.8 \text{ m/s}^2) \sin 21.0°$$

$$= \boxed{2.6 \times 10^2 \text{ N}}$$

Write Newton's 2nd law in the *x* direction for the middle climber, assuming he is at rest.

$$\sum F_x = F_{T1} - F_{T2} - mg \sin \theta = 0 \quad \rightarrow \quad F_{T1} = F_{T2} + mg \sin \theta = 2F_{T2} = \boxed{5.3 \times 10^2 \text{ N}}$$

CHAPTER 5: Circular Motion; Gravitation

Answers to Questions

1. The problem with the statement is that there is nothing to cause an outward force, and so the water removed from the clothes is not thrown outward. Rather, the spinning drum pushes INWARD on the clothes and water. But where there are holes in the drum, the drum can't push on the water, and so the water is not pushed in. Instead, the water moves tangentially to the rotation, out the holes, in a straight line, and so the water is separated from the clothes.

2. The centripetal acceleration for an object moving in circular motion is inversely proportional to the radius of the curve, given a constant speed $\left(a = v^2/r\right)$. So for a gentle curve (which means a large radius), the acceleration is smaller, while for a sharp curve (which means a small radius), the acceleration is larger.

3. The force that the car exerts on the road is the Newton's 3rd law reaction to the normal force of the road on the car, and so we can answer this question in terms of the normal force. The car exerts the greatest force on the road at the dip between two hills. There the normal force from the road has to both support the weight AND provide a centripetal upward force to make the car move in an upward curved path. The car exerts the least force on the road at the top of a hill. We have all felt the "floating upward" sensation as we have driven over the crest of a hill. In that case, there must be a net downward centripetal force to cause the circular motion, and so the normal force from the road does not completely support the weight.

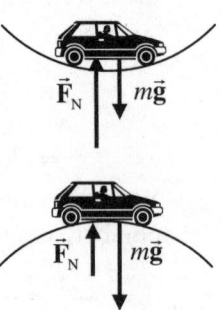

4. There are at least three distinct major forces on the child. The force of gravity is acting downward on the child. There is a normal force from the seat of the horse acting upward on the child. There must be friction between the seat of the horse and the child as well, or the child could not be accelerated by the horse. It is that friction that provides the centripetal acceleration. There may be smaller forces as well, such as a reaction force on the child's hands if the child is holding on to part of the horse. Any force that has a radially inward component will contribute to the centripetal acceleration.

5. For the water to remain in the bucket, there must be a centripetal force forcing the water to move in a circle along with the bucket. That centripetal force gets larger with the tangential velocity of the water, since $F_R = mv^2/r$. The centripetal force at the top of the motion comes from a combination of the downward force of gravity and the downward normal force of the bucket on the water. If the bucket is moving faster than some minimum speed, the water will stay in the bucket. If the bucket is moving too slow, there is insufficient force to keep the water moving in the circular path, and it spills out.

6. The three major "accelerators" are the accelerator pedal, the brake pedal, and the steering wheel. The accelerator pedal (or gas pedal) can be used to increase speed (by depressing the pedal) or to decrease speed in combination with friction (by releasing the pedal). The brake pedal can be used to decrease speed by depressing it. The steering wheel is used to change direction, which also is an acceleration. There are some other controls which could also be considered accelerators. The parking brake can be used to decrease speed by depressing it. The gear shift lever can be used to decrease speed by downshifting. If the car has a manual transmission, then the clutch can be used to

decrease speed by depressing it (friction will slow the car). Finally, shutting the car off can be used to decrease its speed. Any change in speed or direction means that an object is accelerating.

7. When the child is on a level surface, the normal force between his chest and the sled is equal to the child's weight, and thus he has no vertical acceleration. When he goes over the hill, the normal force on him will be reduced. Since the child is moving on a curved path, there must be a net centripetal force towards the center of the path, and so the normal force does not completely support the weight. Write Newton's 2nd law for the radial direction, with inward as positive.

    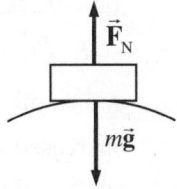

    $$\sum F_R = mg - F_N = mv^2/r \quad \rightarrow \quad F_N = mg - mv^2/r$$

    We see that the normal force is reduced from mg by the centripetal force.

8. When a bicycle rider leans inward, the bike tire pushes down on the ground at an angle. The road surface then pushes back on the tire both vertically (to provide the normal force which counteracts gravity) and horizontally toward the center of the curve (to provide the centripetal frictional force, enabling them to turn).

    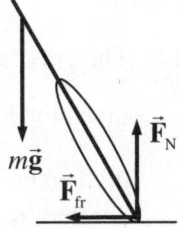

9. Airplanes bank when they turn because in order to turn, there must be a force that will be exerted towards the center of a circle. By tilting the wings, the lift force on the wings has a non-vertical component which points toward the center of the curve, providing the centripetal force. The banking angle can be computed from the free-body diagram. The sum of vertical forces must be zero for the plane to execute a level turn, and so $F_{lift} \cos\theta = mg$. The horizontal component of the lifting force must provide the centripetal force to move the airplane in a circle.

    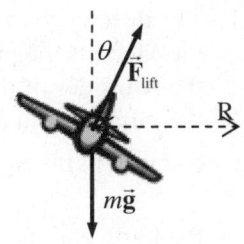

    $$F_{lift} \sin\theta = mv^2/r \quad \rightarrow \quad \frac{mg}{\cos\theta} \sin\theta = mv^2/r \quad \rightarrow \quad \tan\theta = \frac{v^2}{Rg}$$

10. She should let go of the string when the ball is at a position where the tangent line to the circle at the ball's location, when extended, passes through the target's position. That tangent line indicates the direction of the velocity at that instant, and if the centripetal force is removed, then the ball will follow that line horizontally. See the top-view diagram.

    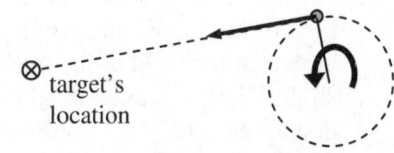

11. The apple does exert a gravitational force on the Earth. By Newton's 3^{d} law, the force on the Earth due to the apple is the same magnitude as the force on the apple due to the Earth– the weight of the apple. The force is also independent of the state of motion of the apple. So for both a hanging apple and a falling apple, the force on the Earth due to the apple is equal to the weight of the apple.

12. The gravitational force on the Moon is given by $G\dfrac{M_{Earth}M_{Moon}}{R^2}$, where R is the radius of the Moon's orbit. This is a radial force, and so can be expressed as $M_{Moon} v_{Moon}^2/R$. This can be changed using the relationship $v_{Moon} = 2\pi R/T$, where T is the orbital period of the Moon, to $4\pi^2 M_{Moon} R/T^2$. If we equate these two expressions for the force, we get the following:

$$G\frac{M_{Earth}M_{Moon}}{R^2} = 4\pi^2 M_{Moon}\,R\big/T^2 \quad \rightarrow \quad \frac{R^3}{T^2} = \frac{GM_{Earth}}{4\pi^2}\,.$$ Thus the mass of the Earth determines the

ratio $R^3\big/T^2$. If the mass of the Earth were doubled, then the ratio $R^3\big/T^2$ would double, and

so $R'^3\big/T'^2 = R^3\big/T^2$, where the primes indicated the "after doubling" conditions. For example, the

radius might stay the same, and the period decrease by a factor of $\sqrt{2}$, which means the speed

increased by a factor of $\sqrt{2}$. Or the period might stay the same, and the radius increase by a factor

of $2^{1/3}$, which means the speed increased by the same factor of $2^{1/3}$. Or if both R and T were to

double, keeping the speed constant, then $R^3\big/T^2$ would double. There are an infinite number of

other combinations that would also satisfy the doubling of $R^3\big/T^2$.

13. The gravitational pull is the same in each case, by Newton's 3rd law. The magnitude of that pull is

    given by $F = G\dfrac{M_{Earth}M_{Moon}}{r^2_{Earth\text{-}Moon}}$. To find the acceleration of each body, the gravitational pulling force is

    divided by the mass of the body. Since the Moon has the smaller mass, it will have the larger
    acceleration.

14. The <u>difference</u> in force on the two sides of the Earth from the gravitational pull of either the Sun or
    the Moon is the primary cause of the tides. That difference in force comes about from the fact that
    the two sides of the Earth are a different distance away from the pulling body. Relative to the Sun,
    the difference in distance (Earth diameter) of the two sides from the Sun, relative to the average

    distance to the Sun, is given by $2R_{Earth}\big/R_{Earth \atop to\ Sun} = 8.5\times10^{-5}$. The corresponding relationship between

    the Earth and the Moon is $2R_{Earth}\big/R_{Earth \atop to\ Moon} = 3.3\times10^{-2}$. Since the relative change in distance is much

    greater for the Earth-Moon combination, we see that the Moon is the primary cause of the Earth's
    tides.

15. An object weighs more at the poles, due to two effects which complement (not oppose) each other.
    First of all, the Earth is slightly flattened at the poles and expanded at the equator, relative to a
    perfect sphere. Thus the mass at the poles is slightly closer to the center, and so experiences a
    slightly larger gravitational force. Secondly, objects at the equator have a centripetal acceleration
    due to the rotation of the Earth that objects at the poles do not have. To provide that centripetal
    acceleration, the apparent weight (the radially outward normal force of the Earth on an object) is
    slightly less than the gravitational pull inward. So the two effects both make the weight of an object
    at the equator less than that at the poles.

16. The Moon is not pulled away from the Earth because both the Moon and the Earth are experiencing
    the same radial acceleration due to the Sun. They both have the same period around the Sun because
    they are both, on average, the same distance from the Sun, and so they travel around the Sun
    together.

17. The centripetal acceleration of Mars is smaller than that of Earth. The acceleration of each planet
    can be found by dividing the gravitational force on each planet by the planet's mass. The resulting
    acceleration is inversely proportional to the square of the distance of the planet from the Sun. Since
    Mars is further from the Sun than the Earth is, the acceleration of Mars will be smaller. Also see the
    equation below.

$$F_{\text{on planet}} = G\frac{M_{\text{sun}}M_{\text{planet}}}{r^2_{\text{Sun to planet}}} \qquad a_{\text{planet}} = \frac{F_{\text{on planet}}}{M_{\text{planet}}} = G\frac{M_{\text{sun}}}{r^2_{\text{Sun to planet}}}$$

18. In order to orbit, a satellite must reach an orbital speed relative to the center of the Earth. Since the satellite is already moving eastward when launched (due to the rotation speed at the surface of the Earth), it requires less additional speed to launch it east to obtain the final orbital speed.

19. The apparent weight (the normal force) would be largest when the elevator is accelerating upward. From the free-body diagram, with up as positive, we have $F_N - mg = ma \;\rightarrow\; F_N = m(g+a)$. With a positive acceleration, the normal force is greater than your weight. The apparent weight would be the least when in free fall, because there the apparent weight is zero, since $a = -g$. When the elevator is moving with constant speed, your apparent weight would be the same as it is on the ground, since $a = 0$ and so $F_N = mg$.

20. A satellite remains in orbit due to the combination of gravitational force on the satellite directed towards the center of the orbit and the tangential speed of the satellite. First, the proper tangential speed had to be established by some other force than the gravitational force. Then, if the satellite has the proper combination of speed and radius such that the force required for circular motion is equal to the force of gravity on the satellite, then the satellite will maintain circular motion.

21. The passengers, as seen in the diagram, are standing on the floor.

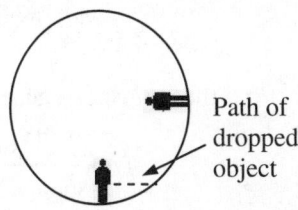

Path of dropped object

   (a) If a passenger held an object beside their waist and then released it, the object would move in a straight line, tangential to the circle in which the passenger's waist was moving when the object was released. In the figure, we see that the released object would hit the rotating shell, and so fall to the floor, but behind the person. The passenger might try to explain such motion by inventing some kind of "retarding" force on dropped objects, when really there is no such force.
   (b) The floor exerts a centripetal force on the feet, pushing them towards the center. This force has the same direction ("upwards", away from the floor) that a passenger would experience on Earth, and so it seems to the passenger that gravity must be pulling them "down". Actually, the passengers are pushing down on the floor, because the floor is pushing up on them.
   (c) The "normal" way of playing catch, for example, would have to change. Since the artificial gravity is not uniform, passengers would have to re-learn how to throw something across the room to each other. There would not be projectile motion as we experience it on Earth. Also, if the cylinder were small, there might be a noticeable difference in the acceleration of our head vs. our feet. Since the head is closer to the center of the circle than the feet, and both the head and the feet have the same period of rotation, the centripetal acceleration $\left(a_R = 4\pi^2 r/T^2\right)$ is smaller for the head. This might cause dizziness or a light-headed feeling.

22. When the runner has both feet off the ground, the only force on the runner is gravity – there is no normal force from the ground on the runner. This lack of normal force is interpreted as "free fall" and "apparent weightlessness".

23. By Kepler's 2nd law, the Earth moves faster around the Sun when it is nearest the Sun. Kepler's 2nd law says that an imaginary line drawn from the Sun to the Earth sweeps out equal areas in equal

times. So when the Earth is close to the Sun, it must move faster to sweep out a given area than when the Earth is far from the Sun. Thus the Earth is closer to the Sun in January.

24. Let the mass of Pluto be M, the mass of the moon be m, the radius of the moon's orbit be R, and the period of the moon's orbit be T. Then Newton's second law for the moon orbiting Pluto will be $F = \dfrac{GmM}{R^2}$. If that moon's orbit is a circle, then the form of the force must be centripetal, and so $F = mv^2/R$. Equate these two expressions for the force on the moon, and substitute the relationship for a circular orbit that $v = 2\pi R/T$.

$$\frac{GmM}{R^2} = \frac{mv^2}{R} = \frac{4\pi^2 mR}{T^2} \quad \rightarrow \quad M = \frac{4\pi^2 R^3}{GT^2}.$$

Thus a value for the mass of Pluto can be calculated knowing the period and radius of the moon's orbit.

Solutions to Problems

1. (a) Find the centripetal acceleration from Eq. 5-1.

    $$a_R = v^2/r = (1.25 \,\text{m/s})^2 / 1.10 \,\text{m} = \boxed{1.42 \,\text{m/s}^2}$$

    (b) The net horizontal force is causing the centripetal motion, and so will be the centripetal force.

    $$F_R = ma_R = (25.0 \,\text{kg})(1.42 \,\text{m/s}^2) = \boxed{35.5 \,\text{N}}$$

2. Find the centripetal acceleration from Eq. 5-1.

    $$a_R = v^2/r = \frac{(525 \,\text{m/s})^2}{6.00 \times 10^3 \,\text{m}} = (45.94 \,\text{m/s}^2) \left(\frac{1 \,g}{9.80 \,\text{m/s}^2} \right) = \boxed{4.69 \,g\text{'s}}$$

3. The centripetal acceleration is $a_R = v^2 / R_{\text{Earth} \atop \text{orbit}} = \dfrac{\left(2\pi R_{\text{Earth} \atop \text{orbit}} / T \right)^2}{R_{\text{Earth} \atop \text{orbit}}} = \dfrac{4\pi^2 R_{\text{Earth} \atop \text{orbit}}}{T^2}$. The force (from

    Newton's 2nd law) is $F_R = m_{\text{Earth}} a_R$. The period is one year, converted into seconds.

    $$a_R = \frac{4\pi^2 R_{\text{Earth} \atop \text{orbit}}}{T^2} = \frac{4\pi^2 (1.50 \times 10^{11} \,\text{m})}{(3.15 \times 10^7 \,\text{sec})^2} = \boxed{5.97 \times 10^{-3} \,\text{m/s}^2}$$

    $$F_R = ma = (5.97 \times 10^{24} \,\text{kg})(5.97 \times 10^{-3} \,\text{m/s}^2) = \boxed{3.56 \times 10^{22} \,\text{N}}$$

    $\boxed{\text{The Sun}}$ exerts this force on the Earth. It is a gravitational force.

4. The speed can be found from the centripetal force and centripetal acceleration.

    $$F_R = ma_R = mv^2/r \quad \rightarrow \quad v = \sqrt{\frac{F_R r}{m}} = \sqrt{\frac{(210 \,\text{N})(0.90 \,\text{m})}{2.0 \,\text{kg}}} = \boxed{9.7 \,\text{m/s}}$$

5. The orbit radius will be the sum of the Earth's radius plus the 400 km orbit height. The orbital period is about 90 minutes. Find the centripetal acceleration from these data.

$$r = 6380\,\text{km} + 400\,\text{km} = 6780\,\text{km} = 6.78 \times 10^6\,\text{m} \qquad T = 90\,\text{min}\left(\frac{60\,\text{sec}}{1\,\text{min}}\right) = 5400\,\text{sec}$$

$$a_R = \frac{4\pi^2 r}{T^2} = \frac{4\pi^2\left(6.78 \times 10^6\,\text{m}\right)}{\left(5400\,\text{sec}\right)^2} = \left(9.18\,\text{m/s}^2\right)\left(\frac{1\,g}{9.80\,\text{m/s}^2}\right) = 0.937 \approx \boxed{0.9\,g's}$$

Notice how close this is to g, because the shuttle is not very far above the surface of the Earth, relative to the radius of the Earth.

6. To find the period, the rotational speed (in rev/min) is reciprocated to have min/rev, and then converted to sec/rev. Use the period to find the speed, and then the centripetal acceleration.

$$T = \left(\frac{1\,\text{min}}{45\,\text{rev}}\right)\left(\frac{60\,\text{sec}}{1\,\text{min}}\right) = 1.333\,\frac{\text{sec}}{\text{rev}} \qquad r = 0.16\,\text{m} \qquad v = \frac{2\pi r}{T} = \frac{2\pi\left(0.16\,\text{m}\right)}{1.333\,\text{sec}} = 0.754\,\text{m/s}$$

$$a_R = v^2/r = \frac{\left(0.754\,\text{m/s}\right)^2}{0.16\,\text{m}} = \boxed{3.6\,\text{m/s}^2}$$

7. See the free-body diagram in the textbook. Since the object is moving in a circle with a constant speed, the net force on the object at any point must point to the center of the circle.
    (*a*) Take positive to be downward. Write Newton's 2nd law in the downward direction.

$$\sum F_R = mg + F_{T1} = ma_R = mv^2/r \rightarrow$$

$$F_{T1} = m\left(v^2/r - g\right) = \left(0.300\,\text{kg}\right)\left(\frac{\left(4.00\,\text{m/s}\right)^2}{0.720\,\text{m}} - 9.80\,\text{m/s}^2\right) = \boxed{3.73\,\text{N}}$$

   This is a downward force, as expected.
    (*b*) Take positive to be upward. Write Newton's 2nd law in the upward direction.

$$\sum F_R = F_{T2} - mg = ma = mv^2/r \rightarrow$$

$$F_{T1} = m\left(v^2/r + g\right) = \left(0.300\,\text{kg}\right)\left(\frac{\left(4.00\,\text{m/s}\right)^2}{0.720\,\text{m}} + 9.80\,\text{m/s}^2\right) = \boxed{9.61\,\text{N}}$$

   This is an upward force, as expected.

8. The centripetal force that the tension provides is given by $F_R = mv^2/r$. Solve that for the speed.

$$v = \sqrt{\frac{F_R r}{m}} = \sqrt{\frac{\left(75\,\text{N}\right)\left(1.3\,\text{m}\right)}{0.45\,\text{kg}}} = \boxed{15\,\text{m/s}}$$

9. A free-body diagram for the car at one instant of time is shown. In the diagram, the car is coming out of the paper at the reader, and the center of the circular path is to the right of the car, in the plane of the paper. If the car has its maximum speed, it would be on the verge of slipping, and the force of static friction would be at its maximum value. The vertical forces (gravity and normal force) are of the same magnitude, because the car is not accelerating vertically. We assume that the force of friction is the force causing the circular motion.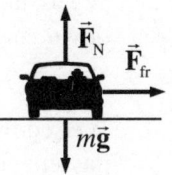

$$F_R = F_{fr} \rightarrow mv^2/r = \mu_s F_N = \mu_s mg \rightarrow v = \sqrt{\mu_s rg} = \sqrt{\left(0.80\right)\left(77\,\text{m}\right)\left(9.8\,\text{m/s}^2\right)} = \boxed{25\,\text{m/s}}$$

Notice that the result is independent of the car's mass.

10. In the free-body diagram, the car is coming out of the paper at the reader, and the center of the circular path is to the right of the car, in the plane of the paper. The vertical forces (gravity and normal force) are of the same magnitude, because the car is not accelerating vertically. We assume that the force of friction is the force causing the circular motion. If the car has its maximum speed, it would be on the verge of slipping, and the force of static friction would be at its maximum value.

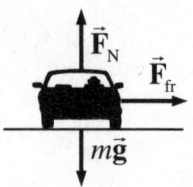

$$F_R = F_{fr} \quad \rightarrow \quad mv^2/r = \mu_s F_N = \mu_s mg \quad \rightarrow \quad \mu_s = \frac{v^2}{rg} = \frac{\left[(95\,\mathrm{km/hr}) \left(\frac{1\,\mathrm{m/s}}{3.6\,\mathrm{km/hr}} \right) \right]^2}{(85\ \mathrm{m})(9.8\,\mathrm{m/s^2})} = \boxed{0.84}$$

Notice that the result is independent of the car's mass.

11. Since the motion is all in a horizontal circle, gravity has no influence on the analysis. Set the general expression for centripetal force equal to the stated force in the problem.

$$F_R = mv^2/r = 7.85W = 7.85mg \quad \rightarrow \quad v = \sqrt{7.85\,rg} = \sqrt{7.85(12.0\mathrm{m})(9.8\,\mathrm{m/s^2})} = \boxed{30.4\,\mathrm{m/s}}$$

$$(30.4\,\mathrm{m/s}) \left(\frac{1\ \mathrm{rev}}{2\pi\,(12.0\ \mathrm{m})} \right) = \boxed{0.403\,\mathrm{rev/s}}$$

12. The force of static friction is causing the circular motion – it is the centripetal force. The coin slides off when the static frictional force is not large enough to move the coin in a circle. The maximum static frictional force is the coefficient of static friction times the normal force, and the normal force is equal to the weight of the coin as seen in the free-body diagram, since there is no vertical acceleration. In the free-body diagram, the coin is coming out of the paper and the center of the circle is to the right of the coin, in the plane of the paper.

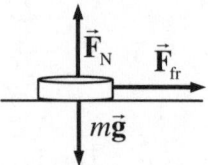

The rotational speed must be changed into a linear speed.

$$v = \left(36\,\frac{\mathrm{rev}}{\mathrm{min}} \right) \left(\frac{1\ \mathrm{min}}{60\ \mathrm{s}} \right) \left(\frac{2\pi\,(0.11\mathrm{m})}{1\ \mathrm{rev}} \right) = 0.4147\,\mathrm{m/s}$$

$$F_R = F_{fr} \quad \rightarrow \quad mv^2/r = \mu_s F_N = \mu_s mg \quad \rightarrow \quad \mu_s = \frac{v^2}{rg} = \frac{(0.4147\,\mathrm{m/s})^2}{(0.11\ \mathrm{m})(9.8\,\mathrm{m/s^2})} = \boxed{0.16}$$

13. At the top of a circle, a free-body diagram for the passengers would be as shown, assuming the passengers are upside down. Then the car's normal force would be pushing DOWN on the passengers, as shown in the diagram. We assume no safety devices are present. Choose the positive direction to be down, and write Newton's 2$^\mathrm{nd}$ law for the passengers.

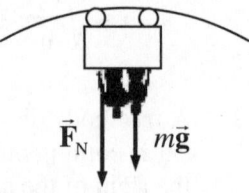

$$\sum F = F_N + mg = ma = mv^2/r \quad \rightarrow \quad F_N = m \left(v^2/r - g \right)$$

We see from this expression that for a high speed, the normal force is positive, meaning the passengers are in contact with the car. But as the speed decreases, the normal force also decreases. If the normal force becomes 0, the passengers are no longer in contact with the car– they are in free fall. The limiting condition is

$$v_{min}^2/r - g = 0 \quad \rightarrow \quad v_{min} = \sqrt{rg} = \sqrt{(9.8\,\mathrm{m/s^2})(7.4\ \mathrm{m})} = \boxed{8.5\,\mathrm{m/s}}$$

14. (*a*) A free-body diagram of the car at the instant it is on the top of the hill is shown. Since the car is moving in a circular path, there must be a net centripetal force downward. Write Newton's 2nd law for the car, with down as the positive direction.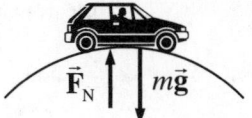

$$\sum F_R = mg - F_N = ma = mv^2/r \quad \rightarrow$$

$$F_N = m\left(g - v^2/r\right) = \left(950\,\text{kg}\right)\left(9.8\,\text{m/s}^2 - \frac{\left(22\,\text{m/s}\right)^2}{95\,\text{m}}\right) = \boxed{4.5 \times 10^3\,\text{N}}$$

(*b*) The free-body diagram for the passengers would be the same as the one for the car, leading to the same equation for the normal force on the passengers.

$$F_N = m\left(g - v^2/r\right) = \left(72\,\text{kg}\right)\left(9.8\,\text{m/s}^2 - \frac{\left(22\,\text{m/s}\right)^2}{95\,\text{m}}\right) = \boxed{3.4 \times 10^2\,\text{N}}$$

Notice that this is significantly less than the 700-N weight of the passenger. Thus the passenger will feel "light" as they drive over the hill.

(*c*) For the normal force to be zero, we see that we must have

$$F_N = m\left(g - v^2/r\right) = 0 \quad \rightarrow \quad g = v^2/r \quad \rightarrow \quad v = \sqrt{gr} = \sqrt{\left(9.8\,\text{m/s}^2\right)\left(95\,\text{m}\right)} = \boxed{31\,\text{m/s}}.$$

15. The free-body diagram for passengers at the top of a Ferris wheel is as shown. F_N is the normal force of the seat pushing up on the passenger. The sum of the forces on the passenger is producing the centripetal motion, and so must be a centripetal force. Call the downward direction positive. Newton's 2nd law for the passenger is: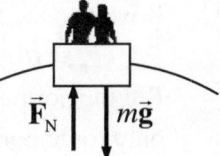

$$\sum F_R = mg - F_N = ma = mv^2/r$$

Since the passenger is to feel "weightless", they must lose contact with their seat, and so the normal force will be 0.

$$mg = mv^2/r \quad \rightarrow \quad v = \sqrt{gr} = \sqrt{\left(9.8\,\text{m/s}^2\right)\left(7.5\,\text{m}\right)} = 8.6\,\text{m/s}$$

$$\left(8.6\,\frac{\text{m}}{\text{s}}\right)\left(\frac{1\,\text{rev}}{2\pi\left(7.5\,\text{m}\right)}\right)\left(\frac{60\,\text{s}}{1\,\text{min}}\right) = \boxed{11\,\text{rpm}}$$

16. (*a*) At the bottom of the motion, a free-body diagram of the bucket would be as shown. Since the bucket is moving in a circle, there must be a net force on it towards the center of the circle, and a centripetal acceleration. Write Newton's 2nd law for the bucket, with up as the positive direction.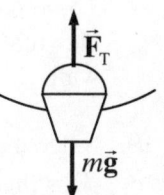

$$\sum F_R = F_T - mg = ma = mv^2/r \quad \rightarrow$$

$$v = \sqrt{\frac{r\left(F_T - mg\right)}{m}} = \sqrt{\frac{\left(1.10\,\text{m}\right)\left[25.0\,\text{N} - \left(2.00\,\text{kg}\right)\left(9.80\,\text{m/s}^2\right)\right]}{2.00\,\text{kg}}} = 1.723 \approx \boxed{1.7\,\text{m/s}}$$

(*b*) A free-body diagram of the bucket at the top of the motion is shown. Since the bucket is moving in a circle, there must be a net force on it towards the center of the circle, and a centripetal acceleration. Write Newton's 2nd law for the bucket, with down as the positive direction.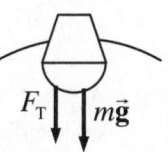

$$\sum F_R = F_T + mg = ma = mv^2/r \quad \rightarrow \quad v = \sqrt{\frac{r\left(F_T + mg\right)}{m}}.$$

If the tension is to be zero, then

$$v = \sqrt{\frac{r(0+mg)}{m}} = \sqrt{rg} = \sqrt{(1.1 \text{ m})(9.8 \text{ m/s}^2)} = \boxed{3.3 \text{ m/s}}$$

The bucket must move faster than 3.3 m/s in order for the rope not to go slack.

17. The centripetal acceleration of a rotating object is given by $a_R = v^2/r$. Thus

$$v = \sqrt{a_R r} = \sqrt{(1.15 \times 10^5 \, g)r} = \sqrt{(1.15 \times 10^5)(9.80 \text{ m/s}^2)(9.00 \times 10^{-2} \text{ m})} = 3.18 \times 10^2 \text{ m/s} .$$

$$\left(3.18 \times 10^2 \text{ m/s}\right)\left(\frac{1 \text{ rev}}{2\pi(9.00 \times 10^{-2} \text{m})}\right)\left(\frac{60 \text{ s}}{1 \text{ min}}\right) = \boxed{3.38 \times 10^4 \text{ rpm}} .$$

18. Consider the free-body diagram for a person in the "Rotor-ride". $\vec{\mathbf{F}}_N$ is the normal force of contact between the rider and the wall, and $\vec{\mathbf{F}}_{fr}$ is the static frictional force between the back of the rider and the wall. Write Newton's 2nd law for the vertical forces, noting that there is no vertical acceleration.

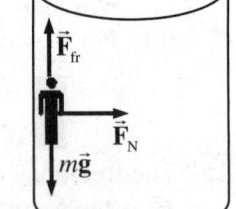

$$\sum F_y = F_{fr} - mg = 0 \quad \rightarrow \quad F_{fr} = mg$$

If we assume that the static friction force is a maximum, then

$$F_{fr} = \mu_s F_N = mg \quad \rightarrow \quad F_N = mg/\mu_s .$$

But the normal force must be the force causing the centripetal motion– it is the only force pointing to the center of rotation. Thus $F_R = F_N = mv^2/r$. Using $v = 2\pi r/T$, we have

$$F_N = \frac{4\pi^2 mr}{T^2} .$$ Equate the two expressions for the normal force and solve for the coefficient of friction. Note that since there are 0.5 rev per sec, the period is 2.0 sec.

$$F_N = \frac{4\pi^2 mr}{T^2} = \frac{mg}{\mu_s} \quad \rightarrow \quad \mu_s = \frac{gT^2}{4\pi^2 r} = \frac{(9.8 \text{ m/s}^2)(2 \text{ s})^2}{4\pi^2 (4.6 \text{ m})} = \boxed{0.22} .$$

Any larger value of the coefficient of friction would mean that the normal force could be smaller to achieve the same frictional force, and so the period could be longer or the cylinder smaller.

There is no force pushing outward on the riders. Rather, the wall pushes against the riders, so by Newton's 3rd law the riders push against the wall. This gives the sensation of being pressed into the wall.

19. Since mass m is dangling, the tension in the cord must be equal to the weight of mass m, and so $F_T = mg$. That same tension is in the other end of the cord, maintaining the circular motion of mass M, and so $F_T = F_R = Ma_R = Mv^2/r$. Equate the two expressions for the tension and solve for the velocity.

$$Mv^2/r = mg \quad \rightarrow \quad v = \boxed{\sqrt{mgR/M}} .$$

20. A free-body diagram for the ball is shown. The tension in the suspending cord must not only hold the ball up, but also provide the centripetal force needed to make the ball move in a circle. Write Newton's 2nd law for the vertical direction, noting that the ball is not accelerating vertically.

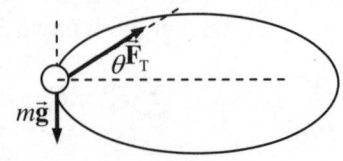

$$\sum F_y = F_T \sin\theta - mg = 0 \quad \rightarrow \quad F_T = \frac{mg}{\sin\theta}$$

The force moving the ball in a circle is the horizontal portion of the tension. Write Newton's 2nd law for that radial motion.

$$\sum F_R = F_T \cos\theta = ma_R = mv^2/r$$

Substitute the expression for the tension from the first equation into the second equation, and solve for the angle. Also substitute in the fact that for a rotating object, $v = 2\pi r/T$. Finally we recognize that if the string is of length L, then the radius of the circle is $r = L\cos\theta$.

$$F_T \cos\theta = \frac{mg}{\sin\theta}\cos\theta = \frac{mv^2}{r} = \frac{4\pi^2 mr}{T^2} = \frac{4\pi^2 mL\cos\theta}{T^2} \quad \rightarrow$$

$$\sin\theta = \frac{gT^2}{4\pi^2 L} \quad \rightarrow \quad \theta = \sin^{-1}\frac{gT^2}{4\pi^2 L} = \sin^{-1}\frac{\left(9.80\,\text{m/s}^2\right)\left(0.500\,\text{s}\right)^2}{4\pi^2\left(0.600\,\text{m}\right)} = \boxed{5.94°}$$

The tension is then given by $F_T = \dfrac{mg}{\sin\theta} = \dfrac{\left(0.150\,\text{kg}\right)\left(9.80\,\text{m/s}^2\right)}{\sin 5.94°} = \boxed{14.2\,\text{N}}$

21. Since the curve is designed for 75 km/h, traveling at a higher speed with the same radius means that more centripetal force will be required. That extra centripetal force will be supplied by a force of static friction, downward along the incline. See the free-body diagram for the car on the incline. Note that from Example 5-7 in the textbook, the no-friction banking angle is given by

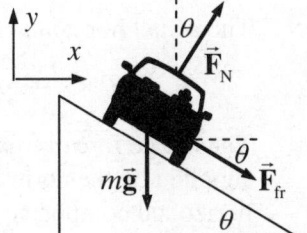

$$\theta = \tan^{-1}\frac{v^2}{rg} = \tan^{-1}\frac{\left[\left(75\,\text{km/h}\right)\left(\dfrac{1.0\,\text{m/s}}{3.6\,\text{km/h}}\right)\right]^2}{\left(88\,\text{m}\right)\left(9.8\,\text{m/s}^2\right)} = 26.7°$$

Write Newton's 2nd law in both the x and y directions. The car will have no acceleration in the y direction, and centripetal acceleration in the x direction. We also assume that the car is on the verge of skidding, so that the static frictional force has its maximum value of $F_{fr} = \mu_s F_N$. Solve each equation for the normal force.

$$\sum F_y = F_N \cos\theta - mg - F_{fr}\sin\theta = 0 \quad \rightarrow \quad F_N \cos\theta - \mu_s F_N \sin\theta = mg \quad \rightarrow$$

$$F_N = \frac{mg}{\left(\cos\theta - \mu_s \sin\theta\right)}$$

$$\sum F_x = F_N \sin\theta + F_{fr}\cos\theta = F_R = mv^2/r \quad \rightarrow \quad F_N \sin\theta + \mu_s F_N \cos\theta = mv^2/r \quad \rightarrow$$

$$F_N = \frac{mv^2/r}{\left(\sin\theta + \mu_s \cos\theta\right)}$$

Equate the two expressions for F_N, and solve for the coefficient of friction. The speed of rounding the curve is given by $v = \left(95\,\text{km/h}\right)\left(\dfrac{1.0\,\text{m/s}}{3.6\,\text{km/h}}\right) = 26.39\,\text{m/s}$.

$$\frac{mg}{\left(\cos\theta - \mu_s \sin\theta\right)} = \frac{mv^2/r}{\left(\sin\theta + \mu_s \cos\theta\right)} \quad \rightarrow$$

$$\mu_s = \frac{\left(\dfrac{v^2}{r}\cos\theta - g\sin\theta\right)}{\left(g\cos\theta + \dfrac{v^2}{r}\sin\theta\right)} = \frac{\left(\dfrac{v^2}{r} - g\tan\theta\right)}{\left(g + \dfrac{v^2}{r}\tan\theta\right)} = \frac{\left(\dfrac{(26.39\,\text{m/s})^2}{88\,\text{m}} - (9.8\,\text{m/s}^2)\tan 26.7^\circ\right)}{\left(9.8\,\text{m/s}^2 + \dfrac{(26.39\,\text{m/s})^2}{88\,\text{m}}\tan 26.7^\circ\right)} = \boxed{0.22}$$

22. The car moves in a horizontal circle, and so there must be a net horizontal centripetal force. The car is not accelerating vertically. Write Newton's 2nd law for both the x and y directions.

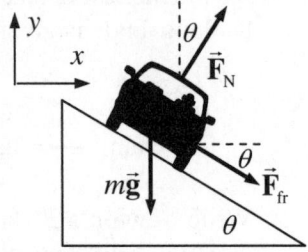

$$\sum F_y = F_N \cos\theta - mg = 0 \quad \rightarrow \quad F_N = \frac{mg}{\cos\theta}$$

$$\sum F_x = \sum F_R = F_N \sin\theta = ma_x$$

The amount of centripetal force needed for the car to round the curve is

$$F_R = mv^2/r = (1200\,\text{kg})\frac{\left[(95\,\text{km/h})\left(\dfrac{1.0\,\text{m/s}}{3.6\,\text{km/h}}\right)\right]^2}{67\,\text{m}} = 1.247\times 10^4\,\text{N}.$$

The actual horizontal force available from the normal force is

$$F_N \sin\theta = \frac{mg}{\cos\theta}\sin\theta = mg\tan\theta = (1200\,\text{kg})(9.80\,\text{m/s}^2)\tan 12^\circ = 2.500\times 10^3\,\text{N}.$$

Thus more force is necessary for the car to round the curve than can be supplied by the normal force. That extra force will have to have a horizontal component to the right in order to provide the extra centripetal force. Accordingly, we add a frictional force pointed down the plane. That corresponds to the car not being able to make the curve without friction.

Again write Newton's 2nd law for both directions, and again the y acceleration is zero.

$$\sum F_y = F_N \cos\theta - mg - F_{fr}\sin\theta = 0 \quad \rightarrow \quad F_N = \frac{mg + F_{fr}\sin\theta}{\cos\theta}$$

$$\sum F_x = F_N \sin\theta + F_{fr}\cos\theta = mv^2/r$$

Substitute the expression for the normal force from the y equation into the x equation, and solve for the friction force.

$$\frac{mg + F_{fr}\sin\theta}{\cos\theta}\sin\theta + F_{fr}\cos\theta = mv^2/r \quad \rightarrow \quad (mg + F_{fr}\sin\theta)\sin\theta + F_{fr}\cos^2\theta = m\frac{v^2}{r}\cos\theta$$

$$F_{fr} = m\frac{v^2}{r}\cos\theta - mg\sin\theta = (1.247\times 10^4\,\text{N})\cos 12^\circ - (1200\,\text{kg})(9.80\,\text{m/s}^2)\sin 12^\circ$$

$$= 9.752\times 10^3\,\text{N}$$

So a frictional force of $\boxed{9.8\times 10^3\,\text{N down the plane}}$ is needed to provide the necessary centripetal force to round the curve at the specified speed.

23. If the masses are in line and both have the same frequency, then they will always stay in line. Consider a free-body diagram for both masses, from a side view, at the instant that they are to the left of the post. Note that the same tension that pulls inward on mass 2 pulls outward on mass 1, by Newton's 3rd law. Also notice that since there is no vertical acceleration, the normal force on each mass is equal to its weight. Write Newton's 2nd law for the horizontal direction for both masses, noting that they are in uniform circular motion.

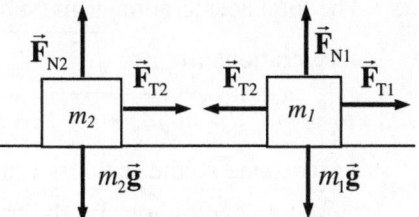

$$\sum F_{1R} = F_{T1} - F_{T2} = m_1 a_1 = m_1 v_1^2 / r_1 \qquad \sum F_{2R} = F_{T2} = m_2 a_2 = m_2 v_2^2 / r_2$$

The speeds can be expressed in terms of the frequency as follows: $v = \left(f \dfrac{\text{rev}}{\text{sec}} \right)\left(\dfrac{2\pi r}{1 \text{ rev}} \right) = 2\pi r f$.

$$F_{T2} = m_2 v_2^2 / r_2 = m_2 \left(2\pi r_2 f \right)^2 / r_2 = \boxed{4\pi^2 m_2 r_2 f^2}$$

$$F_{T1} = F_{T2} + m_1 v_1^2 / r_1 = 4\pi m_2 r_2 f^2 + m_1 \left(2\pi r_1 f \right)^2 / r_1 = \boxed{4\pi^2 f^2 \left(m_1 r_1 + m_2 r_2 \right)}$$

24. The fact that the pilot can withstand 9.0 *g*'s without blacking out, along with the speed of the aircraft, will determine the radius of the circle that he must fly as he pulls out of the dive. To just avoid crashing into the sea, he must begin to form that circle (pull out of the dive) at a height equal to the radius of that circle.

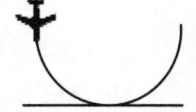

$$a_R = v^2 / r = 9.0g \;\rightarrow\; r = \frac{v^2}{9.0g} = \frac{\left(310 \,\text{m/s} \right)^2}{9.0 \left(9.80 \,\text{m/s}^2 \right)} = \boxed{1.1 \times 10^3 \,\text{m}}$$

25. From example 5.8, we are given that the track radius is 500 m, and the tangential acceleration is 32 m/s². Thus the tangential force is

$$F_{\text{tan}} = m a_{\text{tan}} = \left(1100 \text{ kg} \right)\left(3.2 \,\text{m/s}^2 \right) = \boxed{3.5 \times 10^3 \,\text{N}} .$$

The centripetal force is given by

$$F_R = m v^2 / r = \left(1100 \text{ kg} \right)\left(15 \,\text{m/s} \right)^2 / \left(500 \text{ m} \right) = \boxed{5.0 \times 10^2 \,\text{N}} .$$

26. The car has constant tangential acceleration, which is the acceleration that causes the speed to change. Thus use constant acceleration equations to calculate the tangential acceleration. The initial speed is 0, the final speed is $320 \,\text{km/h} \left(\dfrac{1.0 \,\text{m/s}}{3.6 \,\text{km/h}} \right) = 88.89 \,\text{m/s}$, and the distance traveled is one half of a circular arc of radius 220 m, so $\Delta x_{\text{tan}} = 220\pi$ m . Find the tangential acceleration using Eq. 2-11c.

$$v_{\text{tan}}^2 - v_{0\,\text{tan}}^2 = 2 a_{\text{tan}} \Delta x_{\text{tan}} \;\rightarrow\; a_{\text{tan}} = \frac{v_{\text{tan}}^2 - v_{0\,\text{tan}}^2}{2\Delta x_{\text{tan}}} = \frac{\left(88.89 \,\text{m/s} \right)^2}{2\left(220\pi \text{ m} \right)} = 5.72 \,\text{m/s}^2$$

With this tangential acceleration, we can find the speed that the car has halfway through the turn, using Eq. 2-11c, and then calculate the radial acceleration.

$$v_{\text{tan}}^2 - v_{0\,\text{tan}}^2 = 2 a_{\text{tan}} \Delta x_{\text{tan}} \;\rightarrow\; v_{\text{tan}} = \sqrt{v_{0\,\text{tan}}^2 + 2 a_{\text{tan}} \Delta x_{\text{tan}}} = \sqrt{2\left(5.72 \,\text{m/s}^2 \right)\left(110\pi \text{ m} \right)} = 62.9 \,\text{m/s}$$

$$a_R = v^2 / r = \frac{\left(62.9 \,\text{m/s} \right)^2}{220 \text{ m}} = 18.0 \,\text{m/s}^2$$

The total acceleration is given by the Pythagorean combination of the tangential and centripetal accelerations. $a_{\text{total}} = \sqrt{a_R^2 + a_{\text{tan}}^2}$. If static friction is to provide the total acceleration, then $F_{\text{fr}} = ma_{\text{total}} = m\sqrt{a_R^2 + a_{\text{tan}}^2}$. We assume that the car is on the verge of slipping, and is on a level surface, and so the static frictional force has its maximum value of $F_{\text{fr}} = \mu_s F_N = \mu_s mg$. If we equate these two expressions for the frictional force, we can solve for the coefficient of static friction.

$$F_{\text{fr}} = ma_{\text{total}} = m\sqrt{a_R^2 + a_{\text{tan}}^2} = \mu_s mg \;\; \rightarrow$$

$$\mu_s = \frac{\sqrt{a_R^2 + a_{\text{tan}}^2}}{g} = \frac{\sqrt{\left(18.0\,\text{m/s}^2\right)^2 + \left(5.72\,\text{m/s}^2\right)^2}}{9.80\,\text{m/s}^2} = 1.92 \approx \boxed{1.9}$$

This is an exceptionally large coefficient of friction, and so the curve had better be banked.

27. We show a top view of the particle in circular motion, traveling clockwise. Because the particle is in circular motion, there must be a radially-inward component of the acceleration.

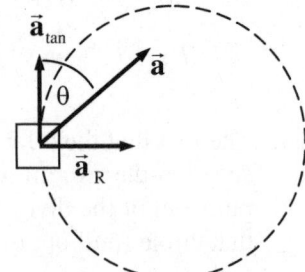

    (*a*) $a_R = a\sin\theta = v^2/r \;\; \rightarrow$

$$v = \sqrt{ar\sin\theta} = \sqrt{\left(1.05\,\text{m/s}^2\right)\left(2.90\,\text{m}\right)\sin 32.0^\circ} = \boxed{1.27\,\text{m/s}}$$

    (*b*)   The particle's speed change comes from the tangential acceleration, which is given by $a_{\text{tan}} = a\cos\theta$. If the tangential acceleration is constant, then using Eq. 2-11a,

$$v_{\text{tan}} - v_{0\,\text{tan}} = a_{\text{tan}}t \;\; \rightarrow$$

$$v_{\text{tan}} = v_{0\,\text{tan}} + a_{\text{tan}}t = 1.27\,\text{m/s} + \left(1.05\,\text{m/s}^2\right)\left(\cos 32.0^\circ\right)\left(2.00\,\text{s}\right) = \boxed{3.05\,\text{m/s}}$$

28. The spacecraft is three times as far from the Earth's center as when at the surface of the Earth. Therefore, since the force as gravity decreases as the square of the distance, the force of gravity on the spacecraft will be one-ninth of its weight at the Earth's surface.

$$F_G = \tfrac{1}{9}mg_{\substack{\text{Earth's}\\\text{surface}}} = \frac{\left(1350\,\text{kg}\right)\left(9.80\,\text{m/s}^2\right)}{9} = \boxed{1.47\times10^3\,\text{N}}$$

This could also have been found using Newton's law of Universal Gravitation.

29. (*a*)   Mass is independent of location and so the mass of the ball is $\boxed{21.0\,\text{kg}}$ on both the Earth and the planet.

    (*b*)   The weight is found by $W = mg$.

$$W_{\text{Earth}} = mg_{\text{Earth}} = \left(21.0\,\text{kg}\right)\left(9.80\,\text{m/s}^2\right) = \boxed{206\,\text{N}}$$

$$W_{\text{Planet}} = mg_{\text{Planet}} = \left(21.0\,\text{kg}\right)\left(12.0\,\text{m/s}^2\right) = \boxed{252\,\text{N}} .$$

30. The force of gravity on an object at the surface of a planet is given by Newton's law of Universal Gravitation, using the mass and radius of the planet. If that is the only force on an object, then the acceleration of a freely-falling object is acceleration due to gravity.

$$F_G = G\frac{M_{\text{Moon}}m}{r_{\text{Moon}}^2} = mg_{\text{Moon}} \;\; \rightarrow$$

$$g_{Moon} = G\frac{M_{Moon}}{r_{Moon}^2} = \left(6.67\times10^{-11}\,N\cdot m^2/kg^2\right)\frac{\left(7.35\times10^{22}\,kg\right)}{\left(1.74\times10^6\,m\right)^2} = \boxed{1.62\,m/s^2}$$

31. The acceleration due to gravity at any location on or above the surface of a planet is given by $g_{planet} = GM_{Planet}/r^2$, where r is the distance from the center of the planet to the location in question.

$$g_{planet} = G\frac{M_{Planet}}{r^2} = G\frac{M_{Earth}}{\left(1.5R_{Earth}\right)^2} = \frac{1}{1.5^2}G\frac{M_{Earth}}{R_{Earth}^2} = \frac{1}{1.5^2}g_{Earth} = \frac{9.8\,m/s^2}{1.5^2} = \boxed{4.4\,m/s^2}$$

32. The acceleration due to gravity at any location at or above the surface of a planet is given by $g_{planet} = GM_{Planet}/r^2$, where r is the distance from the center of the planet to the location in question.

$$g_{planet} = G\frac{M_{Planet}}{r^2} = G\frac{1.66M_{Earth}}{R_{Earth}^2} = 1.66\left(G\frac{M_{Earth}}{R_{Earth}^2}\right) = 1.66g_{Earth} = 1.66\left(9.80\,m/s^2\right) = \boxed{16.3\,m/s^2}$$

33. Assume that the two objects can be treated as point masses, with $m_1 = m$ and $m_2 = 4\,kg - m$. The gravitational force between the two masses is given by

$$F = G\frac{m_1 m_2}{r^2} = G\frac{m(4-m)}{r^2} = \left(6.67\times10^{-11}\,N\cdot m^2/kg^2\right)\frac{4m-m^2}{\left(0.25\,m\right)^2} = 2.5\times10^{-10}\,N.$$

This can be rearranged into a quadratic form of $m^2 - 4m + 0.234 = 0$. Use the quadratic formula to solve for m, resulting in two values which are the two masses.
$$\boxed{m_1 = 3.9\,kg\,,\,m_2 = 0.1\,kg}.$$

34. The acceleration due to gravity at any location at or above the surface of a planet is given by $g_{planet} = GM_{Planet}/r^2$, where r is the distance from the center of the planet to the location in question. For this problem, $M_{Planet} = M_{Earth} = 5.97\times10^{24}\,kg$

(a) $r = R_{Earth} + 3200\,m = 6.38\times10^6\,m + 3200\,m$

$$g = G\frac{M_{Earth}}{r^2} = \left(6.67\times10^{-11}\,N\bullet m^2/kg^2\right)\frac{\left(5.97\times10^{24}\,kg\right)}{\left(6.38\times10^6\,m + 3200\,m\right)^2} = \boxed{9.77\,m/s^2}$$

(b) $r = R_{Earth} + 3200\,km = 6.38\times10^6\,m + 3.20\times10^6\,m = 9.58\times10^6\,m$

$$g = G\frac{M_{Earth}}{r^2} = \left(6.67\times10^{-11}\,N\bullet m^2/kg^2\right)\frac{\left(5.97\times10^{24}\,kg\right)}{\left(9.58\times10^6\,m\right)^2} = \boxed{4.34\,m/s^2}$$

35. In general, the acceleration due to gravity of the Earth is given by $g = GM_{Earth}/r^2$, where r is the distance from the center of the Earth to the location in question. So for the location in question,

$$g = \tfrac{1}{10}g_{surface} \quad\rightarrow\quad G\frac{M_{Earth}}{r^2} = \tfrac{1}{10}G\frac{M_{Earth}}{R_{Earth}^2} \quad\rightarrow\quad r^2 = 10R_{Earth}^2$$

$$r = \sqrt{10}R_{Earth} = \sqrt{10}\left(6.38\times10^6\,m\right) = \boxed{2.02\times10^7\,m}$$

36. The acceleration due to gravity at any location at or above the surface of a star is given by $g_{star} = GM_{star}/r^2$, where r is the distance from the center of the star to the location in question.

$$g_{star} = G\frac{M_{star}}{r^2} = G\frac{5M_{Sun}}{r^2} = \left(6.67\times10^{-11}\ \text{N}\cdot\text{m}^2/\text{kg}^2\right)\frac{5\left(1.99\times10^{30}\ \text{kg}\right)}{\left(1\times10^4\ \text{m}\right)^2} = \boxed{7\times10^{12}\ \text{m}/\text{s}^2}$$

37. The acceleration due to gravity at any location at or above the surface of a star is given by $g_{star} = GM_{star}/r^2$, where r is the distance from the center of the star to the location in question.

$$g_{star} = G\frac{M_{sun}}{R_{Moon}^2} = \left(6.67\times10^{-11}\ \text{N}\cdot\text{m}^2/\text{kg}^2\right)\frac{\left(1.99\times10^{30}\ \text{kg}\right)}{\left(1.74\times10^6\ \text{m}\right)^2} = \boxed{4.38\times10^7\ \text{m}/\text{s}^2}$$

38. The distance from the Earth's center is

$$r = R_{Earth} + 250\ \text{km} = 6.38\times10^6\ \text{m} + 2.5\times10^5\ \text{m} = 6.63\times10^6\ \text{m}.$$

Calculate the acceleration due to gravity at that location.

$$g = G\frac{M_{Earth}}{r^2} = G\frac{M_{Earth}}{r^2} = \left(6.67\times10^{-11}\ \text{N}\cdot\text{m}^2/\text{kg}^2\right)\frac{5.97\times10^{24}\ \text{kg}}{\left(6.63\times10^6\ \text{m}\right)^2} = 9.059\ \text{m}/\text{s}^2$$

$$= 9.059\ \text{m}/\text{s}^2\left(\frac{1"\ g\ "}{9.80\ \text{m}/\text{s}^2}\right) = \boxed{0.924\ g\text{'s}}$$

This is only about a 7.5% reduction from the value of g at the surface of the Earth.

39. Calculate the force on the sphere in the lower left corner, using the free-body diagram shown. From the symmetry of the problem, the net forces in the x and y directions will be the same. Note $\theta = 45°$

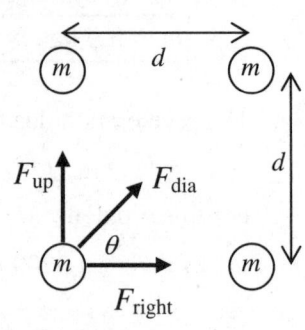

$$F_x = F_{right} + F_{dia}\cos\theta = G\frac{m^2}{d^2} + G\frac{m^2}{\left(\sqrt{2}d\right)^2}\frac{1}{\sqrt{2}} = G\frac{m^2}{d^2}\left(1+\frac{1}{2\sqrt{2}}\right)$$

and so $F_y = F_x = G\dfrac{m^2}{d^2}\left(1+\dfrac{1}{2\sqrt{2}}\right)$. The net force can be found by the

Pythagorean combination of the two component forces. Due to the symmetry of the arrangement, the net force will be along the diagonal of the square.

$$F = \sqrt{F_x^2 + F_y^2} = \sqrt{2F_x^2} = F_x\sqrt{2} = G\frac{m^2}{d^2}\left(1+\frac{1}{2\sqrt{2}}\right)\sqrt{2} = G\frac{m^2}{d^2}\left(\sqrt{2}+\frac{1}{2}\right)$$

$$= \left(6.67\times10^{-11}\ \text{N}\cdot\text{m}^2/\text{kg}^2\right)\frac{\left(9.5\ \text{kg}\right)^2}{\left(0.60\ \text{m}\right)^2}\left(\sqrt{2}+\frac{1}{2}\right) = \boxed{3.2\times10^{-8}\ \text{N at }45°}$$

The force points towards the center of the square.

40. We are to calculate the force on Earth, so we need the distance of each planet from Earth.

$$r_{Earth\atop Venus} = \left(150-108\right)\times10^6\ \text{km} = 4.2\times10^{10}\ \text{m} \qquad r_{Earth\atop Jupiter} = \left(778-150\right)\times10^6\ \text{km} = 6.28\times10^{11}\ \text{m}$$

$$r_{Earth\atop Saturn} = \left(1430-150\right)\times10^6\ \text{km} = 1.28\times10^{12}\ \text{m}$$

Jupiter and Saturn will exert a rightward force, while Venus will exert a leftward force. Take the right direction as positive.

$$F_{\substack{\text{Earth-}\\\text{planets}}} = G\frac{M_{\text{Earth}}M_{\text{Jupiter}}}{r^2_{\substack{\text{Earth}\\\text{Jupiter}}}} + G\frac{M_{\text{Earth}}M_{\text{Saturn}}}{r^2_{\substack{\text{Earth}\\\text{Saturn}}}} - G\frac{M_{\text{Earth}}M_{\text{Venus}}}{r^2_{\substack{\text{Earth}\\\text{Venus}}}}$$

$$= GM^2_{\text{Earth}}\left(\frac{318}{\left(6.28\times10^{11}\,\text{m}\right)^2} + \frac{95.1}{\left(1.28\times10^{12}\,\text{m}\right)^2} - \frac{0.815}{\left(4.2\times10^{10}\,\text{m}\right)^2}\right)$$

$$= \left(6.67\times10^{-11}\,\text{N}\bullet\text{m}^2/\text{kg}^2\right)\left(5.97\times10^{24}\,\text{kg}\right)^2\left(4.02\times10^{-22}\,\text{m}^{-2}\right) = \boxed{9.56\times10^{17}\,\text{N}}$$

The force of the Sun on the Earth is as follows.

$$F_{\substack{\text{Earth-}\\\text{Sun}}} = G\frac{M_{\text{Earth}}M_{\text{Sun}}}{r^2_{\substack{\text{Earth}\\\text{Sun}}}} = \left(6.67\times10^{-11}\,\text{N}\bullet\text{m}^2/\text{kg}^2\right)\frac{\left(5.97\times10^{24}\,\text{kg}\right)\left(1.99\times10^{30}\,\text{kg}\right)}{\left(1.50\times10^{11}\,\text{m}\right)^2} = 3.52\times10^{22}\,\text{N}$$

And so the ratio is $F_{\substack{\text{Earth-}\\\text{planets}}}\Big/F_{\substack{\text{Earth-}\\\text{Sun}}} = 9.56\times10^{17}\,\text{N}\big/3.52\times10^{22}\,\text{N} = \boxed{2.71\times10^{-5}}$, which is 27 millionths.

41. The expression for the acceleration due to gravity at the surface of a body is $g_{\text{body}} = G\dfrac{M_{\text{body}}}{R^2_{\text{body}}}$, where

R_{body} is the radius of the body. For Mars, $g_{\text{Mars}} = 0.38\,g_{\text{Earth}}$. Thus

$$G\frac{M_{\text{Mars}}}{R^2_{\text{Mars}}} = 0.38\,G\frac{M_{\text{Earth}}}{R^2_{\text{Earth}}} \quad\rightarrow$$

$$M_{\text{Mars}} = 0.38\,M_{\text{Earth}}\left(\frac{R_{\text{Mars}}}{R_{\text{Earth}}}\right)^2 = 0.38\left(5.97\times10^{24}\,\text{kg}\right)\left(\frac{3400\,\text{km}}{6380\,\text{km}}\right)^2 = \boxed{6.4\times10^{23}\,\text{kg}}$$

42. The speed of an object in an orbit of radius r around the Sun is given by $v = \sqrt{GM_{\text{Sun}}/r}$, and is also given by $v = 2\pi r/T$, where T is the period of the object in orbit. Equate the two expressions for the speed and solve for M_{Sun} , using data for the Earth.

$$\sqrt{G\frac{M_{\text{Sun}}}{r}} = \frac{2\pi r}{T} \quad\rightarrow\quad M_{\text{Sun}} = \frac{4\pi^2 r^3}{GT^2} = \frac{4\pi^2\left(1.50\times10^{11}\,\text{m}\right)^3}{\left(6.67\times10^{-11}\,\text{N}\bullet\text{m}^2/\text{kg}^2\right)\left(3.15\times10^7\,\text{sec}\right)^2} = \boxed{2.01\times10^{30}\,\text{kg}}$$

This is the same result obtained in Example 5-16 using Kepler's third law.

$\boxed{43.}$ The speed of a satellite in a circular orbit around a body is given by $v = \sqrt{GM_{\text{body}}/r}$, where r is the distance from the satellite to the center of the body. So for this satellite,

$$v = \sqrt{G\frac{M_{\text{body}}}{r}} = \sqrt{G\frac{M_{\text{Earth}}}{R_{\text{Earth}} + 3.6\times10^6\,\text{m}}} = \sqrt{\left(6.67\times10^{-11}\,\text{N}\bullet\text{m}^2/\text{kg}^2\right)\frac{\left(5.97\times10^{24}\,\text{kg}\right)}{\left(9.98\times10^6\,\text{m}\right)}}$$

$$= \boxed{6.32\times10^3\,\text{m/s}}$$

44. The shuttle must be moving at "orbit speed" in order for the satellite to remain in the orbit when released. The speed of a satellite in circular orbit around the Earth is given by

$$v = \sqrt{G\frac{M_{Earth}}{r}} = \sqrt{G\frac{M_{Earth}}{\left(R_{Earth} + 650 \text{ km}\right)}} = \sqrt{\left(6.67 \times 10^{-11} \text{ N} \cdot \text{m}^2 / \text{kg}^2\right) \frac{\left(5.97 \times 10^{24} \text{ kg}\right)}{\left(6.38 \times 10^6 \text{ m} + 6.5 \times 10^5 \text{ m}\right)}}$$

$$= \boxed{7.53 \times 10^3 \text{ m/s}}$$

45. The centripetal acceleration will simulate gravity. Thus $v^2 / r = 0.60g \rightarrow v = \sqrt{0.60gr}$. Also for a rotating object, the speed is given by $v = 2\pi r / T$. Equate the two expressions for the speed and solve for the period.

$$v = \sqrt{0.60gr} = \frac{2\pi r}{T} \rightarrow T = \frac{2\pi r}{\sqrt{0.60gr}} = \frac{2\pi \left(16 \text{ m}\right)}{\sqrt{\left(0.60\right)\left(9.8 \text{ m/s}^2\right)\left(16 \text{ m}\right)}} = \boxed{10 \text{ sec}}$$

46. The speed of an object in an orbit of radius r around the Earth is given by $v = \sqrt{G M_{Earth} / r}$, and is also given by $v = 2\pi r / T$, where T is the period of the object in orbit. Equate the two expressions for the speed and solve for T. Also, for a "near-Earth" orbit, $r = R_{Earth}$.

$$\sqrt{G\frac{M_{Earth}}{r}} = \frac{2\pi r}{T} \rightarrow T = 2\pi\sqrt{\frac{r^3}{GM_{Earth}}}$$

$$T = 2\pi\sqrt{\frac{R_{Earth}^3}{GM_{Earth}}} = 2\pi\sqrt{\frac{\left(6.38 \times 10^6 \text{ m}\right)^3}{\left(6.67 \times 10^{-11} \text{ N} \cdot \text{m}^2 / \text{kg}^2\right)\left(5.98 \times 10^{24} \text{ m}\right)}} = \boxed{5070 \text{ s} \sim 84 \text{ min}}$$

$\boxed{\text{No}}$, the result does not depend on the mass of the satellite.

47. At the top of Mt. Everest (elevation 8848 meters), the distance of the orbit from the center of the Earth would be $r = R_{Earth} + 8848 \text{ m} = 6.38 \times 10^6 \text{ m} + 8848 \text{ m}$. The orbit speed is given by

$$v = \sqrt{G\frac{M_{Earth}}{r}} = \sqrt{\left(6.67 \times 10^{-11} \text{ N} \cdot \text{m}^2 / \text{kg}^2\right) \frac{\left(5.98 \times 10^{24} \text{ m}\right)}{\left(6.38 \times 10^6 \text{ m} + 8848 \text{ m}\right)}} = \boxed{7.90 \times 10^3 \text{ m/s}}.$$

A comment – a launch would have some initial orbit speed from the fact that the Earth is rotating to the east. That is why most space launches are to the east.

48. The speed of an object in an orbit of radius r around the Moon is given by $v = \sqrt{G M_{Moon} / r}$, and is also given by $v = 2\pi r / T$, where T is the period of the object in orbit. Equate the two expressions for the speed and solve for T.

$$\sqrt{G M_{Moon} / r} = 2\pi r / T \rightarrow$$

$$T = 2\pi\sqrt{\frac{r^3}{GM_{Moon}}} = 2\pi\sqrt{\frac{\left(R_{Moon} + 100 \text{ km}\right)^3}{GM_{Moon}}} = 2\pi\sqrt{\frac{\left(1.74 \times 10^6 \text{ m} + 1.0 \times 10^5 \text{ m}\right)^3}{\left(6.67 \times 10^{-11} \text{ N} \cdot \text{m}^2 / \text{kg}^2\right)\left(7.35 \times 10^{22} \text{ kg}\right)}}$$

$$= \boxed{7.08 \times 10^3 \text{ s} \left(\sim 2 \text{ h}\right)}$$

49. The speed of an object in an orbit of radius r around a planet is given by $v = \sqrt{GM_{planet}/r}$, and is also given by $v = 2\pi r/T$, where T is the period of the object in orbit. Equate the two expressions for the speed and solve for T.

$$\sqrt{G\frac{M_{Planet}}{r}} = \frac{2\pi r}{T} \quad \rightarrow \quad T = 2\pi \sqrt{\frac{r^3}{GM_{Planet}}}$$

For this problem, the inner orbit is at $r_{inner} = 7.3 \times 10^7 \, \text{m}$, and the outer orbit is at $r_{inner} = 1.7 \times 10^8 \, \text{m}$. Use these values to calculate the periods.

$$T_{inner} = 2\pi \sqrt{\frac{\left(7.3 \times 10^7 \, \text{m}\right)^3}{\left(6.67 \times 10^{-11} \, \text{N} \cdot \text{m}^2/\text{kg}^2\right)\left(5.7 \times 10^{26} \, \text{kg}\right)}} = \boxed{2.0 \times 10^4 \, \text{s}}$$

$$T_{outer} = 2\pi \sqrt{\frac{\left(1.7 \times 10^8 \, \text{m}\right)^3}{\left(6.67 \times 10^{-11} \, \text{N} \cdot \text{m}^2/\text{kg}^2\right)\left(5.7 \times 10^{26} \, \text{kg}\right)}} = \boxed{7.1 \times 10^4 \, \text{s}}$$

Saturn's rotation period (day) is 10 hr 39 min which is about $3.8 \times 10^4 \, \text{sec}$. Thus the inner ring will appear to move across the sky "faster" than the Sun (about twice per Saturn day), while the outer ring will appear to move across the sky "slower" than the Sun (about once every two Saturn days).

50. The apparent weight is the normal force on the passenger. For a person at rest, the normal force is equal to the actual weight. If there is acceleration in the vertical direction, either up or down, then the normal force (and hence the apparent weight) will be different than the actual weight. The speed of the Ferris wheel is $v = 2\pi r/T = 2\pi \left(12.0 \, \text{m}\right)/15.5 \, \text{s} = 4.86 \, \text{m/s}$.

(a) At the top, consider the free-body diagram shown. We assume the passengers are right-side up, so that the normal force of the Ferris wheel seat is upward. The net force must point to the center of the circle, so write Newton's 2nd law with downward as the positive direction. The acceleration is centripetal since the passengers are moving in a circle.

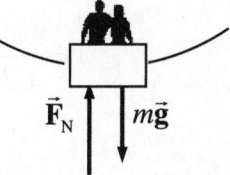

$$\sum F = F_R = mg - F_N = ma = mv^2/r \quad \rightarrow \quad F_N = mg - mv^2/r$$

The ratio of apparent weight to real weight is given by

$$\frac{mg - mv^2/r}{mg} = \frac{g - v^2/r}{g} = 1 - \frac{v^2}{rg} = 1 - \frac{\left(4.86 \, \text{m/s}\right)^2}{\left(12.0 \, \text{m}\right)\left(9.80 \, \text{m/s}^2\right)} = \boxed{0.799}$$

(b) At the bottom, consider the free-body diagram shown. We assume the passengers are right-side up, so that the normal force of the Ferris wheel seat is upward. The net force must point to the center of the circle, so write Newton's 2nd law with upward as the positive direction. The acceleration is centripetal since the passengers are moving in a circle.

$$\sum F = F_R = F_N - mg = ma = mv^2/r \quad \rightarrow \quad F_N = mg + mv^2/r$$

The ratio of apparent weight to real weight is given by

$$\frac{mg + mv^2/r}{mg} = 1 + \frac{v^2}{rg} = \boxed{1.201}$$

51. Consider the free-body diagram for the astronaut in the space vehicle. The Moon is below the astronaut in the figure. We assume that the astronaut is touching the inside of the space vehicle, or in a seat, or strapped in somehow, and so a force will be exerted on the astronaut by the spacecraft. That force has been labeled $\vec{F}_N$. The magnitude of that force is the apparent weight of the astronaut. Take down as the positive direction.

(*a*) If the spacecraft is moving with a constant velocity, then the acceleration of the astronaut must be 0, and so the net force on the astronaut is 0.

$$\sum F = mg - F_N = 0 \;\rightarrow$$

$$F_N = mg = G\frac{mM_{\text{Moon}}}{r^2} = \left(6.67\times10^{-11}\ \text{N}\bullet\text{m}^2/\text{kg}^2\right)\frac{\left(75\ \text{kg}\right)\left(7.4\times10^{22}\ \text{kg}\right)}{\left(4.2\times10^{6}\ \text{m}\right)^2} = 21\ \text{N}$$

Since the value here is positive, the normal force points in the original direction as shown on the free-body diagram. The astronaut will be pushed "upward" by the floor or the seat. Thus the astronaut will perceive that he has a "weight" of $\boxed{21\ \text{N, towards the Moon}}$.

(*b*) Now the astronaut has an acceleration towards the Moon. Write Newton's 2nd law for the astronaut, with down as the positive direction.

$$\sum F = mg - F_N = ma \;\rightarrow\; F_N = mg - ma = 21\ \text{N} - \left(75\ \text{kg}\right)\left(2.9\ \text{m/s}^2\right) = -2.0\times10^{2}\ \text{N}$$

Because of the negative value, the normal force points in the opposite direction from what is shown on the free-body diagram – it is pointing towards the Moon. So perhaps the astronaut is pinned against the "ceiling" of the spacecraft, or safety belts are pulling down on the astronaut. The astronaut will perceive being "pushed downwards", and so has an upward apparent weight of $\boxed{2.0\times10^{2}\ \text{N, away from the Moon}}$.

52. Consider the motion of one of the stars. The gravitational force on the star is given by $F = G\dfrac{mm}{d^2}$, where d is the distance separating the two stars. But since the star is moving in a circle of radius $d/2$, the force on the star can be expressed as $F_R = mv^2/r = m\dfrac{v^2}{d/2}$. Equate these two force expressions, and use $v = 2\pi r/T = d\pi/T$.

$$G\frac{mm}{d^2} = m\frac{v^2}{d/2} = m\frac{\left(d\pi/T\right)^2}{d/2} \;\rightarrow$$

$$m = \frac{2\pi^2 d^3}{GT^2} = \frac{2\pi^2\left(3.6\times10^{11}\ \text{m}\right)^3}{\left(6.67\times10^{-11}\ \text{N}\bullet\text{m}^2/\text{kg}^2\right)\left[\left(5.7\ \text{y}\right)\left(3.15\times10^{7}\ \text{sec/y}\right)\right]^2} = \boxed{4.3\times10^{29}\ \text{kg}}$$

53. Consider a free-body diagram for the woman in the elevator. $\vec{F}_N$ is the force the spring scale exerts. Write Newton's 2nd law for the vertical direction, with up as positive.

$$\sum F = F_N - mg = ma \;\rightarrow\; F_N = m\left(g + a\right)$$

(*a, b*) For constant speed motion in a straight line, the acceleration is 0, and so

$$F_N = mg = \left(55\ \text{kg}\right)\left(9.8\ \text{m/s}^2\right) = \boxed{5.4\times10^{2}\ \text{N}}$$

(*c*) Here $a = +0.33g$ and so $F_N = 1.33mg = 1.33\left(55\ \text{kg}\right)\left(9.8\ \text{m/s}^2\right) = \boxed{7.2\times10^{2}\ \text{N}}$

(d) Here $a = -0.33g$ and so $F_{\text{N}} = 0.67\,mg = 0.67\left(55\text{ kg}\right)\left(9.8\,\text{m/s}^2\right) = \boxed{3.6 \times 10^2\,\text{N}}$

(e) Here $a = -g$ and so $F_{\text{N}} = \boxed{0\,\text{N}}$

54. Draw a free-body diagram of the monkey. Then write Newton's 2nd law for the vertical direction, with up as positive.

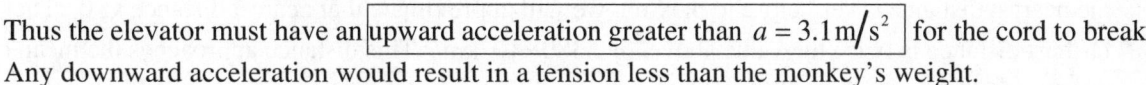

$$\sum F = F_{\text{T}} - mg = ma \;\rightarrow\; a = \frac{F_{\text{T}} - mg}{m}$$

For the maximum tension of 220 N,

$$a = \frac{220\text{ N} - \left(17.0\text{ kg}\right)\left(9.80\,\text{m/s}^2\right)}{\left(17.0\text{ kg}\right)} = 3.1\,\text{m/s}^2$$

Thus the elevator must have an $\boxed{\text{upward acceleration greater than } a = 3.1\,\text{m/s}^2}$ for the cord to break. Any downward acceleration would result in a tension less than the monkey's weight.

55. (a) The speed of an object in near-surface orbit around a planet is given by $v = \sqrt{GM/R}$, where M is the planet mass and R is the planet radius. The speed is also given by $v = 2\pi R/T$, where T is the period of the object in orbit. Equate the two expressions for the speed.

$$\sqrt{G\frac{M}{R}} = \frac{2\pi R}{T} \;\rightarrow\; G\frac{M}{R} = \frac{4\pi^2 R^2}{T^2} \;\rightarrow\; \frac{M}{R^3} = \frac{4\pi^2}{GT^2}$$

The density of a uniform spherical planet is given by $\rho = \dfrac{M}{\text{Volume}} = \dfrac{M}{\frac{4}{3}\pi R^3}$. Thus

$$\rho = \frac{3M}{4\pi R^3} = \frac{3}{4\pi}\frac{4\pi^2}{GT^2} = \frac{3\pi}{GT^2}$$

(b) For Earth,

$$\rho = \frac{3\pi}{GT^2} = \frac{3\pi}{\left(6.67 \times 10^{-11}\,\text{N} \cdot \text{m}^2/\text{kg}^2\right)\left[\left(85\text{ min}\right)\left(60\text{ s/min}\right)\right]^2} = \boxed{5.4 \times 10^3\,\text{kg/m}^3}$$

56. Use Kepler's 3rd law for objects orbiting the Earth. The following are given.

$$T_2 = \text{period of Moon} = \left(27.4\text{ day}\right)\left(\frac{86{,}400\text{ s}}{1\text{ day}}\right) = 2.367 \times 10^6\text{ sec}$$

r_2 = radius of Moon's orbit $= 3.84 \times 10^8\,\text{m}$

r_1 = radius of near-Earth orbit $= R_{\text{Earth}} = 6.38 \times 10^6\,\text{m}$

$$\left(T_1/T_2\right)^2 = \left(r_1/r_2\right)^3 \;\rightarrow$$

$$T_1 = T_2\left(r_1/r_2\right)^{3/2} = \left(2.367 \times 10^6\text{ sec}\right)\left(\frac{6.38 \times 10^6\,\text{m}}{3.84 \times 10^8\,\text{m}}\right)^{3/2} = \boxed{5.07 \times 10^3\text{ sec}}\left(\sim 84.5\text{ min}\right)$$

57. Use Kepler's 3rd law for objects orbiting the Sun.

$$\left(\frac{r_{\text{Icarus}}}{r_{\text{Earth}}}\right)^3 = \left(\frac{T_{\text{Icarus}}}{T_{\text{Earth}}}\right)^2 \;\rightarrow\; r_{\text{Icarus}} = r_{\text{Earth}}\left(\frac{T_{\text{Icarus}}}{T_{\text{Earth}}}\right)^{2/3} = \left(1.50 \times 10^{11}\,\text{m}\right)\left(\frac{410\text{ d}}{365\text{ d}}\right)^{2/3} = \boxed{1.62 \times 10^{11}\,\text{m}}$$

58. Use Kepler's 3rd law for objects orbiting the Sun.

$$\left(T_{Neptune}/T_{Earth}\right)^2 = \left(r_{Neptune}/r_{Earth}\right)^3 \rightarrow$$

$$T_{Neptune} = T_{Earth}\left(\frac{r_{Neptune}}{r_{Earth}}\right)^{3/2} = (1 \text{ year})\left(\frac{4.5 \times 10^9 \text{ km}}{1.5 \times 10^8 \text{ km}}\right)^{3/2} = \boxed{1.6 \times 10^2 \text{ years}}$$

59. Use Kepler's 3rd law to relate the orbits of Earth and Halley's comet around the Sun.

$$\left(r_{Halley}/r_{Earth}\right)^3 = \left(T_{Halley}/T_{Earth}\right)^2 \rightarrow$$

$$r_{Halley} = r_{Earth}\left(T_{Halley}/T_{Earth}\right)^{2/3} = \left(150 \times 10^6 \text{ km}\right)\left(76 \text{ y}/1 \text{ y}\right)^{2/3} = \boxed{2690 \times 10^6 \text{ km}}$$

This value is half the sum of the nearest and farthest distances of Halley's comet from the Sun. Since the nearest distance is very close to the Sun, we will approximate that nearest distance as 0. Then the farthest distance is twice the value above, or $5380 \times 10^6 \text{ km}$. This distance approaches the mean orbit distance of Pluto, which is $5900 \times 10^6 \text{ km}$. $\boxed{\text{It is still in the Solar System, nearest to Pluto's orbit.}}$

60. There are two expressions for the velocity of an object in circular motion around a mass M:
$v = \sqrt{GM/r}$ and $v = 2\pi r/T$. Equate the two expressions and solve for T.

$$\sqrt{GM/r} = 2\pi r/T \rightarrow$$

$$T = 2\pi\sqrt{\frac{r^3}{GM}} = 2\pi\sqrt{\frac{\left(3 \times 10^4 \text{ly}\right)\frac{\left(3 \times 10^8 \text{ m/s}\right)\left(3.16 \times 10^7 \text{ sec}\right)}{1 \text{ ly}}\right)^3}{\left(6.67 \times 10^{-11} \text{ N} \cdot \text{m}^2/\text{kg}^2\right)\left(4 \times 10^{41} \text{ kg}\right)}} = 5.8 \times 10^{15} \text{ s} = 1.8 \times 10^8 \text{ y}$$

$$\approx \boxed{2 \times 10^8 \text{ y}}$$

61. (a) The relationship between satellite period T, mean satellite distance r, and planet mass M can be derived from the two expressions for satellite speed: $v = \sqrt{GM/r}$ and $v = 2\pi r/T$. Equate the two expressions and solve for M.

$$\sqrt{GM/r} = 2\pi r/T \rightarrow M = \frac{4\pi^2 r^3}{GT^2}$$

Substitute the values for Io to get the mass of Jupiter.

$$M_{\substack{Jupiter- \\ Io}} = \frac{4\pi^2\left(4.22 \times 10^8 \text{ m}\right)^3}{\left(6.67 \times 10^{-11} \text{ N} \cdot \text{m}^2/\text{kg}^2\right)\left(1.77\text{d} \times \frac{24 \text{ h}}{1 \text{ d}} \times \frac{3600 \text{ s}}{1 \text{ h}}\right)^2} = \boxed{1.90 \times 10^{27} \text{ kg}} .$$

(b) For the other moons:

$$M_{\substack{Jupiter- \\ Europa}} = \frac{4\pi^2\left(6.71 \times 10^8 \text{ m}\right)^3}{\left(6.67 \times 10^{-11} \text{ N} \cdot \text{m}^2/\text{kg}^2\right)\left(3.55 \times 24 \times 3600 \text{ s}\right)^2} = \boxed{1.90 \times 10^{27} \text{ kg}}$$

$$M_{\substack{Jupiter- \\ Ganymede}} = \frac{4\pi^2\left(1.07 \times 10^9 \text{ m}\right)^3}{\left(6.67 \times 10^{-11} \text{ N} \cdot \text{m}^2/\text{kg}^2\right)\left(7.16 \times 24 \times 3600 \text{ s}\right)^2} = \boxed{1.89 \times 10^{27} \text{ kg}}$$

$$M_{\text{Jupiter-}\atop\text{Callisto}} = \frac{4\pi^2 \left(1.883\times10^9\,\text{m}\right)^3}{\left(6.67\times10^{-11}\,\text{N}\bullet\text{m}^2/\text{kg}^2\right)\left(16.7\times24\times3600\,\text{s}\right)^2} = \boxed{1.90\times10^{27}\,\text{kg}}$$

$\boxed{\text{Yes}}$, the results are consistent – only about 0.5% difference between them.

62. Knowing the period of the Moon and the distance to the Moon, we can calculate the speed of the Moon by $v = 2\pi r/T$. But the speed can also be calculated for any Earth satellite by $v = \sqrt{GM_{\text{Earth}}/r}$. Equate the two expressions for the speed, and solve for the mass of the Earth.

$$\sqrt{GM_{\text{Earth}}/r} = 2\pi r/T \rightarrow$$

$$M_{\text{Earth}} = \frac{4\pi^2 r^3}{GT^2} = \frac{4\pi^2 \left(3.84\times10^8\,\text{m}\right)^3}{\left(6.67\times10^{-11}\,\text{N}\bullet\text{m}^2/\text{kg}^2\right)\left[\left(27.4\,\text{d}\right)\left(86,400\,\text{s/d}\right)\right]^2} = \boxed{5.98\times10^{24}\,\text{kg}}$$

63. Use Kepler's 3rd law to find the radius of each moon of Jupiter, using Io's data for r_2 and T_2.

$$\left(r_1/r_2\right)^3 = \left(T_1/T_2\right)^2 \rightarrow r_1 = r_2 \left(T_1/T_2\right)^{2/3}$$

$$r_{\text{Europa}} = r_{\text{Io}} \left(T_{\text{Europa}}/T_{\text{Io}}\right)^{2/3} = \left(422\times10^3\,\text{km}\right)\left(3.55\,\text{d}/1.77\,\text{d}\right)^{2/3} = \boxed{671\times10^3\,\text{km}}$$

$$r_{\text{Ganymede}} = \left(422\times10^3\,\text{km}\right)\left(7.16\,\text{d}/1.77\,\text{d}\right)^{2/3} = \boxed{1070\times10^3\,\text{km}}$$

$$r_{\text{Callisto}} = \left(422\times10^3\,\text{km}\right)\left(16.7\,\text{d}/1.77\,\text{d}\right)^{2/3} = \boxed{1880\times10^3\,\text{km}}$$

The agreement with the data in the table is excellent.

64. (*a*) Use Kepler's 3rd law to relate the Earth and the hypothetical planet in their orbits around the Sun.

$$\left(T_{\text{planet}}/T_{\text{Earth}}\right)^2 = \left(r_{\text{planet}}/r_{\text{Earth}}\right)^3 \rightarrow T_{\text{planet}} = T_{\text{Earth}}\left(r_{\text{planet}}/r_{\text{Earth}}\right)^{3/2} = \left(1\,\text{y}\right)\left(3/1\right)^{3/2} \approx \boxed{5\,\text{y}}$$

(*b*) No mass data can be calculated from this relationship, because the relationship is mass-independent. Any object at the orbit radius of 3 times the Earth's orbit radius would have a period of 5.2 years, regardless of its mass.

65. If the ring is to produce an apparent gravity equivalent to that of Earth, then the normal force of the ring on objects must be given by $F_{\text{N}} = mg$. The Sun will also exert a force on objects on the ring. See the free-body diagram.

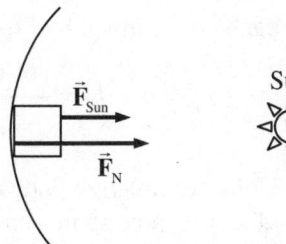

Write Newton's 2nd law for the object, with the fact that the acceleration is centripetal.

$$\sum F = F_{\text{R}} = F_{\text{Sun}} + F_{\text{N}} = mv^2/r$$

Substitute in the relationships that $v = 2\pi r/T$, $F_{\text{N}} = mg$, and $F_{\text{Sun}} = G\dfrac{M_{\text{Sun}}m}{r^2}$, and solve for the

period of the rotation.

$$F_{\text{Sun}} + F_{\text{N}} = mv^2/r \rightarrow G\frac{M_{\text{Sun}}m}{r^2} + mg = \frac{4\pi^2 mr}{T^2} \rightarrow G\frac{M_{\text{Sun}}}{r^2} + g = \frac{4\pi^2 r}{T^2}$$

$$T = \sqrt{\frac{4\pi^2 r}{G\frac{M_{Sun}}{r^2}+g}} = \sqrt{\frac{4\pi^2\left(1.50\times10^{11}\,\text{m}\right)}{\left(6.67\times10^{-11}\,\text{N}\cdot\text{m}^2/\text{kg}^2\right)\dfrac{\left(1.99\times10^{30}\,\text{kg}\right)}{\left(1.50\times10^{11}\,\text{m}\right)^2}+9.8\,\text{m/s}^2}} = 7.8\times10^5\,\text{s} = \boxed{9.0\,\text{d}}$$

The force of the Sun is only about 1/1600 the size of the normal force. The force of the Sun could have been ignored in the calculation with no effect in the result as given above.

66. A free-body diagram of Tarzan at the bottom of his swing is shown. The upward tension force is created by his pulling down on the vine. Write Newton's 2nd law in the vertical direction. Since he is moving in a circle, his acceleration will be centripetal, and points upward when he is at the bottom.

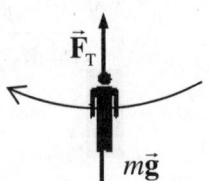

$$\sum F = F_T - mg = ma = mv^2/r \;\rightarrow\; v = \sqrt{\frac{\left(F_T - mg\right)r}{m}}$$

The maximum speed will be obtained with the maximum tension.

$$v_{max} = \sqrt{\frac{\left(\vec{F}_{T\,max} - mg\right)r}{m}} = \sqrt{\frac{\left(1400\,\text{N} - \left(80\,\text{kg}\right)\left(9.8\,\text{m/s}^2\right)\right)5.5\,\text{m}}{80\,\text{kg}}} = \boxed{6.5\,\text{m/s}}$$

67. The acceleration due to the Earth's gravity at a location at or above the surface is given by $g = GM_{Earth}/r^2$, where r is the distance from the center of the Earth to the location in question. Find the location where $g = \frac{1}{2}g_{surface}$.

$$\frac{GM_{Earth}}{r^2} = \frac{1}{2}\frac{GM_{Earth}}{R_{Earth}^2} \;\rightarrow\; r^2 = 2R_{Earth}^2 \;\rightarrow\; r = \sqrt{2}R_{Earth}$$

The distance above the Earth's surface is

$$r - R_{Earth} = \left(\sqrt{2}-1\right)R_{Earth} = \left(\sqrt{2}-1\right)\left(6.38\times10^6\,\text{m}\right) = \boxed{2.64\times10^6\,\text{m}}\,.$$

68. The radius of either skater's motion is 0.80 m, and the period is 2.5 sec. Thus their speed is given by $v = 2\pi r/T = \dfrac{2\pi\left(0.80\,\text{m}\right)}{2.5\,\text{s}} = 2.0\,\text{m/s}$. Since each skater is moving in a circle, the net radial force on each one is given by Eq. 5-3.

$$F_R = mv^2/r = \frac{\left(60.0\,\text{kg}\right)\left(2.0\,\text{m/s}\right)^2}{0.80\,\text{m}} = \boxed{3.0\times10^2\,\text{N}}\,.$$

69. Consider this free-body diagram for an object at the equator. Since the object is moving in a circular path, there must be a net force on the object, pointing towards the center of the Earth, producing a centripetal acceleration. Write Newton's 2nd law, with the inward direction positive.

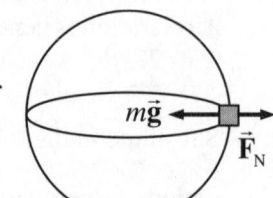

$$\sum F_R = mg - F_N = mv^2/R_{Earth} \;\rightarrow\; F_N = m\left(g - v^2/R_{Earth}\right)$$

We see that the normal force, which without the rotation would be the "expected" value of mg, has now been reduced. This effect can be described as saying that the acceleration due to gravity has been reduced, by an amount equal to v^2/R_{Earth}. To calculate this "change" in g, use $v = 2\pi R_{Earth}/T$ to get the following.

$$\Delta g = -v^2/R_{\text{Earth}} = -\frac{4\pi^2 R_{\text{Earth}}}{T^2} = -\frac{4\pi^2 \left(6.38 \times 10^6 \,\text{m}\right)}{\left[(1 \,\text{d})(86,400 \,\text{s/1 d})\right]^2} = -0.03374 \,\text{m/s}^2$$

This is a reduction of $-0.03374 \,\text{m/s}^2 \times \dfrac{1\, g}{9.80 \,\text{m/s}^2} = \boxed{-3.44 \times 10^{-3}\, g}$.

70. For the forces to balance means that the gravitational force on the spacecraft due to the Earth must be the same as that due to the Moon. Write the gravitational forces on the spacecraft, equate them, and solve for the distance x.

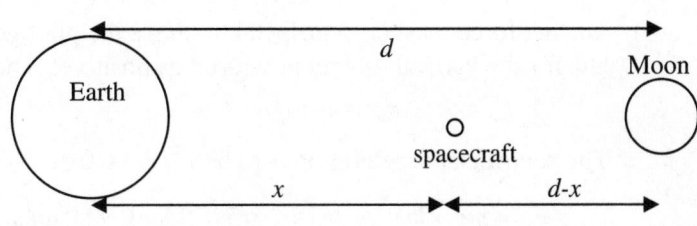

$$F_{\substack{\text{Earth-}\\\text{spacecraft}}} = G\frac{M_{\text{Earth}} m_{\text{spacecraft}}}{x^2} \quad ; \quad F_{\substack{\text{Moon}\\\text{spacecraft}}} = G\frac{M_{\text{Moon}} m_{\text{spacecraft}}}{(d-x)^2}$$

$$G\frac{M_{\text{Earth}} m_{\text{spacecraft}}}{x^2} = G\frac{M_{\text{Moon}} m_{\text{spacecraft}}}{(d-x)^2} \rightarrow \frac{x^2}{M_{\text{Earth}}} = \frac{(d-x)^2}{M_{\text{Moon}}} \rightarrow \frac{x}{\sqrt{M_{\text{Earth}}}} = \frac{d-x}{\sqrt{M_{\text{Moon}}}}$$

$$x = d\frac{\sqrt{M_{\text{Earth}}}}{\left(\sqrt{M_{\text{Moon}}} + \sqrt{M_{\text{Earth}}}\right)} = \left(3.84 \times 10^8 \,\text{m}\right)\frac{\sqrt{5.97 \times 10^{24} \,\text{kg}}}{\left(\sqrt{7.35 \times 10^{22} \,\text{kg}} + \sqrt{5.97 \times 10^{24} \,\text{kg}}\right)} = \boxed{3.46 \times 10^8 \,\text{m}}$$

This is only about 22 Moon radii away from the Moon.

71. Consider a free-body diagram of yourself in the elevator. $\vec{\mathbf{F}}_N$ is the force of the scale pushing up on you, and reads the normal force. Since the scale reads 82 kg, if it were calibrated in Newtons, the normal force would be $F_N = (82 \,\text{kg})(9.8 \,\text{m/s}^2) = 804 \,\text{N}$. Write Newton's 2nd law in the vertical direction, with upward as positive.

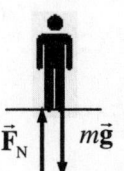

$$\sum F = F_N - mg = ma \rightarrow a = \frac{F_N - mg}{m} = \frac{804 \,\text{N} - (65 \,\text{kg})(9.8 \,\text{m/s}^2)}{65 \,\text{kg}} = \boxed{2.6 \,\text{m/s}^2 \text{ upward}}$$

Since the acceleration is positive, the acceleration is upward.

72. To experience a gravity-type force, objects must be on the inside of the outer wall of the tube, so that there can be a centripetal force to move the objects in a circle. See the free-body diagram for an object on the inside of the outer wall, and a portion of the tube. The normal force of contact between the object and the wall must be maintaining the circular motion. Write Newton's 2nd law for the radial direction.

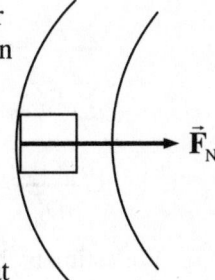

$$\sum F_R = F_N = ma = mv^2/r$$

If this is to have the same effect as Earth gravity, then we must also have that $F_N = mg$. Equate the two expressions for normal force and solve for the speed.

$$F_N = mv^2/r = mg \rightarrow v = \sqrt{gr} = \sqrt{\left(9.8 \,\text{m/s}^2\right)(550 \,\text{m})} = 73 \,\text{m/s}$$

$$(73 \,\text{m/s})\left(\frac{1 \,\text{rev}}{2\pi (550 \,\text{m})}\right)\left(\frac{86,400 \,\text{s}}{1 \,\text{d}}\right) = 1825 \,\text{rev/d} \approx \boxed{1.8 \times 10^3 \,\text{rev/d}}$$

73. (*a*) See the free-body diagram for the pilot in the jet at the bottom of the
loop. For $a_R = v^2/r = 6g$,

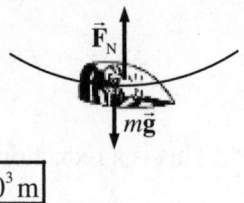

$$v^2/r = 6.0g \quad \rightarrow \quad r = \frac{v^2}{6.0g} = \frac{\left[(1300 \,\text{km/h}) \left(\dfrac{1 \,\text{m/s}}{3.6 \,\text{km/h}} \right) \right]^2}{6.0(9.8 \,\text{m/s}^2)} = \boxed{2.2 \times 10^3 \,\text{m}}$$

(*b*) The net force must be centripetal, to make the pilot go in a circle. Write Newton's 2nd
law for the vertical direction, with up as positive. The normal force is the apparent weight.

$$\sum F_R = F_N - mg = mv^2/r$$

The centripetal acceleration is to be $v^2/r = 6.0g$.

$$F_N = mg + mv^2/r = 7mg = 7(78 \,\text{kg})(9.80 \,\text{m/s}^2) = 5350 \,\text{N} = \boxed{5.4 \times 10^3 \,\text{N}}$$

(*c*) See the free-body diagram for the pilot at the top of the loop. Notice that
the normal force is down, because the pilot is upside down. Write Newton's
2nd law in the vertical direction, with down as positive.

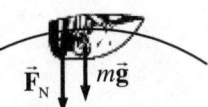

$$\sum F_R = F_N + mg = mv^2/r = 6mg \quad \rightarrow \quad F_N = 5mg = \boxed{3.8 \times 10^3 \,\text{N}}$$

74. The force of gravity on an object at the surface is given by $F_{\text{grav}} = mg_P$. But by Newton's law of
Universal Gravitation, the force of gravity on an object at the surface is given by $F_{\text{grav}} = G\dfrac{mM_{\text{planet}}}{r^2}$.
Equate the expressions for the force of gravity and solve for the mass of the planet.

$$G\frac{mM_{\text{planet}}}{r^2} = mg_P \quad \rightarrow \quad \boxed{M_{\text{planet}} = \frac{r^2 g_P}{G}}.$$

75. (*a*) See the free-body diagram for the plumb bob. The attractive gravitational force
on the plumb bob is $F_M = G\dfrac{mm_M}{D_M^2}$. Since the bob is not accelerating, the net
force in any direction will be zero. Write the net force for both vertical and
horizontal directions. Use $g = G\dfrac{M_{\text{Earth}}}{R_{\text{Earth}}^2}$

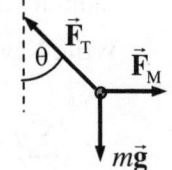

$$\sum F_{\text{vertical}} = F_T \cos\theta - mg = 0 \quad \rightarrow \quad F_T = \frac{mg}{\cos\theta}$$

$$\sum F_{\text{horizontal}} = F_M - F_T \sin\theta = 0 \quad \rightarrow \quad F_M = F_T \sin\theta = mg \tan\theta$$

$$G\frac{mm_M}{D_M^2} = mg \tan\theta \quad \rightarrow \quad \theta = \tan^{-1} G\frac{m_M}{gD_M^2} = \boxed{\tan^{-1}\frac{m_M R_{\text{Earth}}^2}{M_{\text{Earth}} D_M^2}}$$

(*b*) We estimate the mass of Mt. Everest by taking its volume times its mass density. If we
approximate Mt. Everest as a cone with the same size diameter as height, then its volume is
$V = \frac{1}{3}\pi r^2 h = \frac{1}{3}\pi (2000 \,\text{m})^2 (4000 \,\text{m}) = 1.7 \times 10^{10} \,\text{m}^3$. The density is $\rho = 3 \times 10^3 \,\text{kg/m}^3$. Find
the mass by multiplying the volume times the density.

$$M = \rho V = (3 \times 10^3 \,\text{kg/m}^3)(1.7 \times 10^{10} \,\text{m}^3) = \boxed{5 \times 10^{13} \,\text{kg}}$$

(c)   With $D = 5000$ m, use the relationship derived in part (a).

$$\theta = \tan^{-1}\frac{M_M R_{Earth}^2}{M_{Earth} D_M^2} = \tan^{-1}\frac{\left(5\times10^{13}\,\text{kg}\right)\left(6.38\times10^6\,\text{m}\right)^2}{\left(5.97\times10^{24}\,\text{kg}\right)\left(5000\,\text{m}\right)^2} = \boxed{8\times10^{-4}\,\text{degrees}}$$

76.   Since the curve is designed for a speed of 95 km/h, traveling at that speed would mean no friction is needed to round the curve. From Example 5-7 in the textbook, the no-friction banking angle is given by

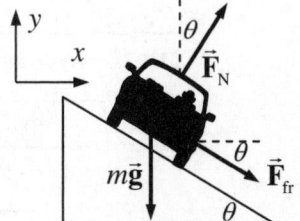

$$\theta = \tan^{-1}\frac{v^2}{rg} = \tan^{-1}\frac{\left[\left(95\,\text{km/h}\right)\left(\dfrac{1\,\text{m/s}}{3.6\,\text{km/h}}\right)\right]^2}{\left(67\,\text{m}\right)\left(9.8\,\text{m/s}^2\right)} = 46.68°$$

Driving at a higher speed with the same radius means that more centripetal force will be required than is present by the normal force alone. That extra centripetal force will be supplied by a force of static friction, downward along the incline, as shown in the first free-body diagram for the car on the incline. Write Newton's 2nd law in both the x and y directions. The car will have no acceleration in the y direction, and centripetal acceleration in the x direction. We also assume that the car is on the verge of skidding, so that the static frictional force has its maximum value of $F_{fr} = \mu_s F_N$.

$$\sum F_y = F_N\cos\theta - mg - F_{fr}\sin\theta = 0 \quad\rightarrow\quad F_N\cos\theta - \mu_s F_N\sin\theta = mg \quad\rightarrow$$

$$F_N = \frac{mg}{\left(\cos\theta - \mu_s\sin\theta\right)}$$

$$\sum F_x = F_N\sin\theta + F_{fr}\cos\theta = mv^2/r \quad\rightarrow\quad F_N\sin\theta + \mu_s F_N\cos\theta = mv^2/r \quad\rightarrow$$

$$F_N = \frac{mv^2/r}{\left(\sin\theta + \mu_s\cos\theta\right)}$$

Equate the two expressions for the normal force, and solve for the speed.

$$\frac{mv^2/r}{\left(\sin\theta + \mu_s\cos\theta\right)} = \frac{mg}{\left(\cos\theta - \mu_s\sin\theta\right)} \quad\rightarrow$$

$$v = \sqrt{rg\frac{\left(\sin\theta + \mu_s\cos\theta\right)}{\left(\cos\theta - \mu_s\sin\theta\right)}} = \sqrt{\left(67\,\text{m}\right)\left(9.8\,\text{m/s}^2\right)\frac{\left(\sin 46.68° + 0.30\cos 46.68°\right)}{\left(\cos 46.68° - 0.30\sin 46.68°\right)}} = 36\,\text{m/s}$$

Now for the slowest possible speed. Driving at a slower speed with the same radius means that less centripetal force will be required than that supplied by the normal force. That decline in centripetal force will be supplied by a force of static friction, upward along the incline, as shown in the second free-body diagram for the car on the incline. Write Newton's 2nd law in both the x and y directions. The car will have no acceleration in the y direction, and centripetal acceleration in the x direction. We also assume that the car is on the verge of skidding, so that the static frictional force has its maximum value of $F_{fr} = \mu_s F_N$.

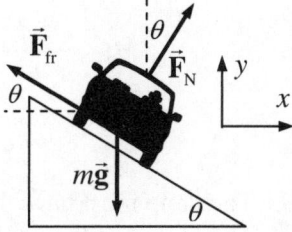

$$\sum F_y = F_N\cos\theta - mg + F_{fr}\sin\theta = 0 \quad\rightarrow$$

$$F_N\cos\theta + \mu_s F_N\sin\theta = mg \quad\rightarrow\quad F_N = \frac{mg}{\left(\cos\theta + \mu_s\sin\theta\right)}$$

$$\sum F_x = F_N \sin\theta - F_{fr}\cos\theta = mv^2/r \quad \rightarrow \quad F_N \sin\theta - \mu_s F_N \cos\theta = mv^2/r \quad \rightarrow$$

$$F_N = \frac{mv^2/r}{(\sin\theta - \mu_s\cos\theta)}$$

Equate the two expressions for the normal force, and solve for the speed.

$$\frac{mv^2/r}{(\sin\theta - \mu_s\cos\theta)} = \frac{mg}{(\cos\theta + \mu_s\sin\theta)} \quad \rightarrow$$

$$v = \sqrt{rg\frac{(\sin\theta - \mu_s\cos\theta)}{(\cos\theta + \mu_s\sin\theta)}} = \sqrt{(67\text{ m})(9.8\text{ m/s}^2)\frac{(\sin 46.67° - 0.30\cos 46.67°)}{(\cos 46.67° + 0.30\sin 46.67°)}} = 19\text{ m/s}$$

Thus the range is $\boxed{19\text{ m/s} \le v \le 36\text{ m/s}}$, which is $\boxed{68\text{ km/h} \le v \le 130\text{ km/h}}$.

77. For an object to be apparently weightless would mean that the object would have a centripetal acceleration equal to *g*. This is really the same as asking what the orbital period would be for an object orbiting the Earth with an orbital radius equal to the Earth's radius. To calculate, use
$g = a_C = v^2/R_{Earth}$, along with $v = 2\pi R_{Earth}/T$, and solve for *T*.

$$g = \frac{v^2}{R_{Earth}} = \frac{4\pi^2 R_{Earth}}{T^2} \quad \rightarrow \quad T = 2\pi\sqrt{\frac{R_{Earth}}{g}} = 2\pi\sqrt{\frac{6.38\times10^6\text{ m}}{9.80\text{ m/s}^2}} = \boxed{5.07\times10^3\text{ s}}\,(\sim 84.5\text{ min})$$

78. See the diagram for the two stars.
    (a) The two stars don't crash into each other because of their circular motion. The force on them is centripetal, and maintains their circular motion. Another way to consider it is that the stars have a velocity, and the gravity force causes CHANGE in velocity, not actual velocity. If the stars were somehow brought to rest and then released under the influence of their mutual gravity, they would crash into each other.

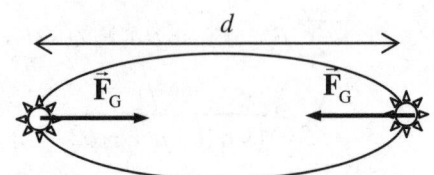

(b) Set the gravity force on one of the stars equal to the centripetal force, using the relationship that $v = 2\pi r/T = \pi d/T$, and solve for the mass.

$$F_G = G\frac{M^2}{d^2} = F_R = M\frac{v^2}{d/2} = M\frac{2(\pi d/T)^2}{d} = \frac{2\pi^2 Md}{T^2} \quad \rightarrow \quad G\frac{M^2}{d^2} = \frac{2\pi^2 Md}{T^2} \quad \rightarrow$$

$$M = \frac{2\pi^2 d^3}{GT^2} = \frac{2\pi^2\left(8.0\times10^{10}\text{ m}\right)^3}{\left(6.67\times10^{-11}\text{ N}\bullet\text{m}^2/\text{kg}^2\right)\left(12.6\text{ y}\times\dfrac{3.15\times10^7\text{ s}}{1\text{ y}}\right)^2} = \boxed{9.6\times10^{26}\text{ kg}}$$

79. The lamp must have the same speed and acceleration as the train. The forces on the lamp as the train rounds the corner are shown in the free-body diagram included. The tension in the suspending cord must not only hold the lamp up, but also provide the centripetal force needed to make the lamp move in a circle. Write Newton's 2nd law for the vertical direction, noting that the lamp is not accelerating vertically.

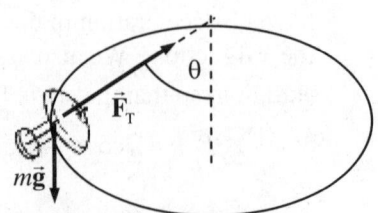

$$\sum F_y = F_T \cos\theta - mg = 0 \quad \rightarrow \quad F_T = \frac{mg}{\cos\theta}$$

The force moving the lamp in a circle is the horizontal portion of the tension. Write Newton's 2nd law for that radial motion.

$$\sum F_R = F_T \sin\theta = ma_R = mv^2/r$$

Substitute the expression for the tension from the first equation into the second equation, and solve for the speed.

$$F_T \sin\theta = \frac{mg}{\cos\theta}\sin\theta = mg\tan\theta = mv^2/r \quad \rightarrow$$

$$v = \sqrt{rg\tan\theta} = \sqrt{(235\text{ m})(9.80\text{ m/s}^2)\tan 17.5°} = \boxed{26.9\text{ m/s}}$$

80. For a body on the equator, the net motion is circular. Consider the free-body diagram as shown. F_N is the normal force, which is the apparent weight. The net force must point to the center of the circle for the object to be moving in a circular path at constant speed. Write Newton's 2nd law with the inward direction as positive.

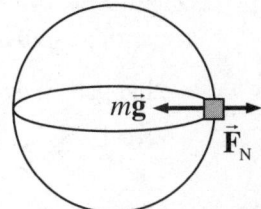

$$\sum F_R = mg_{\text{Jupiter}} - F_N = mv^2/R_{\text{Jupiter}} \quad \rightarrow$$

$$F_N = m\left(g_{\text{Jupiter}} - v^2/R_{\text{Jupiter}}\right) = m\left(G\frac{M_{\text{Jupiter}}}{R_{\text{Jupiter}}^2} - \frac{v^2}{R_{\text{Jupiter}}}\right)$$

Use the fact that for a rotating object, $v = 2\pi r/T$.

$$F_N = m\left(G\frac{M_{\text{Jupiter}}}{R_{\text{Jupiter}}^2} - \frac{4\pi^2 R_{\text{Jupiter}}}{T_{\text{Jupiter}}^2}\right)$$

Thus the perceived acceleration of the object on the surface of Jupiter is

$$G\frac{M_{\text{Jupiter}}}{R_{\text{Jupiter}}^2} - \frac{4\pi^2 R_{\text{Jupiter}}}{T_{\text{Jupiter}}^2} = \left(6.67\times10^{-11}\text{ N}\bullet\text{m}^2/\text{kg}^2\right)\frac{\left(1.9\times10^{27}\text{ kg}\right)}{\left(7.1\times10^7\text{ m}\right)^2} - \frac{4\pi^2\left(7.1\times10^7\text{ m}\right)}{\left[\left(595\text{ min}\right)\left(\frac{60\text{ s}}{1\text{ min}}\right)\right]^2}$$

$$= 22.94\text{ m/s}^2\left(\frac{1\text{ }g}{9.8\text{ m/s}^2}\right) = \boxed{2.3\text{ }g\text{'s}}$$

Thus you would not be crushed at all. You would certainly feel "heavy", but not at all crushed.

81. The speed of an orbiting object is given by $v = \sqrt{GM/r}$, where r is the radius of the orbit, and M is the mass around which the object is orbiting. Solve the equation for M.

$$v = \sqrt{GM/r} \quad \rightarrow \quad M = \frac{rv^2}{G} = \frac{\left(5.7\times10^{17}\text{ m}\right)\left(7.8\times10^5\text{ m/s}\right)^2}{\left(6.67\times10^{-11}\text{ N}\bullet\text{m}^2/\text{kg}^2\right)} = \boxed{5.2\times10^{39}\text{ kg}}$$

The number of solar masses is found by dividing the result by the solar mass.

$$\text{\# solar masses} = \frac{M_{\text{galaxy}}}{M_{\text{Sun}}} = \frac{5.2\times10^{39}\text{ kg}}{2\times10^{30}\text{ kg}} = \boxed{2.6\times10^9\text{ solar masses}}$$

82. A generic free-body diagram for the car at any of the three locations is shown. Write Newton's 2nd law for the vertical direction, with downward positive.

$$\sum F = mg - F_N = ma$$

(a) At point B, the net force is 0, so the acceleration is 0, and so $F_N = mg$. At point A, the net force is positive, so $mg > F_N$, which is interpreted as a relatively small normal force. At point B, the net force is negative, so $mg < F_N$, which is interpreted as a relatively large normal force. And so $\boxed{F_{NC} > F_{NB} > F_{NA}}$.

(b) The driver "feels heavy" when the normal force is larger than his weight, so the driver will feel heavy at point C. The driver "feels light" when the normal force is smaller than his weight, so the driver will feel light at point A. $\boxed{\text{From feels heaviest to feels lightest, C, B, A.}}$

(c) In general, $mg - F_N = mv^2/r$ if the car is executing a part of the road that is curved up or down with a radius of R. If the normal force goes to 0, then the car loses contact with the road. This happens if $mg = mv^2/r \rightarrow \boxed{v_{max} = \sqrt{gR}}$. Any faster and the car will lose contact with the road.

83. (a) The speed of a satellite orbiting the Earth is given by $v = \sqrt{GM_{Earth}/r}$. For the GPS satellites,

$$r = R_{Earth} + (11,000)(1.852 \text{ km}) = 2.68 \times 10^7 \text{ m}.$$

$$v = \sqrt{\left(6.67 \times 10^{-11} \text{ N} \cdot \text{m}^2/\text{kg}^2\right) \frac{\left(5.97 \times 10^{24} \text{ kg}\right)}{2.68 \times 10^7 \text{ m}}} = \boxed{3.86 \times 10^3 \text{ m/s}}$$

(b) The period can be found from the speed and the radius.

$$v = 2\pi r/T \rightarrow T = \frac{2\pi r}{v} = \frac{2\pi \left(2.68 \times 10^7 \text{ m}\right)}{3.86 \times 10^3 \text{ m/s}} = \boxed{4.36 \times 10^4 \text{ sec}} = 12.1 \text{ hours}$$

84. (a) The speed of an object orbiting a mass M is given by $v = \sqrt{GM/r}$. The mass of the asteroid is found by multiplying the density times the volume. The period of an object moving in a circular path is given by $T = 2\pi r/v$. Combine these relationships to find the period.

$$M = \rho V = \left(2.3 \times 10^3 \frac{\text{kg}}{\text{m}^3}\right)\left(40000 \times 6000 \times 6000 \text{ m}^3\right) = 3.312 \times 10^{15} \text{ kg}$$

$$T = \frac{2\pi r}{\sqrt{G\dfrac{M}{r}}} = \frac{2\pi \left(1.5 \times 10^4 \text{ m}\right)}{\sqrt{\left(6.67 \times 10^{-11} \text{ N} \cdot \text{m}^2/\text{kg}^2\right) \dfrac{\left(3.312 \times 10^{15} \text{ kg}\right)}{\left(1.5 \times 10^4 \text{ m}\right)}}} = 2.456 \times 10^4 \text{ sec}$$

$$\approx \boxed{2 \times 10^4 \text{ sec}} \approx 7 \text{ h}$$

(b) If the asteroid were a sphere, then the mass would be given by $M = \rho V = \frac{4}{3}\pi \rho r^3$. Solve this for the radius.

$$r = \left(\frac{3M}{4\pi \rho}\right)^{1/3} = \left(\frac{3\left(3.312 \times 10^{15} \text{ kg}\right)}{4\pi \left(2.3 \times 10^3 \dfrac{\text{kg}}{\text{m}^3}\right)}\right)^{1/3} = 7005 \text{ m} \approx \boxed{7 \times 10^3 \text{ m}}$$

(c) The acceleration due to gravity is found from the mass and the radius.

$$g = GM/r^2 = \left(6.67\times10^{-11}\ \text{N•m}^2/\text{kg}^2\right)\frac{\left(3.312\times10^{15}\ \text{kg}\right)}{\left(7005\ \text{m}\right)^2} = 4.502\times10^{-3}\ \text{m}/\text{s}^2$$

$$\approx \boxed{5\times10^{-3}\ \text{m}/\text{s}^2}$$

85. The relationship between orbital speed and orbital radius for objects in orbit around the Earth is given by $v = \sqrt{GM_{\text{Earth}}/r}$. There are two orbital speeds involved – the one at the original radius, $v_0 = \sqrt{GM_{\text{Earth}}/r_0}$, and the faster speed at the reduced radius, $v = \sqrt{GM_{\text{Earth}}/\left(r_0 - \Delta r\right)}$.

(a) At the faster speed, 25,000 more meters will be traveled during the "catch-up" time, t. Note that $r_0 = 6.38\times10^6\ \text{m} + 4\times10^5\ \text{m} = 6.78\times10^6\ \text{m}$.

$$vt = v_0 t + 2.5\times10^4\ \text{m} \ \rightarrow \ \left(\sqrt{G\frac{M_{\text{Earth}}}{r_0 - \Delta r}}\right)t = \left(\sqrt{G\frac{M_{\text{Earth}}}{r_0}}\right)t + 2.5\times10^4\ \text{m} \ \rightarrow$$

$$t = \frac{2.5\times10^4\ \text{m}}{\sqrt{GM_{\text{Earth}}}}\left(\frac{1}{\sqrt{r_0 - \Delta r}} - \frac{1}{\sqrt{r_0}}\right)$$

$$= \frac{2.5\times10^4\ \text{m}}{\sqrt{\left(6.67\times10^{-11}\ \text{N•m}^2/\text{kg}^2\right)\left(5.97\times10^{24}\ \text{kg}\right)}}\left(\frac{1}{\sqrt{6.78\times10^6\ \text{m} - 1\times10^3\ \text{m}}} - \frac{1}{\sqrt{6.78\times10^6\ \text{m}}}\right)$$

$$= 4.42\times10^4\ \text{s} \approx \boxed{12\,\text{h}}$$

(b) Again, 25,000 more meters must be traveled at the faster speed in order to catch up to the satellite.

$$vt = v_0 t + 2.5\times10^4\ \text{m} \ \rightarrow \ \left(\sqrt{G\frac{M_{\text{Earth}}}{r_0 - \Delta r}}\right)t = \left(\sqrt{G\frac{M_{\text{Earth}}}{r_0}}\right)t + 2.5\times10^4\ \text{m} \ \rightarrow$$

$$\sqrt{\frac{1}{r_0 - \Delta r}} = \frac{1}{\sqrt{r_0}} + \frac{2.5\times10^4\ \text{m}}{t\sqrt{GM_{\text{Earth}}}} \ \rightarrow \ \sqrt{r_0 - \Delta r} = \left[\frac{1}{\sqrt{r_0}} + \frac{2.5\times10^4\ \text{m}}{t\sqrt{GM_{\text{Earth}}}}\right]^{-1} \ \rightarrow$$

$$\Delta r = r_0 + \left[\frac{1}{\sqrt{r_0}} + \frac{2.5\times10^4\ \text{m}}{t\sqrt{GM_{\text{Earth}}}}\right]^{-2} = 1755\ \text{m} \approx \boxed{1.8\times10^3\ \text{m}}$$

86. (a) Use Kepler's 3rd law to relate the orbits of the Earth and the comet around the Sun.

$$\left(\frac{r_{\text{comet}}}{r_{\text{Earth}}}\right)^3 = \left(\frac{T_{\text{comet}}}{T_{\text{Earth}}}\right)^2 \ \rightarrow \ r_{\text{comet}} = r_{\text{Earth}}\left(\frac{T_{\text{comet}}}{T_{\text{Earth}}}\right)^{2/3} = \left(1\ \text{AU}\right)\left(\frac{3000\ \text{y}}{1\ \text{y}}\right)^{2/3} = \boxed{208\ \text{AU}}$$

(b) The mean distance is the numeric average of the closest and farthest distances.

$$208\ \text{AU} = \frac{1\ \text{AU} + r_{\text{max}}}{2} \ \rightarrow \ r_{\text{max}} = \boxed{415\ \text{AU}}\ .$$

(c) Refer to figure 5-29, which illustrates Kepler's second law. If the time for each shaded region is made much shorter, then the area of each region can be approximated as a triangle. The area of each triangle is half the "base" (speed of comet multiplied by the amount of time) times the "height" (distance from Sun). So we have the following.

$$\text{Area}_{\min} = \text{Area}_{\max} \quad \rightarrow \quad \tfrac{1}{2}(v_{\min}t)r_{\min} = \tfrac{1}{2}(v_{\max}t)r_{\max} \quad \rightarrow$$

$$v_{\min}/v_{\max} = r_{\max}/r_{\min} = \boxed{415/1}$$

87. Let us assume that each person has a mass of 70 kg (a weight of ~ 150 lb). We shall assume that the people can be treated as point masses, and that their centers of mass are about 0.5 m apart. Finally, we assume that we can feel a gravitational force of about 1 N. The expression for the gravitational force becomes

$$F = G\frac{m_1 m_2}{r^2} \quad \rightarrow \quad G = \frac{Fr^2}{m_1 m_2} = \frac{(1\,\text{N})(0.5\,\text{m})^2}{(70\,\text{kg})^2} = \boxed{5\times10^{-5}\,\text{N}\cdot\text{m}^2/\text{kg}^2}.$$

This is roughly one million times larger than G actually is.

88. The speed of rotation of the Sun about the galactic center, under the assumptions made, is given by

$$v = \sqrt{G\frac{M_{\text{galaxy}}}{r_{\text{Sun orbit}}}} \quad \text{and so} \quad M_{\text{galaxy}} = \frac{r_{\text{Sun orbit}}\,v^2}{G}. \quad \text{Substitute in the relationship that } v = 2\pi r_{\text{Sun orbit}}/T.$$

$$M_{\text{galaxy}} = \frac{4\pi^2 \left(r_{\text{Sun orbit}}\right)^3}{GT^2} = \frac{4\pi^2\left[(30,000)(9.5\times10^{15}\,\text{m})\right]^3}{\left(6.67\times10^{-11}\,\text{N}\cdot\text{m}^2/\text{kg}^2\right)\left[(200\times10^6\,\text{y})\left(\frac{3.15\times10^7\,\text{s}}{1\,\text{y}}\right)\right]^2}$$

$$= 3.452\times10^{41}\,\text{kg} \approx \boxed{3\times10^{41}\,\text{kg}}$$

The number of solar masses is found by dividing the result by the solar mass.

$$\#\ \text{stars} = \frac{M_{\text{galaxy}}}{M_{\text{Sun}}} = \frac{3.452\times10^{41}\,\text{kg}}{2.0\times10^{30}\,\text{kg}} = 1.726\times10^{11} \approx \boxed{2\times10^{11}\,\text{stars}}$$

89. See the free-body diagram. $\theta = \tan^{-1}0.25/0.50 = 27°$. Because of the symmetry of the problem, the forces $\vec{\mathbf{F}}_L$ and $\vec{\mathbf{F}}_R$ cancel each other. Likewise, the horizontal components of $\vec{\mathbf{F}}_{UR}$ and $\vec{\mathbf{F}}_{UL}$ cancel each other. Thus the only forces on the fifth mass will be the vertical components of $\vec{\mathbf{F}}_{UR}$ and $\vec{\mathbf{F}}_{UL}$. These components are also equal, and so only one needs to be calculated, and then doubled.

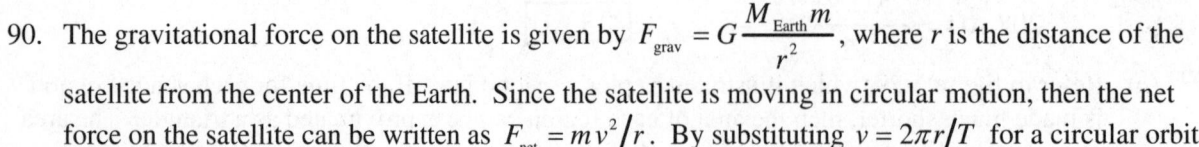

$$F_{\text{net}} = 2F_{UR}\cos\theta = 2G\frac{m^2}{d^2 + (d/2)^2}\cos\theta$$

$$= 2\left(6.67\times10^{-11}\,\text{N}\cdot\text{m}^2/\text{kg}^2\right)\frac{(1.0\,\text{kg})^2}{\tfrac{5}{4}(0.50\,\text{m})^2}\cos27° = \boxed{3.8\times10^{-10}\,\text{N}\,,\ \text{upward}}$$

90. The gravitational force on the satellite is given by $F_{\text{grav}} = G\dfrac{M_{\text{Earth}}\,m}{r^2}$, where r is the distance of the satellite from the center of the Earth. Since the satellite is moving in circular motion, then the net force on the satellite can be written as $F_{\text{net}} = mv^2/r$. By substituting $v = 2\pi r/T$ for a circular orbit,

we have $F_{net} = \dfrac{4\pi^2 mr}{T^2}$. Then, since gravity is the only force on the satellite, the two expressions for force can be equated, and solved for the orbit radius.

$$G\frac{M_{Earth}m}{r^2} = \frac{4\pi^2 mr}{T^2} \rightarrow$$

$$r = \left(\frac{GM_{Earth}T^2}{4\pi^2}\right)^{1/3} = \left[\frac{\left(6.67\times10^{-11}\ \text{N}\bullet\text{m}^2/\text{kg}^2\right)\left(6.0\times10^{24}\ \text{kg}\right)\left(6200\ \text{s}\right)^2}{4\pi^2}\right]^{1/3} = 7.304\times10^6\ \text{m}$$

(a)   From this value the gravitational force on the satellite can be calculated.

$$F_{grav} = G\frac{M_{Earth}m}{r^2} = \left(6.67\times10^{-11}\ \text{N}\bullet\text{m}^2/\text{kg}^2\right)\frac{\left(6.0\times10^{24}\ \text{kg}\right)\left(5500\ \text{kg}\right)}{\left(7.304\times10^6\ \text{m}\right)^2} = 4.126\times10^4\ \text{N}$$

$$\approx \boxed{4.1\times10^4\ \text{N}}$$

(b)   The altitude of the satellite above the Earth's surface is given by

$$r - R_{Earth} = 7.304\times10^6\ \text{m} - 6.38\times10^6\ \text{m} = \boxed{9.2\times10^5\ \text{m}}.$$

91.   The radial acceleration is given by $a_R = v^2/r$. Substitute in the speed of the tip of the sweep hand,

given by $v = 2\pi r/T$, to get $a_R = \dfrac{4\pi^2 r}{T^2}$. For the tip of the sweep hand, $r = 0.015$ m, and $T = 60$ sec.

$$a_R = \frac{4\pi^2 r}{T^2} = \frac{4\pi^2\left(0.015\ \text{m}\right)}{\left(60\ \text{s}\right)^2} = \boxed{1.6\times10^{-4}\ \text{m}/\text{s}^2}.$$

92.   A free-body diagram for the sinker weight is shown. L is the length of the string actually swinging the sinker. The radius of the circle of motion is moving is $r = L\sin\theta$. Write Newton's 2nd law for the vertical direction, noting that the sinker is not accelerating vertically. Take up to be positive.

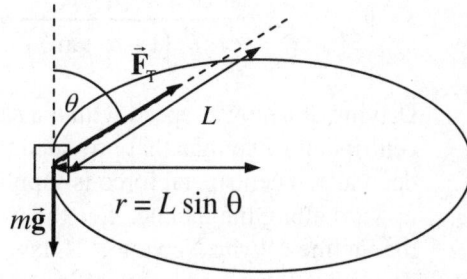

$$\sum F_y = F_T\cos\theta - mg = 0 \rightarrow F_T = \frac{mg}{\cos\theta}$$

The radial force is the horizontal portion of the tension. Write Newton's 2nd law for the radial motion.

$$\sum F_R = F_T\sin\theta = ma_R = mv^2/r$$

Substitute the tension from the vertical equation, and the relationships $r = L\sin\theta$ and $v = 2\pi r/T$.

$$F_T\sin\theta = mv^2/r \rightarrow \frac{mg}{\cos\theta}\sin\theta = \frac{4\pi^2 mL\sin\theta}{T^2} \rightarrow \cos\theta = \frac{gT^2}{4\pi^2 L}$$

$$\theta = \cos^{-1}\frac{gT^2}{4\pi^2 L} = \cos^{-1}\frac{\left(9.8\ \text{m}/\text{s}^2\right)\left(0.50\ \text{s}\right)^2}{4\pi^2\left(0.25\ \text{m}\right)} = \boxed{76^\circ}$$

93. From Example 5-7 in the textbook, the no-friction banking angle is given by $\theta = \tan^{-1}\dfrac{v_0^2}{Rg}$. The

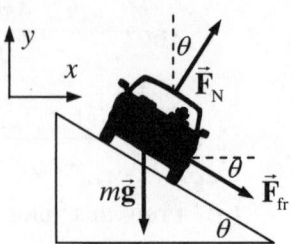

centripetal force in this case is provided by a component of the normal force. Driving at a higher speed with the same radius requires more centripetal force than that provided by the normal force alone. The additional centripetal force is supplied by a force of static friction, downward along the incline. See the free-body diagram for the car on the incline. The center of the circle of the car's motion is to the right of the car in the diagram. Write Newton's 2nd law in both the x and y directions. The car will have no acceleration in the y direction, and centripetal acceleration in the x direction. Assume that the car is on the verge of skidding, so that the static frictional force has its maximum value of $F_{fr} = \mu_s F_N$.

$$\sum F_y = F_N \cos\theta - mg - F_{fr} \sin\theta = 0 \;\to\; F_N \cos\theta - \mu_s F_N \sin\theta = mg \;\to$$

$$F_N = \frac{mg}{\left(\cos\theta - \mu_s \sin\theta\right)}$$

$$\sum F_x = F_R = F_N \sin\theta + F_{fr} \cos\theta = mv^2/R \;\to\; F_N \sin\theta + \mu_s F_N \cos\theta = mv^2/R \;\to$$

$$F_N = \frac{mv^2/R}{\left(\sin\theta + \mu_s \cos\theta\right)}$$

Equate the two expressions for the normal force, and solve for the speed, which is the maximum speed that the car can have.

$$\frac{mv^2/R}{\left(\sin\theta + \mu_s \cos\theta\right)} = \frac{mg}{\left(\cos\theta - \mu_s \sin\theta\right)} \;\to$$

$$v_{max} = \sqrt{Rg\,\frac{\sin\theta}{\cos\theta}\,\frac{\left(1 + \mu_s/\tan\theta\right)}{\left(1 - \mu_s \tan\theta\right)}} = v_0 \sqrt{\frac{\left(1 + Rg\mu_s/v_0^2\right)}{\left(1 - \mu_s v_0^2/Rg\right)}}$$

Driving at a slower speed with the same radius requires less centripetal force than that provided by the normal force alone. The decrease in centripetal force is supplied by a force of static friction, upward along the incline. See the free-body diagram for the car on the incline. Write Newton's 2nd law in both the x and y directions. The car will have no acceleration in the y direction, and centripetal acceleration in the x direction. Assume that the car is on the verge of skidding, so that the static frictional force has its maximum value of

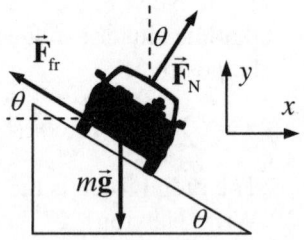

$F_{fr} = \mu_s F_N$.

$$\sum F_y = F_N \cos\theta - mg + F_{fr} \sin\theta = 0 \;\to$$

$$F_N \cos\theta + \mu_s F_N \sin\theta = mg \;\to\; F_N = \frac{mg}{\left(\cos\theta + \mu_s \sin\theta\right)}$$

$$\sum F_x = F_R = F_N \sin\theta - F_{fr} \cos\theta = mv^2/R \;\to\; F_N \sin\theta - \mu_s F_N \cos\theta = mv^2/R \;\to$$

$$F_N = \frac{mv^2/R}{\left(\sin\theta - \mu_s \cos\theta\right)}$$

Equate the two expressions for the normal force, and solve for the speed.

$$\frac{mv^2/R}{\left(\sin\theta - \mu_s\cos\theta\right)} = \frac{mg}{\left(\cos\theta + \mu_s\sin\theta\right)} \rightarrow$$

$$v_{min} = \sqrt{Rg\,\frac{\sin\theta}{\cos\theta}\,\frac{\left(1-\mu_s/\tan\theta\right)}{\left(1+\mu_s\tan\theta\right)}} = v_0\sqrt{\frac{\left(1-\mu_s Rg/v_0^2\right)}{\left(1+\mu_s v_0^2/Rg\right)}}$$

Thus $\boxed{v_{min} = v_0\sqrt{\dfrac{\left(1-\mu_s Rg/v_0^2\right)}{\left(1+\mu_s v_0^2/Rg\right)}}}$ and $\boxed{v_{max} = v_0\sqrt{\dfrac{\left(1+Rg\mu_s/v_0^2\right)}{\left(1-\mu_s v_0^2/Rg\right)}}}$.

94. The speed of the train is $(160\,\text{km/h})\left(\dfrac{1\,\text{m/s}}{3.6\,\text{km/h}}\right) = 44.44\,\text{m/s}$

(a) If there is no tilt, then the friction force must supply the entire centripetal force on the passenger.

$$F_R = mv^2/R = \frac{(75\,\text{kg})(44.44\,\text{m/s})^2}{(620\,\text{m})} = 238.9\,\text{N} \approx \boxed{2.4\times10^2\,\text{N}}$$

(b) For the banked case, the normal force will contribute to the radial force needed. Write Newton's 2nd law for both the x and y directions. The y acceleration is zero, and the x acceleration is radial.

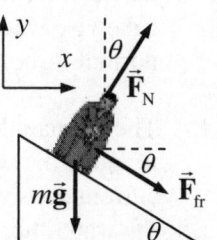

$$\sum F_y = F_N\cos\theta - mg - F_{fr}\sin\theta = 0 \;\rightarrow\; F_N = \frac{mg + F_{fr}\sin\theta}{\cos\theta}$$

$$\sum F_x = F_N\sin\theta + F_{fr}\cos\theta = mv^2/r$$

Substitute the expression for the normal force from the y equation into the x equation, and solve for the friction force.

$$\frac{mg + F_{fr}\sin\theta}{\cos\theta}\sin\theta + F_{fr}\cos\theta = mv^2/r \;\rightarrow$$

$$\left(mg + F_{fr}\sin\theta\right)\sin\theta + F_{fr}\cos^2\theta = m\frac{v^2}{r}\cos\theta \;\rightarrow$$

$$F_{fr} = m\left(\frac{v^2}{r}\cos\theta - g\sin\theta\right)$$

$$= (75\,\text{kg})\left[\frac{(44.44\,\text{m/s})^2}{620\,\text{m}}\cos8.0° - (9.80\,\text{m/s}^2)\sin8.0°\right] = 134\,\text{N} \approx \boxed{1.3\times10^2\,\text{N}}$$

CHAPTER 6: Work and Energy

Answers to Questions

1. Some types of physical labor, particularly if it involves lifting objects, such as shoveling dirt or carrying shingles up to a roof, are "work" in the physics sense of the word. Or, pushing a lawn mower would be work corresponding to the physics definition. When we use the word "work" for employment, such as "go to work" or "school work", there is often no sense of physical labor or of moving something through a distance by a force.

2. Since "centripetal" means "pointing to the center of curvature", then a centripetal force will not do work on an object, because if an object is moving in a curved path, by definition the direction towards the center of curvature is always perpendicular to the direction of motion. For a force to do work, the force must have a component in the direction of displacement. So the centripetal force does no work.

3. The normal force can do work on an object if the normal force has a component in the direction of displacement of an object. If someone were to jump up in the air, then the floor pushing upward on the person (the normal force) would do positive work and increase the person's kinetic energy. Likewise when they hit the floor coming back down, the force of the floor pushing upwards (the normal force) would do negative work and decrease the person's kinetic energy.

4. The woman does work by moving the water with her hands and feet, because she must exert a force to move the water some distance. As she stops swimming and begins to float in the current, the current does work on her because she gains kinetic energy. Once she is floating the same speed as the water, her kinetic energy does not change, and so no net work is being done on her.

5. The kinetic force of friction opposes the relative motion between two objects. As in the example suggested, as the tablecloth is pulled from under the dishes, the relative motion is for the dishes to be left behind as the tablecloth is pulled, and so the kinetic friction opposes that and moves the dishes in the same direction as the tablecloth. This is a force that is in the direction of displacement, and so positive work is done. Also note that the cloth is moving faster than the dishes in this case, so that the friction is kinetic, not static.

6. While it is true that no work is being done on the wall by you, there is work being done inside your arm muscles. Exerting a force via a muscle causes small continual motions in your muscles, which is work, and which causes you to tire. An example of this is holding a heavy load at arm's length. While at first you may hold the load steady, after a time your arm will begin to shake, which indicates the motion of muscles in your arm.

7. (a) In this case, the same force is applied to both springs. Spring 1 will stretch less, and so more work is done on spring 2.
   (b) In this case, both springs are stretched the same distance. It takes more force to stretch spring 1, and so more work is done on spring 1.

8. At point C the block's speed will be less than $2v_B$. The same amount of work was done on the block in going from A to B as from B to C since the force and the displacement are the same for each segment. Thus the change in kinetic energy will be the same for each segment. From A to B, the

block gained $\frac{1}{2}mv_B^2$ of kinetic energy. If the same amount is gained from B to C, then the total kinetic energy at C is $\frac{1}{2}mv_C^2 = 2\left(\frac{1}{2}mv_B^2\right)$ which results in $v_C = \sqrt{2}\,v_B$, or $v_C \approx 1.4 v_B$

9. Your gravitational PE will change according to $\Delta PE = mg\Delta y$. If we choose some typical values of $m = 80$ kg and $\Delta y = 0.75$ m, then $\Delta PE = (80 \text{ kg})(9.8 \text{ m/s}^2)(0.75 \text{ m}) = 590$ J

10. Since each balloon has the same initial kinetic energy, and each balloon undergoes the same overall change in gravitational PE, each balloon will have the same kinetic energy at the ground, and so each one has the same speed at impact.

11. The two launches will result in the same largest angle. Applying conservation of energy between the launching point and the highest point, we have $E_1 = E_2 \rightarrow \frac{1}{2}mv^2 + mgh = mgh_{max}$. The direction of the launching velocity does not matter, and so the same maximum height (and hence maximum angle) will results from both launches. Also, for the first launch, the ball will rise to some maximum height and then come back to the launch point with the same speed as when launched. That then exactly duplicates the second launch.

12. The spring can leave the table if it is compressed enough. If the spring is compressed an amount x_0, then the gain in elastic PE is $\frac{1}{2}kx_0^2$. As the spring is compressed, its center of mass is lowered by some amount. If the spring is uniform, then the center of mass is lowered by $x_0/2$, and the amount of decrease in gravitational PE is $\frac{1}{2}mgx_0$. If the gain in elastic PE is more than the loss in gravitational PE, so that $\frac{1}{2}kx_0^2 > \frac{1}{2}mgx_0$ or $x_0 > mg/k$, then the released spring should rise up off of the table, because there is more than enough elastic PE to restore the spring to its original position. That extra elastic energy will enable the spring to "jump" off the table – it can raise its center of mass to a higher point and thus rise up off the table. Where does that "extra" energy come from? From the work you did in compressing the spring.

13. If the instructor releases the ball without pushing it, the ball should return to exactly the same height (barring any dissipative forces) and just touch the instructor's nose as it stops. But if the instructor pushes the ball, giving it extra kinetic energy and hence a larger total energy, the ball will then swing to a higher point before stopping, and hit the instructor in the face when it returns.

14. When water at the top of a waterfall falls to the pool below, initially the water's gravitational PE is turned into kinetic energy. That kinetic energy then can do work on the pool water when it hits it, and so some of the pool water is given energy, which makes it splash upwards and outwards and creates outgoing water waves, which carry energy. Some of the energy will become heat, due to viscous friction between the falling water and the pool water. Some of the energy will become kinetic energy of air molecules, making sound waves that give the waterfall its "roar".

15. Start the description with the child suspended in mid-air, at the top of a hop. All of the energy is gravitational PE at that point. Then, the child falls, and gains kinetic energy. When the child reaches the ground, most of the energy is kinetic. As the spring begins to compress, the kinetic energy is changed into elastic PE. The child also goes down a little bit further as the spring compresses, and so more gravitational PE is also changed into elastic PE. At the very bottom of a hop, the energy is all elastic PE. Then as the child rebounds, the elastic PE is turned into kinetic energy and gravitational PE. When the child reaches the top of the bounce, all of the elastic PE has

been changed into gravitational PE, because the child has a speed of 0 at the top. Then the cycle starts over again. Due to friction, the child must also add energy to the system by pushing down on the pogo stick while it is on the ground, getting a more forceful reaction from the ground.

16. As the skier goes down the hill, the gravitational PE is transformed mostly into kinetic energy, and small amount is transformed into heat energy due to the friction between the skis and the snow and air friction. As the skier strikes the snowdrift, the kinetic energy of the skier turns into kinetic energy of the snow (by making the snow move), and also into some heat from the friction in moving through the snowdrift.

17. (*a*) If there is no friction to dissipate any of the energy, then the gravitational PE that the child has at the top of the hill all turns into kinetic energy at the bottom of the hill. The same kinetic energy will be present regardless of the slope – the final speed is completely determined by the height. The time it takes to reach the bottom of the hill will be longer for a smaller slope.

   (*b*) If there is friction, then the longer the path is, the more work that friction will do, and so the slower the speed will be at the bottom. So for a steep hill, the sled will have a greater speed at the bottom than for a shallow hill.

18. Stepping on the log requires that the entire body mass be raised up the height of the log, requiring work (that is not recoverable) proportional to the entire body mass. Stepping over the log only requires the raising of the legs, making for a small mass being raised and thus less work. Also, when jumping down, energy is expended to stop the "fall" from the log. The potential energy that you had at the top of the log is lost when coming down from the log.

19. If we assume that all of the arrow's kinetic energy is converted into work done against friction, then the following relationship exists:

$$W = \Delta KE = KE_f - KE_i \quad \rightarrow \quad F_{fr}d\cos 180^\circ = \tfrac{1}{2}mv_f^2 - \tfrac{1}{2}mv_0^2 \quad \rightarrow \quad -F_{fr}d = -\tfrac{1}{2}mv_0^2 \quad \rightarrow$$

$$d = \frac{mv_0^2}{2F_{fr}}$$

Thus the distance is proportional to the square of the initial velocity. So if the initial velocity is doubled, the distance will be multiplied by a factor of 4. Thus the faster arrow penetrates 4 times further than the slower arrow.

20. (*a*) Consider that there is no friction to dissipate any energy. Start the pendulum at the top of a swing, and define the lowest point of the swing as the zero location for gravitational PE. The pendulum has maximum gravitational PE at the top of a swing. Then as it falls, the gravitational PE is changed to kinetic energy. At the bottom of the swing, the energy is all kinetic energy. Then the pendulum starts to rise, and kinetic energy is changed to gravitational PE. Since there is no dissipation, all of the original gravitational PE is converted to kinetic energy, and all of the kinetic energy is converted to gravitational PE. The pendulum rises to the same height on both sides of every swing, and reaches the same maximum speed at the bottom on every swing.

   (*b*) If there is friction to dissipate the energy, then on each downward swing, the pendulum will have less kinetic energy at the bottom than it had gravitational PE at the top. And then on each swing up, the pendulum will not rise as high as the previous swing, because energy is being lost to frictional dissipation any time the pendulum is moving. So each time it swings, it has a smaller maximum displacement. When a grandfather clock is wound up, a weight is elevated so that it has some PE. That weight then falls at the proper rate to put energy back in to the pendulum to replace the energy that was lost to dissipation.

21. The superball cannot rebound to a height greater than its original height when dropped. If it did, it would violate conservation of energy. When a ball collides with the floor, the KE of the ball is converted into elastic PE by deforming the ball, much like compressing a spring. Then as the ball springs back to its original shape, that elastic PE is converted to back to KE. But that process is "lossy" – not all of the elastic PE gets converted back to KE. Some of the PE is lost, primarily to friction. The superball rebounds higher than many other balls because it is less "lossy" in its rebound than many other materials.

22. The work done to lift the suitcase is equal to the change in PE of the suitcase, which is the weight of the suitcase times the change in height (the height of the table).
    (*a*) Work does NOT depend on the path, as long as there are no non-conservative forces doing work.
    (*b*) Work does NOT depend on the time taken.
    (*c*) Work DOES depend on the height of the table – the higher the table, the more work it takes to lift the suitcase.
    (*d*) Work DOES depend on the weight of the suitcase – the more the suitcase weighs, the more work it takes to lift the suitcase.

23. The power needed to lift the suitcase is the work required to lift the suitcase, divided by the time that it takes.
    (*a*) Since work does NOT depend on the path, the power will not depend on the path either, assuming the time is the same for all paths.
    (*b*) The power DOES depend on the time taken. The more time taken, the lower the power needed.
    (*c*) The power needed DOES depend on the height of the table. A higher table requires more work to lift the suitcase. If we assume that the time to lift the suitcase is the same in both cases, then to lift to the higher table takes more power.
    (*d*) The power DOES depend on the weight of the suitcase. A heavier suitcase requires more force to lift, and so requires more work. Thus the heavier the suitcase, the more power is needed to lift it (in the same amount of time).

24. The climber does the same amount of work whether climbing straight up or via a zig-zag path, ignoring dissipative forces. But if a longer zig-zag path is taken, it takes more time to do the work, and so the power output needed from the climber is less. That will make the climb easier. It is easier for the human body to generate a small amount of power for long periods of time rather than to generate a large power for a small period of time.

25. Assuming that there are no dissipative forces to consider, for every meter that the load is raised, two meters of rope must be pulled up. This is due to the rope passing over the bottom pulley. The work done by the person pulling must be equal to the work done on the piano. Since the force on the piano is twice that exerted by the person pulling, and since work is force times distance, the person must exert their smaller force over twice the distance that the larger pulley force moves the piano.

Solutions to Problems

1. The force and the displacement are both downwards, so the angle between them is $0°$.
$$W_G = mgd \cos\theta = (265 \text{ kg})(9.80 \text{ m/s}^2)(2.80 \text{ m}) \cos 0° = \boxed{7.27 \times 10^3 \text{ J}}$$

2.   The minimum force required to lift the firefighter is equal to his weight. The force and the displacement are both upwards, so the angle between them is $0°$.

$$W_{climb} = F_{climb} d \cos\theta = mgd\cos\theta = (65.0\text{ kg})(9.80\text{ m/s}^2)(20.0\text{m})\cos 0° = \boxed{1.27\times10^4\text{ J}}$$

3.   (a) See the free-body diagram for the crate as it is being pulled. Since the crate is not accelerating horizontally, $F_P = F_{fr} = 230\text{ N}$. The work done to move it across the floor is the work done by the pulling force. The angle between the pulling force and the direction of motion is $0°$.

$$W_P = F_P d\cos 0° = (230\text{ N})(4.0\text{ m})(1) = \boxed{9.2\times10^2\text{ J}}$$

(b) See the free-body diagram for the crate as it is being lifted. Since the crate is not accelerating vertically, the pulling force is the same magnitude as the weight. The angle between the pulling force and the direction of motion is $0°$.

$$W_P = F_P d\cos 0° = mgd = (1300\text{ N})(4.0\text{ m}) = \boxed{5.2\times10^3\text{ J}}$$

4.   Draw a free-body diagram for the crate as it is being pushed across the floor. Since it is not accelerating vertically, $F_N = mg$. Since it is not accelerating horizontally, $F_P = F_{fr} = \mu_k F_N = \mu_k mg$. The work done to move it across the floor is the work done by the pushing force. The angle between the pushing force and the direction of motion is $0°$.

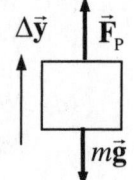

$$W_{push} = F_{push} d\cos 0° = \mu_k mgd(1) = (0.50)(160\text{ kg})(9.80\text{ m/s}^2)(10.3\text{ m})$$

$$= \boxed{8.1\times10^3\text{ J}}$$

5.   Since the acceleration of the box is constant, use Eq. 2-11b to find the distance moved. Assume that the box starts from rest.

$$\Delta x = x - x_0 = v_0 t + \tfrac{1}{2}at^2 = 0 + \tfrac{1}{2}(2.0\text{ m/s}^2)(7\text{ s})^2 = 49\text{ m}$$

Then the work done in moving the crate is

$$W = F\Delta x\cos 0° = ma\Delta x = (5\text{ kg})(2.0\text{ m/s}^2)(49\text{ m}) = \boxed{4.9\times10^2\text{ J}}$$

6.   The first book is already in position, so no work is required to position it. The second book must be moved upwards by a distance d, by a force equal to its weight, mg. The force and the displacement are in the same direction, so the work is mgd. The third book will need to be moved a distance of $2d$ by the same size force, so the work is $2mgd$, This continues through all seven books, with each needing to be raised by an additional amount of d by a force of mg. The total work done is

$$W = mgd + 2mgd + 3mgd + 4mgd + 5mgd + 6mgd + 7mgd$$

$$= 28mgd = 28(1.7\text{ kg})(9.8\text{ m/s}^2)(0.043\text{ m}) = \boxed{2.0\times10^1\text{ J}}.$$

7. Consider the diagram shown. If we assume that the man pushes straight down on the end of the lever, then the work done by the man (the "input" work) is given by $W_I = F_I h_I$. The object moves a shorter distance, as seen from the diagram, and so $W_O = F_O h_O$. Equate the two amounts of work.

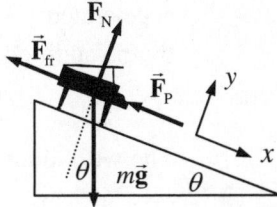

$$F_O h_O = F_I h_I \quad \rightarrow \quad \frac{F_O}{F_I} = \frac{h_I}{h_O}$$

But by similar triangles, we see that $\dfrac{h_I}{h_O} = \dfrac{l_I}{l_O}$, and so $\boxed{\dfrac{F_O}{F_I} = \dfrac{l_I}{l_O}}$.

8. The piano is moving with a constant velocity down the plane. $\vec{F}_P$ is the force of the man pushing on the piano.

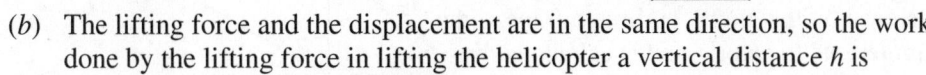

   (a) Write Newton's 2nd law on each direction for the piano, with an acceleration of 0.

$$\sum F_y = F_N - mg\cos\theta = 0 \quad \rightarrow \quad F_N = mg\cos\theta$$

$$\sum F_x = mg\sin\theta - F_P - F_{fr} = 0 \quad \rightarrow$$

$$F_P = mg\sin\theta - F_{fr} = mg\left(\sin\theta - \mu_k\cos\theta\right)$$

$$= (330\,\text{kg})(9.80\,\text{m/s}^2)(\sin 28° - 0.40\cos 28°) = \boxed{3.8\times10^2\,\text{N}}$$

   (b) The work done by the man is the work done by $\vec{F}_P$. The angle between $\vec{F}_P$ and the direction of motion is 180°.

$$W_P = F_P d\cos 180° = -(380\,\text{N})(3.6\,\text{m}) = \boxed{-1.4\times10^3\,\text{J}}.$$

   (c) The angle between $\vec{F}_{fr}$ and the direction of motion is 180°.

$$W_{fr} = F_{fr}d\cos 180° = -\mu_k mgd\cos\theta = -(0.40)(330\,\text{kg})(9.8\,\text{m/s}^2)(3.6\,\text{m})\cos 28°$$

$$= \boxed{-4.1\times10^3\,\text{J}}$$

   (d) The angle between the force of gravity and the direction of motion is 62°. So the work done by gravity is

$$W_G = F_G d\cos 62° = mgd\cos 62° = (330\,\text{kg})(9.8\,\text{m/s}^2)(3.6\,\text{m})\cos 62° = \boxed{5.5\times10^3\,\text{J}}.$$

   (e) Since the piano is unaccelerated, the net force on the piano is 0, and so the net work done on the piano is also 0. This can also be seen by adding the three work amounts calculated.

$$W_{Net} = W_P + W_{fr} + W_G = -1400\,\text{J} - 4100\,\text{J} + 5500\,\text{J} = \boxed{0\,\text{J}}$$

9. (a) Write Newton's 2nd law for the vertical direction, with up as positive.

$$\sum F_y = F_L - Mg = Ma = M(0.10g) \quad \rightarrow \quad F_L = \boxed{1.10\,Mg}$$

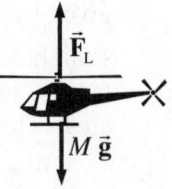

   (b) The lifting force and the displacement are in the same direction, so the work done by the lifting force in lifting the helicopter a vertical distance h is

$$W_L = F_L h\cos 0° = \boxed{1.10\,Mgh}.$$

10. Draw a free-body diagram of the car on the incline. Include a frictional force, but ignore it in part (*a*) of the problem. The minimum work will occur when the car is moved at a constant velocity.

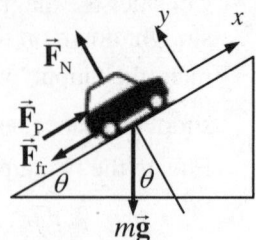

(*a*) Write Newton's 2nd law in both the *x* and *y* directions, noting that the car is unaccelerated.

$$\sum F_y = F_N - mg\cos\theta = 0 \;\rightarrow\; F_N = mg\cos\theta$$

$$\sum F_x = F_P - mg\sin\theta = 0 \;\rightarrow\; F_P = mg\sin\theta$$

The work done by $\vec{F}_P$ in moving the car a distance *d* along the plane (parallel to $\vec{F}_P$) is given by

$$W_P = F_P d\cos 0^\circ = mgd\sin\theta = (950\text{ kg})(9.80\text{ m/s}^2)(810\text{ m})\sin 9.0^\circ = \boxed{1.2\times 10^6\text{ J}}$$

(*b*) Now include the frictional force, given by $F_{fr} = \mu_k F_N$. We still assume that the car is not accelerated. We again write Newton's 2nd law for each direction. The *y*-forces are unchanged by the addition of friction, and so we still have $F_N = mg\cos\theta$.

$$\sum F_x = F_P - F_{fr} - mg\sin\theta = 0 \;\rightarrow\; F_P = F_{fr} + mg\sin\theta = \mu_k mg\cos\theta + mg\sin\theta.$$

The work done by $\vec{F}_P$ in moving the car a distance *d* along the plane (parallel to $\vec{F}_P$) is given by

$$W_P = F_P d\cos 0^\circ = mgd(\sin\theta + \mu_k\cos\theta)$$

$$= (950\text{ kg})(9.80\text{ m/s}^2)(810\text{ m})(\sin 9.0^\circ + 0.25\cos 9.0^\circ) = \boxed{3.0\times 10^6\text{ J}}$$

11. The work done is equal to the area under the graph. The area is roughly trapezoidal, and so the area of the region is found as follows.

$$W = \tfrac{1}{2}\left(F_{\|max} + F_{\|min}\right)(d_B - d_A) = \tfrac{1}{2}(250\text{ N} + 150\text{ N})(35.0\text{ m} - 10.0\text{ m}) = \boxed{5.0\times 10^3\text{ J}}$$

12. The work done will be the area under the F_x vs. *x* graph.

(*a*) From $x = 0.0$ to $x = 10.0\text{ m}$, the shape under the graph is trapezoidal. The area is

$$W_a = (400\text{ N})\frac{10\text{ m} + 4\text{ m}}{2} = \boxed{2.8\times 10^3\text{ J}}$$

(*b*) From $x = 10.0\text{ m}$ to $x = 15.0\text{ m}$, the force is in the opposite direction from the direction of motion, and so the work will be negative. Again, since the shape is trapezoidal, we find

$$W_a = (-200\text{ N})\frac{5\text{ m} + 2\text{ m}}{2} = -700\text{ J}.$$

Thus the total work from $x = 0.0$ to $x = 15.0\text{ m}$ is $2800\text{ J} - 700\text{ J} = \boxed{2.1\times 10^3\text{ J}}$.

13. The force exerted to stretch a spring is given by $F_{stretch} = kx$ (the opposite of the force exerted by the spring, which is given by $F = -kx$. A graph of $F_{stretch}$ vs. *x* will be a straight line of slope *k* thorough the origin. The stretch from x_1 to x_2, as shown on the graph, outlines a trapezoidal area. This area represents the work, and is calculated by

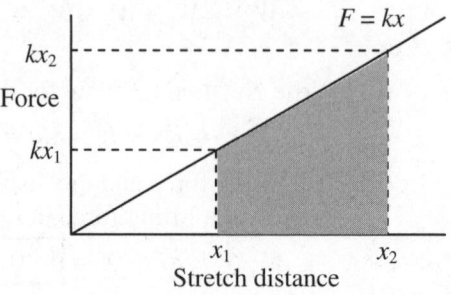

$$W = \tfrac{1}{2}(kx_1 + kx_2)(x_2 - x_1) = \tfrac{1}{2}k(x_1 + x_2)(x_2 - x_1)$$

$$= \tfrac{1}{2}(88\text{ N/m})(0.096\text{ m})(0.020\text{ m}) = \boxed{8.4\times 10^{-2}\text{ J}}.$$

14. See the graph of force vs. distance. The work done is the area under the graph. It can be found from the formula for a trapezoid.

$$W = \tfrac{1}{2}(13.0 \text{ m} + 5.0 \text{ m})(24.0 \text{ N}) = \boxed{216 \text{ J}}$$

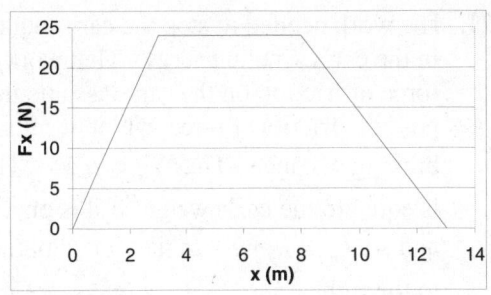

15. Find the velocity from the kinetic energy, using Eq. 6-3.

$$KE = \tfrac{1}{2}mv^2 \quad \rightarrow \quad v = \sqrt{\frac{2(KE)}{m}} = \sqrt{\frac{2(6.21 \times 10^{-21}\text{J})}{5.31 \times 10^{-26}}} = \boxed{484 \text{ m/s}}$$

16. (a) Since $KE = \tfrac{1}{2}mv^2$, then $v = \sqrt{2(KE)/m}$ and so $v \propto \sqrt{KE}$. Thus if the kinetic energy is doubled, the speed will be multiplied by a factor of $\boxed{\sqrt{2}}$.

  (b) Since $KE = \tfrac{1}{2}mv^2$, then $KE \propto v^2$. Thus if the speed is doubled, the kinetic energy will be multiplied by a factor of $\boxed{4}$.

17. The work done on the electron is equal to the change in its kinetic energy.

$$W = \Delta KE = \tfrac{1}{2}mv_2^2 - \tfrac{1}{2}mv_1^2 = 0 - \tfrac{1}{2}(9.11 \times 10^{-31}\text{kg})(1.90 \times 10^6 \text{ m/s})^2 = \boxed{-1.64 \times 10^{-18}\text{J}}$$

18. The work done on the car is equal to the change in its kinetic energy, and so

$$W = KE = \tfrac{1}{2}mv_2^2 - \tfrac{1}{2}mv_1^2 = 0 - \tfrac{1}{2}(1250 \text{ kg})\left[(105 \text{ km/h})\left(\frac{1 \text{ m/s}}{3.6 \text{ km/h}}\right)\right]^2 = \boxed{-5.32 \times 10^5 \text{J}}$$

19. The force exerted by the bow on the arrow is in the same direction as the displacement of the arrow. Thus $W = Fd \cos 0° = Fd = (110 \text{ N})(0.78 \text{ m}) = 85.8 \text{ J}$. But that work changes the KE of the arrow, by the work-energy theorem. Thus

$$Fd = W = KE_2 - KE_1 = \tfrac{1}{2}mv_2^2 - \tfrac{1}{2}mv_1^2 \quad \rightarrow \quad v_2 = \sqrt{\frac{2Fd}{m} + v_1^2} = \sqrt{\frac{2(85.8 \text{ J})}{0.088 \text{ kg}} + 0} = \boxed{44 \text{ m/s}}$$

20. The work done by the ball on the glove will be the opposite of the work done by the glove on the ball. The work done on the ball is equal to the change in the kinetic energy of the ball.

$$W_{\text{on ball}} = (KE_2 - KE_1)_{\text{ball}} = \tfrac{1}{2}mv_2^2 - \tfrac{1}{2}mv_1^2 = 0 - \tfrac{1}{2}(0.140 \text{ kg})(32 \text{ m/s})^2 = -72 \text{ J}$$

So $W_{\text{on glove}} = 72 \text{ J}$. But $W_{\text{on glove}} = F_{\text{on glove}}d \cos 0°$, because the force on the glove is in the same direction as the motion of the glove.

$$72 \text{ J} = F_{\text{on glove}}(0.25 \text{ m}) \quad \rightarrow \quad F_{\text{on glove}} = \frac{72 \text{ J}}{0.25 \text{ m}} = \boxed{2.9 \times 10^2 \text{N}}.$$

21. The work needed to stop the car is equal to the change in the car's kinetic energy. That work comes from the force of friction on the car. Assume the maximum possible frictional force, which results in the minimum braking distance. Thus $F_{fr} = \mu_s F_N$. The normal force is equal to the car's weight if it is on a level surface, and so $F_{fr} = \mu_s mg$. In the diagram, the car is traveling to the right.

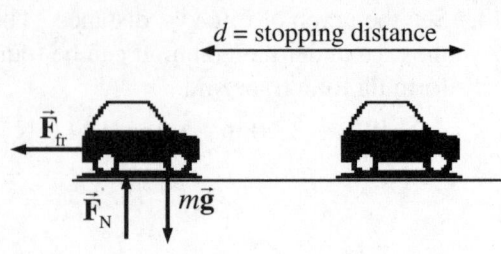

d = stopping distance

$$W = \Delta KE \ \rightarrow \ F_{fr} d \cos 180° = \tfrac{1}{2} mv_2^2 - \tfrac{1}{2} mv_1^2 \ \rightarrow \ -\mu_s mgd = -\tfrac{1}{2} mv_1^2 \ \rightarrow \ d = \frac{v_1^2}{2 g \mu_s}$$

Since $d \propto v_1^2$, if v_1 increases by 50%, or is multiplied by 1.5, then d will be multiplied by a factor of $(1.5)^2$, or $\boxed{2.25}$.

$\boxed{22.}$ The work needed to stop the car is equal to the change in the car's kinetic energy. That work comes from the force of friction on the car, which is assumed to be static friction since the driver locked the brakes. Thus $F_{fr} = \mu_k F_N$. Since the car is on a level surface, the normal force is equal to the car's weight, and so $F_{fr} = \mu_k mg$ if it is on a level surface. See the diagram for the car. The car is traveling to the right.

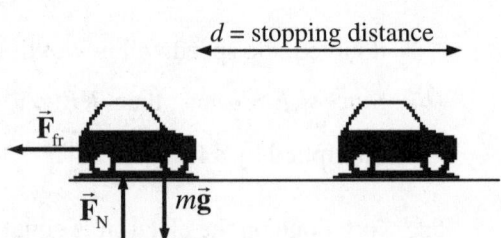

d = stopping distance

$$W = \Delta KE \ \rightarrow \ F_{fr} d \cos 180° = \tfrac{1}{2} mv_2^2 - \tfrac{1}{2} mv_1^2 \ \rightarrow \ -\mu_k mgd = 0 - \tfrac{1}{2} mv_1^2 \ \rightarrow$$

$$v_1 = \sqrt{2 \mu_k gd} = \sqrt{2(0.42)(9.8 \,\text{m/s}^2)(88 \,\text{m})} = \boxed{27 \,\text{m/s}}$$

The mass does not affect the problem, since both the change in kinetic energy and the work done by friction are proportional to the mass. The mass cancels out of the equation.

23. The original speed of the softball is $(95 \,\text{km/h}) \left(\dfrac{1 \,\text{m/s}}{3.6 \,\text{km/h}} \right) = 26.39 \,\text{m/s}$. The final speed is 90% of this, or 23.75 m/s. The work done by air friction causes a change in the kinetic energy of the ball, and thus the speed change. In calculating the work, notice that the force of friction is directed oppositely to the direction of motion of the ball.

$$W_{fr} = F_{fr} d \cos 180° = KE_2 - KE_1 = \tfrac{1}{2} m \left(v_2^2 - v_1^2 \right) \ \rightarrow$$

$$F_{fr} = \frac{m \left(v_2^2 - v_1^2 \right)}{-2d} = \frac{mv_1^2 \left(0.9^2 - 1 \right)}{-2d} = \frac{(0.25 \,\text{kg})(26.39 \,\text{m/s})^2 \left(0.9^2 - 1 \right)}{-2(15 \,\text{m})} = \boxed{1.1 \,\text{N}}$$

24. If the rock has 80.0 J of work done to it, and it loses all 80.0 J by stopping, then the force of gravity must have done –80.0 J of work on the rock. The force is straight down, and the displacement is straight up, so the angle between the force and the displacement is 180°. The work done by the gravity force can be used to find the distance the rock rises.

$$W_G = F_G d \cos \theta = mgd \cos 180° = -80.0 \,\text{J}$$

$$d = \frac{W_G}{-mg} = \frac{-80.0\ \text{J}}{-(1.85\ \text{kg})(9.80\ \text{m/s}^2)} = \boxed{4.41\ \text{m}}$$

25. (a) From the free-body diagram for the load being lifted, write Newton's 2nd law for the vertical direction, with up being positive.

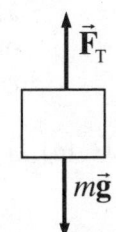

$$\sum F = F_T - mg = ma = 0.160mg \quad \rightarrow$$

$$F_T = 1.16mg = 1.16(285\ \text{kg})(9.80\ \text{m/s}^2) = \boxed{3.24 \times 10^3\ \text{N}}$$

(b) The net work done on the load is found from the net force.

$$W_{\text{net}} = F_{\text{net}}d\cos 0° = (0.160mg)d = 0.160(285\ \text{kg})(9.80\ \text{m/s}^2)(22.0\ \text{m})$$

$$= \boxed{9.83 \times 10^3\ \text{J}}$$

(c) The work done by the cable on the load is

$$W_{\text{cable}} = F_T d\cos 0° = (1.160mg)d = 1.16(285\ \text{kg})(9.80\ \text{m/s}^2)(22.0\ \text{m}) = \boxed{7.13 \times 10^4\ \text{J}}$$

(d) The work done by gravity on the load is

$$W_G = mgd\cos 180° = -mgd = -(285\ \text{kg})(9.80\ \text{m/s}^2)(22.0\ \text{m}) = \boxed{-6.14 \times 10^4\ \text{J}}$$

(e) Use the work-energy theory to find the final speed, with an initial speed of 0.

$$W_{\text{net}} = KE_2 - KE_1 = \tfrac{1}{2}mv_2^2 - \tfrac{1}{2}mv_1^2 \quad \rightarrow$$

$$v_2 = \sqrt{\frac{2W_{\text{net}}}{m} + v_1^2} = \sqrt{\frac{2(9.83 \times 10^3\ \text{J})}{285\ \text{kg}} + 0} = \boxed{8.31\ \text{m/s}}$$

26. The elastic PE is given by $PE_{\text{elastic}} = \tfrac{1}{2}kx^2$ where x is the distance of stretching or compressing of the spring from its natural length.

$$x = \sqrt{\frac{2PE_{\text{elastic}}}{k}} = \sqrt{\frac{2(25\ \text{J})}{440\ \text{N/m}}} = \boxed{0.34\ \text{m}}$$

27. Subtract the initial gravitational PE from the final gravitational PE.

$$\Delta PE_G = mgy_2 - mgy_1 = mg(y_2 - y_1) = (7.0\ \text{kg})(9.8\ \text{m/s}^2)(1.2\ \text{m}) = \boxed{82\ \text{J}}$$

28. Subtract the initial gravitational PE from the final gravitational PE.

$$\Delta PE_{\text{grav}} = mgy_2 - mgy_1 = mg(y_2 - y_1) = (64\ \text{kg})(9.8\ \text{m/s}^2)(4.0\ \text{m}) = \boxed{2.5 \times 10^3\ \text{J}}$$

29. Assume that all of the kinetic energy of the car becomes PE of the compressed spring.

$$\tfrac{1}{2}mv^2 = \tfrac{1}{2}kx^2 \quad \rightarrow \quad k = \frac{mv^2}{x^2} = \frac{(1200\ \text{kg})\left[(65\ \text{km/h})\left(\dfrac{1\ \text{m/s}}{3.6\ \text{km/h}}\right)\right]^2}{(2.2\ \text{m})^2} = \boxed{8.1 \times 10^4\ \text{N/m}}$$

30. (a) Relative to the ground, the PE is given by

$$PE_G = mg(y_{\text{book}} - y_{\text{ground}}) = (2.10\ \text{kg})(9.80\ \text{m/s}^2)(2.20\ \text{m}) = \boxed{45.3\ \text{J}}$$

(b) Relative to the top of the person's head, the PE is given by

$$PE_G = mg\left(y_{book} - y_{head}\right)h = (2.10\text{ kg})(9.80\text{ m/s}^2)(0.60\text{ m}) = \boxed{12\text{ J}}$$

(c) The work done by the person in lifting the book from the ground to the final height is the same as the answer to part (a), $\boxed{45.3\text{ J}}$. In part (a), the PE is calculated relative to the starting location of the application of the force on the book. The work done by the person is not related to the answer to part (b).

31. (a) The change in PE is given by

$$\Delta PE_G = mg\left(y_2 - y_1\right) = (55\text{ kg})(9.80\text{ m/s}^2)(3300\text{ m} - 1600\text{ m}) = \boxed{9.2\times10^5\text{ J}}$$

(b) The minimum work required by the hiker would equal the change in PE, which is $\boxed{9.2\times10^5\text{ J}}$.

(c) $\boxed{\text{Yes}}$. The actual work may be more than this, because the climber almost certainly had to overcome some dissipative forces such as air friction. Also, as the person steps up and down, they do not get the full amount of work back from each up-down event. For example, there will be friction in their joints and muscles.

32. The spring will stretch enough to hold up the mass. The force exerted by the spring will be equal to the weight of the mass.

$$mg = k\left(\Delta x\right) \quad \rightarrow \quad \Delta x = \frac{mg}{k} = \frac{(2.5\text{ kg})(9.80\text{ m/s}^2)}{53\text{ N/m}} = 0.46\text{ m}$$

Thus the ruler reading will be $\boxed{46\text{ cm} + 15\text{ cm} = 61\text{ cm}}$.

33. The only forces acting on Jane are gravity and the vine tension. The tension pulls in a centripetal direction, and so can do no work– the tension force is perpendicular at all times to her motion. So Jane's mechanical energy is conserved. Subscript 1 represents Jane at the point where she grabs the vine, and subscript 2 represents Jane at the highest point of her swing. The ground is the zero location for PE $(y = 0)$. We have $v_1 = 5.3\text{ m/s}$, $y_1 = 0$, and $v_2 = 0$ (top of swing). Solve for y_2, the height of her swing.

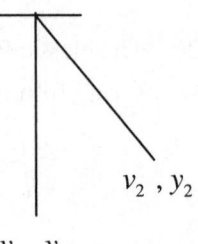

$$\tfrac{1}{2}mv_1^2 + mgy_1 = \tfrac{1}{2}mv_2^2 + mgy_2 \quad \rightarrow \quad \tfrac{1}{2}mv_1^2 + 0 = 0 + mgy_2 \quad \rightarrow$$

$$y_2 = \frac{v_1^2}{2g} = \frac{(5.3\text{ m/s})^2}{2(9.8\text{ m/s}^2)} = \boxed{1.4\text{ m}}$$

$\boxed{\text{No}}$, the length of the vine does not enter into the calculation, unless the vine is less than 0.7 m long. If that were the case, she could not rise 1.4 m high. Instead she would wrap the vine around the tree branch.

34. The forces on the skier are gravity and the normal force. The normal force is perpendicular to the direction of motion, and so does no work. Thus the skier's mechanical energy is conserved. Subscript 1 represents the skier at the top of the hill, and subscript 2 represents the skier at the bottom of the hill. The ground is the zero location for PE $(y = 0)$. We have $v_1 = 0$, $y_1 = 185\text{ m}$, and

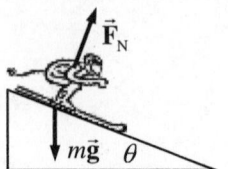

$y_2 = 0$ (bottom of the hill). Solve for v_2, the speed at the bottom.

$$\tfrac{1}{2}mv_1^2 + mgy_1 = \tfrac{1}{2}mv_2^2 + mgy_2 \quad \rightarrow \quad 0 + mgy_1 = \tfrac{1}{2}mv_2^2 + 0 \quad \rightarrow$$

$$v_2 = \sqrt{2gy_1} = \sqrt{2(9.80 \text{ m/s}^2)(185 \text{ m})} = \boxed{60.2 \text{ m/s}} (\approx 135 \text{ mi/h})$$

35. The forces on the sled are gravity and the normal force. The normal force is perpendicular to the direction of motion, and so does no work. Thus the sled's mechanical energy is conserved. Subscript 1 represents the sled at the bottom of the hill, and subscript 2 represents the sled at the top of the hill. The ground is the zero location for PE $(y = 0)$. We have $y_1 = 0$, $v_2 = 0$, and $y_2 = 1.35$ m. Solve for v_1, the speed at the bottom.

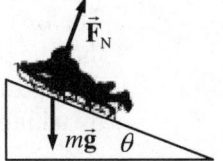

$$\tfrac{1}{2}mv_1^2 + mgy_1 = \tfrac{1}{2}mv_2^2 + mgy_2 \quad \rightarrow \quad \tfrac{1}{2}mv_1^2 + 0 = 0 + mgy_2 \quad \rightarrow$$

$$v_1 = \sqrt{2gy_2} = \sqrt{2(9.80 \text{ m/s}^2)(1.35 \text{ m})} = \boxed{5.14 \text{ m/s}}$$

Notice that the angle is not used in the calculation.

36. We assume that all the forces on the jumper are conservative, so that the mechanical energy of the jumper is conserved. Subscript 1 represents the jumper at the bottom of the jump, and subscript 2 represents the jumper at the top of the jump. Call the ground the zero location for PE $(y = 0)$. We have $y_1 = 0$, $v_2 = 0.70 \text{ m/s}$, and $y_2 = 2.10$ m. Solve for v_1, the speed at the bottom.

$$\tfrac{1}{2}mv_1^2 + mgy_1 = \tfrac{1}{2}mv_2^2 + mgy_2 \quad \rightarrow \quad \tfrac{1}{2}mv_1^2 + 0 = \tfrac{1}{2}mv_2^2 + mgy_2 \quad \rightarrow$$

$$v_1 = \sqrt{v_2^2 + 2gy_2} = \sqrt{(0.70 \text{ m/s})^2 + 2(9.80 \text{ m/s}^2)(2.10 \text{ m})} = \boxed{6.45 \text{ m/s}}$$

37. (a) Since there are no dissipative forces present, the mechanical energy of the person – trampoline – Earth combination will be conserved. The level of the unstretched trampoline is the zero level for both the elastic and gravitational PE. Call up the positive direction. Subscript 1 represents the jumper at the top of the jump, and subscript 2 represents the jumper upon arriving at the trampoline. There is no elastic PE involved in this part of the problem. We have $v_1 = 5.0 \text{ m/s}$, $y_1 = 3.0$ m, and $y_2 = 0$. Solve for v_2, the speed upon arriving at the trampoline.

$$E_1 = E_2 \quad \rightarrow \quad \tfrac{1}{2}mv_1^2 + mgy_1 = \tfrac{1}{2}mv_2^2 + mgy_2 \quad \rightarrow \quad \tfrac{1}{2}mv_1^2 + mgy_1 = \tfrac{1}{2}mv_2^2 + 0 \quad \rightarrow$$

$$v_2 = \pm\sqrt{v_1^2 + 2gy_1} = \pm\sqrt{(5.0 \text{ m/s})^2 + 2(9.8 \text{ m/s}^2)(3.0 \text{ m})} = \pm 9.154 \text{ m/s} \approx \boxed{9.2 \text{ m/s}}$$

The speed is the absolute value of v_2.

(b) Now let subscript 3 represent the jumper at the maximum stretch of the trampoline. We have $v_2 = 9.154 \text{ m/s}$, $y_2 = 0$, $x_2 = 0$, $v_3 = 0$, and $x_3 = y_3$. There is no elastic energy at position 2, but there is elastic energy at position 3. Also, the gravitational PE at position 3 is negative, and so $y_3 < 0$. A quadratic relationship results from the conservation of energy condition.

$$E_2 = E_3 \quad \rightarrow \quad \tfrac{1}{2}mv_2^2 + mgy_2 + \tfrac{1}{2}kx_2^2 = \tfrac{1}{2}mv_3^2 + mgy_3 + \tfrac{1}{2}kx_3^2 \quad \rightarrow$$

$$\tfrac{1}{2}mv_2^2 + 0 + 0 = 0 + mgy_3 + \tfrac{1}{2}ky_3^2 \quad \rightarrow \quad \tfrac{1}{2}ky_3^2 + mgy_3 - \tfrac{1}{2}mv_2^2 = 0 \quad \rightarrow$$

$$y_3 = \frac{-mg \pm \sqrt{m^2g^2 - 4(\tfrac{1}{2}k)(-\tfrac{1}{2}mv_2^2)}}{2(\tfrac{1}{2}k)} = \frac{-mg \pm \sqrt{m^2g^2 + kmv_2^2}}{k}$$

$$= \frac{-(65 \text{ kg})(9.8 \text{ m/s}^2) \pm \sqrt{(65 \text{ kg})^2(9.8 \text{ m/s}^2)^2 + (6.2 \times 10^4 \text{ N/m})(65 \text{ kg})(9.154 \text{ m/s})^2}}{(6.2 \times 10^4 \text{ N/m})}$$

$$= -0.307 \text{ m} , 0.286 \text{ m}$$

Since $y_3 < 0$, $y_3 = \boxed{-0.31 \text{ m}}$.

The first term under the quadratic is about 1000 times smaller than the second term, indicating that the problem could have been approximated by not even including gravitational PE for the final position. If that approximation would have been made, the result would have been found by taking the negative result from the following solution.

$$E_2 = E_3 \;\rightarrow\; \tfrac{1}{2}mv_2^2 = \tfrac{1}{2}ky_3^2 \;\rightarrow\; y_3 = v_2\sqrt{\frac{m}{k}} = (9.2 \text{ m/s})\sqrt{\frac{65 \text{ kg}}{6.2 \times 10^4 \text{ N/m}}} = \pm 0.30 \text{ m}$$

38. Use conservation of energy. Subscript 1 represents the projectile at the launch point, and subscript 2 represents the projectile as it reaches the ground. The ground is the zero location for PE $(y = 0)$. We have $v_1 = 185 \text{ m/s}$, $y_1 = 265 \text{ m}$, and $y_2 = 0$. Solve for v_2.

$$E_1 = E_2 \;\rightarrow\; \tfrac{1}{2}mv_1^2 + mgy_1 = \tfrac{1}{2}mv_2^2 + mgy_2 \;\rightarrow\; \tfrac{1}{2}mv_1^2 + mgy_1 = \tfrac{1}{2}mv_2^2 + 0 \;\rightarrow\;$$

$$v_2 = \sqrt{v_1^2 + 2gy_1} = \sqrt{(185 \text{ m/s})^2 + 2(9.80 \text{ m/s}^2)(265 \text{ m})} = \boxed{199 \text{ m/s}}$$

Note that the angle of launch does not enter into the problem.

39. Use conservation of energy. The level of the ball on the uncompressed spring taken as the zero location for both gravitational PE $(y = 0)$ and elastic PE $(x = 0)$. Take up to be positive for both.

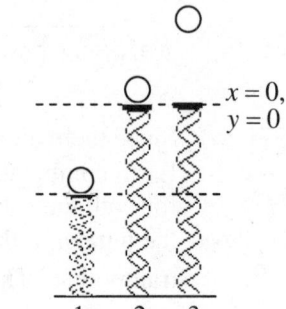

(*a*) Subscript 1 represents the ball at the launch point, and subscript 2 represents the ball at the location where it just leaves the spring, at the uncompressed length. We have $v_1 = 0$, $x_1 = y_1 = -0.150 \text{ m}$, and $x_2 = y_2 = 0$. Solve for v_2.

$$E_1 = E_2 \;\rightarrow\; \tfrac{1}{2}mv_1^2 + mgy_1 + \tfrac{1}{2}kx_1^2 = \tfrac{1}{2}mv_2^2 + mgy_2 + \tfrac{1}{2}kx_2^2 \;\rightarrow\;$$

$$0 + mgy_1 + \tfrac{1}{2}kx_1^2 = \tfrac{1}{2}mv_2^2 + 0 + 0 \;\rightarrow\; v_2 = \sqrt{\frac{kx_1^2 + 2mgy_1}{m}}$$

$$v_2 = \sqrt{\frac{(950 \text{ N/m})(0.150 \text{ m})^2 + 2(0.30 \text{ kg})(9.80 \text{ m/s}^2)(-0.150 \text{ m})}{(0.30 \text{ kg})}} = \boxed{8.3 \text{ m/s}}$$

(*b*) Subscript 3 represents the ball at its highest point. We have $v_1 = 0$, $x_1 = y_1 = -0.150 \text{ m}$, $v_3 = 0$, and $x_3 = 0$. Solve for y_3.

$$E_1 = E_3 \;\rightarrow\; \tfrac{1}{2}mv_1^2 + mgy_1 + \tfrac{1}{2}kx_1^2 = \tfrac{1}{2}mv_3^2 + mgy_3 + \tfrac{1}{2}kx_3^2 \;\rightarrow\;$$

$$0 + mgy_1 + \tfrac{1}{2}kx_1^2 = 0 + mgy_2 + 0 \;\rightarrow\; y_2 - y_1 = \frac{kx_1^2}{2mg} = \frac{(950 \text{ N/m})(0.150 \text{ m})^2}{2(0.30 \text{ kg})(9.80 \text{ m/s}^2)} = \boxed{3.6 \text{ m}}$$

40. Draw a free-body diagram for the block at the top of the curve. Since the block is moving in a circle, the net force is centripetal. Write Newton's 2nd law for the block, with down as positive. If the block is to be on the verge of falling off the track, then $F_N = 0$.

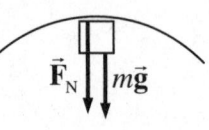

$$\sum F_R = F_N + mg = mv^2/r \quad \rightarrow \quad mg = mv_{top}^2/r \quad \rightarrow \quad v_{top} = \sqrt{gr}$$

Now use conservation of energy for the block. Since the track is frictionless, there are no non-conservative forces, and mechanical energy will be conserved. Subscript 1 represents the block at the release point, and subscript 2 represents the block at the top of the loop. The ground is the zero location for PE $(y = 0)$. We have $v_1 = 0$, $y_1 = h$, $v_2 = \sqrt{gr}$, and $y_2 = 2r$. Solve for h.

$$E_1 = E_2 \quad \rightarrow \quad \tfrac{1}{2}mv_1^2 + mgy_1 = \tfrac{1}{2}mv_2^2 + mgy_2 \quad \rightarrow \quad 0 + mgh = \tfrac{1}{2}mgr + 2mgr \quad \rightarrow \quad \boxed{h = 2.5\,r}$$

41. The block-spring combination is assumed to initially be at equilibrium, so the spring is neither stretched nor unstretched. At the release point, the speed of the mass is 0, and so the initial energy is all PE, given by $\tfrac{1}{2}kx_0^2$. That is the total energy of the system. Thus the energy of the system when the block is at a general location with some non-zero speed will still have this same total energy value. This is expressed by $E_{\text{total}} = \boxed{\tfrac{1}{2}mv^2 + \tfrac{1}{2}kx^2 = \tfrac{1}{2}kx_0^2}$.

42. Consider this diagram for the jumper's fall.
    (a) The mechanical energy of the jumper is conserved. Use y for the distance from the 0 of gravitational PE and x for the amount of bungee cord "stretch" from its unstretched length. Subscript 1 represents the jumper at the start of the fall, and subscript 2 represents the jumper at the lowest point of the fall. The bottom of the fall is the zero location for gravitational PE $(y = 0)$, and the location where the bungee cord just starts to be stretched is the zero location for elastic PE $(x = 0)$. We have $v_1 = 0$, $y_1 = 31\text{ m}$, $x_1 = 0$, $v_2 = 0$, $y_2 = 0$, and $x_2 = 19\text{ m}$. Apply conservation of energy.

    $$E_1 = E_2 \quad \rightarrow \quad \tfrac{1}{2}mv_1^2 + mgy_1 + \tfrac{1}{2}kx_1^2 = \tfrac{1}{2}mv_2^2 + mgy_2 + \tfrac{1}{2}kx_2^2 \quad \rightarrow \quad mgy_1 = \tfrac{1}{2}kx_2^2 \quad \rightarrow$$

    $$k = \frac{2mgy_1}{x_2^2} = \frac{2(62\text{ kg})(9.8\text{ m/s}^2)(31\text{ m})}{(19\text{ m})^2} = 104.4\text{ N/m} \approx \boxed{1.0 \times 10^2\text{ N/m}}$$

    (b) The maximum acceleration occurs at the location of the maximum force, which occurs when the bungee cord has its maximum stretch, at the bottom of the fall. Write Newton's 2nd law for the force on the jumper, with upward as positive.

    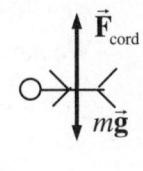

    $$F_{net} = F_{cord} - mg = kx_2 - mg = ma \quad \rightarrow$$

    $$a = \frac{kx_2}{m} - g = \frac{(104.4\text{ N/m})(19\text{ m})}{(62\text{ kg})} - 9.8\text{ m/s}^2 = 22.2\text{ m/s}^2 \approx \boxed{22\text{ m/s}^2}$$

43. Since there are no dissipative forces present, the mechanical energy of the roller coaster will be conserved. Subscript 1 represents the coaster at point 1, etc. The height of point 2 is the zero location for gravitational PE. We have $v_1 = 0$ and $y_1 = 35\text{ m}$.

    Point 2: $\tfrac{1}{2}mv_1^2 + mgy_1 = \tfrac{1}{2}mv_2^2 + mgy_2$; $y_2 = 0 \quad \rightarrow \quad mgy_1 = \tfrac{1}{2}mv_2^2 \quad \rightarrow$

    $$v_2 = \sqrt{2gy_1} = \sqrt{2(9.80\text{ m/s}^2)(35\text{ m})} = \boxed{26\text{ m/s}}$$

Point 3: $\frac{1}{2}mv_1^2 + mgy_1 = \frac{1}{2}mv_3^2 + mgy_3$; $y_3 = 28$ m $\rightarrow$ $mgy_1 = \frac{1}{2}mv_3^2 + mgy_3$ $\rightarrow$

$$v_3 = \sqrt{2g(y_1 - y_3)} = \sqrt{2(9.80\,\text{m/s}^2)(7\,\text{m})} = \boxed{12\,\text{m/s}}$$

Point 4: $\frac{1}{2}mv_1^2 + mgy_1 = \frac{1}{2}mv_4^2 + mgy_4$; $y_4 = 15$ m $\rightarrow$ $mgy_1 = \frac{1}{2}mv_4^2 + mgy_1$ $\rightarrow$

$$v_4 = \sqrt{2g(y_1 - y_4)} = \sqrt{2(9.80\,\text{m/s}^2)(20\,\text{m})} = \boxed{20\,\text{m/s}}$$

44. (*a*) See the diagram for the thrown ball. The speed at the top of the path will be the horizontal component of the original velocity.

$$v_{\text{top}} = v_0 \cos\theta = (12\,\text{m/s})\cos 33° = \boxed{10\,\text{m/s}}$$

(*b*) Since there are no dissipative forces in the problem, the mechanical energy of the ball is conserved. Subscript 1 represents the ball at the release point, and subscript 2 represents the ball at the top of the path. The ground is the zero location for PE $(y = 0)$. We have $v_1 = 12\,\text{m/s}$, $y_1 = 0$, and $v_2 = v_1 \cos\theta$. Solve for y_2.

$$E_1 = E_2 \rightarrow \frac{1}{2}mv_1^2 + mgy_1 = \frac{1}{2}mv_2^2 + mgy_2 \rightarrow \frac{1}{2}mv_1^2 + 0 = \frac{1}{2}mv_1^2\cos^2\theta + mgy_2 \rightarrow$$

$$y_2 = \frac{v_1^2(1 - \cos^2\theta)}{2g} = \frac{(12\,\text{m/s})^2(1 - \cos^2 33°)}{2(9.8\,\text{m/s}^2)} = \boxed{2.2\,\text{m}}$$

45. The maximum acceleration of 5.0 *g* occurs where the force is at a maximum. The maximum force occurs at the bottom of the motion, where the spring is at its maximum compression. Write Newton's 2nd law for the elevator at the bottom of the motion, with up as the positive direction.

$$F_{\text{net}} = F_{\text{spring}} - Mg = Ma = 5.0Mg \rightarrow F_{\text{spring}} = 6.0Mg$$

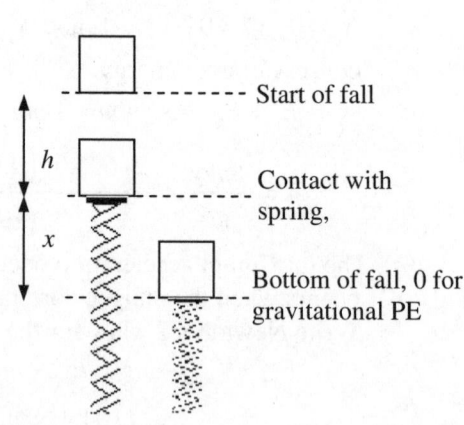

Now consider the diagram for the elevator at various points in its motion. If there are no non-conservative forces, then mechanical energy is conserved. Subscript 1 represents the elevator at the start of its fall, and subscript 2 represents the elevator at the bottom of its fall. The bottom of the fall is the zero location for gravitational PE $(y = 0)$. There is also a point at the top of the spring that we will define as the zero location for elastic PE $(x = 0)$. We have $v_1 = 0$, $y_1 = x + h$, $x_1 = 0$, $v_2 = 0$, $y_2 = 0$, and $x_2 = x$. Apply conservation of energy.

$$E_1 = E_2 \rightarrow \frac{1}{2}Mv_1^2 + Mgy_1 + \frac{1}{2}kx_1^2 = \frac{1}{2}Mv_2^2 + Mgy_2 + \frac{1}{2}kx_2^2 \rightarrow$$

$$0 + Mg(x + h) + 0 = 0 + 0 + \frac{1}{2}kx_2^2 \rightarrow Mg(x + h) = \frac{1}{2}kx_2^2$$

$$F_{\text{spring}} = 6.0Mg = kx \rightarrow x = \frac{6.0Mg}{k} \rightarrow Mg\left(\frac{6Mg}{k} + h\right) = \frac{1}{2}k\left(\frac{6Mg}{k}\right)^2 \rightarrow \boxed{k = \frac{12Mg}{h}}$$

46. (*a*) The work done against gravity is the change in PE.

$$W_{\substack{\text{against} \\ \text{gravity}}} = \Delta PE = mg(y_2 - y_1) = (75\,\text{kg})(9.8\,\text{m/s}^2)(150\,\text{m}) = \boxed{1.1 \times 10^5\,\text{J}}$$

(b) The work done by the force on the pedals in one revolution is equal to the tangential force times the circumference of the circular path of the pedals. That work is alsoequal to the energy change of the bicycle during that revolution. Note that a vertical rise on the incline is related to the distance along the incline by $\text{rise} = \text{distance}(\sin\theta)$.

$$W_{\substack{\text{pedal} \\ \text{force}}} = F_{\text{tan}}\, 2\pi r = \Delta PE_{1\,\text{rev}} = mg\,(\Delta y)_{1\,\text{rev}} = mgd_{1\,\text{rev}}\sin\theta \;\rightarrow$$

$$F_{\text{tan}} = \frac{mgd_{1\,\text{rev}}\sin\theta}{2\pi r} = \frac{(75\ \text{kg})(9.8\ \text{m/s}^2)(5.1\ \text{m})\sin 7.8^\circ}{2\pi(0.18\ \text{m})} = \boxed{4.5\times10^2\ \text{N}}$$

47. Use conservation of energy, where all of the kinetic energy is transformed to thermal energy.

$$E_{\text{initial}} = E_{\text{final}} \;\rightarrow\; \tfrac{1}{2}mv^2 = E_{\text{thermal}} = \tfrac{1}{2}(2)(7650\ \text{kg})\left[(95\ \text{km/h})\left(\frac{0.238\ \text{m/s}}{1\ \text{km/h}}\right)\right]^2 = \boxed{5.3\times10^6\ \text{J}}$$

48. Apply the conservation of energy to the child, considering work done by gravity and work changed into thermal energy. Subscript 1 represents the child at the top of the slide, and subscript 2 represents the child at the bottom of the slide. The ground is the zero location for $PE\,(y=0)$. We have $v_1 = 0$, $y_1 = 3.5\ \text{m}$, $v_2 = 2.2\ \text{m/s}$, and $y_2 = 0$. Solve for the work changed into thermal energy.

$$E_1 = E_2 \;\rightarrow\; \tfrac{1}{2}mv_1^2 + mgy_1 = \tfrac{1}{2}mv_2^2 + mgy_2 + W_{\text{thermal}} \;\rightarrow$$

$$W_{\text{thermal}} = mgy_1 - \tfrac{1}{2}mv_2^2 = (21.7\ \text{kg})(9.8\ \text{m/s}^2)(3.5\ \text{m}) - \tfrac{1}{2}(21.7\ \text{kg})(2.2\ \text{m/s})^2 = \boxed{6.9\times10^2\ \text{J}}$$

49. (a) See the free-body diagram for the ski. Write Newton's 2nd law for forces perpendicular to the direction of motion, noting that there is no acceleration perpendicular to the plane.

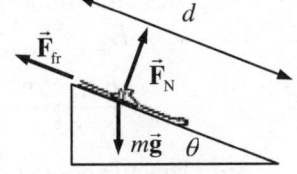

$$\sum F_\perp = F_N - mg\cos\theta \;\rightarrow\; F_N = mg\cos\theta \;\rightarrow$$

$$F_{\text{fr}} = \mu_k F_N = \mu_k mg\cos\theta$$

Now use conservation of energy, including the non-conservative friction force. Subscript 1 represents the ski at the top of the slope, and subscript 2 represents the ski at the bottom of the slope. The location of the ski at the bottom of the incline is the zero location for gravitational PE $(y=0)$. We have $v_1 = 0$, $y_1 = d\sin\theta$, and $y_2 = 0$. Write the conservation of energy condition, and solve for the final speed. Note that $F_{\text{fr}} = \mu_k F_N = \mu_k mg\cos\theta$

$$W_{\text{NC}} = \Delta KE + \Delta PE = \tfrac{1}{2}mv_2^2 - \tfrac{1}{2}mv_1^2 + mgy_2 - mgy_1 \;\rightarrow\; W_{\text{NC}} + E_1 = E_2$$

$$F_{\text{fr}}d\cos 180^\circ + \tfrac{1}{2}mv_1^2 + mgy_1 = \tfrac{1}{2}mv_2^2 + mgy_2 \;\rightarrow\; -\mu_k mgd\cos\theta + mgd\sin\theta = \tfrac{1}{2}mv_2^2 \;\rightarrow$$

$$v_2 = \sqrt{2gd(\sin\theta - \mu_k\cos\theta)} = \sqrt{2(9.80\ \text{m/s}^2)(75\ \text{m})(\sin 22^\circ - 0.090\cos 22^\circ)}$$

$$= 20.69\ \text{m/s} \approx \boxed{21\ \text{m/s}}$$

(b) Now, on the level ground, $F_f = \mu_k mg$, and there is no change in PE. Let us again use conservation of energy, including the non-conservative friction force, to relate position 2 with position 3. Subscript 3 represents the ski at the end of the travel on the level, having traveled a distance d_3 on the level. We have $v_2 = 20.69\ \text{m/s}$, $y_2 = 0$, $v_3 = 0$, and $y_3 = 0$.

$$W_{NC} + E_2 = E_3 \quad \rightarrow \quad F_f d_3 \cos 180° + \tfrac{1}{2}mv_2^2 + mgy_2 = \tfrac{1}{2}mv_3^2 + mgy_3 \quad \rightarrow$$

$$-\mu_k mgd_3 + \tfrac{1}{2}mv_2^2 = 0 \quad \rightarrow \quad d_3 = \frac{v_2^2}{2g\mu_k} = \frac{(20.69\,\text{m/s})^2}{2(9.80\,\text{m/s}^2)(0.090)} = 242.7\,\text{m} \approx \boxed{2.4 \times 10^2\,\text{m}}$$

50. (*a*) Apply energy conservation with no non-conservative work. Subscript 1 represents the ball as it is dropped, and subscript 2 represents the ball as it reaches the ground. The ground is the zero location for gravitational PE. We have $v_1 = 0$, $y_1 = 13.0\,\text{m}$, and $y_2 = 0$. Solve for v_2.

$$E_1 = E_2 \quad \rightarrow \quad \tfrac{1}{2}mv_1^2 + mgy_1 = \tfrac{1}{2}mv_2^2 + mgy_2 \quad \rightarrow \quad mgy_1 = \tfrac{1}{2}mv_2^2 \quad \rightarrow$$

$$v_2 = \sqrt{2gy_1} = \sqrt{2(9.80\,\text{m/s}^2)(13.0\,\text{m})} = \boxed{16.0\,\text{m/s}}$$

(*b*) Apply energy conservation, but with non-conservative work due to friction included. The work done by friction will be given by $W_{NC} = F_{fr} d \cos 180°$, since the force of friction is in the opposite direction as the motion. The distance d over which the frictional force acts will be the 13.0 m distance of fall. With the same parameters as above, and $v_2 = 8.00\,\text{m/s}$, solve for the force of friction.

$$W_{nc} + E_1 = E_2 \quad \rightarrow \quad -F_{fr}d + \tfrac{1}{2}mv_1^2 + mgy_1 = \tfrac{1}{2}mv_2^2 + mgy_2 \quad \rightarrow \quad -F_{fr}d + mgy_1 = \tfrac{1}{2}mv_2^2 \quad \rightarrow$$

$$F_{fr} = m\left(g\frac{y_1}{d} - \frac{v_2^2}{2d}\right) = (0.145\,\text{kg})\left(9.80\,\text{m/s}^2 - \frac{(8.00\,\text{m/s})^2}{2(13.0\,\text{m})}\right) = \boxed{1.06\,\text{N}}$$

51. (*a*) Calculate the energy of the ball at the two maximum heights, and subtract to find the amount of energy "lost". The energy at the two heights is all gravitational PE, since the ball has no KE at those maximum heights.

$$E_{lost} = E_{initial} - E_{final} = mgy_{initial} - mgy_{final}$$

$$\frac{E_{lost}}{E_{initial}} = \frac{mgy_{initial} - mgy_{final}}{mgy_{initial}} = \frac{y_{initial} - y_{final}}{y_{initial}} = \frac{2.0\,\text{m} - 1.5\,\text{m}}{2.0\,\text{m}} = 0.25 = \boxed{25\%}$$

(*b*) Due to energy conservation, the KE of the ball just as it leaves the ground is equal to its final PE.

$$PE_{final} = KE_{ground} \quad \rightarrow \quad mgy_{final} = \tfrac{1}{2}mv_{ground}^2 \quad \rightarrow$$

$$v_{ground} = \sqrt{2gy_{final}} = \sqrt{2(9.8\,\text{m/s}^2)(1.5\,\text{m})} = \boxed{5.4\,\text{m/s}}$$

(*c*) The energy "lost" was changed primarily into heat energy – the temperature of the ball and the ground would have increased slightly after the bounce. Some of the energy may have been changed into acoustic energy (sound waves). Some may have been lost due to non-elastic deformation of the ball or ground.

52. Since the crate moves along the floor, there is no change in gravitational PE, so use the work-energy theorem: $W_{net} = KE_2 - KE_1$. There are two forces doing work: F_P, the pulling force, and $F_{fr} = \mu_k F_N = \mu_k mg$, the frictional force. $KE_1 = 0$ since the crate starts from rest. Note that the two forces doing work do work over different distances.

$$W_P = F_P d_P \cos 0° \qquad W_{fr} = F_{fr} d_{fr} \cos 180° = -\mu_k mgd_{fr}$$

$$W_{\text{net}} = W_{\text{P}} + W_{\text{fr}} = KE_2 - KE_1 = \tfrac{1}{2}mv_2^2 - 0 \;\rightarrow$$

$$v_2 = \sqrt{\frac{2}{m}\left(W_{\text{P}} + W_{\text{fr}}\right)} = \sqrt{\frac{2}{m}\left(F_{\text{P}}d_{\text{P}} - \mu_k mgd_{\text{fr}}\right)}$$

$$= \sqrt{\frac{2}{(110\text{ kg})}\left[(350\text{ N})(30\text{ m}) - (0.30)(110\text{ kg})(9.8\text{ m/s}^2)(15\text{ m})\right]} = \boxed{10\,\text{m/s}}$$

53. Since there is a non-conservative force, consider energy conservation with non-conservative work included. Subscript 1 represents the roller coaster at point 1, and subscript 2 represents the roller coaster at point 2. Point 2 is taken as the zero location for gravitational PE. We have $v_1 = 1.70\,\text{m/s}$, $y_1 = 35\text{ m}$, and $y_2 = 0$. Solve for v_2. The work done by the non-conservative friction force is given by $W_{\text{NC}} = F_{\text{fr}}d\cos 180° = -0.20mgd$, since the force is one-fifth of mg, and the force is directed exactly opposite to the direction of motion.

$$W_{\text{NC}} + E_1 = E_2 \;\rightarrow\; -0.2mgd + \tfrac{1}{2}mv_1^2 + mgy_1 = \tfrac{1}{2}mv_2^2 + mgy_2 \;\rightarrow$$

$$v_2 = \sqrt{-0.4gd + v_1^2 + 2gy_1} = \sqrt{-0.4(9.80\text{ m/s}^2)(45.0\text{ m}) + (1.70\text{ m/s})^2 + 2(9.80\text{ m/s}^2)(35\text{ m})}$$

$$= 22.64\text{ m/s} \approx \boxed{23\,\text{m/s}}$$

54. Consider the free-body diagram for the skier in the midst of the motion. Write Newton's 2ⁿᵈ law for the direction perpendicular to the plane, with an acceleration of 0.

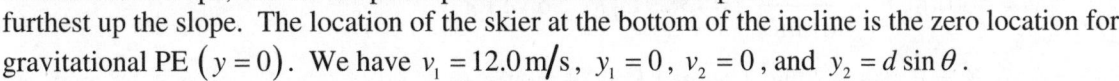

$$\sum F_\perp = F_{\text{N}} - mg\cos\theta = 0 \;\rightarrow\; F_{\text{N}} = mg\cos\theta \;\rightarrow$$

$$F_{\text{fr}} = \mu_k F_{\text{N}} = \mu_k mg\cos\theta$$

Apply conservation of energy to the skier, including the non-conservative friction force. Subscript 1 represents the skier at the bottom of the slope, and subscript 2 represents the skier at the point furthest up the slope. The location of the skier at the bottom of the incline is the zero location for gravitational PE $(y = 0)$. We have $v_1 = 12.0\,\text{m/s}$, $y_1 = 0$, $v_2 = 0$, and $y_2 = d\sin\theta$.

$$W_{\text{NC}} + E_1 = E_2 \;\rightarrow\; F_{\text{fr}}d\cos 180° + \tfrac{1}{2}mv_1^2 + mgy_1 = \tfrac{1}{2}mv_2^2 + mgy_2 \;\rightarrow$$

$$-\mu_k mgd\cos\theta + \tfrac{1}{2}mv_1^2 + 0 = 0 + mgd\sin\theta \;\rightarrow$$

$$\mu_k = \frac{\tfrac{1}{2}v_1^2 - gd\sin\theta}{gd\cos\theta} = \frac{v_1^2}{2gd\cos\theta} - \tan\theta = \frac{(12.0\text{ m/s})^2}{2(9.80\text{ m/s}^2)(12.2\text{ m})\cos 18.0°} - \tan 18.0°$$

$$= \boxed{0.308}$$

55. Use conservation of energy, including the non-conservative frictional force. The block is on a level surface, so there is no gravitational PE change to consider. The frictional force is given by $F_{\text{fr}} = \mu_k F_{\text{N}} = \mu_k mg$, since the normal force is equal to the weight. Subscript 1 represents the block at the compressed location, and subscript 2 represents the block at the maximum stretched position. The location of the block when the spring is neither stretched nor compressed is the zero location for elastic PE $(x = 0)$. Take right to be the positive direction. We have $v_1 = 0$, $x_1 = -0.050\text{ m}$, $v_2 = 0$, and $x_2 = 0.023\text{ m}$.

$$W_{NC} + E_1 = E_2 \rightarrow F_{fr}\Delta x \cos 180° + \tfrac{1}{2}mv_1^2 + \tfrac{1}{2}kx_1^2 = \tfrac{1}{2}mv_2^2 + \tfrac{1}{2}kx_2^2 \rightarrow$$

$$-\mu_k mg \Delta x + \tfrac{1}{2}kx_1^2 = \tfrac{1}{2}kx_2^2 \rightarrow$$

$$\mu_k = \frac{k\left(x_1^2 - x_2^2\right)}{2mg\Delta x} = \frac{(180\,\text{N/m})\left[(0.050\,\text{m})^2 - (0.023\,\text{m})^2\right]}{2(0.620\,\text{kg})(9.80\,\text{m/s}^2)(0.073\,\text{m})} = \boxed{0.40}$$

56. Use conservation of energy, including the non-conservative frictional force. The block is on a level surface, so there is no gravitational PE change to consider. Since the normal force is equal to the weight, the frictional force is $F_{fr} = \mu_k F_N = \mu_k mg$. Subscript 1 represents the block at the compressed location, and subscript 2 represents the block at the maximum stretched position. The location of the block when the spring is neither stretched nor compressed is the zero location for elastic PE ($x = 0$). Take right to be the positive direction. We have $v_1 = 0$, $x_1 = -0.18$ m, and $v_2 = 0$. The value of the spring constant is found from the fact that a 20-N force compresses the spring 18 cm, and so $k = F/x = 22\,\text{N}/0.18\,\text{m} = 122.2\,\text{N/m}$. The value of x_2 must be positive.

$$W_{NC} + E_1 = E_2 \rightarrow F_{fr}\Delta x \cos 180° + \tfrac{1}{2}mv_1^2 + \tfrac{1}{2}kx_1^2 = \tfrac{1}{2}mv_2^2 + \tfrac{1}{2}kx_2^2 \rightarrow$$

$$-\mu_k mg\left(x_2 - x_1\right) + \tfrac{1}{2}kx_1^2 = \tfrac{1}{2}kx_2^2 \rightarrow x_2^2 + \frac{2\mu_k mg}{k}x_2 - \left(\frac{2\mu_k mg}{k}x_1 + x_1^2\right) = 0 \rightarrow$$

$$x_2^2 + \frac{2(0.30)(0.28)(9.80)}{122.2}x_2 - \left(\frac{2(0.30)(0.28)(9.80)}{122.2}(-0.18) + (-0.18)^2\right) = 0 \rightarrow$$

$$x_2^2 + 0.01347x_2 - 0.02997 = 0 \rightarrow x_2 = 0.1665\,\text{m}, -0.1800\,\text{m} \rightarrow x_2 = \boxed{0.17\,\text{m}}$$

57. (a) If there is no air resistance, then conservation of mechanical energy can be used. Subscript 1 represents the glider when at launch, at subscript 2 represents the glider at landing. The landing location is the zero location for elastic PE ($x = 0$). We have $y_1 = 500$ m, $y_2 = 0$, and

$$v_1 = 500\,\text{km/h}\left(\frac{1\,\text{m/s}}{3.6\,\text{km/h}}\right) = 138.9\,\text{m/s}. \text{ Solve for } v_2$$

$$E_1 = E_2 \rightarrow \tfrac{1}{2}mv_1^2 + mgy_1 = \tfrac{1}{2}mv_2^2 + mgy_2 \rightarrow$$

$$v_2 = \sqrt{v_1^2 + 2gy_1} = \sqrt{(138.9\,\text{m/s})^2 + 2(9.80\,\text{m/s}^2)(3500\,\text{m})} = 296\,\text{m/s}\left(\frac{3.6\,\text{km/h}}{1\,\text{m/s}}\right)$$

$$= 1067\,\text{km/h} \approx \boxed{1.1 \times 10^3\,\text{km/h}}$$

(b) Now include the work done by the non-conservative frictional force. Consider the diagram of the glider. Calculate the work done by friction.

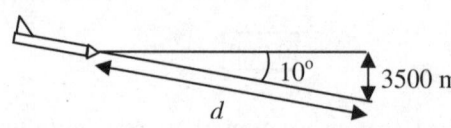

$$W_{NC} = F_{fr}d \cos 180° = -F_{fr}d = -F_{fr}\frac{3500\,\text{m}}{\sin 10°}$$

Use the same subscript representations as above, with y_1, v_1, and y_2 as before, and

$$v_2 = 200\,\text{km/h}\left(\frac{1\,\text{m/s}}{3.6\,\text{km/h}}\right) = 55.56\,\text{m/s}. \text{ Write the energy conservation equation and solve for}$$

the frictional force.

$$W_{NC} + E_1 = E_2 \rightarrow -F_{fr}d + \tfrac{1}{2}mv_1^2 + mgy_1 = \tfrac{1}{2}mv_2^2 + mgy_2 \rightarrow F_f = \frac{m\left(v_1^2 - v_2^2 + 2gy_1\right)}{2d}$$

$$= \frac{(980 \text{ kg})\left[(138.9 \text{ m/s})^2 - (55.56 \text{ m/s})^2 + 2(9.80 \text{ m/s}^2)(3500 \text{ m})\right]}{2\left(\dfrac{3500 \text{ m}}{\sin 10^\circ}\right)}$$

$$= 2062 \text{ N} \approx \boxed{2 \times 10^3 \text{ N}}$$

58. The work necessary to lift the piano is the work done by an upward force, equal in magnitude to the weight of the piano. Thus $W = Fd\cos 0^\circ = mgh$. The average power output required to lift the piano is the work done divided by the time to lift the piano.

$$P = \frac{W}{t} = \frac{mgh}{t} \rightarrow t = \frac{mgh}{P} = \frac{(315 \text{ kg})(9.80 \text{ m/s}^2)(16.0 \text{ m})}{1750 \text{ W}} = \boxed{28.2 \text{ s}}$$

59. The 18 hp is the power generated by the engine in creating a force on the ground to propel the car forward. The relationship between the power and the force is given by $P = \dfrac{W}{t} = \dfrac{Fd}{t} = F\dfrac{d}{t} = Fv$.

Thus the force to propel the car forward is found by $F = P/v$. If the car has a constant velocity, then the total resistive force must be of the same magnitude as the engine force, so that the net force is zero. Thus the total resistive force is also found by $F = P/v$.

$$F = \frac{P}{v} = \frac{(18 \text{ hp})(746 \text{ W/1 hp})}{(88 \text{ km/h})\left(\dfrac{1 \text{ m/s}}{3.6 \text{ km/h}}\right)} = \boxed{5.5 \times 10^2 \text{ N}}$$

60. The power is given by Eq. 6-16. The energy transformed is the change in kinetic energy of the car.

$$P = \frac{\text{energy transformed}}{\text{time}} = \frac{\Delta KE}{t} = \frac{\tfrac{1}{2}m\left(v_2^2 - v_1^2\right)}{t} = \frac{(1400 \text{ kg})\left[(95 \text{ km/h})\left(\dfrac{1 \text{ m/s}}{3.6 \text{ km/h}}\right)\right]^2}{2(7.4 \text{ s})}$$

$$= \boxed{6.6 \times 10^4 \text{ W}} \approx 88 \text{ hp}$$

61. (a) $1 \text{ hp} = (1 \text{ hp})\left(\dfrac{550 \text{ ft} \cdot \text{lb/s}}{1 \text{ hp}}\right)\left(\dfrac{4.45 \text{ N}}{1 \text{ lb}}\right)\left(\dfrac{1 \text{ m}}{3.28 \text{ ft}}\right) = 746 \text{ N} \cdot \text{m/s} = \boxed{746 \text{ W}}$

   (b) $75 \text{ W} = (75 \text{ W})\left(\dfrac{1 \text{ hp}}{746 \text{ W}}\right) = \boxed{0.10 \text{ hp}}$

62. (a) $1 \text{ kW} \cdot \text{h} = 1 \text{ kW} \cdot \text{h}\left(\dfrac{1000 \text{ W}}{1 \text{ kW}}\right)\left(\dfrac{3600 \text{ s}}{1 \text{ h}}\right)\left(\dfrac{1 \text{ J/s}}{1 \text{ W}}\right) = \boxed{3.6 \times 10^6 \text{ J}}$

   (b) $(520 \text{ W})(1 \text{ month}) = (520 \text{ W})(1 \text{ month})\left(\dfrac{1 \text{ kW}}{1000 \text{ W}}\right)\left(\dfrac{30 \text{ d}}{1 \text{ month}}\right)\left(\dfrac{24 \text{ h}}{1 \text{ d}}\right) = 374 \text{ kW} \cdot \text{h}$

$$\approx \boxed{370 \text{ kW} \cdot \text{h}}$$

(*c*) $374 \text{ kW} \cdot \text{h} = 374 \text{ kW} \cdot \text{h} \left(\dfrac{3.6 \times 10^6 \text{ J}}{1 \text{ kW} \cdot \text{h}} \right) = \boxed{1.3 \times 10^9 \text{ J}}$

(*d*) $\left(374 \text{ kW} \cdot \text{h} \right) \left(\dfrac{\$0.12}{1 \text{ kW} \cdot \text{h}} \right) = \$44.88 \approx \boxed{\$45}$

Kilowatt-hours is a measure of energy, not power, and so $\boxed{\text{no}}$, the actual rate at which the energy is used does not figure into the bill. They could use the energy at a constant rate, or at a widely varying rate, and as long as the total used is 370 kilowatt-hours, the price would be $45.

63.   The energy transfer from the engine must replace the lost kinetic energy. From the two speeds, calculate the average rate of loss in kinetic energy while in neutral.

$$v_1 = 85 \text{ km/h} \left(\dfrac{1 \text{ m/s}}{3.6 \text{ km/h}} \right) = 23.61 \text{ m/s} \qquad v_2 = 65 \text{ km/h} \left(\dfrac{1 \text{ m/s}}{3.6 \text{ km/h}} \right) = 18.06 \text{ m/s}$$

$$\Delta KE = \tfrac{1}{2} m v_2^2 - \tfrac{1}{2} m v_1^2 = \tfrac{1}{2} \left(1150 \text{ kg} \right) \left[\left(18.06 \text{ m/s} \right)^2 - \left(23.61 \text{ m/s} \right)^2 \right] = -1.330 \times 10^5 \text{ J}$$

$$P = \dfrac{W}{t} = \dfrac{1.330 \times 10^5 \text{ J}}{6.0 \text{ s}} = 2.216 \times 10^4 \text{ W} \text{ , or } \left(2.216 \times 10^4 \text{ W} \right) \dfrac{1 \text{ hp}}{746 \text{ W}} = 29.71 \text{ hp}$$

So $\boxed{2.2 \times 10^4 \text{ W}}$ or $\boxed{3.0 \times 10^1 \text{ hp}}$ is needed from the engine.

64.   Since $P = \dfrac{W}{t}$, we have $W = Pt = 3.0 \text{ hp} \left(\dfrac{746 \text{ W}}{1 \text{ hp}} \right) \left(1 \text{ hr} \right) \left(\dfrac{3600 \text{ s}}{1 \text{ h}} \right) = \boxed{8.1 \times 10^6 \text{ J}}$

$\boxed{65.}$ The work done in accelerating the shot put is given by its change in kinetic energy: The power is the energy change per unit time.

$$P = \dfrac{W}{t} = \dfrac{KE_2 - KE_1}{t} = \dfrac{\tfrac{1}{2} m \left(v_2^2 - v_1^2 \right)}{t} = \dfrac{\tfrac{1}{2} \left(7.3 \text{ kg} \right) \left[\left(14 \text{ m/s} \right)^2 - 0 \right]}{1.5 \text{ s}} = 476.9 \text{ W} \approx \boxed{4.8 \times 10^2 \text{ W}}$$

66.   The force to lift the water is equal to its weight, and so the work to lift the water is equal to the weight times the distance. The power is the work done per unit time.

$$P = \dfrac{W}{t} = \dfrac{mgh}{t} = \dfrac{\left(18.0 \text{ kg} \right) \left(9.80 \text{ m/s}^2 \right) \left(3.60 \text{ m} \right)}{60 \text{ sec}} = \boxed{10.6 \text{ W}}$$

67.   The minimum force needed to lift the football player vertically is equal to his weight, *mg*. The distance over which that force would do work would be the change in height,

$\Delta y = \left(140 \text{ m} \right) \sin 32° = 74.2 \text{ m}$. So the work done in raising the player is $W = mg \Delta y$ and the power output required is the work done per unit time.

$$P = \dfrac{W}{t} = \dfrac{mg \Delta y}{t} = \dfrac{\left(95 \text{ kg} \right) \left(9.80 \text{ m/s}^2 \right) \left(74.2 \text{ m} \right)}{66 \text{ sec}} = 1047 \text{ W} \approx \boxed{1.0 \times 10^3 \text{ W}} .$$

68. See the free-body diagram for the bicycle on the hill. Write Newton's 2nd law for the x direction, noting that the acceleration is 0. Solve for the magnitude of $\vec{F}_P$. The power output related to that force is given by Eq. 6-17, $P = F_P v$. Use that relationship to find the velocity.

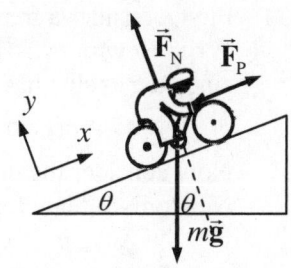

$$\sum F_x = F_P - mg\sin\theta = 0 \quad\rightarrow\quad F_P = mg\sin\theta$$

$$P = vF_P \quad\rightarrow\quad v = \frac{P}{F_P} = \frac{P}{mg\sin\theta} = \frac{(0.25\,\text{hp})(746\,\text{W/hp})}{(68\,\text{kg})(9.8\,\text{m/s}^2)\sin 6.0^\circ}$$

$$= \boxed{2.7\,\text{m/s}}$$

69. Consider the free-body diagram for the car. The car has a constant velocity, so the net force on the car is zero. F_{fr} is the friction force, and F_{car} is the force of the road pushing on the car. It is equal in magnitude to the force of the car pushing on the road, and so we can think of F_{car} as the force the car is able to generate by the engine. Write Newton's 2nd law in the x direction.

$$\sum F_x = F_{car} - F_{fr} - mg\sin\theta \quad\rightarrow\quad F_{car} = F_{fr} + mg\sin\theta$$

Use Eq. 6-17 to express the power output of the car, and then calculate the angle from that expression.

$$P = (F_{fr} + mg\sin\theta)v \quad\rightarrow$$

$$\theta = \sin^{-1}\left[\frac{1}{mg}\left(\frac{P}{v} - F_{fr}\right)\right] = \sin^{-1}\left[\frac{1}{(1200\,\text{kg})(9.80\,\text{m/s}^2)}\left(\frac{120\text{hp}(746\,\text{W/1 hp})}{(75\,\text{km/h})\left(\frac{1\,\text{m/s}}{3.6\,\text{km/h}}\right)} - 650\,\text{N}\right)\right]$$

$$= \boxed{18^\circ}$$

70. Draw a free-body diagram for the box being dragged along the floor. The box has a constant speed, so the acceleration is 0 in all directions. Write Newton's 2nd law for both the x (horizontal) and y (vertical) directions.

$$\sum F_y = F_N - mg = 0 \quad\rightarrow\quad F_N = mg$$

$$\sum F_x = F_P - F_{fr} = 0 \quad\rightarrow\quad F_P = F_{fr} = \mu_k F_N = \mu_k mg$$

The work done by F_P in moving the crate a distance Δx is given by $W = F_P \Delta x \cos 0^\circ = \mu_k mg\Delta x$. The power required is the work done per unit time.

$$P = \frac{W}{t} = \frac{\mu_k mg\Delta x}{t} = \mu_k mg\frac{\Delta x}{t} = \mu_k mg v_x = (0.45)(310\,\text{kg})(9.80\,\text{m/s}^2)(1.20\,\text{m/s}) = 1641\,\text{W}$$

$$1641\,\text{W}\left(\frac{1\,\text{hp}}{746\,\text{W}}\right) = \boxed{2.2\,\text{hp}}$$

71. First, consider a free-body diagram for the cyclist going down hill. Write Newton's 2nd law for the *x* direction, with an acceleration of 0 since the cyclist has a constant speed.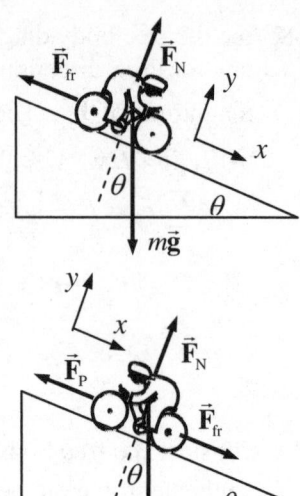

$$\sum F_x = mg \sin \theta - F_{fr} = 0 \quad \rightarrow \quad F_{fr} = mg \sin \theta$$

Now consider the diagram for the cyclist going up the hill. Again, write Newton's 2nd law for the x direction, with an acceleration of 0.

$$\sum F_x = F_{fr} - F_P + mg \sin \theta = 0 \quad \rightarrow \quad F_P = F_{fr} + mg \sin \theta$$

Assume that the friction force is the same when the speed is the same, so the friction force when going uphill is the same magnitude as when going downhill.

$$F_P = F_{fr} + mg \sin \theta = 2mg \sin \theta$$

The power output due to this force is given by Eq. 6-17.

$$P = F_P v = 2mgv \sin \theta = 2(75 \text{ kg})(9.8 \text{ m/s}^2)(5.0 \text{ m/s}) \sin 7.0°$$

$$= \boxed{9.0 \times 10^2 \text{ W}}$$

72. The kinetic energy of the moving car is changed into the elastic PE of the bumper, before it deforms.

$$\tfrac{1}{2}mv^2 = \tfrac{1}{2}kx^2 \quad \rightarrow \quad k = \frac{mv^2}{x^2} = \frac{(1300 \text{ kg})\left[(8 \text{ km/h})\left(\dfrac{1 \text{ m/s}}{3.6 \text{ km/h}}\right)\right]^2}{(0.015 \text{ m})^2} = \boxed{2.9 \times 10^7 \text{ N/m}}$$

73. The minimum work required to shelve a book is equal to the weight of the book times the vertical distance the book is moved – its increase in PE. See the diagram. Each book that is placed on the lowest shelf has its center of mass moved upwards by 20.5 cm. So the work done to move 25 books to the lowest shelf is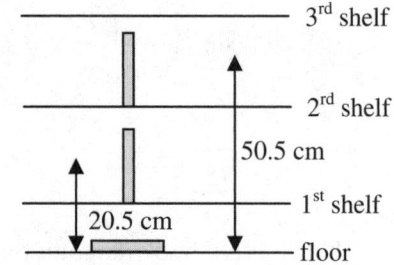
$W_1 = 25mg\,(0.205 \text{ m})$. Each book that is placed on the second shelf has its center of mass moved upwards by 50.5 cm, so the work done to move 25 books to the second shelf is
$W_2 = 25mg\,(0.505 \text{ m})$. Similarly, $W_3 = 25mg\,(0.805 \text{ m})$, $W_4 = 25mg\,(1.105 \text{ m})$, and $W_5 = 25mg\,(1.405 \text{ m})$. The total work done is the sum of the five work expressions.

$$W = 25mg\,(0.205 \text{ m} + .505 \text{ m} + .805 \text{ m} + 1.105 \text{ m} + 1.405 \text{ m})$$

$$= 25(1.5 \text{ kg})(9.80 \text{ m/s}^2)(4.025 \text{ m}) = 1479 \text{ J} \approx \boxed{1.5 \times 10^3 \text{ J}}$$

74. Assume that there are no non-conservative forces doing work, so the mechanical energy of the jumper will be conserved. Subscript 1 represents the jumper at the launch point of the jump, and subscript 2 represents the jumper at the highest point. The starting height of the jump is the zero location for PE $(y = 0)$. We have $y_1 = 0$, $y_2 = 1.1$ m, and $v_2 = 6.5$ m/s. Solve for v_1.

$$E_1 = E_2 \quad \rightarrow \quad \tfrac{1}{2}mv_1^2 + mgy_1 = \tfrac{1}{2}mv_2^2 + mgy_2 \quad \rightarrow$$

$$v_1 = \sqrt{v_2^2 + 2gy_2} = \sqrt{(6.5 \text{ m/s})^2 + 2(9.8 \text{ m/s}^2)(1.1 \text{ m})} = \boxed{8.0 \text{ m/s}}$$

75. (a) Consider a free-body diagram for the block at the top of the curve. Since the block is moving in a circle, the net force is centripetal. Write Newton's 2nd law for the block, with down as vertical. If the block is to be on the verge of falling off the track, then $F_N = 0$.

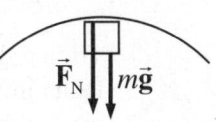

$$\sum F_R = F_N + mg = mv_{top}^2/r \;\rightarrow\; mg = mv_{top}^2/r \;\rightarrow\; v_{top} = \sqrt{gr}$$

Now use conservation of energy for the block. Since the track is frictionless, there are no non-conservative forces, and mechanical energy will be conserved. Subscript 1 represents the block at the release point, and subscript 2 represents the block at the top of the loop. The ground is the zero location for PE $(y = 0)$. We have $v_1 = 0$, $y_1 = h$, $v_2 = v_{top} = \sqrt{gr}$, and $y_2 = 2r$. Solve for h.

$$E_1 = E_2 \;\rightarrow\; \tfrac{1}{2}mv_1^2 + mgy_1 = \tfrac{1}{2}mv_2^2 + mgy_2 \;\rightarrow\; mgh = \tfrac{1}{2}mgr + 2mgr \;\rightarrow\; h = \boxed{2.5\,r}$$

(b) Now the release height is $2h = 5r$. Use conservation of energy again. Subscript 1 represents the block at the (new) release point, and subscript 2 represents the block at the bottom of the loop. We have $v_1 = 0$, $y_1 = 5r$, and $y_2 = 0$. Solve for v_2^2.

$$E_1 = E_2 \;\rightarrow\; \tfrac{1}{2}mv_1^2 + mgy_1 = \tfrac{1}{2}mv_2^2 + mgy_2 \;\rightarrow\; v_2^2 = 10rg\;.$$

Now consider the free-body diagram for the block at the bottom of the loop. The net force must be upward and radial. Write Newton's 2nd law for the vertical direction, with up as positive.

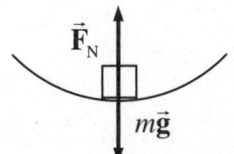

$$\sum F_R = F_N - mg = mv^2/r \;\rightarrow$$

$$F_N = mg + mv^2/r = mg + \frac{m10rg}{r} = \boxed{11mg}$$

(c) Use conservation of energy again. Subscript 2 is as in part (b) above, and subscript 3 represents the block at the top of the loop. We have $y_2 = 0$, $v_2 = \sqrt{10rg}$, and $y_3 = 2r$. Solve for v_3^2.

$$E_2 = E_3 \;\rightarrow\; \tfrac{1}{2}mv_2^2 + mgy_2 = \tfrac{1}{2}mv_3^2 + mgy_3 \;\rightarrow\; 5mrg + 0 = \tfrac{1}{2}mv_3^2 + 2rmg \;\rightarrow$$

$$v_3^2 = 6rg$$

Refer to the free-body diagram and analysis of part (a) to find the normal force.

$$\sum F_R = F_N + mg = mv_{top}^2/r \;\rightarrow\; F_N = mv^2/r - mg = \frac{6rmg}{r} - mg = \boxed{5mg}$$

(d) When moving on the level, the normal force is the same as the weight, $F_N = \boxed{mg}$.

76. (a) Use conservation of energy, including the work done by the non-conservative force of the snow on the pilot. Subscript 1 represents the pilot at the top of the snowbank, and subscript 2 represents the pilot at the bottom of the crater. The bottom of the crater is the zero location for PE $(y = 0)$. We have $v_1 = 35$ m/s, $y_1 = 1.1$ m, $v_2 = 0$, and $y_2 = 0$. Solve for the non-conservative work.

$$W_{NC} + E_1 = E_2 \;\rightarrow\; W_{NC} + \tfrac{1}{2}mv_1^2 + mgy_1 = \tfrac{1}{2}mv_2^2 + mgy_2 \;\rightarrow$$

$$W_{NC} = -\tfrac{1}{2}mv_1^2 - mgy_1 = -\tfrac{1}{2}(78 \text{ kg})(35 \text{ m/s})^2 - (78 \text{ kg})(9.8 \text{ m/s}^2)(1.1 \text{ m})$$

$$= -4.862 \times 10^4 \text{ J} \approx \boxed{-4.9 \times 10^4 \text{ J}}$$

(b) The work done by the snowbank is done by an upward force, while the pilot moves down.

$$W_{NC} = F_{snow}d\cos 180° = -F_{snow}d \;\rightarrow$$

$$F_{snow} = -\frac{W_{NC}}{d} = -\frac{-4.862 \times 10^4 \text{ J}}{1.1 \text{ m}} = 4.420 \times 10^4 \text{ N} \approx \boxed{4.4 \times 10^4 \text{ N}}$$

(c) To find the work done by air friction, another non-conservative force, use energy conservation including the work done by the non-conservative force of air friction. Subscript 1 represents the pilot at the start of the descent, and subscript 3 represents the pilot at the top of the snowbank. The top of the snowbank is the zero location for PE $(y = 0)$. We have $v_1 = 0$ m/s, $y_1 = 370$ m, $v_2 = 35$ m/s, and $y_2 = 0$. Solve for the non-conservative work.

$$W_{NC} + E_1 = E_2 \quad \rightarrow \quad W_{NC} + \tfrac{1}{2}mv_1^2 + mgy_1 = \tfrac{1}{2}mv_2^2 + mgy_2 \quad \rightarrow$$

$$W_{NC} = \tfrac{1}{2}mv_2^2 - mgy_1 = \tfrac{1}{2}(78 \text{ kg})(35 \text{ m/s})^2 - (78 \text{ kg})(9.8 \text{ m/s}^2)(370 \text{ m})$$

$$= -2.351 \times 10^5 \text{ J} \approx \boxed{-2.4 \times 10^5 \text{ J}}$$

77. (a) The tension in the cord is perpendicular to the path at all times, and so the tension in the cord does not do any work on the ball. Thus the mechanical energy of the ball is conserved. Subscript 1 represents the ball when it is horizontal, and subscript 2 represents the ball at the lowest point on its path. The lowest point on the path is the zero location for PE $(y = 0)$. We have $v_1 = 0$, $y_1 = L$, and $y_2 = 0$. Solve for v_2.

$$E_1 = E_2 \quad \rightarrow \quad \tfrac{1}{2}mv_1^2 + mgy_1 = \tfrac{1}{2}mv_2^2 + mgy_2 \quad \rightarrow \quad mgL = \tfrac{1}{2}mv_2^2 \quad \rightarrow \quad v_2 = \boxed{\sqrt{2gL}}$$

(b) Use conservation of energy, to relate points 2 and 3. Point 2 is as described above. Subscript 3 represents the ball at the top of its circular path around the peg. The lowest point on the path is the zero location for PE $(y = 0)$. We have $v_1 = \sqrt{2gL}$, $y_1 = 0$, and $y_2 = 2(L - h) = 2(L - 0.80L) = 0.40L$. Solve for v_2.

$$E_2 = E_3 \quad \rightarrow \quad \tfrac{1}{2}mv_2^2 + mgy_2 = \tfrac{1}{2}mv_3^2 + mgy_3 \quad \rightarrow \quad \tfrac{1}{2}m(2gL) = \tfrac{1}{2}mv_2^2 + mg(0.40L) \quad \rightarrow$$

$$\boxed{v_2 = \sqrt{1.2gL}}$$

78. (a) The work done by the hiker against gravity is the change in gravitational PE.

$$W_G = mg\Delta y = (65 \text{ kg})(9.8 \text{ m/s}^2)(3700 \text{ m} - 2300 \text{ m}) = 8.918 \times 10^5 \text{ J} \cong \boxed{8.9 \times 10^5 \text{ J}}$$

(b) The average power output is found by dividing the work by the time taken.

$$P_{output} = \frac{W_{grav}}{t} = \frac{8.918 \times 10^5 \text{ J}}{(5 \text{ h})(3600 \text{ s}/1 \text{ h})} = 49.54 \text{ W} \approx \boxed{50 \text{ W}}$$

$$49.54 \text{ W}\left(\frac{1 \text{ hp}}{746 \text{ W}}\right) = \boxed{6.6 \times 10^{-2} \text{ hp}}$$

(c) The output power is the efficiency times the input power.

$$P_{output} = 0.15 P_{input} \quad \rightarrow \quad P_{input} = \frac{P_{output}}{0.15} = \frac{49.54 \text{ W}}{0.15} = \boxed{3.3 \times 10^2 \text{ W}} = \boxed{0.44 \text{ hp}}$$

79. (a) The work done by gravity as the elevator falls is the opposite of the change in gravitational PE.

$$W_G = -\Delta PE = PE_1 - PE_2 = mg(y_1 - y_2) = (920 \text{ kg})(9.8 \text{ m/s}^2)(28 \text{ m})$$

$$= 2.524 \times 10^5 \text{ J} \approx \boxed{2.5 \times 10^5 \text{ J}}$$

Gravity is the only force doing work on the elevator as it falls (ignoring friction), so this result is also the net work done on the elevator as it falls.

(b) The net work done on the elevator is equal to its change in kinetic energy. The net work done just before striking the spring is the work done by gravity found above.

$$W_G = KE_2 - KE_1 \quad \rightarrow \quad mg(y_1 - y_2) = \tfrac{1}{2}mv_2^2 - 0 \quad \rightarrow$$

$$v_2 = \sqrt{2g(y_1 - y_2)} = \sqrt{2(9.8\,\text{m/s}^2)(28\text{ m})} = 23.43\,\text{m/s} \approx \boxed{23\,\text{m/s}}$$

(c) Use conservation of energy. Subscript 1 represents the elevator just before striking the spring, and subscript 2 represents the elevator at the bottom of its motion. The level of the elevator just before striking the spring is the zero location for both gravitational PE and elastic PE. We have $v_1 = 23.43\,\text{m/s}$, $y_1 = 0$, and $v_2 = 0$. We assume that $y_2 < 0$.

$$E_1 = E_2 \quad \rightarrow \quad \tfrac{1}{2}mv_1^2 + mgy_1 + \tfrac{1}{2}ky_1^2 = \tfrac{1}{2}mv_2^2 + mgy_2 + \tfrac{1}{2}ky_2^2 \quad \rightarrow$$

$$y_2^2 + 2\frac{mg}{k}y_2 - \frac{m}{k}v_1^2 = 0 \quad \rightarrow \quad y_2 = \frac{-\dfrac{2mg}{k} \pm \sqrt{\dfrac{4m^2g^2}{k^2} + 4\dfrac{mv_1^2}{k}}}{2} = \frac{-mg \pm \sqrt{m^2g^2 + mkv_1^2}}{k}$$

We must choose the negative root so that y_2 is negative. Thus

$$y_2 = \frac{-(920\text{ kg})(9.8\,\text{m/s}^2) - \sqrt{(920\text{ kg})^2(9.8\,\text{m/s}^2) + (920\text{ kg})(2.2\times10^5\text{ N/m})(23.43\,\text{m/s})^2}}{2.2\times10^5\text{ N/m}}$$

$$= \boxed{-1.56\text{ m}}$$

80. The force to lift a person is equal to the person's weight, so the work to lift a person up a vertical distance h is equal to mgh. The work needed to lift N people is $Nmgh$, and so the power needed is the total work divided by the total time. We assume the mass of the average person to be 70 kg,

$$P = \frac{W}{t} = \frac{Nmgh}{t} = \frac{47000(70\text{ kg})(9.80\,\text{m/s}^2)(200\text{ m})}{3600\text{ s}} = 1.79\times10^6\,\text{W} \approx \boxed{2\times10^6\,\text{W}}.$$

81. (a) Use conservation of mechanical energy, assuming there are no non-conservative forces. Subscript 1 represents the water at the top of the dam, and subscript 2 represents the water as it strikes the turbine blades. The level of the turbine blades is the zero location for PE $(y = 0)$.

We have $v_1 = 0$, $y_1 = 80$ m, and $y_2 = 0$. Solve for v_2.

$$E_1 = E_2 \quad \rightarrow \quad \tfrac{1}{2}mv_1^2 + mgy_1 = \tfrac{1}{2}mv_2^2 + mgy_2 \quad \rightarrow \quad mgy_1 = \tfrac{1}{2}mv_2^2 \quad \rightarrow$$

$$v_2 = \sqrt{2gy_1} = \sqrt{2(9.8\,\text{m/s}^2)(81\text{ m})} = 39.84\,\text{m/s} \approx \boxed{4.0\times10^1\text{ m/s}}$$

(b) The energy of the water at the level of the turbine blades is all kinetic energy, and so is given by $\tfrac{1}{2}mv_2^2$. 58% of that energy gets transferred to the turbine blades. The rate of energy transfer to the turbine blades is the power developed by the water.

$$P = 0.58\left(\tfrac{1}{2}\frac{m}{t}v_2^2\right) = \frac{(0.58)(650\text{ kg/s})(39.84\,\text{m/s})^2}{2} = \boxed{3.0\times10^5\,\text{W}}$$

82. Consider the free-body diagram for the coaster at the bottom of the loop. The
     net force must be an upward centripetal force.

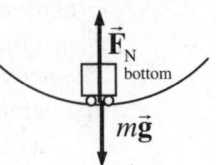

$$\sum F_{\text{bottom}} = F_{N_{\text{bottom}}} - mg = m v_{\text{bottom}}^2 / R \;\;\rightarrow\;\; F_{N_{\text{bottom}}} = mg + m v_{\text{bottom}}^2 / R$$

Now consider the force diagram at the top of the loop. Again, the net force
must be centripetal, and so must be downward.

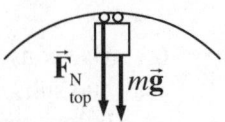

$$\sum F_{\text{top}} = F_{N_{\text{top}}} + mg = m v_{\text{top}}^2 / R \;\;\rightarrow\;\; F_{N_{\text{top}}} = m v_{\text{top}}^2 / R - mg .$$

Assume that the speed at the top is large enough that $F_{N_{\text{top}}} > 0$, and so

$v_{\text{top}} > \sqrt{Rg}$. Now apply the conservation of mechanical energy. Subscript 1 represents the coaster
at the bottom of the loop, and subscript 2 represents the coaster at the top of the loop. The level of
the bottom of the loop is the zero location for PE $(y = 0)$. We have $y_1 = 0$ and $y_2 = 2R$.

$$E_1 = E_2 \;\;\rightarrow\;\; \tfrac{1}{2}mv_1^2 + mgy_1 = \tfrac{1}{2}mv_2^2 + mgy_2 \;\;\rightarrow\;\; v_{\text{bottom}}^2 = v_{\text{top}}^2 + 4gR .$$

The difference in apparent weights is the difference in the normal forces.

$$F_{N_{\text{bottom}}} - F_{N_{\text{top}}} = \left(mg + m v_{\text{bottom}}^2 / R\right) - \left(m v_{\text{top}}^2 / R - mg\right) = 2mg + m\left(v_{\text{bottom}}^2 - v_{\text{top}}^2\right) / R$$

$$= 2mg + m\left(4gR\right) / R = \boxed{6mg}$$

Notice that the result does not depend on either v or R .

83. (*a*) Assume that the energy of the candy bar is completely converted into a change of PE:

$$E_{\text{candy bar}} = \Delta PE = mg\Delta y \;\;\rightarrow\;\; \Delta y = \frac{E_{\text{candy bar}}}{mg} = \frac{1.1 \times 10^6 \, \text{J}}{\left(82 \, \text{kg}\right)\left(9.8 \, \text{m/s}^2\right)} = \boxed{1.4 \times 10^3 \, \text{m}} .$$

     (*b*) If the person jumped to the ground, the same energy is all converted into kinetic energy.

$$E_{\text{candy bar}} = \tfrac{1}{2}mv^2 \;\;\rightarrow\;\; v = \sqrt{\frac{2E_{\text{candy bar}}}{m}} = \sqrt{\frac{2\left(1.1 \times 10^6 \, \text{J}\right)}{\left(82 \, \text{kg}\right)}} = \boxed{1.6 \times 10^2 \, \text{m/s}}$$

84. Since there are no non-conservative forces, the mechanical energy of the projectile will be
     conserved. Subscript 1 represents the projectile at launch and subscript 2 represents the projectile as
     it strikes the ground. The ground is the zero location for PE $(y = 0)$. We have $v_1 = 175 \, \text{m/s}$,

     $y_1 = 165 \, \text{m}$, and $y_2 = 0$. Solve for v_2.

$$E_1 = E_2 \;\;\rightarrow\;\; \tfrac{1}{2}mv_1^2 + mgy_1 = \tfrac{1}{2}mv_2^2 + mgy_2 \;\;\rightarrow\;\; \tfrac{1}{2}mv_1^2 + mgy_1 = \tfrac{1}{2}mv_2^2 \;\;\rightarrow$$

$$v_2 = \sqrt{v_1^2 + 2gy_1} = \sqrt{\left(175 \, \text{m/s}\right)^2 + 2\left(9.8 \, \text{m/s}^2\right)\left(165 \, \text{m}\right)} = \boxed{184 \, \text{m/s}}$$

Notice that the launch angle does not enter the problem, and so does not influence the final speed.

85. The spring constant for the scale can be found from the 0.6 mm compression due to the 710 N force.

$$k = \frac{F}{x} = \frac{710 \, \text{N}}{6.0 \times 10^{-4} \, \text{m}} = 1.183 \times 10^6 \, \text{N/m} .$$ Use conservation of energy for the jump. Subscript 1

represents the initial location, and subscript 2 represents the location at maximum compression of the
scale spring. Assume that the location of the uncompressed scale spring is the 0 location for
gravitational PE. We have $v_1 = v_2 = 0$ and $y_1 = 1.0 \, \text{m}$. Solve for y_2, which must be negative.

$$E_1 = E_2 \quad \rightarrow \quad \tfrac{1}{2}mv_1^2 + mgy_1 = \tfrac{1}{2}mv_2^2 + mgy_2 + \tfrac{1}{2}ky_2^2 \quad \rightarrow$$

$$mgy_1 = mgy_2 + \tfrac{1}{2}ky_2^2 \quad \rightarrow \quad y_2^2 + 2\frac{mg}{k}y_2 - 2\frac{mg}{k}y_1 = y_2^2 + 1.200 \times 10^{-3}\,y_2 - 1.200 \times 10^{-3} = 0$$

$$y_2 = -3.52 \times 10^{-2}\,\text{m}, 3.40 \times 10^{-2}\,\text{m}$$

$$F_{\text{scale}} = k|x| = \left(1.183 \times 10^6\,\text{N/m}\right)\left(3.52 \times 10^{-2}\,\text{m}\right) = \boxed{4.2 \times 10^4\,\text{N}}$$

86. (*a*) Use conservation of energy for the swinging motion. Subscript 1 represents the student initially grabbing the rope, and subscript 2 represents the student at the top of the swing. The location where the student initially grabs the rope is the zero location for PE $(y = 0)$.

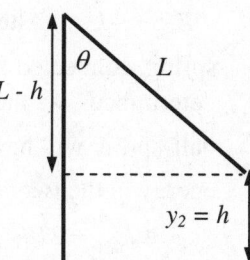

We have $v_1 = 5.0\,\text{m/s}$, $y_1 = 0$, and $v_2 = 0$. Solve for y_2.

$$E_1 = E_2 \quad \rightarrow \quad \tfrac{1}{2}mv_1^2 + mgy_1 = \tfrac{1}{2}mv_2^2 + mgy_2 \quad \rightarrow$$

$$\tfrac{1}{2}mv_1^2 = mgy_2 \quad \rightarrow \quad y_2 = \frac{v_1^2}{2g} = h$$

Calculate the angle from the relationship in the diagram.

$$\cos\theta = \frac{L-h}{L} = 1 - \frac{h}{L} = 1 - \frac{v_1^2}{2gL} \quad \rightarrow$$

$$\theta = \cos^{-1}\left(1 - \frac{v_1^2}{2gL}\right) = \cos^{-1}\left(1 - \frac{(5.0\,\text{m/s})^2}{2(9.8\,\text{m/s}^2)(10\,\text{m})}\right) = \boxed{29°}$$

(*b*) At the release point, the speed is 0, and so there is no radial acceleration, since $a_R = v^2/r$. Thus the centripetal force must be 0. Use the free-body diagram to write Newton's 2nd law for the radial direction.

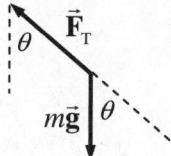

$$\sum F_R = F_T - mg\cos\theta = 0 \quad \rightarrow$$

$$F_T = mg\cos\theta = (65\,\text{kg})(9.8\,\text{m/s}^2)\cos 29° = \boxed{5.6 \times 10^2\,\text{N}}$$

(*c*) Write Newton's 2nd law for the radial direction for any angle, and solve for the tension.

$$\sum F_R = F_T - mg\cos\theta = mv^2/r \quad \rightarrow \quad F_T = mg\cos\theta + mv^2/r$$

As the angle decreases, the tension increases, and as the speed increases, the tension increases. Both effects are greatest at the bottom of the swing, and so that is where the tension will be at its maximum.

$$F_{T_{\max}} = mg\cos 0 + mv_1^2/r = (65\,\text{kg})(9.8\,\text{m/s}^2) + \frac{(65\,\text{kg})(5.0\,\text{m/s})^2}{10\,\text{m}} = \boxed{8.0 \times 10^2\,\text{N}}$$

87. The minimum vertical force needed to raise the athlete is equal to the athlete's weight. If the athlete moves upward a distance Δy, then the work done by the lifting force is $W = Fd\cos 0° = mg\Delta y$, the change in PE. The power output needed to accomplish this work in a certain time t is the work divided by the time.

$$P = \frac{W}{t} = \frac{mg\Delta y}{t} = \frac{(72\,\text{kg})(9.8\,\text{m/s}^2)(5.0\,\text{m})}{9.0\,\text{s}} = \boxed{3.9 \times 10^2\,\text{W}}$$

88. The energy to be stored is the power multiplied by the time: $E = Pt$. The energy will be stored as the gravitational PE increase in the water: $E = \Delta PE = mg\Delta y = \rho V g \Delta y$, where ρ is the density of the water, and V is the volume of the water.

$$Pt = \rho V g \Delta y \rightarrow V = \frac{Pt}{\rho g \Delta y} = \frac{\left(120 \times 10^6 \, \text{W}\right)\left(3600 \, \text{s}\right)}{\left(1000 \, \text{kg/m}^3\right)\left(9.8 \, \text{m/s}^2\right)\left(520 \, \text{m}\right)} = \boxed{8.5 \times 10^4 \, \text{m}^3}$$

89. If the original spring is stretched a distance x from equilibrium, then the potential energy stored is $PE_{\text{full}} = \frac{1}{2}kx^2$. Alternatively, think of the original spring as being made up of the two halves of the spring, connected from end to end. Each half of the spring has a spring constant k', to be determined. As the spring is stretched a distance x, each half-spring is stretched a distance $x/2$. Each half-spring will have an amount of potential energy stored of $PE_{\text{half}} = \frac{1}{2}k'\left(x/2\right)^2$. The amount of energy in the two half-springs must equal the amount of energy in the full spring.

$$PE_{\text{full}} = 2PE_{\text{half}} \rightarrow \tfrac{1}{2}kx^2 = 2\left[\tfrac{1}{2}k'\left(x/2\right)^2\right] \rightarrow k' = \boxed{2k}$$

90. Consider the free-body diagram for the block. The block is moving up the plane.

    (a) $KE_1 = \frac{1}{2}mv_1^2 = \frac{1}{2}\left(6.0 \, \text{kg}\right)\left(2.2 \, \text{m/s}\right)^2 = 14.52 \, \text{J} \approx \boxed{15 \, \text{J}}$

    (b) $W_P = F_P d \cos 37° = \left(75 \, \text{N}\right)\left(8.0 \, \text{m}\right)\cos 37° = 479.2 \, \text{J} \approx \boxed{4.8 \times 10^2 \, \text{J}}$

    (c) $W_{\text{fr}} = F_{\text{fr}} d \cos 180° = -\left(25 \, \text{N}\right)\left(8.0 \, \text{m}\right) = \boxed{-2.0 \times 10^2 \, \text{J}}$

    (d) $W_G = mgd \cos 127° = \left(6.0 \, \text{kg}\right)\left(9.8 \, \text{m/s}^2\right)\left(8.0 \, \text{m}\right)\cos 127°$

    $\quad\quad = -283.1 \, \text{J} \approx \boxed{-2.8 \times 10^2 \, \text{J}}$

    (e) $W_N = F_N d \cos 90° = \boxed{0 \, \text{J}}$

    (f) By the work-energy theorem,

    $\quad\quad W_{\text{total}} = KE_2 - KE_1 \rightarrow$

    $\quad\quad KE_2 = W_{\text{total}} + KE_1 = W_P + W_{\text{fr}} + W_G + W_N + KE_1 = 10.62 \, \text{J} \approx \boxed{11 \, \text{J}}$

91. The power output for either scenario is given by the change in kinetic energy, divided by the time required to change the kinetic energy. Subscripts of f and i are used for final and initial values of speed and kinetic energy. Subscript 1 represents the acceleration from 35 km/h to 55 km/h, and subscript 2 represents the acceleration from 55 km/h to 75 km/h.

$$P_1 = \frac{KE_{1f} - KE_{1i}}{t_1} = \frac{\frac{1}{2}m\left(v_{1f}^2 - v_{1i}^2\right)}{t_1} \quad\quad P_2 = \frac{KE_{2f} - KE_{2i}}{t_2} = \frac{\frac{1}{2}m\left(v_{2f}^2 - v_{2i}^2\right)}{t_2}$$

Equate the two expressions for power, and solve for t_2.

$$\frac{\frac{1}{2}m\left(v_{1f}^2 - v_{1i}^2\right)}{t_1} = \frac{\frac{1}{2}m\left(v_{2f}^2 - v_{2i}^2\right)}{t_2} \rightarrow t_2 = t_1\frac{\left(v_{2f}^2 - v_{2i}^2\right)}{\left(v_{1f}^2 - v_{1i}^2\right)}$$

Since the velocities are included as a ratio, any consistent set of units may be used for the velocities. Thus no conversion from km/h to some other units is needed.

$$t_2 = t_1\frac{\left(v_{2f}^2 - v_{2i}^2\right)}{\left(v_{1f}^2 - v_{1i}^2\right)} = \left(3.2 \, \text{s}\right)\frac{\left(75 \, \text{km/h}\right)^2 - \left(55 \, \text{km/h}\right)^2}{\left(55 \, \text{km/h}\right)^2 - \left(35 \, \text{km/h}\right)^2} = \boxed{4.6 \, \text{s}}$$

92. See the free-body diagram for the patient on the treadmill. We assume that there are no dissipative forces. Since the patient has a constant velocity, the net force parallel to the plane must be 0. Write Newton's 2nd law for forces parallel to the plane, and then calculate the power output of force $\vec{F}_P$.

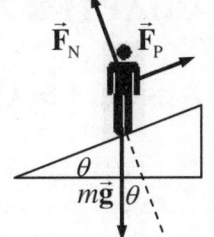

$$\sum F_{parallel} = F_P - mg\sin\theta = 0 \;\rightarrow\; F_P = mg\sin\theta$$

$$P = F_P v = mgv\sin\theta = (75\text{ kg})(9.8\,\text{m/s}^2)(3.3\,\text{km/h})\left(\frac{1\,\text{m/s}}{3.6\,\text{km/h}}\right)\sin 15°$$

$$= 174.4\text{ W} \approx \boxed{170\text{ W}}$$

This is about 2 to 3 times the wattage of typical household light bulbs (60-100 W).

93. (a) Assume that there are no non-conservative forces on the rock, and so its mechanical energy is conserved. Subscript 1 represents the rock as it leaves the volcano, and subscript 2 represents the rock at its highest point. The location as the rock leaves the volcano is the zero location for PE $(y = 0)$. We have $y_1 = 0$, $y_2 = 500\text{ m}$, and $v_2 = 0$. Solve for v_1.

$$E_1 = E_2 \;\rightarrow\; \tfrac{1}{2}mv_1^2 + mgy_1 = \tfrac{1}{2}mv_2^2 + mgy_2 \;\rightarrow\; \tfrac{1}{2}mv_1^2 = mgy_2 \;\rightarrow$$

$$v_1 = \sqrt{2gy_2} = \sqrt{2(9.80\,\text{m/s}^2)(500\text{ m})} = 98.99\,\text{m/s} \approx \boxed{1\times10^2\,\text{m/s}}$$

(b) The power output is the energy transferred to the launched rocks per unit time. The launching energy of a single rock is $\tfrac{1}{2}mv_1^2$, and so the energy of 1000 rocks is $1000\left(\tfrac{1}{2}mv_1^2\right)$. Divide this energy by the time it takes to launch 1000 rocks to find the power output needed to launch the rocks.

$$P = \frac{1000\left(\tfrac{1}{2}mv_1^2\right)}{t} = \frac{500(500\text{ kg})(98.99\,\text{m/s})^2}{60\text{ sec}} = \boxed{4\times10^7\,\text{W}}$$

94. (a) The maximum power output from the falling water would occur if all of the potential energy available were converted into work to turn the wheel. The rate of potential energy delivery to the wheel from the falling water is the power available.

$$P = \frac{W}{t} = \frac{mgh}{t} = \frac{(95\text{ kg})(9.8\,\text{m/s}^2)(2.0\,\text{m})}{1\text{ sec}} = \boxed{1.9\times10^3\,\text{W}}$$

(b) To find the speed of the water as it hits the wheel, use energy conservation with no non-conservative forces. Subscript 1 represents the water at the start of the descent, and subscript 2 represents the water as it hits the wheel at the bottom of the descent. The bottom of the descent is the zero location for PE $(y = 0)$. We have $v_1 = 0$, $y_1 = 2.0\text{ m}$, and $y_2 = 0$. Solve for v_2.

$$\tfrac{1}{2}mv_1^2 + mgy_1 = \tfrac{1}{2}mv_2^2 + mgy_2 \;\rightarrow\; mgy_1 = \tfrac{1}{2}mv_2^2 \;\rightarrow$$

$$v_2 = \sqrt{2gy_1} = \sqrt{2(9.8\,\text{m/s}^2)(2.0\text{ m})} = \boxed{6.3\,\text{m/s}}$$

CHAPTER 7: Linear Momentum

Answers to Questions

1. For momentum to be conserved, the system under analysis must be "closed" – not have any forces on it from outside the system. A coasting car has air friction and road friction on it, for example, which are "outside" forces and thus reduce the momentum of the car. If the ground and the air were considered part of the system, and their velocities analyzed, then the momentum of the entire system would be conserved, but not necessarily the momentum of any single component, like the car.

2. Consider this problem as a very light object hitting and sticking to a very heavy object. The large object – small object combination (Earth + jumper) would have some momentum after the collision, but due to the very large mass of the Earth, the velocity of the combination is so small that it is not measurable. Thus the jumper lands on the Earth, and nothing more happens.

3. When you release an inflated but untied balloon at rest, the gas inside the balloon (at high pressure) rushes out the open end of the balloon. That escaping gas and the balloon form a closed system, and so the momentum of the system is conserved. The balloon and remaining gas acquires a momentum equal and opposite to the momentum of the escaping gas, and so move in the opposite direction to the escaping gas.

4. If the rich man would have faced away from the shore and thrown the bag of coins directly away from the shore, he would have acquired a velocity towards the shore by conservation of momentum. Since the ice is frictionless, he would slide all the way to the shore.

5. When a rocket expels gas in a given direction, it puts a force on that gas. The momentum of the gas-rocket system stays constant, and so if the gas is pushed to the left, the rocket will be pushed to the right due to Newton's 3rd law. So the rocket must carry some kind of material to be ejected (usually exhaust from some kind of engine) to change direction.

6. The air bag greatly increases the amount of time over which the stopping force acts on the driver. If a hard object like a steering wheel or windshield is what stops the driver, then a large force is exerted over a very short time. If a soft object like an air bag stops the driver, then a much smaller force is exerted over a much longer time. For instance, if the air bag is able to increase the time of stopping by a factor of 10, then the average force on the person will be decreased by a factor of 10. This greatly reduces the possibility of serious injury or death.

7. "Crumple zones" are similar to air bags in that they increase the time of interaction during a collision, and therefore lower the average force required for the change in momentum that the car undergoes in the collision.

8. From Eq. 7-7 for a 1-D elastic collision, $v_A - v_B = v'_B - v'_A$. Let "A" represent the bat, and let "B" represent the ball. The positive direction will be the (assumed horizontal) direction that the bat is moving when the ball is hit. We assume the batter can swing the bat with equal strength in either case, so that v_A is the same in both pitching situations. Because the bat is so much heavier than the ball, we assume that $v'_A \approx v_A$ – the speed of the bat doesn't change significantly during the collision. Then the velocity of the baseball after being hit is $v'_B = v'_A + v_A - v_B \approx 2v_A - v_B$. If $v_B = 0$, the ball tossed up into the air by the batter, then $v'_B \approx 2v_A$ – the ball moves away with twice the speed of the

bat. But if $v_B < 0$, the pitched ball situation, we see that the magnitude of $v_B' > 2v_A$, and so the ball moves away with greater speed. If, for example, the pitching speed of the ball was about twice the speed at which the batter could swing the bat, then we would have $v_B' \approx 4v_A$. Thus the ball has greater speed after being struck, and thus it is easier to hit a home run. This is similar to the "gravitational slingshot" effect discussed in problem 85.

9. The impulse is the product of the force and the time duration that the force is applied. So the impulse from a small force applied over a long time can be larger than the impulse applied by a large force over a small time.

10. The momentum of an object can be expressed in terms of its kinetic energy, as follows.
$$p = mv = \sqrt{m^2 v^2} = \sqrt{m\left(mv^2\right)} = \sqrt{2m\left(\tfrac{1}{2}mv^2\right)} = \sqrt{2mKE} \; .$$
Thus if two objects have the same kinetic energy, then the one with more mass has the greater momentum.

11. Consider two objects, each with the same magnitude of momentum, moving in opposite directions. They have a total momentum of 0. If they collide and have a totally inelastic collision, in which they stick together, then their final common speed must be 0 so that momentum is conserved. But since they are not moving after the collision, they have no kinetic energy, and so all of their kinetic energy has been lost.

12. The turbine blades should be designed so that the water rebounds. If the water rebounds, that means that a larger momentum change for the water has occurred than if it just came to a stop. And if there is a larger momentum change for the water, there will also be a larger momentum change for the blades, making them spin faster.

13. (*a*) The downward component of the momentum is unchanged. The horizontal component of momentum changes from rightward to leftward. Thus the change in momentum is to the left in the picture.
    (*b*) Since the force on the wall is opposite that on the ball, the force on the wall is to the right.

14. (*a*) The momentum of the ball is not conserved during any part of the process, because there is an external force acting on the ball at all times – the force of gravity. And there is an upward force on the ball during the collision. So considering the ball as the system, there are always external forces on it, and so its momentum is not conserved.
    (*b*) With this definition of the system, all of the forces are internal, and so the momentum of the Earth-ball system is conserved during the entire process.
    (*c*) The answer here is the same as for part (*b*).

15. In order to maintain balance, your CM must be located directly above your feet. If you have a heavy load in your arms, your CM will be out in front of your body and not above your feet. So you lean backwards to get your CM directly above your feet. Otherwise, you would fall over forwards.

16. The 1-m length of pipe is uniform – it has the same density throughout, and so its CM is at its geometric center, which is its midpoint. The arm and leg are not uniform – they are more dense where there is muscle, primarily in the parts that are closest to the body. Thus the CM of the arm or leg is closer the body than the geometric center. The CM is located closer to the more massive part of the arm or leg.

17. When you are lying flat on the floor, your CM is inside of the volume of your body. When you sit up on the floor with your legs extended, your CM is outside of the volume of your body.

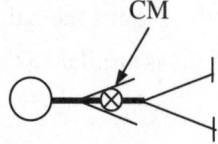

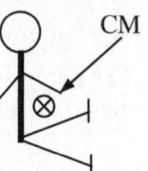

18. The engine does not directly accelerate the car. The engine puts a force on the driving wheels, making them rotate. The wheels then push backwards on the roadway as they spin. The Newton's 3rd law reaction to this force is the forward-pushing of the roadway on the wheels, which accelerates the car. So it is the (external) road surface that accelerates the car.

19. The motion of the center of mass of the rocket will follow the original parabolic path, both before and after explosion. Each individual piece of the rocket will follow a separate path after the explosion, but since the explosion was internal to the system (consisting of the rocket), the center of mass of all the exploded pieces will follow the original path.

Solutions to Problems

1. $p = mv = (0.028 \text{ kg})(8.4 \text{ m/s}) = \boxed{0.24 \text{ kg} \cdot \text{m/s}}$

2. From Newton's second law, $\Delta \vec{\mathbf{p}} = \vec{\mathbf{F}} \Delta t$. For a constant mass object, $\Delta \vec{\mathbf{p}} = m \Delta \vec{\mathbf{v}}$. Equate the two expressions for $\Delta \vec{\mathbf{p}}$.

$$\vec{\mathbf{F}} \Delta t = m \Delta \vec{\mathbf{v}} \quad \rightarrow \quad \Delta \vec{\mathbf{v}} = \frac{\vec{\mathbf{F}} \Delta t}{m}.$$

If the skier moves to the right, then the speed will decrease, because the friction force is to the left.

$$\Delta v = -\frac{F \Delta t}{m} = -\frac{(25 \text{ N})(20 \text{ s})}{65 \text{ kg}} = \boxed{-7.7 \text{ m/s}}$$

The skier loses 7.7 m/s of speed.

3. Choose the direction from the batter to the pitcher to be the positive direction. Calculate the average force from the change in momentum of the ball.

$$\Delta p = F \Delta t = m \Delta v \quad \rightarrow$$

$$F = m \frac{\Delta v}{\Delta t} = (0.145 \text{ kg}) \left(\frac{52.0 \text{ m/s} - -39.0 \text{ m/s}}{3.00 \times 10^{-3} \text{ s}} \right) = \boxed{4.40 \times 10^{3} \text{ N, towards the pitcher}}$$

4. The throwing of the package is a momentum-conserving action, if the water resistance is ignored. Let "A" represent the boat and child together, and let "B" represent the package. Choose the direction that the package is thrown as the positive direction. Apply conservation of momentum, with the initial velocity of both objects being 0.

$$p_{\text{initial}} = p_{\text{final}} \quad \rightarrow \quad (m_A + m_B) v = m_A v_A' + m_B v_B' \quad \rightarrow$$

$$v_A' = -\frac{m_B v_B'}{m_A} = -\frac{(6.40 \text{ kg})(10.0 \text{ m/s})}{(26.0 \text{ kg} + 45.0 \text{ kg})} = \boxed{-0.901 \text{ m/s}}$$

The boat and child move in the opposite direction as the thrown package.

5. The force on the gas can be found from its change in momentum.

$$F = \frac{\Delta p}{\Delta t} = \frac{v\Delta m}{\Delta t} = v\frac{\Delta m}{\Delta t} = \left(4.0\times10^4 \text{ m/s}\right)\left(1500 \text{ kg/s}\right) = 6.0\times10^7 \text{ N downward}$$

The force on the rocket is the Newton's 3rd law pair (equal and opposite) to the force on the gas, and

so is $\boxed{6.0\times10^7 \text{ N upward}}$.

6. The tackle will be analyzed as a one-dimensional momentum conserving situation. Let "A" represent the halfback, and "B" represent the tackling cornerback.

$$p_{\text{initial}} = p_{\text{final}} \quad \rightarrow \quad m_A v_A + m_B v_B = \left(m_A + m_B\right)v' \quad \rightarrow$$

$$v' = \frac{m_A v_A + m_B v_B}{m_A + m_B} = \frac{\left(95 \text{ kg}\right)\left(4.1 \text{ m/s}\right) + \left(85 \text{ kg}\right)\left(5.5 \text{ m/s}\right)}{\left(95 \text{ kg}\right) + \left(85 \text{ kg}\right)} = \boxed{4.8 \text{ m/s}}$$

7. Consider the horizontal motion of the objects. The momentum in the horizontal direction will be conserved. Let "A" represent the car, and "B" represent the load. The positive direction is the direction of the original motion of the car.

$$p_{\text{initial}} = p_{\text{final}} \quad \rightarrow \quad m_A v_A + m_B v_B = \left(m_A + m_B\right)v' \quad \rightarrow$$

$$v' = \frac{m_A v_A + m_B v_B}{m_A + m_B} = \frac{\left(12,600 \text{ kg}\right)\left(18.0 \text{ m/s}\right) + 0}{\left(12,600 \text{ kg}\right) + \left(5350 \text{ kg}\right)} = \boxed{12.6 \text{ m/s}}$$

8. Consider the motion in one dimension, with the positive direction being the direction of motion of the first car. Let "A" represent the first car, and "B" represent the second car. Momentum will be conserved in the collision. Note that $v_B = 0$.

$$p_{\text{initial}} = p_{\text{final}} \quad \rightarrow \quad m_A v_A + m_B v_B = \left(m_A + m_B\right)v' \quad \rightarrow$$

$$m_B = \frac{m_A\left(v_A - v'\right)}{v'} = \frac{\left(9300 \text{ kg}\right)\left(15.0 \text{ m/s} - 6.0 \text{ m/s}\right)}{6.0 \text{ m/s}} = \boxed{1.4\times10^4 \text{ kg}}$$

9. The force stopping the wind is exerted by the person, so the force on the person would be equal in magnitude and opposite in direction to the force stopping the wind. Calculate the force from Eq. 7-2, in magnitude only.

$$\frac{m_{\text{wind}}}{\Delta t} = \frac{40 \text{ kg/s}}{\text{m}^2}\left(1.50 \text{ m}\right)\left(0.50 \text{ m}\right) = 30 \text{ kg/s} \qquad \Delta v_{\text{wind}} = 100 \text{ km/h}\left(\frac{1 \text{ m/s}}{3.6 \text{ km/h}}\right) = 27.8 \text{ m/s}$$

$$F_{\substack{\text{on} \\ \text{person}}} = F_{\substack{\text{on} \\ \text{wind}}} = \frac{\Delta p_{\text{wind}}}{\Delta t} = \frac{m_{\text{wind}}\Delta v_{\text{wind}}}{\Delta t} = \frac{m_{\text{wind}}}{\Delta t}\Delta v_{\text{wind}} = \left(30 \text{ kg/s}\right)\left(27.8 \text{ m/s}\right)$$

$$= 833 \text{ N} \approx \boxed{8\times10^2 \text{ N}}$$

The typical maximum frictional force is $F_{\text{fr}} = \mu_s mg = \left(1.0\right)\left(70 \text{ kg}\right)\left(9.8 \text{ m/s}^2\right) = 690 \text{ N}$, and so we

see that $\boxed{F_{\substack{\text{on} \\ \text{person}}} > F_{\text{fr}}}$ – the wind is literally strong enough to blow a person off his feet.

10. Momentum will be conserved in the horizontal direction. Let "A" represent the car, and "B" represent the snow. For the horizontal motion, $v_B = 0$ and $v'_B = v'_A$. Momentum conservation gives the following.

$$p_{initial} = p_{final} \quad \rightarrow \quad m_A v_A = (m_A + m_B) v_A'$$

$$v_A' = \frac{m_A v_A}{m_A + m_B} = \frac{(3800 \text{ kg})(8.60 \text{ m/s})}{3800 \text{ kg} + \left(\dfrac{3.50 \text{ kg}}{\text{min}}\right)(90.0 \text{ min})} = 7.94 \text{ m/s} \approx \boxed{7.9 \text{ m/s}}$$

11. Consider the motion in one dimension, with the positive direction being the direction of motion of the original nucleus. Let "A" represent the alpha particle, with a mass of 4 u, and "B" represent the new nucleus, with a mass of 218 u. Momentum conservation gives the following.

$$p_{initial} = p_{final} \quad \rightarrow \quad (m_A + m_B) v = m_A v_A' + m_B v_B' \quad \rightarrow$$

$$v_A' = \frac{(m_A + m_B) v - m_B v_B'}{m_A} = \frac{(222 \text{ u})(420 \text{ m/s}) - (218 \text{ u})(350 \text{ m/s})}{4.0 \text{ u}} = \boxed{4.2 \times 10^3 \text{ m/s}}$$

Note that the masses do not have to be converted to kg, since all masses are in the same units, and a ratio of masses is what is significant.

12. Consider the motion in one dimension with the positive direction being the direction of motion of the bullet. Let "A" represent the bullet, and "B" represent the block. Since there is no net force outside of the block-bullet system (like frictions with the table), the momentum of the block and bullet combination is conserved. Note that $v_B = 0$.

$$p_{initial} = p_{final} \quad \rightarrow \quad m_A v_A + m_B v_B = m_A v_A' + m_B v_B' \quad \rightarrow$$

$$v_B' = \frac{m_A (v_A - v_A')}{m_B} = \frac{(0.023 \text{ kg})(230 \text{ m/s} - 170 \text{ m/s})}{2.0 \text{ kg}} = \boxed{0.69 \text{ m/s}}$$

13. (a) Consider the motion in one dimension with the positive direction being the direction of motion before the separation. Let "A" represent the upper stage (that moves away faster) and "B" represent the lower stage. It is given that $m_A = m_B$, $v_A = v_B = v$, and $v_B' = v_A' - v_{rel}$. Momentum conservation gives the following.

$$p_{initial} = p_{final} \quad \rightarrow \quad (m_A + m_B) v = m_A v_A' + m_B v_B' = m_A v_A' + m_B (v_A' - v_{rel}) \quad \rightarrow$$

$$v_A' = \frac{(m_A + m_B) v + m_B v_{rel}}{(m_A + m_B)} = \frac{(975 \text{ kg})(5800 \text{ m/s}) + \frac{1}{2}(975 \text{ kg})(2200 \text{ m/s})}{(975 \text{ kg})}$$

$$= \boxed{6.9 \times 10^3 \text{ m/s} \text{ , away from Earth}}$$

$$v_B' = v_A' - v_{rel} = 6.9 \times 10^3 \text{ m/s} - 2.20 \times 10^3 \text{ m/s} = \boxed{4.7 \times 10^3 \text{ m/s} \text{ , away from Earth}}$$

(b) The change in KE had to be supplied by the explosion.

$$\Delta KE = KE_f - KE_i = \left(\tfrac{1}{2} m_A v_A'^2 + \tfrac{1}{2} m_B v_B'^2\right) - \tfrac{1}{2}(m_A + m_B) v^2$$

$$= \tfrac{1}{2}(487.5 \text{ kg})\left[(6900 \text{ m/s})^2 + (4700 \text{ m/s})^2\right] - \tfrac{1}{2}(975 \text{ kg})(5800 \text{ m/s})^2$$

$$= \boxed{5.9 \times 10^8 \text{ J}}$$

14. To alter the course by $35.0°$, a velocity perpendicular to the original velocity must be added. Call the direction of the added velocity, $\vec{v}_{add}$, the positive direction. From the diagram, we see that $v_{add} = v_{orig} \tan \theta$. The momentum in the perpendicular direction will be conserved, considering that the gases are given perpendicular momentum in the opposite direction of $\vec{v}_{add}$. The gas is expelled in the opposite direction to $\vec{v}_{add}$, and so a negative value is used for $v_{\perp gas}$.

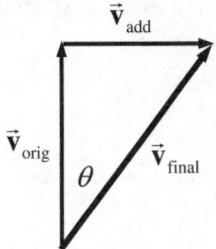

$$\underset{\text{before}}{p_\perp} = \underset{\text{after}}{p_\perp} \quad \rightarrow \quad 0 = m_{gas} v_{\perp gas} + \left(m_{rocket} - m_{gas} \right) v_{add} \quad \rightarrow$$

$$m_{gas} = \frac{m_{rocket} v_{add}}{\left(v_{add} - v_{\perp gas} \right)} = \frac{(3180 \text{ kg})(115 \text{ m/s}) \tan 35.0°}{\left[(115 \text{ m/s}) \tan 35° - -1750 \text{ m/s} \right]} = \boxed{1.40 \times 10^1 \text{ kg}}$$

15. (a) The impulse is the change in momentum. The direction of travel of the struck ball is the positive direction.
$$\Delta p = m \Delta v = \left(4.5 \times 10^{-2} \text{ kg} \right) (45 \text{ m/s} - 0) = \boxed{2.0 \text{ kg} \cdot \text{m/s}}$$

(b) The average force is the impulse divided by the interaction time.
$$\overline{F} = \frac{\Delta p}{\Delta t} = \frac{2.0 \text{ kg} \cdot \text{m/s}}{3.5 \times 10^{-3} \text{ s}} = \boxed{5.8 \times 10^2 \text{ N}}$$

16. (a) The impulse given to the nail is the opposite of the impulse given to the hammer. This is the change in momentum. Call the direction of the initial velocity of the hammer the positive direction.
$$\Delta p_{nail} = -\Delta p_{hammer} = m v_i - m v_f = (12 \text{ kg})(8.5 \text{ m/s}) - 0 = \boxed{1.0 \times 10^2 \text{ kg} \cdot \text{m/s}}$$

(b) The average force is the impulse divided by the time of contact.
$$F_{avg} = \frac{\Delta p}{\Delta t} = \frac{1.0 \times 10^2 \text{ kg} \cdot \text{m/s}}{8.0 \times 10^{-3} \text{ s}} = \boxed{1.3 \times 10^4 \text{ N}}$$

17. The impulse given the ball is the change in the ball's momentum. From the symmetry of the problem, the vertical momentum of the ball does not change, and so there is no vertical impulse. Call the direction AWAY from the wall the positive direction for momentum perpendicular to the wall.
$$\Delta p_\perp = \underset{\text{final}}{m v_\perp} - \underset{\text{initial}}{m v_\perp} = m \left(v \sin 45° - -v \sin 45° \right) = 2 m v \sin 45°$$

$$= 2 \left(6.0 \times 10^{-2} \text{ km} \right) (25 \text{ m/s}) \sin 45° = \boxed{2.1 \text{ kg} \cdot \text{m/s} \text{ , to the left}}$$

18. (a) The average force on the car is the impulse (change in momentum) divided by the time of interaction. The positive direction is the direction of the car's initial velocity.
$$\overline{F} = \frac{\Delta p}{\Delta t} = \frac{m \Delta v}{\Delta t} = (1500 \text{ kg}) \left(\frac{0 - 50 \text{ km/h} \left(\frac{1 \text{m/s}}{3.6 \text{ km/h}} \right)}{0.15 \text{ s}} \right) = -1.389 \times 10^5 \text{ N} \approx \boxed{-1.4 \times 10^5 \text{ N}}$$

(b)   The deceleration is found from Newton's 2nd law.

$$\overline{F} = m\overline{a} \;\rightarrow\; \overline{a} = \frac{\overline{F}}{m} = \frac{\left(-1.389 \times 10^5\,\text{N}\right)}{1500\,\text{kg}} = \boxed{-93\,\text{m/s}^2}$$

19.   Call east the positive direction.

(a) $P_{\text{original} \atop \text{fullback}} = mv_{\text{original} \atop \text{fullback}} = (95\,\text{kg})(4.0\,\text{m/s}) = \boxed{3.8 \times 10^2\,\text{kg·m/s}}$

(b)   The impulse on the fullback is the change in the fullback's momentum.

$$\Delta p_{\text{fullback}} = m\left(v_{\text{final} \atop \text{fullback}} - v_{\text{final} \atop \text{fullback}} \right) = (95\,\text{kg})(0 - 4.0\,\text{m/s}) = \boxed{-3.8 \times 10^2\,\text{kg·m/s}}$$

(c)   The impulse on the tackler is the opposite of the impulse on the fullback, so $\boxed{3.8 \times 10^2\,\text{kg·m/s}}$

(d)   The average force on the tackler is the impulse on the tackler divided by the time of interaction.

$$\overline{F} = \frac{\Delta p}{\Delta t} = \frac{3.8 \times 10^2\,\text{kg·m/s}}{0.75\,\text{s}} = \boxed{5.1 \times 10^2\,\text{N}}$$

20.   (a)   The impulse given the ball is the area under the F vs. t graph. Approximate the area as a triangle of "height" 250 N, and "width" 0.01 sec.

$$\Delta p = \tfrac{1}{2}(250\,\text{N})(0.01\,\text{s}) = \boxed{1.25\,\text{N·s}}$$

(b)   The velocity can be found from the change in momentum. Call the positive direction the direction of the ball's travel after being served.

$$\Delta p = m\Delta v = m(v_f - v_i) \;\rightarrow\; v_f = v_i + \frac{\Delta p}{m} = 0 + \frac{1.25\,\text{N·s}}{6.0 \times 10^{-2}\,\text{kg}} = \boxed{21\,\text{m/s}}$$

21.   Find the velocity upon reaching the ground from energy conservation. Assume that all of the initial potential energy at the maximum height h_{max} is converted into kinetic energy. Take down to be the positive direction, so the velocity at the ground is positive.

$$mgh_{\text{max}} = \tfrac{1}{2}mv_{\text{ground}}^2 \;\rightarrow\; v_{\text{ground}} = \sqrt{2gh_{\text{max}}}$$

When contacting the ground, the impulse on the person causes a change in momentum. That relationship is used to find the time of the stopping interaction. The force of the ground acting on the person is negative since it acts in the upward direction.

$$\overline{F}\Delta t = m\left(0 - v_{\text{ground}}\right) \;\rightarrow\; \Delta t = -\frac{mv_{\text{ground}}}{\overline{F}}$$

We assume that the stopping force is so large that we call it the total force on the person – we ignore gravity for the stopping motion. The average acceleration of the person during stopping $\left(\overline{a} = \overline{F}/m\right)$ is used with Eq. 2-11b to find the displacement during stopping, h_{stop}.

$$y - y_0 = v_0 t + \tfrac{1}{2}at^2 \;\rightarrow\; h_{\text{stop}} = v_{\text{ground}}\left(-\frac{mv_{\text{ground}}}{\overline{F}}\right) + \tfrac{1}{2}\left(\frac{\overline{F}}{m}\right)\left(-\frac{mv_{\text{ground}}}{\overline{F}}\right)^2 \;\rightarrow\;$$

$$h_{\text{stop}} = -\frac{mv_{\text{ground}}^2}{\overline{F}} + \tfrac{1}{2}\frac{mv_{\text{ground}}^2}{\overline{F}} = -\tfrac{1}{2}\frac{mv_{\text{ground}}^2}{\overline{F}} = -\frac{gh_{\text{max}}m}{\overline{F}} \;\rightarrow\; h_{\text{max}} = -\frac{\overline{F}h_{\text{stop}}}{mg}$$

We assume that the person lands with both feet striking the ground simultaneously, so the stopping force is divided between both legs. Thus the critical average stopping force is twice the breaking strength of a single leg.

$$h_{max} = -\frac{\bar{F}h_{stop}}{mg} = \frac{2F_{break}h_{stop}}{mg} = \frac{2(170 \times 10^6 \text{ N/m}^2)(2.5 \times 10^{-4} \text{ m}^2)(0.60 \text{ m})}{(75 \text{ kg})(9.8 \text{ m/s}^2)} = \boxed{69 \text{ m}}$$

22. Let A represent the 0.440-kg ball, and B represent the 0.220-kg ball. We have $v_A = 3.30$ m/s and $v_B = 0$. Use Eq. 7-7 to obtain a relationship between the velocities.

$$v_A - v_B = -(v_A' - v_B') \rightarrow v_B' = v_A + v_A'$$

Substitute this relationship into the momentum conservation equation for the collision.

$$m_A v_A + m_B v_B = m_A v_A' + m_B v_B' \rightarrow m_A v_A = m_A v_A' + m_B (v_A + v_A') \rightarrow$$

$$v_A' = \frac{(m_A - m_B)}{(m_A + m_B)}v_A = \frac{0.220 \text{ kg}}{0.660 \text{ kg}}(3.30 \text{ m/s}) = \boxed{1.10 \text{ m/s (east)}}$$

$$v_B' = v_A + v_A' = 3.30 \text{ m/s} + 1.10 \text{ m/s} = \boxed{4.40 \text{ m/s (east)}}$$

23. Let A represent the 0.450-kg puck, and let B represent the 0.900-kg puck. The initial direction of puck A is the positive direction. We have $v_A = 3.00$ m/s and $v_B = 0$. Use Eq. 7-7 to obtain a relationship between the velocities.

$$v_A - v_B = -(v_A' - v_B') \rightarrow v_B' = v_A + v_A'$$

Substitute this relationship into the momentum conservation equation for the collision.

$$m_A v_A + m_B v_B = m_A v_A' + m_B v_B' \rightarrow m_A v_A = m_A v_A' + m_B (v_A + v_A') \rightarrow$$

$$v_A' = \frac{(m_A - m_B)}{(m_A + m_B)}v_A = \frac{-0.450 \text{ kg}}{1.350 \text{ kg}}(3.00 \text{ m/s}) = -1.00 \text{ m/s} = \boxed{1.00 \text{ m/s (west)}}$$

$$v_B' = v_A + v_A' = 3.00 \text{ m/s} - 1.00 \text{ m/s} = \boxed{2.00 \text{ m/s (east)}}$$

24. Let A represent the ball moving at 2.00 m/s, and call that direction the positive direction. Let B represent the ball moving at 3.00 m/s in the opposite direction. So $v_A = 2.00$ m/s and $v_B = -3.00$ m/s. Use Eq. 7-7 to obtain a relationship between the velocities.

$$v_A - v_B = -(v_A' - v_B') \rightarrow v_B' = 5.00 \text{ m/s} + v_A'$$

Substitute this relationship into the momentum conservation equation for the collision, noting that $m_A = m_B$.

$$m_A v_A + m_B v_B = m_A v_A' + m_B v_B' \rightarrow v_A + v_B = v_A' + v_B' \rightarrow$$

$$-1.00 \text{ m/s} = v_A' + (v_A' + 5.00 \text{ m/s}) \rightarrow 2v_A' = -6.00 \text{ m/s} \rightarrow v_A' = \boxed{-3.00 \text{ m/s}}$$

$$v_B' = 5.00 \text{ m/s} + v_A' = \boxed{2.00 \text{ m/s}}$$

The two balls have exchanged velocities. This will always be true for 1-D elastic collisions of objects of equal mass.

25. Let A represent the 0.060-kg tennis ball, and let B represent the 0.090-kg ball. The initial direction of the balls is the positive direction. We have $v_A = 2.50\,\text{m/s}$ and $v_B = 1.15\,\text{m/s}$. Use Eq. 7-7 to obtain a relationship between the velocities.

$$v_A - v_B = -\left(v_A' - v_B'\right) \quad \rightarrow \quad v_B' = 1.35\,\text{m/s} + v_A'$$

Substitute this relationship into the momentum conservation equation for the collision.

$$m_A v_A + m_B v_B = m_A v_A' + m_B v_B' \quad \rightarrow \quad m_A v_A + m_B v_B = m_A v_A' + m_B\left(1.35\,\text{m/s} + v_A'\right) \quad \rightarrow$$

$$v_A' = \frac{m_A v_A + m_B\left(v_B - 1.35\,\text{m/s}\right)}{m_A + m_B} = \frac{\left(0.060\,\text{kg}\right)\left(2.50\,\text{m/s}\right) + \left(0.090\,\text{kg}\right)\left(1.15\,\text{m/s} - 1.35\,\text{m/s}\right)}{0.150\,\text{kg}}$$

$$= \boxed{0.88\,\text{m/s}}$$

$$v_B' = 1.35\,\text{m/s} + v_A' = \boxed{2.23\,\text{m/s}}$$

Both balls move in the direction of the tennis ball's initial motion.

26. Let A represent the moving softball, and let B represent the ball initially at rest. The initial direction of the softball is the positive direction. We have $v_A = 8.5\,\text{m/s}$, $v_B = 0$, and $v_A' = -3.7\,\text{m/s}$.

(*a*) Use Eq. 7-7 to obtain a relationship between the velocities.

$$v_A - v_B = -\left(v_A' - v_B'\right) \quad \rightarrow \quad v_B' = v_A - v_B + v_A' = 8.5\,\text{m/s} - 0 - 3.7\,\text{m/s} = \boxed{4.8\,\text{m/s}}$$

(*b*) Use momentum conservation to solve for the mass of the target ball.

$$m_A v_A + m_B v_B = m_A v_A' + m_B v_B' \quad \rightarrow$$

$$m_B = m_A \frac{\left(v_A - v_A'\right)}{\left(v_B' - v_B\right)} = \left(0.220\,\text{kg}\right)\frac{\left(8.5\,\text{m/s} - -3.7\,\text{m/s}\right)}{4.8\,\text{m/s}} = \boxed{0.56\,\text{kg}}$$

27. Let the original direction of the cars be the positive direction. We have $v_A = 4.50\,\text{m/s}$ and $v_B = 3.70\,\text{m/s}$

(*a*) Use Eq. 7-7 to obtain a relationship between the velocities.

$$v_A - v_B = -\left(v_A' - v_B'\right) \quad \rightarrow \quad v_B' = v_A - v_B + v_A' = 0.80\,\text{m/s} + v_A'$$

Substitute this relationship into the momentum conservation equation for the collision.

$$m_A v_A + m_B v_B = m_A v_A' + m_B v_B' \quad \rightarrow \quad m_A v_A + m_B v_B = m_A v_A' + m_B\left(0.80\,\text{m/s} + v_A'\right) \quad \rightarrow$$

$$v_A' = \frac{m_A v_A + m_B\left(v_B - 0.80\,\text{m/s}\right)}{m_A + m_B} = \frac{\left(450\,\text{kg}\right)\left(4.50\,\text{m/s}\right) + \left(550\,\text{kg}\right)\left(2.90\,\text{m/s}\right)}{1000\,\text{kg}} = \boxed{3.62\,\text{m/s}}$$

$$v_B' = 0.80\,\text{m/s} + v_A' = \boxed{4.42\,\text{m/s}}$$

(*b*) Calculate $\Delta p = p' - p$ for each car.

$$\Delta p_A = m_A v_A' - m_A v_A = \left(450\,\text{kg}\right)\left(3.62\,\text{m/s} - 4.50\,\text{m/s}\right) = -3.96 \times 10^2\,\text{kg·m/s}$$

$$\approx \boxed{-4.0 \times 10^2\,\text{kg·m/s}}$$

$$\Delta p_B = m_B v_B' - m_B v_B = \left(550\,\text{kg}\right)\left(4.42\,\text{m/s} - 3.70\,\text{m/s}\right) = 3.96 \times 10^2\,\text{kg·m/s}$$

$$\approx \boxed{4.0 \times 10^2\,\text{kg·m/s}}$$

The two changes are equal and opposite because momentum was conserved.

28.	(*a*)	Momentum will be conserved in one dimension. Call the direction of the first ball the positive direction. Let A represent the first ball, and B represent the second ball. We have $v_B = 0$ and $v'_B = \frac{1}{2}v_A$. Use Eq. 7-7 to obtain a relationship between the velocities.

$$v_A - v_B = -\left(v'_A - v'_B\right) \quad \rightarrow \quad v'_A = -\frac{1}{2}v_A$$

Substitute this relationship into the momentum conservation equation for the collision.

$$p_{initial} = p_{final} \quad \rightarrow \quad m_A v_A + m_B v_B = m_A v'_A + m_B v'_B \quad \rightarrow \quad m_A v_A = -\frac{1}{2}m_A v_A + m_B \frac{1}{2} v_A \quad \rightarrow$$

$$m_B = 3m_A = 3\left(0.280 \text{ kg}\right) = \boxed{0.840 \text{ kg}}$$

(*b*)	The fraction of the kinetic energy given to the second ball is as follows.

$$\frac{KE'_B}{KE_A} = \frac{\frac{1}{2}m_B v'^2_B}{\frac{1}{2}m_A v^2_A} = \frac{3m_A \left(\frac{1}{2}v_A\right)^2}{m_A v^2_A} = \boxed{0.75}$$

29.	Let A represent the cube of mass M, and B represent the cube of mass m. Find the speed of A immediately before the collision, v_A, by using energy conservation.

$$Mgh = \frac{1}{2}Mv^2_A \quad \rightarrow \quad v_A = \sqrt{2gh} = \sqrt{2\left(9.8 \text{ m/s}^2\right)\left(0.30 \text{ m}\right)} = 2.42 \text{ m/s}$$

Use Eq. 7-7 for elastic collisions to obtain a relationship between the velocities in the collision. We have $v_B = 0$ and $M = 2m$.

$$v_A - v_B = -\left(v'_A - v'_B\right) \quad \rightarrow \quad v'_B = v_A + v'_A$$

Substitute this relationship into the momentum conservation equation for the collision.

$$m_A v_A + m_B v_B = m_A v'_A + m_B v'_B \quad \rightarrow \quad m_A v_A = m_A v'_A + m_B\left(v_A + v'_A\right) \quad \rightarrow$$

$$2mv_A = 2mv'_A + m\left(v_A + v'_A\right) \quad \rightarrow \quad v'_A = \frac{v_A}{3} = \frac{\sqrt{2gh}}{3} = \frac{\sqrt{2\left(9.8 \text{ m/s}^2\right)\left(0.30 \text{ m}\right)}}{3} = 0.808 \text{ m/s}$$

$$v'_B = v_A + v'_A = \frac{4}{3}v_A = 3.23 \text{ m/s}$$

Each mass is moving horizontally initially after the collision, and so each has a vertical velocity of 0 as they start to fall. Use constant acceleration Eq. 2-11b with down as positive and the table top as the vertical origin to find the time of fall.

$$y = y_0 + v_0 t + \frac{1}{2}at^2 \quad \rightarrow \quad H = 0 + 0 + \frac{1}{2}gt^2 \quad \rightarrow \quad t = \sqrt{2H/g}$$

Each cube then travels a horiztonal distance found by $\Delta x = v_x \Delta t$.

$$\Delta x_m = v'_A \Delta t = \frac{\sqrt{2gh}}{3}\sqrt{\frac{2H}{g}} = \frac{2}{3}\sqrt{hH} = \frac{2}{3}\sqrt{\left(0.30 \text{ m}\right)\left(0.90 \text{ m}\right)} = 0.3464 \text{ m} \approx \boxed{0.35 \text{ m}}$$

$$\Delta x_M = v'_B \Delta t = \frac{4\sqrt{2gh}}{3}\sqrt{\frac{2H}{g}} = \frac{8}{3}\sqrt{hH} = \frac{8}{3}\sqrt{\left(0.30 \text{ m}\right)\left(0.90 \text{ m}\right)} = 1.386 \text{ m} \approx \boxed{1.4 \text{ m}}$$

30.	(*a*)	Use Eq. 7-7, along with $v_B = 0$, to obtain a relationship between the velocities.

$$v_A - v_B = -\left(v'_A - v'_B\right) \quad \rightarrow \quad v'_B = v_A + v'_A$$

Substitute this relationship into the momentum conservation equation for the collision.

$$m_A v_A + m_B v_B = m_A v'_A + m_B v'_B = m_A v'_A + m_B\left(v_A + v'_A\right) = m_A v'_A + m_B v_A + m_B v'_A \quad \rightarrow$$

$$m_A v_A - m_B v_A = m_A v'_A + m_B v'_A \quad \rightarrow \quad \left(m_A - m_B\right)v_A = \left(m_A + m_B\right)v'_A \quad \rightarrow \quad v'_A = \frac{\left(m_A - m_B\right)}{\left(m_A + m_B\right)}v_A$$

Substitute this result into the result of Eq. 7-7.

$$v'_B = v_A + v'_A = v_A + \frac{(m_A - m_B)}{(m_A + m_B)} v_A = v_A \frac{(m_A + m_B)}{(m_A + m_B)} + \frac{(m_A - m_B)}{(m_A + m_B)} v_A = v_A \frac{2m_A}{(m_A + m_B)}$$

(b) If $m_A \ll m_B$, then approximate $m_A = 0$

$$v'_A = \frac{(m_A - m_B)}{(m_A + m_B)} v_A = \frac{(-m_B)}{(+m_B)} v_A = -v_A \qquad v'_B = \frac{2m_A v_A}{(m_A + m_B)} = 0$$

The result is $\boxed{v'_A = -v_A \ ; \ v'_B = 0}$. An example of this is a ball bouncing off of the floor. The massive floor has no speed after the collision, and the velocity of the ball is reversed (if dissipative forces are not present).

(c) If $m_A \gg m_B$, then approximate $m_B = 0$.

$$v'_A = \frac{(m_A - m_B)}{(m_A + m_B)} v_A = \frac{(m_A)}{(m_A)} v_A = v_A \qquad v'_B = \frac{2m_A v_A}{(m_A + m_B)} = \frac{2m_A v_A}{(m_A)} = 2v_A$$

The result is $\boxed{v'_A = v_A \ ; \ v'_B = 2v_A}$. An example of this would be a golf club hitting a golf ball. The speed of the club immediately after the collision is essentially the same as its speed before the collision, and the golf ball takes off with twice the speed of the club.

(d) If $m_A = m_B$, then set $m_A = m_B = m$.

$$v'_A = \frac{(m - m)}{(m + m)} v_A = 0 \qquad v'_B = \frac{2m v_A}{(m + m)} = \frac{2m v_A}{2m} = v_A$$

The result is $\boxed{v'_A = 0 \ ; \ v'_B = v_A}$. An example of this is one billiard ball making a head-on collision with another. The first ball stops, and the second ball takes off with the same speed that the first one had.

31. From the analysis in Example 7-10, the initial projectile speed is given by $v = \dfrac{m+M}{m}\sqrt{2gh}$.

Compare the two speeds with the same masses.

$$\frac{v_2}{v_1} = \frac{\dfrac{m+M}{m}\sqrt{2gh_2}}{\dfrac{m+M}{m}\sqrt{2gh_1}} = \frac{\sqrt{h_2}}{\sqrt{h_1}} = \sqrt{\frac{h_2}{h_1}} = \sqrt{\frac{5.2}{2.6}} = \sqrt{2} \quad \rightarrow \quad \boxed{v_2 = \sqrt{2}v_1}$$

32. From the analysis in the Example 7-10, we know that

$$v = \frac{m+M}{m}\sqrt{2gh} \quad \rightarrow$$

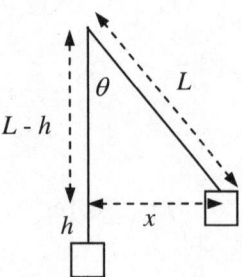

$$h = \frac{1}{2g}\left(\frac{mv}{m+M}\right)^2 = \frac{1}{2(9.8\,\text{m/s}^2)}\left(\frac{(0.028\,\text{kg})(230\,\text{m/s})}{0.028\,\text{kg} + 3.6\,\text{kg}}\right)^2$$

$$= 0.1607\,\text{m} \approx \boxed{0.16\,\text{m}}$$

From the diagram we see that

$$L^2 = (L - h)^2 + x^2$$

$$x = \sqrt{L^2 - (L-h)^2} = \sqrt{(2.8\,\text{m})^2 - (2.8\,\text{m} - 0.1607\,\text{m})^2} = \boxed{0.94\,\text{m}}$$

33. (*a*) In example 7-10, $KE_i = \frac{1}{2}mv^2$ and $KE_f = \frac{1}{2}(m+M)v'^2$. The speeds are related by

$$v' = \frac{m}{m+M}v.$$

$$\frac{\Delta KE}{KE_i} = \frac{KE_f - KE_i}{KE_i} = \frac{\frac{1}{2}(m+M)v'^2 - \frac{1}{2}mv^2}{\frac{1}{2}mv^2} = \frac{(m+M)\left(\frac{m}{m+M}v\right)^2 - mv^2}{mv^2}$$

$$= \frac{\frac{m^2v^2}{m+M} - mv^2}{mv^2} = \frac{m}{m+M} - 1 = \boxed{\frac{-M}{m+M}}$$

(*b*) For the given values, $\dfrac{-M}{m+M} = \dfrac{-380 \text{ g}}{394 \text{ g}} = -0.96$. Thus 96% of the energy is lost.

34. Use conservation of momentum in one dimension, since the particles will separate and travel in opposite directions. Call the direction of the heavier particle's motion the positive direction. Let A represent the heavier particle, and B represent the lighter particle. We have $m_A = 1.5m_B$, and $v_A = v_B = 0$.

$$p_{\text{initial}} = p_{\text{final}} \rightarrow 0 = m_A v'_A + m_B v'_B \rightarrow v'_A = -\frac{m_B v'_B}{m_A} = -\frac{2}{3}v'_B$$

The negative sign indicates direction.

Since there was no mechanical energy before the explosion, the kinetic energy of the particles after the explosion must equal the energy added.

$$E_{\text{added}} = KE'_A + KE'_B = \frac{1}{2}m_A v'^2_A + \frac{1}{2}m_B v'^2_B = \frac{1}{2}(1.5m_B)\left(\frac{2}{3}v'_B\right)^2 + \frac{1}{2}m_B v'^2_B = \frac{5}{3}\left(\frac{1}{2}m_B v'^2_B\right) = \frac{5}{3}KE'_B$$

$$KE'_B = \frac{3}{5}E_{\text{added}} = \frac{3}{5}(7500 \text{ J}) = 4500 \text{ J} \qquad KE'_A = E_{\text{added}} - KE'_B = 7500 \text{ J} - 4500 \text{ J} = 3000 \text{ J}$$

Thus $\boxed{KE'_A = 3.0 \times 10^3 \text{ J} \quad KE'_B = 4.5 \times 10^3 \text{ J}}$

35 Use conservation of momentum in one dimension. Call the direction of the sports car's velocity the positive *x* direction. Let A represent the sports car, and B represent the SUV. We have $v_B = 0$ and $v'_A = v'_B$. Solve for v_A.

$$p_{\text{initial}} = p_{\text{final}} \rightarrow m_A v_A + 0 = (m_A + m_B)v'_A \rightarrow v_A = \frac{m_A + m_B}{m_A}v'_A$$

The kinetic energy that the cars have immediately after the collision is lost due to negative work done by friction. The work done by friction can also be calculated using the definition of work. We assume the cars are on a level surface, so that the normal force is equal to the weight. The distance the cars slide forward is Δx. Equate the two expressions for the work done by friction, solve for v'_A, and use that to find v_A.

$$W_{\text{fr}} = \left(KE_{\text{final}} - KE_{\text{initial}}\right)_{\substack{\text{after} \\ \text{collision}}} = 0 - \frac{1}{2}(m_A + m_B)v'^2_A$$

$$W_{\text{fr}} = F_{\text{fr}}\Delta x \cos 180° = -\mu_k(m_A + m_B)g\Delta x$$

$$-\frac{1}{2}(m_A + m_B)v'^2_A = -\mu_k(m_A + m_B)g\Delta x \rightarrow v'_A = \sqrt{2\mu_k g\Delta x}$$

$$v_A = \frac{m_A + m_B}{m_A} v_A' = \frac{m_A + m_B}{m_A} \sqrt{2\mu_k g \Delta x} = \frac{920\,\text{kg} + 2300\,\text{kg}}{920\,\text{kg}} \sqrt{2(0.80)(9.8\,\text{m/s}^2)(2.8\,\text{m})}$$

$$= 23.191\,\text{m/s} \approx \boxed{23\,\text{m/s}}$$

36. Consider conservation of energy during the rising and falling of the ball, between contacts with the floor. The gravitational potential energy at the top of a path will be equal to the kinetic energy at the start and the end of each rising-falling cycle. Thus $mgh = \frac{1}{2}mv^2$ for any particular bounce cycle.

    Thus for an interaction with the floor, the ratio of the energies before and after the bounce is

    $$\frac{KE_{after}}{KE_{before}} = \frac{mgh'}{mgh} = \frac{1.20\,\text{m}}{1.50\,\text{m}} = 0.80.$$ We assume that each bounce will further reduce the energy to

    80% of its pre-bounce amount. The number of bounces to lose 90% of the energy can be expressed as follows.

    $$(0.8)^n = 0.1 \quad \rightarrow \quad n = \frac{\log 0.1}{\log 0.8} = 10.3$$

    Thus after $\boxed{11 \text{ bounces}}$, more than 90% of the energy is lost.

    As an alternate method, after each bounce, 80% of the available energy is left. So after 1 bounce, 80% of the original energy is left. After the second bounce, only 80% of 80%, or 64% of the available energy is left. After the third bounce, 51 %. After the fourth bounce, 41%. After the fifth bounce, 33 %. After the sixth bounce, 26%. After the seventh bounce, 21%. After the eight bounce, 17%. After the ninth bounce, 13%. After the tenth bounce, 11%. After the eleventh bounce, 9% is left. So again, it takes 11 bounces.

37. (a) For a perfectly elastic collision, Eq. 7-7 says $v_A - v_B = -(v_A' - v_B')$. Substitute that into the coefficient of restitution definition.

    $$e = \frac{v_A' - v_B'}{v_B - v_A} = -\frac{(v_A - v_B)}{v_B - v_A} = 1.$$

    For a completely inelastic collision, $v_A' = v_B'$. Substitute that into the coefficient of restitution definition.

    $$e = \frac{v_A' - v_B'}{v_B - v_A} = 0.$$

    (b) Let A represent the falling object, and B represent the heavy steel plate. The speeds of the steel plate are $v_B = 0$ and $v_B' = 0$. Thus $e = -v_A'/v_A$. Consider energy conservation during the falling or rising path. The potential energy of body A at height h is transformed into kinetic energy just before it collides with the plate. Choose down to be the positive direction.

    $$mgh = \frac{1}{2}mv_A^2 \quad \rightarrow \quad v_A = \sqrt{2gh}$$

    The kinetic energy of body A immediately after the collision is transformed into potential energy as it rises. Also, since it is moving upwards, it has a negative velocity.

    $$mgh' = \frac{1}{2}mv_A'^2 \quad \rightarrow \quad v_A' = -\sqrt{2gh'}$$

    Substitute the expressions for the velocities into the definition of the coefficient of restitution.

    $$e = -v_A'/v_A = -\frac{-\sqrt{2gh'}}{\sqrt{2gh}} \quad \rightarrow \quad \boxed{e = \sqrt{h'/h}}$$

38. Let A represent the more massive piece, and B the less massive piece. Thus $m_A = 3m_B$. In the explosion, momentum is conserved. We have $v_A = v_B = 0$.

$$p_{initial} = p_{final} \rightarrow 0 = m_A v_A' + m_B v_B' = 3m_B v_A' + m_B v_B' \rightarrow v_A' = -\tfrac{1}{3} v_B'$$

For each block, the kinetic energy gained during the explosion is lost to negative work done by friction on the block.

$$W_{fr} = KE_f - KE_i = -\tfrac{1}{2} mv^2$$

But work is also calculated in terms of the force doing the work and the distance traveled.

$$W_{fr} = F_{fr} \Delta x \cos 180° = -\mu_k F_N \Delta x = -\mu_k mg \Delta x$$

Equate the two work expressions, solve for the distance traveled, and find the ratio of distances.

$$-\tfrac{1}{2} mv^2 = -\mu_k mg \Delta x \rightarrow \Delta x = \frac{v^2}{g\mu_k} \qquad \frac{(\Delta x)_A}{(\Delta x)_B} = \frac{\dfrac{v_A'^2}{g\mu_k}}{\dfrac{v_B'^2}{g\mu_k}} = \frac{v_A'^2}{v_B'^2} = \frac{\left(-\tfrac{1}{3} v_B'\right)^2}{v_B'^2} = \frac{1}{9}$$

And so $\boxed{(\Delta x)_{heavy} / (\Delta x)_{light} = 1/9}$

39. In each case, use momentum conservation. Let A represent the 15.0-kg object, and let B represent the 10.0-kg object. We have $v_A = 5.5\,\text{m/s}$ and $v_B = -4.0\,\text{m/s}$.

(a) In this case, $v_A' = v_B'$.

$$m_A v_A + m_B v_B = (m_A + m_B) v_A' \rightarrow$$

$$v_B' = v_A' = \frac{m_A v_A + m_B v_B}{m_A + m_B} = \frac{(15.0\,\text{kg})(5.5\,\text{m/s}) + (10.0\,\text{kg})(-4.0\,\text{m/s})}{25.0\,\text{kg}} = \boxed{1.7\,\text{m/s}}$$

(b) In this case, use Eq. 7-7 to find a relationship between the velocities.

$$v_A - v_B = -(v_A' - v_B') \rightarrow v_B' = v_A - v_B + v_A'$$

$$m_A v_A + m_B v_B = m_A v_A' + m_B v_B' = m_A v_A' + m_B (v_A - v_B + v_A') \rightarrow$$

$$v_A' = \frac{(m_A - m_B) v_A + 2 m_B v_B}{m_A + m_B} = \frac{(5.0\,\text{kg})(5.5\,\text{m/s}) + 2(10.0\,\text{kg})(-4.0\,\text{m/s})}{25.0\,\text{kg}} = \boxed{-2.1\,\text{m/s}}$$

$$v_B' = v_A - v_B + v_A' = 5.5\,\text{m/s} - (-4.0\,\text{m/s}) - 2.1\,\text{m/s} = \boxed{7.4\,\text{m/s}}$$

(c) In this case, $v_A' = 0$.

$$m_A v_A + m_B v_B = m_B v_B' \rightarrow$$

$$v_B' = \frac{m_A v_A + m_B v_B}{m_B} = \frac{(15.0\,\text{kg})(5.5\,\text{m/s}) + (10.0\,\text{kg})(-4.0\,\text{m/s})}{10.0\,\text{kg}} = \boxed{4.3\,\text{m/s}}$$

To check for "reasonableness", first note the final directions of motion. A has stopped, and B has gone in the opposite direction. This is reasonable. Secondly, calculate the change in kinetic energy.

$$\Delta KE = \tfrac{1}{2} m_B v_B'^2 - \left(\tfrac{1}{2} m_A v_A^2 + \tfrac{1}{2} m_B v_B^2\right)$$

$$= \tfrac{1}{2}(10.0\,\text{kg}) - \left[\tfrac{1}{2}(15.0\,\text{kg})(5.5\,\text{m/s})^2 + \tfrac{1}{2}(10.0\,\text{kg})(-4.0\,\text{m/s})^2\right] = -220\,\text{J}$$

Since the system has lost kinetic energy and the directions are possible, this interaction is $\boxed{\text{"reasonable"}}$.

(*d*) In this case, $v_B' = 0$.

$$m_A v_A + m_B v_B = m_A v_A' \rightarrow$$

$$v_A' = \frac{m_A v_A + m_B v_B}{m_A} = \frac{(15.0\,\text{kg})(5.5\,\text{m/s}) + (10.0\,\text{kg})(-4.0\,\text{m/s})}{15.0\,\text{kg}} = \boxed{2.8\,\text{m/s}}$$

This answer is $\boxed{\text{not reasonable}}$ because it has A moving in its original direction while B has stopped. Thus A has somehow passed through B. If B has stopped, A should have rebounded in the negative direction.

(*e*) In this case, $v_A' = -4.0\,\text{m/s}$.

$$m_A v_A + m_B v_B = m_A v_A' + m_B v_B' \rightarrow$$

$$v_B' = \frac{(15.0\,\text{kg})(5.5\,\text{m/s} - -4.0\,\text{m/s}) + (10.0\,\text{kg})(-4.0\,\text{m/s})}{10.0\,\text{kg}} = \boxed{10.3\,\text{m/s}}$$

The directions are reasonable, in that each object rebounds. However, the speed of both objects is larger than its speed in the perfectly elastic case (b). Thus the system has gained kinetic energy, and unless there is some other source adding energy, this is $\boxed{\text{not reasonable}}$.

40. Use this diagram for the momenta after the decay. Since there was no momentum before the decay, the three momenta shown must add to 0 in both the *x* and *y* directions.

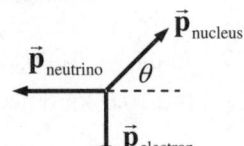

$$\left(p_{\text{nucleus}}\right)_x = p_{\text{neutrino}} \qquad \left(p_{\text{nucleus}}\right)_y = p_{\text{electron}}$$

$$p_{\text{nucleus}} = \sqrt{\left(p_{\text{nucleus}}\right)_x^2 + \left(p_{\text{nucleus}}\right)_y^2} = \sqrt{\left(p_{\text{neutrino}}\right)^2 + \left(p_{\text{electron}}\right)^2}$$

$$= \sqrt{\left(5.40 \times 10^{-23}\,\text{kg•m/s}\right)^2 + \left(9.30 \times 10^{-23}\,\text{kg•m/s}\right)^2} = \boxed{1.08 \times 10^{-22}\,\text{kg•m/s}}$$

$$\theta = \tan^{-1}\frac{\left(p_{\text{nucleus}}\right)_y}{\left(p_{\text{nucleus}}\right)_x} = \tan^{-1}\frac{\left(p_{\text{electron}}\right)}{\left(p_{\text{neutrino}}\right)} = \tan^{-1}\frac{\left(9.30 \times 10^{-23}\,\text{kg•m/s}\right)}{\left(5.40 \times 10^{-23}\,\text{kg•m/s}\right)} = 59.9°$$

The second nucleus' momentum is $\boxed{150° \text{ from the momentum of the electron}}$.

41. Consider the diagram for the momenta of the eagles. Momentum will be conserved in both the *x* and *y* directions.

$$\vec{\mathbf{p}}' = \left(m_A + m_B\right)\vec{\mathbf{v}}'$$

$$\vec{\mathbf{p}}_A = m_A\vec{\mathbf{v}}_A$$

$$\vec{\mathbf{p}}_B = m_B\vec{\mathbf{v}}_B$$

$$p_x' = \left(m_A + m_B\right)v_x' = m_A v_A \rightarrow v_x' = \frac{m_A v_A}{m_A + m_B}$$

$$p_y' = \left(m_A + m_B\right)v_y' = m_B v_B \rightarrow v_y' = \frac{m_B v_B}{m_A + m_B}$$

$$v' = \sqrt{v_x'^2 + v_y'^2} = \sqrt{\left(\frac{m_A v_A}{m_A + m_B}\right)^2 + \left(\frac{m_B v_B}{m_A + m_B}\right)^2} = \frac{\sqrt{\left(m_A v_A\right)^2 + \left(m_B v_B\right)^2}}{m_A + m_B}$$

$$= \frac{\sqrt{\left(4.3\,\text{kg}\right)^2\left(7.8\,\text{m/s}\right)^2 + \left(5.6\,\text{kg}\right)^2\left(10.2\,\text{m/s}\right)^2}}{4.3\,\text{kg} + 5.6\,\text{kg}} = \boxed{6.7\,\text{m/s}}$$

$$\theta = \tan^{-1}\frac{v_y'}{v_x'} = \tan^{-1}\frac{\dfrac{m_B v_B}{m_A + m_B}}{\dfrac{m_A v_A}{m_A + m_B}} = \tan^{-1}\frac{m_B v_B}{m_A v_A} = \tan^{-1}\frac{(5.6\,\text{kg})(10.2\,\text{m/s})}{(4.3\,\text{kg})(7.8\,\text{m/s})} = \boxed{60°\ \text{rel. to eagle A}}$$

42. (a) $p_x:\quad m_A v_A = m_A v_A' \cos\theta_A' + m_B v_B' \cos\theta_B'$

   $p_y:\quad 0 = m_A v_A' \sin\theta_A' - m_B v_B' \sin\theta_B'$

   (b) Solve the x equation for $\cos\theta_B'$ and the y equation for $\sin\theta_B'$, and then find the angle from the tangent function.

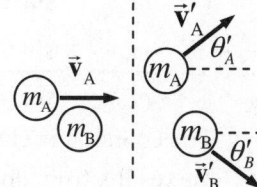

$$\tan\theta_B' = \frac{\sin\theta_B'}{\cos\theta_B'} = \frac{\dfrac{m_A v_A' \sin\theta_A'}{m_B v_B'}}{\dfrac{m_A\left(v_A - v_A' \cos\theta_A'\right)}{m_B v_B'}} = \frac{v_A' \sin\theta_A'}{\left(v_A - v_A' \cos\theta_A'\right)}$$

$$\theta_B' = \tan^{-1}\frac{v_A' \sin\theta_A'}{v_A - v_A' \cos\theta_A'} = \tan^{-1}\frac{(1.10\,\text{m/s})\sin 30.0°}{1.80\,\text{m/s} - (1.10\,\text{m/s})\cos 30.0°} = \boxed{33.0°}$$

With the value of the angle, solve the y equation for the velocity.

$$v_B' = \frac{m_A v_A' \sin\theta_A'}{m_B \sin\theta_B'} = \frac{(0.400\,\text{kg})(1.10\,\text{m/s})\sin 30.0°}{(0.500\,\text{kg})\sin 33.0°} = \boxed{0.808\,\text{m/s}}$$

43. Call the final direction of the joined objects the positive x axis. A diagram of the collision is shown. Momentum will be conserved in both the x and y directions. Note that $v_A = v_B = v$ and $v' = v/3$.

   $p_y:\quad -mv\sin\theta_1 + mv\sin\theta_2 = 0 \quad\rightarrow\quad \sin\theta_1 = \sin\theta_2 \quad\rightarrow\quad \theta_1 = \theta_2$

   $p_x:\quad mv\cos\theta_1 + mv\cos\theta_2 = (2m)(v/3) \quad\rightarrow\quad \cos\theta_1 + \cos\theta_2 = \tfrac{2}{3}$

   $\cos\theta_1 + \cos\theta_2 = 2\cos\theta_1 = \tfrac{2}{3} \quad\rightarrow\quad \theta_1 = \cos^{-1}\tfrac{1}{3} = 70.5° = \theta_2$

   $\theta_1 + \theta_2 = \boxed{141°}$

44. Write momentum conservation in the x and y directions, and KE conservation. Note that both masses are the same. We allow $\vec{\mathbf{v}}_A$ to have both x and y components.

   $p_x:\quad mv_B = mv_{Ax}' \quad\rightarrow\quad v_B = v_{Ax}'$

   $p_y:\quad mv_A = mv_{Ay}' + mv_B' \quad\rightarrow\quad v_A = v_{Ay}' + v_B'$

   $KE:\quad \tfrac{1}{2}mv_A^2 + \tfrac{1}{2}mv_B^2 = \tfrac{1}{2}mv_A'^2 + \tfrac{1}{2}mv_B'^2 \quad\rightarrow\quad v_A^2 + v_B^2 = v_A'^2 + v_B'^2$

   Substitute the results from the momentum equations into the KE equation.

   $\left(v_{Ay}' + v_B'\right)^2 + \left(v_{Ax}'\right)^2 = v_A'^2 + v_B'^2 \quad\rightarrow\quad v_{Ay}'^2 + 2v_{Ay}'v_B' + v_B'^2 + v_{Ax}'^2 = v_A'^2 + v_B'^2 \quad\rightarrow$

   $v_A'^2 + 2v_{Ay}'v_B' + v_B'^2 = v_A'^2 + v_B'^2 \quad\rightarrow\quad 2v_{Ay}'v_B' = 0 \quad\rightarrow\quad v_{Ay}' = 0 \text{ or } v_B' = 0$

   Since we are given that $v_B' \neq 0$, we must have $v_{Ay}' = 0$. This means that the final direction of A is the $\boxed{x\ \text{direction}}$. Put this result into the momentum equations to find the final speeds.

   $v_A' = v_{Ax}' = v_B = \boxed{3.7\,\text{m/s}} \qquad v_B' = v_A = \boxed{2.0\,\text{m/s}}$

45. Let A represent the incoming neon atom, and B represent the target atom. A momentum diagram of the collision looks like the first figure. The figure can be re-drawn as a triangle, the second figure, since $m_A \vec{v}_A = m_A \vec{v}'_A + m_B \vec{v}'_B$. Write the law of sines for this triangle, relating each final momentum magnitude to the initial momentum magnitude.

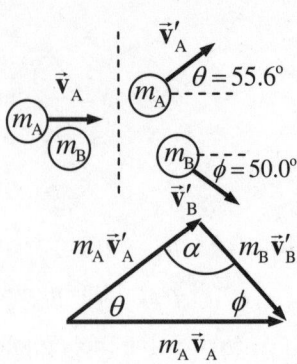

$$\frac{m_A v'_A}{m_A v_A} = \frac{\sin \phi}{\sin \alpha} \quad \rightarrow \quad v'_A = v_A \frac{\sin \phi}{\sin \alpha}$$

$$\frac{m_B v'_B}{m_A v_A} = \frac{\sin \theta}{\sin \alpha} \quad \rightarrow \quad v'_B = v_A \frac{m_A}{m_B} \frac{\sin \theta}{\sin \alpha}$$

The collision is elastic, so write the KE conservation equation, and substitute the results from above. Also note that $\alpha = 180.0 - 55.6° - 50.0° = 74.4°$

$$\tfrac{1}{2} m_A v_A^2 = \tfrac{1}{2} m_A v_A'^2 + \tfrac{1}{2} m_B v_B'^2 \quad \rightarrow \quad m_A v_A^2 = m_A \left(v_A \frac{\sin \phi}{\sin \alpha} \right)^2 + m_B \left(v_A \frac{m_A}{m_B} \frac{\sin \theta}{\sin \alpha} \right)^2 \quad \rightarrow$$

$$m_B = \frac{m_A \sin^2 \theta}{\sin^2 \alpha - \sin^2 \phi} = \frac{(20.0 \text{ u}) \sin^2 55.6°}{\sin^2 74.4 - \sin^2 50.0°} = \boxed{39.9 \text{ u}}$$

46. Use Eq. 7-9a, extended to three particles.

$$x_{CM} = \frac{m_A x_A + m_B x_B + m_C x_C}{m_A + m_B + m_C} = \frac{(1.00 \text{ kg})(0) + (1.50 \text{ kg})(0.50 \text{ m}) + (1.10 \text{ kg})(0.75 \text{ m})}{1.00 \text{ kg} + 1.50 \text{ kg} + 1.10 \text{ kg}}$$

$$= \boxed{0.44 \text{ m}}$$

47. Choose the carbon atom as the origin of coordinates.

$$x_{CM} = \frac{m_C x_C + m_O x_O}{m_C + m_O} = \frac{(12 \text{ u})(0) + (16 \text{ u})(1.13 \times 10^{-10} \text{ m})}{12 \text{ u} + 16 \text{ u}} = \boxed{6.5 \times 10^{-11} \text{ m}} \text{ from the C atom.}$$

48. Find the CM relative to the front of the car.

$$x_{CM} = \frac{m_{car} x_{car} + m_{front} x_{front} + m_{back} x_{back}}{m_{car} + m_{front} + m_{back}}$$

$$= \frac{(1050 \text{ kg})(2.50 \text{ m}) + 2(70.0 \text{ kg})(2.80 \text{ m}) + 3(70.0 \text{ kg})(3.90 \text{ m})}{1050 \text{ kg} + 2(70.0 \text{ kg}) + 3(70.0 \text{ kg})} = \boxed{2.74 \text{ m}}$$

49. Consider this diagram of the cars on the raft. Notice that the origin of coordinates is located at the CM of the raft. Reference all distances to that location.

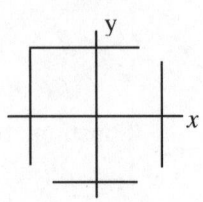

$$x_{CM} = \frac{(1200 \text{ kg})(9 \text{ m}) + (1200 \text{ kg})(9 \text{ m}) + (1200 \text{ kg})(-9 \text{ m})}{3(1200 \text{ kg}) + 6800 \text{ kg}} = \boxed{1.04 \text{ m}}$$

$$y_{CM} = \frac{(1200 \text{ kg})(9 \text{ m}) + (1200 \text{ kg})(-9 \text{ m}) + (1200 \text{ kg})(-9 \text{ m})}{3(1200 \text{ kg}) + 6800 \text{ kg}} = \boxed{-1.04 \text{ m}}$$

50. By the symmetry of the problem, since the centers of the cubes are along a straight line, the vertical CM coordinate will be 0, and the depth CM coordinate will be 0. The only CM coordinate to calculate is the one along the straight line joining the centers. The mass of each cube will be the volume times the density, and so $m_1 = \rho(l_0)^3$, $m_2 = \rho(2l_0)^3$, $m_3 = \rho(3l_0)^3$. Measuring from the left edge of the smallest block, the locations of the CM's of the individual cubes are $x_1 = \frac{1}{2}l_0$, $x_2 = 2l_0$, $x_3 = 4.5l_0$. Use Eq. 7-9a to calculate the CM of the system.

$$x_{CM} = \frac{m_1 x_1 + m_2 x_2 + m_3 x_3}{m_1 + m_2 + m_3} = \frac{\rho l_0^3 \left(\frac{1}{2}l_0\right) + 8\rho l_0^3 (2l_0) + 27\rho l_0^3 (4.5l_0)}{\rho l_0^3 + 8\rho l_0^3 + 27\rho l_0^3}$$

$$= \boxed{3.8\, l_0 \text{ from the left edge of the smallest cube}}$$

51. Let each crate have a mass M. A top view of the pallet is shown, with the total mass of each stack listed. Take the origin to be the back left corner of the pallet.

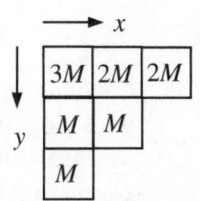

$$x_{CM} = \frac{(5M)(l/2) + (3M)(3l/2) + (2M)(5l/2)}{10M} = \boxed{1.2l}$$

$$y_{CM} = \frac{(7M)(l/2) + (2M)(3l/2) + (1M)(5l/2)}{10M} = \boxed{0.9l}$$

52. Consider the following. We start with a full circle of radius $2R$, with its CM at the origin. Then we draw a circle of radius R, with its CM at the coordinates $(0.80R, 0)$.

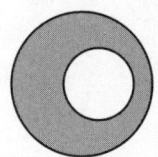

The full circle can now be labeled as a "gray" part and a "white" part. The y coordinate of the CM of the entire circle, the CM of the gray part, and the CM of the white part are all at $y = 0$ by the symmetry of the system. The x coordinate of the entire circle is at $x_{CM} = 0$, and can be calculated by $x_{CM} = \dfrac{m_{gray} x_{gray} + m_{white} x_{white}}{m_{total}}$. Rearrange this equation.

$$x_{CM} = \frac{m_{gray} x_{gray} + m_{white} x_{white}}{m_{total}} \rightarrow$$

$$x_{gray} = \frac{m_{total} x_{CM} - m_{white} x_{white}}{m_{gray}} = \frac{m_{total} x_{CM} - m_{white} x_{white}}{m_{total} - m_{white}} = \frac{-m_{white} x_{white}}{m_{total} - m_{white}}$$

This is functionally the same as treating the white part of the figure as a hole of negative mass. The mass of each part can be found by multiplying the area of the part times the uniform density of the plate.

$$x_{gray} = \frac{-m_{white} x_{white}}{m_{total} - m_{white}} = \frac{-\rho \pi R^2 (0.80R)}{\rho \pi (2R)^2 - \rho \pi R^2} = \frac{-0.80R}{3} = \boxed{-0.27R}$$

53. Take the upper leg, lower leg, and foot all together. Note that Table 7-1 gives the relative mass of BOTH legs and feet, so a factor of 1/2 is needed. Assume a person of mass 70 kg.

$$(70 \text{ kg})\frac{(21.5 + 9.6 + 3.4)}{100}\frac{1}{2} = \boxed{12 \text{ kg}}.$$

54. With the shoulder as the origin of coordinates for measuring the center of mass, we have the following relative locations from Table 7-1 for the arm components, as percentages of the height. Down is positive.

$$x_{\underset{arm}{upper}} = 81.2 - 7.7 = 9.5 \quad x_{\underset{arm}{lower}} = 81.2 - 55.3 = 25.9 \quad x_{hand} = 81.2 - 43.1 = 38.1$$

To find the CM, we can also use relative mass percentages. Since the expression includes the total mass in the denominator, there is no need to divide all masses by 2 to find single component masses. Simply use the relative mass percentages given in the table.

$$x_{CM} = \frac{x_{\underset{arm}{upper}} m_{\underset{arm}{upper}} + x_{\underset{arm}{lower}} m_{\underset{arm}{lower}} + x_{hand} m_{hand}}{m_{\underset{arm}{upper}} + m_{\underset{arm}{lower}} + m_{hand}} = \frac{(9.5)(6.6) + (25.9)(4.2) + (38.1)(1.7)}{6.6 + 4.2 + 1.7}$$

$$= \boxed{19\% \text{ of the person's height along the line from the shoulder to the hand}}$$

55. Take the shoulder to be the origin of coordinates. We assume that the arm is held with the upper arm parallel to the floor and the lower arm and hand extended upward. Measure x horizontally from the shoulder, and y vertically. Since the expression includes the total mass in the denominator, there is no need to divide all masses by 2 to find single component masses. Simply use the relative mass percentages given in the table.

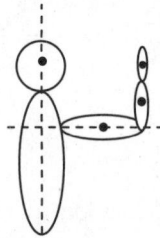

$$x_{CM} = \frac{x_{\underset{arm}{upper}} m_{\underset{arm}{upper}} + x_{\underset{arm}{lower}} m_{\underset{arm}{lower}} + x_{hand} m_{hand}}{m_{\underset{arm}{upper}} + m_{\underset{arm}{lower}} + m_{hand}}$$

$$= \frac{(81.2 - 71.7)(6.6) + (81.2 - 62.2)(4.2 + 1.7)}{6.6 + 4.2 + 1.7} = 14.0$$

$$y_{CM} = \frac{y_{\underset{arm}{upper}} m_{\underset{arm}{upper}} + y_{\underset{arm}{lower}} m_{\underset{arm}{lower}} + y_{hand} m_{hand}}{m_{\underset{arm}{upper}} + m_{\underset{arm}{lower}} + m_{hand}}$$

$$= \frac{(0)(6.6) + (62.2 - 55.3)(4.2) + (62.2 - 43.1)(1.7)}{6.6 + 4.2 + 1.7} = 4.92$$

Convert the distance percentages to actual distance using the person's height.

$$x_{CM} = (14.0\%)(155 \text{ cm}) = \boxed{21.7 \text{ cm}} \qquad y_{CM} = (4.92\%)(155 \text{ cm}) = \boxed{7.6 \text{ cm}}$$

56. See the diagram of the person. The head, trunk, and neck are all lined up so that their CM's are on the torso's median line. Call down the positive y direction. The y distances of the CM of each body part from the median line, in terms of percentage of full height, are shown below, followed by the percentage each body part is of the full body mass.

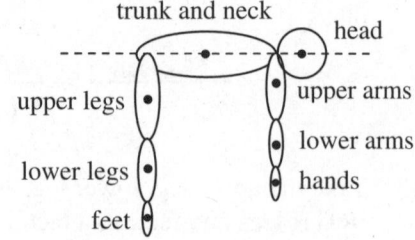

On median line:	head (h):	0	;	6.9% body mass
	Trunk & neck (t n):	0	;	46.1% body mass
From shoulder hinge point:	upper arms (u a):	81.2 − 71.7 = 9.5	;	6.6% body mass
	lower arms (l a):	81.2 − 55.3 = 25.9	;	4.2% body mass
	hands (ha):	81.2 − 43.1 = 38.1	;	1.7% body mass

From hip hinge point:
upper legs (u l): $52.1 - 42.5 = 9.6$; 21.5% body mass
lower legs (l l): $52.1 - 18.2 = 33.9$; 9.6% body mass
feet (f): $52.1 - 1.8 = 50.3$; 3.4% body mass

Using this data, calculate the vertical location of the CM.

$$y_{CM} = \frac{y_h m_h + y_{tn} m_{tn} + y_{ua} m_{ua} + y_{la} m_{la} + y_{ha} m_{ha} + y_{ul} m_{ul} + y_{ll} m_{ll} + y_f m_f}{m_{\substack{full \\ body}}}$$

$$= \frac{0 + 0 + (9.5)(6.6) + (25.9)(4.2) + (38.1)(1.7) + (9.6)(21.5) + (33.9)(9.6) + (50.3)(3.4)}{100}$$

$$= 9.4$$

Thus the center of mass is $\boxed{\text{9.4\% of the full body height below the torso's median line}}$. For a person of height 1.7 m, this is about 16 cm. That is most likely slightly $\boxed{\text{outside the body}}$.

57. (a) Find the CM relative to the center of the Earth.

$$x_{CM} = \frac{m_E x_E + m_M x_M}{m_E + m_M} = \frac{\left(5.98 \times 10^{24}\,\text{kg}\right)(0) + \left(7.35 \times 10^{22}\,\text{kg}\right)\left(3.84 \times 10^8\,\text{m}\right)}{5.98 \times 10^{24}\,\text{kg} + 7.35 \times 10^{22}\,\text{kg}}$$

$$= \boxed{4.66 \times 10^6\,\text{m from the center of the Earth}}$$

This is actually inside the volume of the Earth, since $R_E = 6.38 \times 10^6\,\text{m}$

(b) It is this Earth – Moon CM location that actually traces out the orbit as discussed in chapter 5. The Earth and Moon will orbit about this location in (approximately) circular orbits. The motion of the Moon, for example, around the Sun would then be a sum of two motions: i) the motion of the Moon about the Earth – Moon CM; and ii) the motion of the Earth – Moon CM about the Sun. To an external observer, the Moon's motion would appear to be a small radius, higher frequency circular motion (motion about the Earth – Moon CM) combined with a large radius, lower frequency circular motion (motion about the Sun).

58. (a) Measure all distances from the <u>original</u> position of the woman.

$$x_{CM} = \frac{m_w x_w + m_M x_M}{m_w + m_M} = \frac{(55\,\text{kg})(0) + (80\,\text{kg})(10.0\,\text{m})}{135\,\text{kg}} = \boxed{\text{5.9 m from the woman}}$$

(b) Since there is no force external to the man-woman system, the CM will not move, relative to the <u>original</u> position of the woman. The woman's distance will no longer be 0, and the man's distance has changed to 7.5 m.

$$x_{CM} = \frac{m_w x_w + m_M x_M}{m_w + m_M} = \frac{(55\,\text{kg})x_w + (80\,\text{kg})(7.5\,\text{m})}{135\,\text{kg}} = 5.9\,\text{m} \quad \rightarrow$$

$$x_w = \frac{(5.9\,\text{m})(135\,\text{kg}) - (80\,\text{kg})(7.5\,\text{m})}{55\,\text{kg}} = 3.6\,\text{m}$$

$$x_M - x_w = 7.5\,\text{m} - 3.6\,\text{m} = \boxed{3.9\,\text{m}}$$

(c) When the man collides with the woman, he will be at the original location of the center of mass.

$$x_{\substack{M \\ final}} - x_{\substack{M \\ initial}} = 5.9\,\text{m} - 10.0\,\text{m} = -4.1\,\text{m}$$

He has moved $\boxed{4.1\,\text{m}}$ from his original position.

59. The point that will follow a parabolic trajectory is the center of mass. Find the CM relative to the bottom of the mallet. Each part of the hammer (handle and head) can be treated as a point mass located at the CM of the respective piece. So the CM of the handle is 12.0 cm from the bottom of the handle, and the CM of the head is 28.0 cm from the bottom of the handle.

$$x_{CM} = \frac{m_{handle}x_{handle} + m_{head}x_{head}}{m_{handle} + m_{head}} = \frac{(0.500\text{ kg})(24.0\text{ cm}) + (2.00\text{ kg})(28.0\text{ cm})}{2.50\text{ kg}} = \boxed{24.8\text{ cm}}$$

Note that this is inside the head of the mallet.

60. The CM of the system will follow the same path regardless of the way the mass splits, and so will still be $2d$ from the launch point when the parts land. Assume that the explosion is designed so that m_1 still is stopped in midair and falls straight down.

(a) $x_{CM} = \dfrac{m_1 x_1 + m_{II} x_{II}}{m_1 + m_{II}} \rightarrow 2d = \dfrac{m_1 d + 3m_1 x_{II}}{4m_1} = \dfrac{d + 3x_{II}}{4} \rightarrow x_{II} = \boxed{\frac{7}{3}d}$

(b) $x_{CM} = \dfrac{m_1 x_1 + m_{II} x_{II}}{m_1 + m_{II}} \rightarrow 2d = \dfrac{3m_{II} d + m_{II} x_{II}}{4m_{II}} = \dfrac{3d + x_{II}}{4} \rightarrow x_{II} = \boxed{5d}$

61. Call the origin of coordinates the CM of the balloon, gondola, and person at rest. Since the CM is at rest, the total momentum of the system relative to the ground is 0. The man climbing the rope cannot change the total momentum of the system, and so the CM must stay at rest. Call the upward direction positive. Then the velocity of the man with respect to the balloon is $-v$. Call the velocity of the balloon with respect to the ground v_{BG}. Then the velocity of the man with respect to the ground is $v_{MG} = -v + v_{BG}$. Apply Eq. 7-10.

$$0 = mv_{MG} + Mv_{BG} = m(-v + v_{BG}) + Mv_{BG} \rightarrow \boxed{v_{BG} = v\frac{m}{m+M}, \text{ upward}}$$

If the passenger stops, $\boxed{\text{the balloon also stops}}$, and the CM of the system remains at rest.

62. To find the average force, divide the change in momentum by the time over which the momentum changes. Choose the x direction to be the opposite of the baseball's incoming direction. The velocity with which the ball is moving after hitting the bat can be found from conservation of energy, and knowing the height the ball rises.

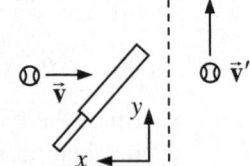

$$\left(KE_{initial} = PE_{final}\right)_{\substack{after \\ collision}} \rightarrow \tfrac{1}{2}mv'^2 = mg\Delta y \rightarrow$$

$$v' = \sqrt{2g\Delta y} = \sqrt{2(9.80\text{ m/s}^2)(55.6\text{ m})} = 33.0\text{ m/s}$$

The average force can be calculated from the change in momentum and the time of contact.

$$\overline{F}_x = \frac{\Delta p_x}{\Delta t} = \frac{m(v'_x - v_x)}{\Delta t} = \frac{(0.145\text{ kg})(0--35.0\text{ m/s})}{1.4\times10^{-3}\text{s}} = 3.6\times10^3\text{ N}$$

$$\overline{F}_y = \frac{\Delta p_y}{\Delta t} = \frac{m(v'_y - v_y)}{\Delta t} = \frac{(0.145\text{ kg})(33.0\text{ m/s}-0)}{1.4\times10^{-3}\text{s}} = 3.4\times10^3\text{ N}$$

$$\overline{F} = \sqrt{\overline{F}_x^2 + \overline{F}_y^2} = \boxed{5.0\times10^3\text{ N}} \qquad \theta = \tan^{-1}\frac{\overline{F}_y}{\overline{F}_x} = \boxed{43°}$$

63. Momentum will be conserved in two dimensions. The fuel was ejected in the *y* direction as seen from the ground, and so the fuel had no *x*-component of velocity.

$$p_x: \quad m_{rocket}v_0 = \left(m_{rocket} - m_{fuel}\right)v_x' + m_{fuel}0 = \tfrac{2}{3}m_{rocket}v_x' \quad \rightarrow \quad \boxed{v_x' = \tfrac{3}{2}v_0}$$

$$p_y: \quad 0 = m_{fuel}v_{fuel} + \left(m_{rocket} - m_{fuel}\right)v_y' = \tfrac{1}{3}m_{rocket}\left(2v_0\right) + \tfrac{2}{3}m_{rocket}v_y' \quad \rightarrow \quad \boxed{v_y' = -v_0}$$

64. In an elastic collision between two objects of equal mass, with the target object initially stationary, the angle between the final velocities of the objects is 90°. Here is a proof of that fact. Momentum conservation as a vector relationship says $m\vec{v} = m\vec{v}_A' + m\vec{v}_B' \rightarrow \vec{v} = \vec{v}_A' + \vec{v}_B'$. Kinetic energy conservation says $\tfrac{1}{2}mv^2 = \tfrac{1}{2}mv_A'^2 + \tfrac{1}{2}mv_B'^2 \rightarrow v^2 = v_A'^2 + v_B'^2$. The vector equation resulting from momentum conservation can be illustrated by the second diagram. Apply the law of cosines to that triangle of vectors, and then equate the two expressions for v^2.

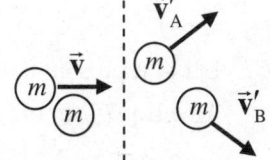

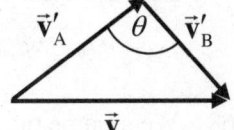

$$v^2 = v_A'^2 + v_B'^2 - 2v_A'v_B'\cos\theta$$

Equating the two expressions for v^2 gives

$$v_A'^2 + v_B'^2 - 2v_A'v_B'\cos\theta = v_A'^2 + v_B'^2 \quad \rightarrow \quad \cos\theta = 0 \quad \rightarrow \quad \theta = 90°$$

For this specific circumstance, see the third diagram. We assume that the target ball is hit "correctly" so that it goes in the pocket. Find θ_1 from

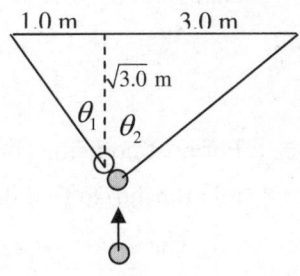

the geometry of the "left" triangle: $\theta_1 = \tan^{-1}\dfrac{1.0}{\sqrt{3.0}} = 30°$. Find θ_2 from

the geometry of the "right" triangle: $\theta_2 = \tan^{-1}\dfrac{3.0}{\sqrt{3.0}} = 60°$. Since the

balls will separate at a 90° angle, if the target ball goes in the pocket, this does appear to be a $\boxed{\text{good possibility of a scratch shot}}$.

65. (a) The momentum of the astronaut – space capsule combination will be conserved since the only forces are "internal" to that system. Let A represent the astronaut and B represent the space capsule, and let the direction the astronaut moves be the positive direction. Due to the choice of reference frame, $v_A = v_B = 0$. We also have $v_A' = 2.50\,\text{m/s}$.

$$p_{initial} = p_{final} \quad \rightarrow \quad m_A v_A + m_B v_B = 0 = m_A v_A' + m_B v_B' \quad \rightarrow$$

$$v_B' = -v_A'\frac{m_A}{m_B} = -\left(2.50\,\text{m/s}\right)\frac{140\,\text{kg}}{1800\,\text{kg}} = \boxed{-0.194\,\text{m/s}}$$

The negative sign indicates that the space capsule is moving in the opposite direction to the astronaut.

(b) The average force on the astronaut is the astronaut's change in momentum, divided by the time of interaction.

$$\overline{F} = \frac{\Delta p}{\Delta t} = \frac{m\left(v_A' - v_A\right)}{\Delta t} = \frac{\left(140\,\text{kg}\right)\left(2.50\,\text{m/s} - 0\right)}{0.40\,\text{s}} = \boxed{8.8 \times 10^2\,\text{N}}$$

66. Since the only forces on the astronauts are internal to the 2-astronaut system, their CM will not change. Call the CM location the origin of coordinates. That is also the original location of the two astronauts.

$$x_{CM} = \frac{m_A x_A + m_B x_B}{m_A + m_B} \rightarrow 0 = \frac{(60 \text{ kg})(12 \text{ m}) + (80 \text{ kg}) x_B}{140 \text{ kg}} \rightarrow x = -9 \text{ m}$$

Their distance apart is $x_A - x_B = 12 \text{ m} - (-9\text{m}) = \boxed{21 \text{ m}}$.

67. Let A represent the incoming ball, and B represent the target ball. We have $v_B = 0$ and $v_A' = -\frac{1}{4} v_A$. Use Eq. 7-7 to obtain a relationship between the velocities.

$$v_A - v_B = -(v_A' - v_B') \rightarrow v_B' = v_A + v_A' = \frac{3}{4} v_A$$

Substitute this relationship into the momentum conservation equation for the collision.

$$p_{\text{initial}} = p_{\text{final}} \rightarrow m_A v_A = m_A v_A' + m_B v_B' = m_A \left(-\frac{1}{4} v_A\right) + m_B \left(\frac{3}{4} v_A\right) \rightarrow \boxed{m_B = \frac{5}{3} m_A}$$

68. We assume that all motion is along a single direction. The distance of sliding can be related to the change in the kinetic energy of a car, as follows.

$$W_{\text{fr}} = \Delta KE = \frac{1}{2} m \left(v_f^2 - v_i^2\right) \quad W_{\text{fr}} = F_{\text{fr}} \Delta x \cos 180° \theta = -\mu_k F_N \Delta x = -\mu_k mg \Delta x \rightarrow$$

$$-\mu_k g \Delta x = \frac{1}{2}\left(v_f^2 - v_i^2\right)$$

For post-collision sliding, $v_f = 0$ and v_i is the speed immediately after the collision, v'. Use this relationship to find the speed of each car immediately after the collision.

Car A: $-\mu_k g \Delta x_A' = -\frac{1}{2} v_A'^2 \rightarrow v_A' = \sqrt{2\mu_k g \Delta x_A'} = \sqrt{2(0.60)(9.8 \text{ m/s}^2)(18 \text{ m})} = 14.55 \text{ m/s}$

Car B: $-\mu_k g \Delta x_B' = -\frac{1}{2} v_B'^2 \rightarrow v_B' = \sqrt{2\mu_k g \Delta x_B'} = \sqrt{2(0.60)(9.8 \text{ m/s}^2)(30 \text{ m})} = 18.78 \text{ m/s}$

During the collision, momentum is conserved in one dimension. Note that $v_B = 0$.

$$p_{\text{initial}} = p_{\text{final}} \rightarrow m_A v_A = m_A v_A' + m_B v_B'$$

$$v_A = \frac{m_A v_A' + m_B v_B'}{m_A} = \frac{(1900 \text{ kg})(14.55 \text{ m/s}) + (1100 \text{ kg})(18.78 \text{ m/s})}{1900 \text{ kg}} = 25.42 \text{ m/s}$$

For pre-collision sliding, again apply the friction – energy relationship, with $v_f = v_A$ and v_i is the speed when the brakes were first applied.

$$-\mu_k g \Delta x_A = \frac{1}{2}\left(v_A^2 - v_i^2\right) \rightarrow v_i = \sqrt{v_A^2 + 2\mu_k g \Delta x_A} = \sqrt{(25.42 \text{ m/s})^2 + 2(0.60)(9.8 \text{ m/s}^2)(15 \text{ m})}$$

$$= 28.68 \text{ m/s} \left(\frac{1 \text{ mi/h}}{0.447 \text{ m/s}}\right) = \boxed{64 \text{ mi/h}}$$

69. Because all of the collisions are perfectly elastic, no energy is lost in the collisions. With each collision, the horizontal velocity is constant, and the vertical velocity reverses direction. So, after each collision, the ball rises again to the same height from which it dropped. Thus, after five bounces, the bounce height will be $\boxed{4.00 \text{ m}}$, the same as the starting height.

70. This is a ballistic "pendulum" of sorts, similar to Example 7-10 in the textbook. There is no difference in the fact that the block and bullet are moving vertically instead of horizontally. The collision is still totally inelastic and conserves momentum, and the energy is still conserved in the

rising of the block and embedded bullet after the collision. So we simply quote the equation from that example.

$$v = \frac{m+M}{m}\sqrt{2gh} \quad \rightarrow$$

$$h = \frac{1}{2g}\left(\frac{mv}{m+M}\right)^2 = \frac{1}{2\left(9.80\,\text{m/s}^2\right)}\left(\frac{\left(0.0290\,\text{kg}\right)\left(510\,\text{m/s}\right)}{0.0290\,\text{kg}+1.40\,\text{kg}}\right)^2 = \boxed{5.47\,\text{m}}$$

71. This is a ballistic "pendulum" of sorts, similar to Example 7-10 in the textbook. Momentum is conserved in the totally inelastic collision, and so $mv = (m+M)v'$. The kinetic energy present immediately after the collision is lost due to negative work being done by friction.

$$W_{\text{fr}} = \Delta KE = \tfrac{1}{2}m\left(v_f^2 - v_i^2\right)_{\substack{\text{after}\\\text{collision}}} \qquad W_{\text{fr}} = F_{\text{fr}}\Delta x\cos 180°\,\theta = -\mu_k F_N \Delta x = -\mu_k mg\Delta x \quad \rightarrow$$

$$-\mu_k g\Delta x = \tfrac{1}{2}\left(v_f^2 - v_i^2\right) = -\tfrac{1}{2}v'^2 \quad \rightarrow \quad v' = \sqrt{2\mu_k g\Delta x}$$

Use this expression for v' in the momentum equation in order to solve for v.

$$mv = (m+M)v' = (m+M)\sqrt{2\mu_k g\Delta x} \quad \rightarrow$$

$$v = \left(\frac{m+M}{m}\right)\sqrt{2\mu_k g\Delta x} = \left(\frac{0.025\,\text{kg}+1.35\,\text{kg}}{0.025\,\text{kg}}\right)\sqrt{2(0.25)\left(9.8\,\text{m/s}^2\right)(9.5\,\text{m})} = \boxed{3.8\times 10^2\,\text{m/s}}$$

72. Calculate the CM relative to the 60-kg person's seat, at one end of the boat. See the first diagram. Don't forget to include the boat's mass.

$$x_{\text{CM}} = \frac{m_A x_A + m_B x_B + m_C x_C}{m_A + m_B + m_C}$$

$$= \frac{\left(60\,\text{kg}\right)(0)+\left(80\,\text{kg}\right)(1.6\,\text{m})+\left(75\,\text{kg}\right)(3.2\,\text{m})}{215\,\text{kg}} = 1.712\,\text{m}$$

Now, when the passengers exchange positions, the boat will move some distance "d" as shown, but the CM will not move. We measure the location of the CM from the same place as before, but now the boat has moved relative to that origin.

$$x_{\text{CM}} = \frac{m_A x_A + m_B x_B + m_C x_C}{m_A + m_B + m_C}$$

$$1.712\,\text{m} = \frac{\left(75\,\text{kg}\right)(d)+\left(80\,\text{kg}\right)(1.6\,\text{m}+d)+\left(60\,\text{kg}\right)(3.2\,\text{m}+d)}{215\,\text{kg}} = \frac{215d\,\text{kg}{\cdot}\text{m}+320\,\text{kg}{\cdot}\text{m}}{215\,\text{kg}}$$

$$d = 0.224\,\text{m}$$

Thus the boat will move $\boxed{0.22\,\text{m towards the initial position of the 75 kg person}}$.

73. (a) The meteor striking and coming to rest in the Earth is a totally inelastic collision. Let A represent the Earth and B represent the meteor. Use the frame of reference in which the Earth is at rest before the collision, and so $v_A = 0$. Write momentum conservation for the collision.

$$m_B v_B = (m_A + m_B)v' \quad \rightarrow$$

$$v' = v_B \frac{m_B}{m_A + m_B} = \left(1.5 \times 10^4 \text{ m/s}\right) \frac{1.0 \times 10^8 \text{ kg}}{6.0 \times 10^{24} \text{ kg} + 1.0 \times 10^8 \text{ kg}} = \boxed{2.5 \times 10^{-13} \text{ m/s}}$$

(*b*) The fraction of the meteor's KE transferred to the Earth is the final KE of the Earth divided by the initial KE of the meteor.

$$\frac{KE_{\text{final}\atop\text{Earth}}}{KE_{\text{initial}\atop\text{meteor}}} = \frac{\frac{1}{2} m_A v'^2}{\frac{1}{2} m_B v_B^2} = \frac{\frac{1}{2}\left(6.0 \times 10^{24} \text{ kg}\right)\left(2.5 \times 10^{-13} \text{ m/s}\right)^2}{\frac{1}{2}\left(1.0 \times 10^8 \text{ kg}\right)\left(1.5 \times 10^4 \text{ m/s}\right)^2} = \boxed{1.7 \times 10^{-17}}$$

(*c*) The Earth's change in KE can be calculated directly.

$$\Delta KE_{\text{Earth}} = KE_{\text{final}\atop\text{Earth}} - KE_{\text{initial}\atop\text{Earth}} = \frac{1}{2} m_A v'^2 - 0 = \frac{1}{2}\left(6.0 \times 10^{24} \text{ kg}\right)\left(2.5 \times 10^{-13} \text{ m/s}\right) = \boxed{0.19 \text{ J}}$$

74. Momentum will be conserved in one dimension in the explosion. Let A represent the fragment with the larger KE.

$$p_{\text{initial}} = p_{\text{final}} \quad \rightarrow \quad 0 = m_A v'_A + m_B v'_B \quad \rightarrow \quad v'_B = -\frac{m_A v'_A}{m_B}$$

$$KE_A = 2KE_B \quad \rightarrow \quad \frac{1}{2} m_A v'^2_A = 2\left(\frac{1}{2} m_B v'^2_B\right) = m_B\left(-\frac{m_A v'_A}{m_B}\right)^2 \quad \rightarrow \quad \frac{m_A}{m_B} = \boxed{\frac{1}{2}}$$

The fragment with the larger KE energy has half the mass of the other fragment.

75. (*a*) The force is linear, with a maximum force of 580 N at 0 seconds, and a minimum force of 40 N at 3 milliseconds.

(*b*) The impulse given the bullet is the "area" under the *F* vs. *t* graph. The area is trapezoidal.

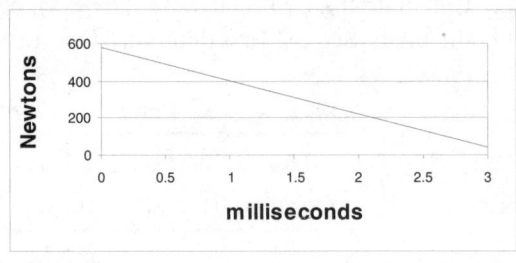

$$\text{Impulse} = \left(\frac{580 \text{ N} + 40 \text{ N}}{2}\right)\left(3.0 \times 10^{-3} \text{ s}\right)$$

$$= \boxed{0.93 \text{ N} \cdot \text{s}}$$

(*c*) The impulse given the bullet is the change in momentum of the bullet. The starting speed of the bullet is 0.

$$\text{Impulse} = \Delta p = m(v - v_0) \quad \rightarrow \quad m = \frac{\text{Impulse}}{v} = \frac{0.93 \text{ N} \cdot \text{s}}{220 \text{ m/s}} = \boxed{4.2 \times 10^{-3} \text{ kg}}$$

76. For the swinging balls, their velocity at the bottom of the swing and the height to which they rise are related by conservation of energy. If the zero of gravitational potential energy is taken to be the lowest point of the swing, then the kinetic energy at the low point is equal to the potential energy at the highest point of the swing, where the speed is zero. Thus we have $\frac{1}{2} m v_{\text{bottom}}^2 = mgh$ for any swinging ball, and so the relationship between speed and height is $v_{\text{bottom}}^2 = 2gh$.

(*a*) Calculate the speed of the lighter ball at the bottom of its swing.

$$v_A = \sqrt{2gh_A} = \sqrt{2\left(9.8 \text{ m/s}^2\right)\left(0.30 \text{ m} - 0.30 \text{ m} \cos 60°\right)} = 1.715 \text{ m/s} \approx \boxed{1.7 \text{ m/s}}$$

(*b*) Assume that the collision is elastic, and use the results of problem 30. Take the direction that ball A is moving just before the collision as the positive direction.

$$v'_A = \frac{(m_A - m_B)}{(m_A + m_B)}v_A = \frac{(0.040\,\text{kg} - 0.060\,\text{kg})}{(0.040\,\text{kg} + 0.060\,\text{kg})}(1.715\,\text{m/s}) = -0.343\,\text{m/s} \approx \boxed{-0.34\,\text{m/s}}$$

$$v'_B = \frac{2m_A}{(m_A + m_B)}v_A = \frac{2(0.040\,\text{kg})}{(0.040\,\text{kg} + 0.060\,\text{kg})}(1.715\,\text{m/s}) = 1.372\,\text{m/s} \approx \boxed{1.4\,\text{m/s}}$$

Notice that ball A has rebounded backwards.

(c)　After each collision, use the conservation of energy relationship again.

$$h'_A = \frac{v'^2_A}{2g} = \frac{(-0.343\,\text{m/s})^2}{2(9.8\,\text{m/s}^2)} = \boxed{6.0 \times 10^{-3}\,\text{m}} \qquad h'_B = \frac{v'^2_B}{2g} = \frac{(1.372\,\text{m/s})^2}{2(9.8\,\text{m/s}^2)} = \boxed{9.6 \times 10^{-2}\,\text{m}}$$

77.　Use conservation of momentum in one dimension, since the particles will separate and travel in opposite directions. Let A represent the alpha particle, and B represent the smaller nucleus. Call the direction of the alpha particle's motion the positive direction. We have $m_B = 57m_A$, $v_A = v_B = 0$, and $v'_A = 3.8 \times 10^5$ m/s .

$$p_{\text{initial}} = p_{\text{final}} \quad \rightarrow \quad 0 = m_A v'_A + m_B v'_B \quad \rightarrow$$

$$v'_B = -\frac{m_A v'_A}{m_B} = -\frac{v'_A}{57} = -\frac{3.8 \times 10^5\,\text{m/s}}{57} = -6.7 \times 10^3\,\text{m/s} \; , \; |v'_B| = \boxed{6.7 \times 10^3\,\text{m/s}}$$

The negative sign indicates that the nucleus is moving in the opposite direction of the alpha particle.

78.　The original horizontal distance can be found from the range formula from Example 3-8.

$$R = v_0^2 \sin 2\theta_0 / g = (25\,\text{m/s})^2 (\sin 60°)/(9.8\,\text{m/s}^2) = 55.2\,\text{m}$$

The height at which the objects collide can be found from Eq. 2-11c for the vertical motion, with $v_y = 0$ at the top of the path. Take up to be positive.

$$v_y^2 = v_{y0}^2 + 2a(y - y_0) \quad \rightarrow \quad (y - y_0) = \frac{v_y^2 - v_{y0}^2}{2a} = \frac{0 - [(25\,\text{m/s})\sin 30°]^2}{2(-9.8\,\text{m/s}^2)} = 7.97\,\text{m}$$

Let *m* represent the bullet and *M* the skeet. When the objects collide, the skeet is moving horizontally at $v_0 \cos\theta = (25\,\text{m/s})\cos 30° = 21.65\,\text{m/s} = v_x$, and the bullet is moving vertically at $v_y = 200\,\text{m/s}$. Write momentum conservation in both directions to find the velocities after the totally inelastic collision.

$$p_x: \quad Mv_x = (M + m)v'_x \quad \rightarrow \quad v'_x = \frac{Mv_x}{M + m} = \frac{(0.25\,\text{kg})(21.65\,\text{m/s})}{(0.25 + 0.015)\,\text{kg}} = 20.42\,\text{m/s}$$

$$p_y: \quad mv_y = (M + m)v'_y \quad \rightarrow \quad v'_y = \frac{mv_y}{M + m} = \frac{(0.015\,\text{kg})(200\,\text{m/s})}{(0.25 + 0.015)\,\text{kg}} = 11.32\,\text{m/s}$$

(a)　The speed v'_y can be used as the starting vertical speed in Eq. 2-11c to find the height that the skeet-bullet combination rises above the point of collision.

$$v_y^2 = v_{y0}^2 + 2a(y - y_0)_{\text{extra}} \quad \rightarrow \quad (y - y_0)_{\text{extra}} = \frac{v_y^2 - v_{y0}^2}{2a} = \frac{0 - (11.32\,\text{m/s})^2}{2(-9.8\,\text{m/s}^2)} = \boxed{6.5\,\text{m}}$$

(b)　From Eq. 2-11b applied to the vertical motion after the collision, we can find the time for the skeet-bullet combination to reach the ground.

$$y = y_0 + v_y't + \tfrac{1}{2}at^2 \quad \rightarrow \quad 0 = 7.97 \text{ m} + (11.32 \text{ m/s})t + \tfrac{1}{2}(-9.8 \text{ m/s}^2)t^2 \quad \rightarrow$$

$$4.9t^2 - 11.32t - 7.97 = 0 \quad \rightarrow \quad t = 2.88 \text{ s}, \; -0.565 \text{ s}$$

The positive time root is used to find the horizontal distance traveled by the combination after the collision.

$$x_{\text{after}} = v_x't = (20.42 \text{ m/s})(2.88 \text{ s}) = 58.7 \text{ m}$$

If the collision would not have happened, the skeet would have gone $\tfrac{1}{2}R$ horizontally.

$$\Delta x = x_{\text{after}} - \tfrac{1}{2}R = 58.7 \text{ m} - \tfrac{1}{2}(55.2 \text{ m}) = 31.1 \text{ m} \approx \boxed{31 \text{ m}}$$

79. (*a*) Use conservation of energy to find the speed of mass m before the collision. The potential energy at the starting point is all transformed into kinetic energy just before the collision.

$$mgh_A = \tfrac{1}{2}mv_A^2 \quad \rightarrow \quad v_A = \sqrt{2gh_A} = \sqrt{2(9.80 \text{ m/s}^2)(3.60 \text{ m})} = 8.40 \text{ m/s}$$

Use Eq. 7-7 to obtain a relationship between the velocities, noting that $v_B = 0$.

$$v_A - v_B = v_B' - v_A' \quad \rightarrow \quad v_B' = v_A' + v_A$$

Apply momentum conservation for the collision, and substitute the result from Eq. 7-7.

$$mv_A = mv_A' + Mv_B' = mv_A' + M(v_A + v_A') \quad \rightarrow$$

$$v_A' = \frac{m-M}{m+M}v_A = \left(\frac{2.20 \text{ kg} - 7.00 \text{ kg}}{9.20 \text{ kg}}\right)(8.4 \text{ m/s}) = -4.38 \text{ m/s} \approx \boxed{-4.4 \text{ m/s}}$$

$$v_B' = v_A' + v_A = -4.4 \text{ m/s} + 8.4 \text{ m/s} = \boxed{4.0 \text{ m/s}}$$

(*b*) Again use energy conservation to find the height to which mass m rises after the collision. The kinetic energy of m immediately after the collision is all transformed into potential energy. Use the angle of the plane to change the final height into a distance along the incline.

$$\tfrac{1}{2}mv_A'^2 = mgh_A' \quad \rightarrow \quad h_A' = \frac{v_A'^2}{2g}$$

$$d_A' = \frac{h_A'}{\sin 30} = \frac{v_A'^2}{2g \sin 30} = \frac{(-4.38 \text{ m/s})^2}{2(9.8 \text{ m/s}^2)g \sin 30} = 1.96 \text{ m} \approx \boxed{2.0 \text{ m}}$$

80. Let A represent mass m, and B represent mass M. Use Eq. 7-7 to obtain a relationship between the velocities, noting that $v_B = 0$.

$$v_A - v_B = v_B' - v_A' \quad \rightarrow \quad v_A' = v_B' - v_A.$$

After the collision, v_A' will be negative since m is moving in the negative direction. For there to be a second collision, then after m moves up the ramp and comes back down, with a positive velocity at the bottom of the incline of $-v_A'$, the speed of m must be greater than the speed of M so that m can catch M. Thus $-v_A' > v_B'$, or $v_A' < -v_B'$. Substitute the result from Eq. 7-7 into the inequality.

$$v_B' - v_A < -v_B' \quad \rightarrow \quad v_B' < \tfrac{1}{2}v_A.$$

Now write momentum conservation for the original collision, and substitute the result from Eq. 7-7.

$$mv_A = mv_A' + Mv_B' = m(v_B' - v_A) + Mv_B' \quad \rightarrow \quad v_B' = \frac{2m}{m+M}v_A$$

Finally, combine the above result with the inequality from above.

$$\frac{2m}{m+M}v_A < \tfrac{1}{2}v_A \quad \rightarrow \quad 4m < m+M \quad \rightarrow \quad \boxed{m < \tfrac{1}{3}M = 2.33\,\text{kg}}$$

81. The interaction between the planet and the spacecraft is elastic, because the force of gravity is conservative. Thus kinetic energy is conserved in the interaction. Consider the problem a 1-dimensional collision, with A representing the spacecraft and B representing Saturn. Because the mass of Saturn is so much bigger than the mass of the spacecraft, Saturn's speed is not changed appreciably during the interaction. Use Eq. 7-7, with $v_A = 10.4\,\text{km/s}$ and $v_B = v_B' = -9.6\,\text{km/s}$.

$$v_A - v_B = -v_A' + v_B' \quad \rightarrow \quad v_A' = 2v_B - v_A = 2(-9.6\,\text{km/s}) - 10.4\,\text{km/s} = \boxed{-29.6\,\text{km/s}}$$

Thus there is almost a threefold increase in the spacecraft's speed.

CHAPTER 8: Rotational Motion

Answers to Questions

1. The odometer designed for 27-inch wheels increases its reading by the circumference of a 27-inch wheel $(27\pi")$ for every revolution of the wheel. If a 24-inch wheel is used, the odometer will still register $(27\pi")$ for every revolution, but only $24\pi"$ of linear distance will have been traveled. Thus the odometer will read a distance that is further than you actually traveled, by a factor of $27/24 = 1.125$. The odometer will read 12.5% too high.

2. If a disk rotates at constant angular velocity, a point on the rim has radial acceleration only – no tangential acceleration. If the disk's angular velocity increases uniformly, the point will have both radial and tangential acceleration. If the disk rotates at constant angular velocity, neither component of linear acceleration is changing – both radial and tangential acceleration are constant. If the disk rotates with a uniformly increasing angular velocity, then the radial acceleration is changing, but the tangential acceleration is a constant non-zero value.

3. A non-rigid body cannot be described by a single value of angular velocity. Since the body is non-rigid, the angular position of one part of the body changes with respect to other parts of the body. Consider the solar system as an example of a non-rigid body or system. Each planet orbits in basically the same direction around the Sun, but each planet has its own angular velocity which is different than that of the other planets.

4. Since the torque involves the product of force times lever arm, a small force can exert a greater torque than a larger force if the small force has a large enough lever arm.

5. If the lever arm is zero, then the force does not exert any torque and so cannot produce an angular acceleration. There will be no change in the angular state of motion. However, the force will add to the net force on the body and so will change the linear acceleration of the body. The body's linear state of motion will change.

6. When you do a sit-up, torque from your abdomen muscles must rotate the upper half of the body from a laying-down position to a sitting-up position. The larger the moment of inertia of the upper half of the body, the more torque is needed, and thus the harder the sit-up is to do. With the hands behind the head, the moment of inertia of the upper half of the body is larger than with the hands outstretched in front.

7. The tension force in the bicycle chain can be assumed to be the same at both the front and rear sprockets. The force is related to the torque at each sprocket by $F = \tau/R$, and so $\tau_R/R_R = \tau_F/R_F$. The torque at the rear sprocket is what actually accelerates the bicycle, and so $\tau_R = \tau_F\,R_R/R_F$.

   We see that, to achieve a given torque at the back sprocket, a larger front torque (due to pedaling) must be present when the rear sprocket is small. Thus it is harder to pedal with a small rear sprocket.

   Likewise, to achieve a given torque at the back sprocket, a larger front torque (due to pedaling) must be present when the front sprocket is larger. Thus it is harder to pedal with a larger front sprocket.

8. The legs have a lower moment of inertia when the leg mass is concentrated next to the body. That means the legs will require less torque to have a given angular acceleration, or, alternatively, a higher angular acceleration can be developed. Thus the animal can run fast.

9. The long beam increases the rotational inertia of the walker. If the walker gets off-center from the tightrope, gravity will exert a torque on the walker causing the walker to rotate with their feet as a pivot point. With a larger rotational inertia, the angular acceleration caused by that gravitational torque will be smaller, and the walker will therefore have more time to compensate.

    The long size of the beam allows the walker to make relatively small shifts in their center of mass to bring them back to being centered on the tightrope. It is much easier for the walker to move a long, narrow object with the precision needed for small adjustments than a short, heavy object like a barbell.

10. Just because the net force on a system is zero, the net torque need not be zero. Consider a uniform object with two equal forces on it, and shown in the first diagram. The net force on the object is zero (it would not start to translate under the action of these forces), but there is a net counterclockwise torque about the center of the rod (it would start to rotate under the action of these forces).

    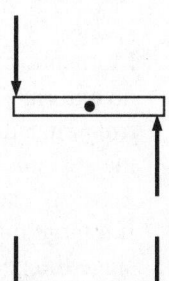

    Just because the net torque on a system is zero, the net force need not be zero. Consider an object with two equal forces on it, as shown in the second diagram. The net torque on the object is zero (it would not start to rotate under the action of these forces), but there is a net downward force on the rod (it would start to translate under the action of these forces).

11. Applying conservation of energy at the top and bottom of the incline, assuming that there is no work done by friction, gives $E_{top} = E_{bottom} \rightarrow Mgh = \frac{1}{2}Mv^2 + \frac{1}{2}I\omega^2$. For a solid ball, $I = \frac{2}{5}MR^2$. If the ball rolls without slipping (no work done by friction) then $\omega = v/R$, and so
$$Mgh = \frac{1}{2}Mv^2 + \frac{1}{2}\frac{2}{5}MR^2 v^2/R^2 \rightarrow v = \sqrt{10gh/7} \ .$$
    This speed is independent of the angle of the incline, and so both balls will have the same speed at the bottom. The ball on the incline with the smaller angle will take more time to reach the bottom than the ball on the incline with the larger angle.

12. Applying conservation of energy at the top and bottom of the incline, and assuming that there is no work done by friction, gives $E_{top} = E_{bottom} \rightarrow Mgh = \frac{1}{2}Mv^2 + \frac{1}{2}I\omega^2$. For a solid ball,

    $I = \frac{2}{5}MR^2$. If the ball rolls without slipping (no work done by friction) then $\omega = v/R$, and so
$$Mgh = \frac{1}{2}Mv^2 + \frac{1}{2}\frac{2}{5}MR^2 v^2/R^2 \rightarrow v = \sqrt{10gh/7}$$
    This speed is independent of the mass and radius of the ball, and so both balls will have the same speed at the bottom. In fact, this is true for ANY height of fall, so the two balls will have identical instantaneous speeds all along their descent, and so both balls will take the same time to reach the bottom. The total kinetic energy is $KE = KE_{trans} + KE_{rot} = \frac{1}{2}Mv^2 + \frac{1}{2}\frac{2}{5}MR^2 v^2/R^2 = \frac{7}{10}Mv^2$, and so the ball with the larger mass has the greater total kinetic energy. Another way to consider this is that the initial potential energy of Mgh is all converted to kinetic energy. The larger mass has more potential energy to begin with (due to the larger mass), and so has more kinetic energy at the bottom.

13. Applying conservation of energy at the top and bottom of the incline, assuming that there is no work done by friction, gives $E_{top} = E_{bottom}$ → $Mgh = \frac{1}{2}Mv^2 + \frac{1}{2}I\omega^2$. If the objects roll without

slipping, then $\omega = v/R$, and so $Mgh = \frac{1}{2}Mv^2 + \frac{1}{2}I(v/R)^2$ → $v = \sqrt{\dfrac{2Mgh}{M + I/R^2}}$. For a solid ball,

$I = \frac{2}{5}MR^2$, and for a cylinder, $I = \frac{1}{2}MR^2$. Thus $v_{sphere} = \sqrt{10gh/7}$ and $v_{cyl} = \sqrt{4gh/3}$. Since

$v_{sphere} > v_{cyl}$, the sphere has the greater speed at the bottom. That is true for any amount of height change, and so the sphere is always moving faster than the cylinder after they start to move. Thus the sphere will reach the bottom first. Since both objects started with the same potential energy, both have the same total kinetic energy at the bottom. But since both objects have the same mass and the cylinder is moving slower, the cylinder has the smaller translational KE and thus the greater rotational KE.

14. Momentum and angular momentum are conserved for closed systems – systems in which there are no external forces or torques applied to the system. Probably no macroscopic systems on Earth are truly closed, and so external forces and torques (like those applied by air friction, for example) affect the systems over time.

15. If a large number of people went to the equator, the rotational inertia of the Earth would increase, since the people would be further from the axis of rotation. Angular momentum would be conserved in such an interaction, and so since the rotational inertia increased, the angular velocity would decrease – the Earth would "slow down" a small amount. The length of a day would therefore increase.

16. In order to do a somersault, the diver needs some initial angular momentum when she leaves the diving board, because angular momentum will be conserved during the free-fall motion of the dive. She cannot exert a torque on herself in isolation, and so if there is no angular momentum initially, there will be no rotation during the rest of the dive.

17. The moment of inertia will increase, because most the mass of the disk will be further from the axis of rotation than it was with the original axis position.

18. Your angular velocity will not change. Before you let go of the masses, your body has a certain angular momentum, which is the product of your moment of inertia and your angular velocity. No torques are put upon you by the act of dropping the masses, and so your angular momentum does not change. If you don't change your moment of inertia by changing the position of your body, then your angular velocity will not change. The masses, when dropped, will have a horizontal motion that is tangential to the circle in which they were moving before they were dropped. An object traveling horizontally at some distance from a vertical line (like your axis of rotation) has angular momentum relative to that vertical line. The masses keep the angular momentum that they had before being dropped.

19. The two spheres would have different rotational inertias. The sphere that is hollow will have a larger rotational inertia than the solid sphere. If the two spheres are allowed to roll down an incline without slipping, the sphere with the smaller moment of inertia (the solid one) will reach the bottom of the ramp first. See question number 13 for an explanation of why this happens.

20. Using the right hand rule, point the fingers in the direction of the Earth's rotation, from west to east. Then the thumb points north. Thus the Earth's angular velocity points along its axis of rotation, towards the North Star.

21. See the diagram. To the left is west, the direction of the angular velocity. The direction of the linear velocity of a point on the top of the wheel would be into the paper, which is north. If the angular acceleration is east, which is opposite the angular velocity, the wheel is slowing down – its angular speed is decreasing. The tangential linear acceleration of the point on top will be in the opposite direction to its linear velocity – it will point south.

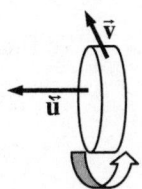

22. The angular momentum of the turntable – person system will be conserved, since no external torques are being applied as the person walks to the center. As the person walks to the center, the overall moment of inertia of the system gets smaller, since the person is closer to the axis of rotation. Since the angular momentum is constant, the angular velocity must increase. So the turntable will begin to rotate faster as you walk to the center. This is similar to the spinning ice skater who pulls her arms in to increase her angular speed.

23. The shortstop, while in mid-air, cannot exert a torque on himself, and so his angular momentum will be conserved while in the air. If the upper half of his body rotates in a certain direction during the throwing motion, then to conserve angular momentum, the lower half of his body will rotate in the opposite direction.

24. Consider a helicopter in the air with the rotor spinning. To change the rotor's angular speed, a torque must be applied to the rotor. That torque has to come from the helicopter, and so by Newton's 3rd law, and equal and opposite torque will be applied by the rotor to the helicopter. Any change in rotor speed would therefore cause the body of the helicopter to spin in a direction opposite to the change in the rotor's angular velocity.

    Some large helicopters have two rotor systems, spinning in opposite directions. That makes any change in the speed of the rotor pair require a net torque of 0, and so the helicopter body would not tend to spin. Smaller helicopters have a tail rotor which rotates in a vertical plane, causing a force on the tail of the helicopter in the opposite direction of the tendency of the tail to spin.

Solutions to Problems

1. (a) $\left(30°\right)\left(2\pi \text{ rad}/360°\right) = \boxed{\pi/6\,\text{rad}} = \boxed{0.52\text{ rad}}$

   (b) $\left(57°\right)\left(2\pi \text{ rad}/360°\right) = \boxed{19\pi/60\,\text{rad}} = \boxed{0.99\text{ rad}}$

   (c) $\left(90°\right)\left(2\pi \text{ rad}/360°\right) = \boxed{\pi/2\,\text{rad}} = \boxed{1.57\text{ rad}}$

   (d) $\left(360°\right)\left(2\pi \text{ rad}/360°\right) = \boxed{2\pi \text{ rad}} = \boxed{6.28\text{ rad}}$

   (e) $\left(420°\right)\left(2\pi \text{ rad}/360°\right) = \boxed{7\pi/3\,\text{rad}} = \boxed{7.33\text{ rad}}$

2. The angle in radians is the diameter of the object divided by the distance to the object.

$$\Delta\theta_{\text{Sun}} = \frac{2R_{\text{Sun}}}{r_{\text{Earth-Sun}}} = \frac{2\left(6.96\times10^5\,\text{km}\right)}{149.6\times10^6\,\text{km}} = \boxed{9.30\times10^{-3}\,\text{rad}}$$

$$\Delta\theta_{Moon} = \frac{2R_{Moon}}{r_{Earth-Moon}} = \frac{2(1.74\times10^3\,km)}{384\times10^3\,km} = \boxed{9.06\times10^{-3}\,rad}$$

Since these angles are practically the same, solar eclipses occur.

3. We find the diameter of the spot from

$$\theta = \frac{diameter}{r_{Earth-Moon}} \rightarrow diameter = \theta\, r_{Earth-Moon} = (1.4\times10^{-5}\,rad)(3.8\times10^8\,m) = \boxed{5.3\times10^3\,m}$$

4. The initial angular velocity is $\omega_o = \left(6500\dfrac{rev}{min}\right)\left(\dfrac{2\pi\,rad}{1\,rev}\right)\left(\dfrac{1\,min}{60\,sec}\right) = 681\,rad/s$. Use the definition of angular acceleration.

$$\alpha = \frac{\Delta\omega}{\Delta t} = \frac{0-681\,rad/s}{3.0\,s} = -227\,rad/s^2 \approx \boxed{-2.3\times10^2\,rad/s^2}$$

5. The ball rolls $2\pi r = \pi d$ of linear distance with each revolution.

$$15.0\,rev\left(\frac{\pi d\ m}{1\,rev}\right) = 3.5\,m \rightarrow d = \frac{3.5\,m}{15.0\,\pi} = \boxed{7.4\times10^{-2}\,m}$$

6. In each revolution, the wheel moves forward a distance equal to its circumference, πd .

$$\Delta x = N_{rev}(\pi d) \rightarrow N = \frac{\Delta x}{\pi d} = \frac{8000\,m}{\pi(0.68\,m)} = \boxed{3.7\times10^3\,rev}$$

7. (a) $\omega = \left(\dfrac{2500\,rev}{1\,min}\right)\left(\dfrac{2\pi\,rad}{1\,rev}\right)\left(\dfrac{1\,min}{60\,s}\right) = 261.8\,rad/sec \sim \boxed{2.6\times10^2\,rad/sec}$

   (b) $v = \omega r = (261.8\,rad/sec)(0.175\,m) = \boxed{46\,m/s}$

   $$a_R = \omega^2 r = (261.8\,rad/sec)^2(0.175\,m) = \boxed{1.2\times10^4\,m/s^2}$$

8. The angular speed of the merry-go-round is $2\pi\,rad/4.0\,s = 1.57\,rad/s$

   (a) $v = \omega r = (1.57\,rad/sec)(1.2\,m) = \boxed{1.9\,m/s}$

   (b) The acceleration is radial. There is no tangential acceleration.

   $$a_R = \omega^2 r = (1.57\,rad/sec)^2(1.2\,m) = \boxed{3.0\,m/s^2\ \text{towards the center}}$$

9. (a) The Earth makes one orbit around the Sun in one year.

   $$\omega_{orbit} = \frac{\Delta\theta}{\Delta t} = \left(\frac{2\pi\,rad}{1\,yr}\right)\left(\frac{1\,yr}{3.16\times10^7\,s}\right) = \boxed{1.99\times10^{-7}\,rad/s}$$

   (b) The Earth makes one revolution about its axis in one day.

   $$\omega_{rotation} = \frac{\Delta\theta}{\Delta t} = \left(\frac{2\pi\,rad}{1\,d}\right)\left(\frac{1\,d}{86,400\,s}\right) = \boxed{7.27\times10^{-5}\,rad/s}$$

10. Each location will have the same angular velocity (1 revolution per day), but the radius of the circular path varies with the location. From the diagram, we see $r = R\cos\theta$, where R is the radius of the Earth, and r is the radius at latitude θ.

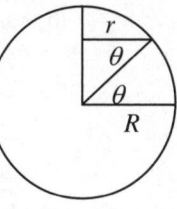

(a) $\quad v = \omega r = \dfrac{2\pi}{T} r = \left(\dfrac{2\pi \text{ rad}}{1\text{ d}}\right)\left(\dfrac{1\text{ d}}{86400\text{ s}}\right)\left(6.38\times10^{6}\text{ m}\right) = \boxed{4.64\times10^{2}\text{ m/s}}$

(b) $\quad v = \omega r = \dfrac{2\pi}{T} r = \left(\dfrac{2\pi \text{ rad}}{1\text{ d}}\right)\left(\dfrac{1\text{ d}}{86400\text{ s}}\right)\left(6.38\times10^{6}\text{ m}\right)\cos 66.5^{\circ} = \boxed{1.85\times10^{2}\text{ m/s}}$

(c) $\quad v = \omega r = \dfrac{2\pi}{T} r = \left(\dfrac{2\pi \text{ rad}}{1\text{ d}}\right)\left(\dfrac{1\text{ d}}{86400\text{ s}}\right)\left(6.38\times10^{6}\text{ m}\right)\cos 45.0^{\circ} = \boxed{3.28\times10^{2}\text{ m/s}}$

11. The centripetal acceleration is given by $a = \omega^{2} r$. Solve for the angular velocity.

$$\omega = \sqrt{\dfrac{a}{r}} = \sqrt{\dfrac{(100,000)\left(9.8\text{ m/s}^{2}\right)}{0.070\text{ m}}} = 3741\dfrac{\text{rad}}{\text{s}}\left(\dfrac{1\text{ rev}}{2\pi\text{ rad}}\right)\left(\dfrac{60\text{ s}}{1\text{ min}}\right) = \boxed{3.6\times10^{4}\text{ rpm}}$$

12. Convert the rpm values to angular velocities.

$$\omega_{0} = \left(130\dfrac{\text{rev}}{\text{min}}\right)\left(\dfrac{2\pi \text{ rad}}{1\text{ rev}}\right)\left(\dfrac{1\text{ min}}{60\text{ sec}}\right) = 13.6\text{ rad/s}$$

$$\omega = \left(280\dfrac{\text{rev}}{\text{min}}\right)\left(\dfrac{2\pi \text{ rad}}{1\text{ rev}}\right)\left(\dfrac{1\text{ min}}{60\text{ sec}}\right) = 29.3\text{ rad/s}$$

(a) The angular acceleration is found from Eq. 8-9a.

$$\omega = \omega_{0} + \alpha t \quad \rightarrow \quad \alpha = \dfrac{\omega - \omega_{0}}{t} = \dfrac{29.3\text{ rad/s} - 13.6\text{ rad/s}}{4.0\text{ s}} = 3.93\text{ rad/s}^{2} \approx \boxed{3.9\text{ rad/s}^{2}}$$

(b) To find the components of the acceleration, the instantaneous angular velocity is needed.

$$\omega = \omega_{0} + \alpha t = 13.6\text{ rad/s} + \left(3.93\text{ rad/s}^{2}\right)\left(2.0\text{ s}\right) = 21.5\text{ rad/s}$$

The instantaneous radial acceleration is given by $a_{R} = \omega^{2} r$.

$$a_{R} = \omega^{2} r = \left(21.5\text{ rad/s}\right)^{2}\left(0.35\text{ m}\right) = \boxed{1.6\times10^{2}\text{ m/s}^{2}}$$

The tangential acceleration is given by $a_{\text{tan}} = \alpha r$.

$$a_{\text{tan}} = \alpha r = \left(3.93\text{ rad/s}^{2}\right)\left(0.35\text{ m}\right) = \boxed{1.4\text{ m/s}^{2}}$$

13. The tangential speed of the turntable must be equal to the tangential speed of the roller, if there is no slippage.

$$v_{1} = v_{2} \quad \rightarrow \quad \omega_{1}R_{1} = \omega_{2}R_{2} \quad \rightarrow \quad \boxed{\omega_{1}/\omega_{2} = R_{2}/R_{1}}$$

14. (a) The angular rotation can be found from Eq. 8-3a. The initial angular frequency is 0 and the final angular frequency is 1 rpm.

$$\alpha = \dfrac{\omega - \omega_{0}}{t} = \dfrac{\left(1\dfrac{\text{rev}}{\text{min}}\right)\left(\dfrac{2\pi \text{ rad}}{1\text{ rev}}\right)\left(\dfrac{1.0\text{ min}}{60\text{ s}}\right) - 0}{720\text{ s}} = 1.454\times10^{-4}\text{ rad/s}^{2} \approx \boxed{1.5\times10^{-4}\text{ rad/s}^{2}}$$

(b) After 5.0 min (300 s), the angular speed is as follows.

$$\omega = \omega_{0} + \alpha t = 0 + \left(1.454\times10^{-4}\text{ rad/s}^{2}\right)\left(300\text{ s}\right) = 4.363\times10^{-2}\text{ rad/s}$$

Find the components of the acceleration of a point on the outer skin from the angular speed and the radius.

$$a_{tan} = \alpha R = \left(1.454 \times 10^{-4} \text{ rad/s}^2\right)\left(4.25 \text{ m}\right) = \boxed{6.2 \times 10^{-4} \text{ m/s}^2}$$

$$a_{rad} = \omega^2 R = \left(4.363 \times 10^{-2} \text{ rad/s}\right)^2\left(4.25 \text{ m}\right) = \boxed{8.1 \times 10^{-3} \text{ m/s}^2}$$

15. The angular displacement can be found from the following uniform angular acceleration relationship.

$$\theta = \tfrac{1}{2}\left(\omega_o + \omega\right)t = \tfrac{1}{2}\left(0 + 15000 \text{ rev/min}\right)\left(220 \text{ s}\right)\left(1 \text{ min}/60 \text{ s}\right) = \boxed{2.8 \times 10^4 \text{ rev}}$$

16. (*a*) For constant angular acceleration:

$$\alpha = \frac{\omega - \omega_o}{t} = \frac{1200 \text{ rev/min} - 4500 \text{ rev/min}}{2.5 \text{ s}} = \frac{-3300 \text{ rev/min}}{2.5 \text{ s}}\left(\frac{2\pi \text{ rad}}{1 \text{ rev}}\right)\left(\frac{1 \text{ min}}{60 \text{ s}}\right)$$

$$= \boxed{-1.4 \times 10^2 \text{ rad/s}^2}$$

(*b*) For the angular displacement, given constant angular acceleration:

$$\theta = \tfrac{1}{2}\left(\omega_o + \omega\right)t = \tfrac{1}{2}\left(4500 \text{ rev/min} + 1200 \text{ rev/min}\right)\left(2.5 \text{ s}\right)\left(\frac{1 \text{ min}}{60 \text{ s}}\right) = \boxed{1.2 \times 10^2 \text{ rev}}$$

17. (*a*) The angular acceleration can be found from $\theta = \omega_o t + \tfrac{1}{2}\alpha t^2$ with $\omega_o = 0$.

$$\alpha = \frac{2\theta}{t^2} = \frac{2\left(20 \text{ rev}\right)}{\left(1.0 \text{ min}\right)^2} = \boxed{4.0 \times 10^1 \text{ rev/min}^2}$$

(*b*) The final angular speed can be found from $\theta = \tfrac{1}{2}\left(\omega_o + \omega\right)t$, with $\omega_o = 0$.

$$\omega = \frac{2\theta}{t} - \omega_o = \frac{2\left(20 \text{ rev}\right)}{1.0 \text{ min}} = \boxed{4.0 \times 10^1 \text{ rpm}}$$

18. Use Eq. 8-9d combined with Eq. 8-2a.

$$\overline{\omega} = \frac{\omega + \omega_0}{2} = \frac{240 \text{ rpm} + 360 \text{ rpm}}{2} = 300 \text{ rpm}$$

$$\theta = \overline{\omega} t = \left(300 \frac{\text{rev}}{\text{min}}\right)\left(\frac{1 \text{ min}}{60 \text{ sec}}\right)\left(6.5 \text{ s}\right) = 32.5 \text{ rev}$$

Each revolution corresponds to a circumference of travel distance.

$$32.5 \text{ rev}\left[\frac{\pi\left(0.33 \text{ m}\right)}{1 \text{ rev}}\right] = \boxed{34 \text{ m}}$$

19. (*a*) The angular acceleration can be found from $\omega^2 = \omega_o^2 + 2\alpha\theta$.

$$\alpha = \frac{\omega^2 - \omega_o^2}{2\theta} = \frac{0 - \left(850 \text{ rev/min}\right)^2}{2\left(1500 \text{ rev}\right)} = \left(-241 \frac{\text{rev}}{\text{min}^2}\right)\left(\frac{2\pi \text{ rad}}{1 \text{ rev}}\right)\left(\frac{1 \text{ min}}{60 \text{ s}}\right)^2 = \boxed{-0.42 \frac{\text{rad}}{\text{s}^2}}$$

(*b*) The time to come to a stop can be found from $\theta = \tfrac{1}{2}\left(\omega_o + \omega\right)t$.

$$t = \frac{2\theta}{\omega_o + \omega} = \frac{2\left(1500 \text{ rev}\right)}{850 \text{ rev/min}}\left(\frac{60 \text{ s}}{1 \text{ min}}\right) = \boxed{210 \text{ s}}$$

20. Since there is no slipping between the wheels, the tangential component of the linear acceleration of each wheel must be the same.

(a) $a_{\text{tan}\atop\text{small}} = a_{\text{tan}\atop\text{argel}} \rightarrow \alpha_{\text{small}} r_{\text{small}} = \alpha_{\text{large}} r_{\text{large}} \rightarrow$

$$\alpha_{\text{large}} = \alpha_{\text{small}} \frac{r_{\text{small}}}{r_{\text{large}}} = \left(7.2\,\text{rad/s}^2\right)\left(\frac{2.0\ \text{cm}}{25.0\ \text{cm}}\right) = 0.576\,\text{rad/s}^2 \approx \boxed{0.58\,\text{rad/s}^2}$$

(b) Assume the pottery wheel starts from rest. Convert the speed to an angular speed, and then use Eq. 8-9a.

$$\omega = \left(65\frac{\text{rev}}{\text{min}}\right)\left(\frac{2\pi\ \text{rad}}{1\ \text{rev}}\right)\left(\frac{1\ \text{min}}{60\ \text{s}}\right) = 6.81\,\text{rad/s}$$

$$\omega = \omega_0 + \alpha t \rightarrow t = \frac{\omega - \omega_0}{\alpha} = \frac{6.81\,\text{rad/s}}{0.576\,\text{rad/s}^2} = \boxed{12\ \text{s}}$$

$\boxed{21.}$ (a) The angular acceleration can be found from $\omega^2 = \omega_o^2 + 2\alpha\theta$, with the angular velocities being found from $\omega = v/r$.

$$\alpha = \frac{\omega^2 - \omega_o^2}{2\theta} = \frac{\left(v^2 - v_o^2\right)}{2r^2\theta} = \frac{\left[\left(45\,\text{km/h}\right)^2 - \left(95\,\text{km/h}\right)^2\right]\left(\frac{1\,\text{m/s}}{3.6\,\text{km/h}}\right)^2}{2\left(0.40\ \text{m}\right)^2\left(65\ \text{rev}\right)\left(\frac{2\pi\ \text{rad}}{\text{rev}}\right)}$$

$$= -4.133\,\text{rad/s}^2 \approx \boxed{-4.1\,\text{rad/s}^2}$$

(b) The time to stop can be found from $\omega = \omega_o + \alpha t$, with a final angular velocity of 0.

$$t = \frac{\omega - \omega_o}{\alpha} = \frac{v - v_o}{r\alpha} = \frac{-\left(45\,\text{km/h}\right)\left(\frac{1\,\text{m/s}}{3.6\,\text{km/h}}\right)}{\left(0.40\ \text{m}\right)\left(-4.133\,\text{rad/s}^2\right)} = \boxed{7.6\ \text{s}}$$

22. (a) The maximum torque will be exerted by the force of her weight, pushing tangential to the circle in which the pedal moves.

$$\tau = r_\perp F = r_\perp mg = \left(0.17\ \text{m}\right)\left(55\ \text{kg}\right)\left(9.8\,\text{m/s}^2\right) = \boxed{92\,\text{m}\cdot\text{N}}$$

(b) She could exert more torque by pushing down harder with her legs, raising her center of mass. She could also pull upwards on the handle bars as she pedals, which will increase the downward force of her legs.

23. The torque is calculated by $\tau = rF\sin\theta$. See the diagram, from the top view.

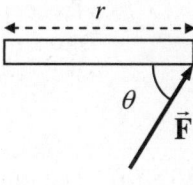

(a) For the first case, $\theta = 90°$.

$$\tau = rF\sin\theta = \left(0.74\ \text{m}\right)\left(55\ \text{N}\right)\sin 90° = \boxed{41\ \text{m}\cdot\text{N}}$$

(b) For the second case, $\theta = 45°$.

$$\tau = rF\sin\theta = \left(0.74\ \text{m}\right)\left(55\ \text{N}\right)\sin 45° = \boxed{29\ \text{m}\cdot\text{N}}$$

24. Each force is oriented so that it is perpendicular to its lever arm. Call counterclockwise torques positive. The torque due to the three applied forces is given by

$$\tau_{\substack{applied \\ forces}} = (28 \text{ N})(0.24 \text{ m}) - (18 \text{ N})(0.24 \text{ m}) - (35 \text{ N})(0.12 \text{ m}) = -1.8 \text{ m} \cdot \text{N} .$$

Since this torque is clockwise, we assume the wheel is rotating clockwise, and so the frictional torque is counterclockwise. Thus the net torque is

$$\tau_{net} = (28 \text{ N})(0.24 \text{ m}) - (18 \text{ N})(0.24 \text{ m}) - (35 \text{ N})(0.12 \text{ m}) + 0.40 \text{ m} \cdot \text{N} = -1.4 \text{ m} \cdot \text{N}$$

$$= \boxed{1.4 \text{ m} \cdot \text{N , clockwise}}$$

25. There is a counterclockwise torque due to the force of gravity on the left block, and a clockwise torque due to the force of gravity on the right block. Call clockwise the positive direction.

$$\sum \tau = mgL_2 - mgL_1 = \boxed{mg\left(L_2 - L_1\right) \text{ , clockwise}}$$

26. (a) The force required to produce the torque can be found from $\tau = rF \sin \theta$. The force is applied perpendicularly to the wrench, so $\theta = 90°$. Thus

$$F = \frac{\tau}{r} = \frac{88 \text{ m} \cdot \text{N}}{0.28 \text{ m}} = \boxed{3.1 \times 10^2 \text{ N}}$$

   (b) The net torque still must be 88 m·N. This is produced by 6 forces, one at each of the 6 points. Those forces are also perpendicular to the lever arm, and so

$$\tau_{net} = \left(6F_{point}\right) r_{point} \quad \rightarrow \quad F_{point} = \frac{\tau}{6r} = \frac{88 \text{ m} \cdot \text{N}}{6(0.0075 \text{ m})} = \boxed{2.0 \times 10^3 \text{ N}}$$

27. For a sphere rotating about an axis through its center, the moment of inertia is given by

$$I = \tfrac{2}{5} MR^2 = \tfrac{2}{5}(10.8 \text{ kg})(0.648 \text{ m})^2 = \boxed{1.81 \text{ kg} \cdot \text{m}^2} \quad .$$

28. Since all of the significant mass is located at the same distance from the axis of rotation, the moment of inertia is given by

$$I = MR^2 = (1.25 \text{ kg})\left(\frac{0.667}{2} \text{ m}\right)^2 = \boxed{0.139 \text{ kg} \cdot \text{m}^2} .$$

The hub mass can be ignored because its distance from the axis of rotation is very small, and so it has a very small rotational inertia.

29. (a) The small ball can be treated as a particle for calculating its moment of inertia.

$$I = MR^2 = (0.650 \text{ kg})(1.2 \text{ m})^2 = \boxed{0.94 \text{ kg} \cdot \text{m}^2}$$

   (b) To keep a constant angular velocity, the net torque must be zero, and so the torque needed is the same magnitude as the torque caused by friction.

$$\sum \tau = \tau_{applied} - \tau_{fr} = 0 \quad \rightarrow \quad \tau_{applied} = \tau_{fr} = F_{fr} r = (0.020 \text{ N})(1.2 \text{ m}) = \boxed{2.4 \times 10^{-2} \text{ m} \cdot \text{N}}$$

30. (a) The torque exerted by the frictional force is $\tau = rF_{fr} \sin \theta$. The frictional force is assumed to be tangential to the clay, and so the angle is $\theta = 90°$.

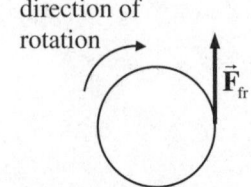

direction of rotation

$$\tau_{total} = rF_{fr} \sin \theta = (6.0 \times 10^{-2} \text{ m})(1.5 \text{ N}) \sin 90° = \boxed{9.0 \times 10^{-2} \text{ m} \cdot \text{N}}$$

(b) The time to stop is found from $\omega = \omega_o + \alpha t$, with a final angular velocity of 0. The angular acceleration can be found from $\tau_{total} = I\alpha$. The net torque (and angular acceleration) is negative since the object is slowing.

$$t = \frac{\omega - \omega_o}{\alpha} = \frac{\omega - \omega_o}{\tau/I} = \frac{0 - (1.6\,\text{rev/s})(2\pi\,\text{rad/rev})}{(-9.0\times10^{-2}\,\text{m}\cdot\text{N})/(0.11\,\text{kg}\cdot\text{m}^2)} = \boxed{12\,\text{s}}$$

31. (a) To calculate the moment of inertia about the *y*-axis (vertical), use

$$I = \sum M_i R_{ix}^2 = m(0.50\,\text{m})^2 + M(0.50\,\text{m})^2 + m(1.00\,\text{m})^2 + M(1.00\,\text{m})^2$$

$$= (m + M)\left[(0.50\,\text{m})^2 + (1.00\,\text{m})^2\right] = (4.9\,\text{kg})\left[(0.50\,\text{m})^2 + (1.00\,\text{m})^2\right] = \boxed{6.1\,\text{kg}\cdot\text{m}^2}$$

(b) To calculate the moment of inertia about the *x*-axis (horizontal), use

$$I = \sum M_i R_{iy}^2 = (2m + 2M)(0.25\,\text{m})^2 = \boxed{0.61\,\text{kg}\cdot\text{m}^2}.$$

(c) Because of the larger *I* value, it is harder to accelerate the array about the $\boxed{\text{vertical axis}}$.

32 The oxygen molecule has a "dumbbell" geometry, rotating about the dashed line, as shown in the diagram. If the total mass is *M*, then each atom has a mass of *M*/2. If the distance between them is *d*, then the distance from the axis of rotation to each atom is *d*/2. Treat each atom as a particle for calculating the moment of inertia.

$$I = (M/2)(d/2)^2 + (M/2)(d/2)^2 = 2(M/2)(d/2)^2 = \tfrac{1}{4}Md^2 \quad\rightarrow$$

$$d = \sqrt{4I/M} = \sqrt{4(1.9\times10^{-46}\,\text{kg}\cdot\text{m}^2)/(5.3\times10^{-26}\,\text{kg})} = \boxed{1.2\times10^{-10}\,\text{m}}$$

33. The firing force of the rockets will create a net torque, but no net force. Since each rocket fires tangentially, each force has a lever arm equal to the radius of the satellite, and each force is perpendicular to the lever arm. Thus $\tau_{net} = 4FR$. This torque will cause an angular acceleration according to $\tau = I\alpha$, where $I = \tfrac{1}{2}MR^2$ for a cylinder. The angular acceleration can be found from the kinematics by $\alpha = \dfrac{\Delta\omega}{\Delta t}$. Equating the two expressions for the torque and substituting enables us to solve for the force.

$$4FR = I\alpha = \tfrac{1}{2}MR^2\frac{\Delta\omega}{\Delta\tau}$$

$$F = \frac{MR\Delta\omega}{8\Delta t} = \frac{(3600\,\text{kg})(4.0\,\text{m})(32\,\text{rev/min})(2\pi\,\text{rad/rev})(1\,\text{min}/60\,\text{s})}{8(5.0\,\text{min})(60\,\text{s/min})}$$

$$= 20.11\,\text{N} \approx \boxed{2.0\times10^1\,\text{N}}$$

34. (a) The moment of inertia of a cylinder is found in Figure 8-21.

$$I = \tfrac{1}{2}MR^2 = \tfrac{1}{2}(0.580\,\text{kg})(8.50\times10^{-2}\,\text{m})^2 = 2.0953\times10^{-3}\,\text{kg}\cdot\text{m}^2 \approx \boxed{2.10\times10^{-3}\,\text{kg}\cdot\text{m}^2}$$

(b) The wheel slows down "on its own" from 1500 rpm to rest in 55.0s. This is used to calculate the frictional torque.

$$\tau_{fr} = I\alpha_{fr} = I\frac{\Delta\omega}{\Delta t} = (2.0953\times10^{-3}\,\text{kg}\cdot\text{m}^2)\frac{(0 - 1500\,\text{rev/min})(2\pi\,\text{rad/rev})(1\,\text{min}/60\,\text{s})}{55.0\,\text{s}}$$

$$= -5.984\times10^{-3}\,\text{m}\cdot\text{N}$$

The net torque causing the angular acceleration is the applied torque plus the (negative) frictional torque.

$$\sum \tau = \tau_{applied} + \tau_{fr} = I\alpha \rightarrow$$

$$\tau_{applied} = I\alpha - \tau_{fr} = I\frac{\Delta\omega}{\Delta t} - \tau_{fr}$$

$$= (2.0953 \times 10^{-3} \text{ kg}\cdot\text{m}^2)\frac{(1500 \text{ rev/min})(2\pi \text{ rad/rev})(1 \text{ min/60 s})}{5.00 \text{ s}} + (5.984 \times 10^{-3} \text{ m}\cdot\text{N})$$

$$= \boxed{7.2 \times 10^{-2} \text{ m}\cdot\text{N}}$$

35. The torque can be calculated from $\tau = I\alpha$. The rotational inertia of a rod about its end is given by $I = \frac{1}{3}ML^2$.

$$\tau = I\alpha = \frac{1}{3}ML^2\frac{\Delta\omega}{\Delta t} = \frac{1}{3}(2.2 \text{ kg})(0.95 \text{ m})^2\frac{(3.0 \text{ rev/s})(2\pi \text{ rad/rev})}{0.20 \text{ s}} = \boxed{62 \text{ m}\cdot\text{N}}$$

36. The torque needed is the moment of inertia of the system (merry-go-round and children) times the angular acceleration of the system. Let the subscript "mgr" represent the merry-go-round.

$$\tau = I\alpha = (I_{mgr} + I_{children})\frac{\Delta\omega}{\Delta t} = (\frac{1}{2}M_{mgr}R^2 + 2m_{child}R^2)\frac{\omega - \omega_0}{t}$$

$$= [\frac{1}{2}(760 \text{ kg}) + 2(25 \text{ kg})](2.5 \text{ m})^2\frac{(15 \text{ rev/min})(2\pi \text{ rad/rev})(1 \text{ min/60 s})}{10.0 \text{ s}}$$

$$= 422.15 \text{ m}\cdot\text{N} \approx \boxed{4.2 \times 10^2 \text{ m}\cdot\text{N}}$$

The force needed is calculated from the torque and the radius. Assume that the force is all directed perpendicularly to the radius.

$$\tau = F_\perp R\sin\theta \rightarrow F_\perp = \tau/R = 4.2215 \times 10^2 \text{ m}\cdot\text{N}/2.5 \text{ m} = \boxed{1.7 \times 10^2 \text{ N}}$$

37. The torque on the rotor will cause an angular acceleration given by $\alpha = \tau/I$. The torque and angular acceleration will have the opposite sign of the initial angular velocity because the rotor is being brought to rest. The rotational inertia is that of a solid cylinder. Substitute the expressions for angular acceleration and rotational inertia into the equation $\omega^2 = \omega_o^2 + 2\alpha\theta$, and solve for the angular displacement.

$$\omega^2 = \omega_o^2 + 2\alpha\theta$$

$$\theta = \frac{\omega^2 - \omega_o^2}{2\alpha} = \frac{0 - \omega_o^2}{2(\tau/I)} = \frac{-\omega_o^2}{2(\tau/\frac{1}{2}MR^2)} = \frac{-MR^2\omega_o^2}{4\tau}$$

$$= \frac{-(4.80 \text{ kg})(0.0710 \text{ m})^2\left[(10,300\frac{\text{rev}}{\text{min}})(\frac{2\pi \text{ rad}}{1 \text{ rev}})(\frac{1 \text{ min}}{60 \text{ s}})\right]^2}{4(-1.20 \text{ N}\cdot\text{m})} = 5865 \text{ rad}(\frac{1 \text{ rev}}{2\pi \text{ rad}})$$

$$= \boxed{993 \text{ rev}}$$

The time can be found from $\theta = \frac{1}{2}(\omega_o + \omega)t$.

$$t = \frac{2\theta}{\omega_o + \omega} = \frac{2(993 \text{ rev})}{10,300 \text{ rev/min}} \left(\frac{60 \text{ s}}{1 \text{ min}} \right) = \boxed{10.9 \text{ s}}$$

38. (a) The torque gives angular acceleration to the ball only, since the arm is considered massless. The angular acceleration of the ball is found from the given tangential acceleration.

$$\tau = I\alpha = MR^2\alpha = MR^2 \frac{a_{\text{tan}}}{R} = MRa_{\text{tan}} = (3.6 \text{ kg})(0.31 \text{ m})(7.0 \text{ m/s}^2)$$

$$= 7.812 \text{ m·N} \approx \boxed{7.8 \text{ m·N}}$$

(b) The triceps muscle must produce the torque required, but with a lever arm of only 2.5 cm, perpendicular to the triceps muscle force.

$$\tau = Fr_\perp \quad \rightarrow \quad F = \tau/r_\perp = 7.812 \text{ m·N}/(2.5 \times 10^{-2} \text{ m}) = \boxed{3.1 \times 10^2 \text{ N}}$$

39. (a) The angular acceleration can be found from

$$\alpha = \frac{\Delta\omega}{\Delta t} = \frac{\omega}{t} = \frac{v/r}{t} = \frac{(10.0 \text{ m/s})/(0.31 \text{ m})}{0.350 \text{ s}} = 92.17 \text{ rad/s}^2 \approx \boxed{92 \text{ rad/s}^2}$$

(b) The force required can be found from the torque, since $\tau = Fr\sin\theta$. In this situation the force is perpendicular to the lever arm, and so $\theta = 90°$. The torque is also given by $\tau = I\alpha$, where I is the moment of inertia of the arm-ball combination. Equate the two expressions for the torque, and solve for the force.

$$Fr\sin\theta = I\alpha$$

$$F = \frac{I\alpha}{r\sin\theta} = \frac{m_{\text{ball}}d_{\text{ball}}^2 + \frac{1}{3}m_{\text{arm}}L_{\text{arm}}^2}{r\sin 90°}\alpha$$

$$= \frac{(1.00 \text{ kg})(0.31 \text{ m})^2 + \frac{1}{3}(3.70 \text{ kg})(0.31 \text{ m})^2}{(0.025 \text{ m})}(92.17 \text{ rad/s}^2) = \boxed{7.9 \times 10^2 \text{ N}}$$

40. (a) The moment of inertia of a thin rod, rotating about its end, is given in Figure 8-21(g). There are three blades to add.

$$I_{\text{total}} = 3\left(\frac{1}{3}ML^2\right) = ML^2 = (160 \text{ kg})(3.75 \text{ m})^2 = 2250 \text{ kg·m}^2 \approx \boxed{2.3 \times 10^2 \text{ kg·m}^2}$$

(b) The torque required is the rotational inertia times the angular acceleration, assumed constant.

$$\tau = I_{\text{total}}\alpha = I_{\text{total}}\frac{\omega - \omega_0}{t} = (2250 \text{ kg·m}^2)\frac{(5.0 \text{ rev/sec})(2\pi \text{ rad/rev})}{8.0 \text{ s}} = \boxed{8.8 \times 10^3 \text{ m·N}}$$

41. We assume that $m_2 > m_1$, and so m_2 will accelerate down, m_1 will accelerate up, and the pulley will accelerate clockwise. Call the direction of acceleration the positive direction for each object. The masses will have the same acceleration since they are connected by a cord. The rim of the pulley will have that same acceleration since the cord is making it rotate, and so $\alpha_{\text{pulley}} = a/r$. From the free-body diagrams for each object, we have the following.

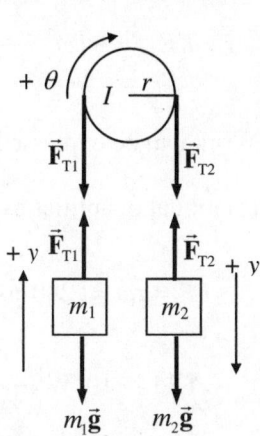

$$\sum F_{y1} = F_{\text{T1}} - m_1g = m_1a \quad \rightarrow \quad F_{\text{T1}} = m_1g + m_1a$$

$$\sum F_{y2} = m_2g - F_{\text{T2}} = m_2a \quad \rightarrow \quad F_{\text{T2}} = m_2g - m_2a$$

$$\sum \tau = F_{T2}r - F_{T1}r = I\alpha = I\frac{a}{r}$$

Substitute the expressions for the tensions into the torque equation, and solve for the acceleration.

$$F_{T2}r - F_{T1}r = I\frac{a}{r} \ \rightarrow \ (m_2 g - m_2 a)r - (m_1 g + m_1 a)r = I\frac{a}{r} \ \rightarrow \ \boxed{a = \frac{(m_2 - m_1)}{(m_1 + m_2 + I/r^2)}g}$$

If the moment of inertia is ignored, then from the torque equation we see that $F_{T2} = F_{T1}$, and the

acceleration will be $\boxed{a_{I=0} = \frac{(m_2 - m_1)}{(m_1 + m_2)}g}$. We see that the acceleration with the moment of inertia

included will be smaller than if the moment of inertia is ignored.

42. A top view diagram of the hammer is shown, just at the instant of release, along with the acceleration vectors.

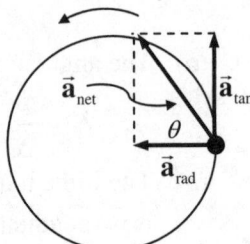

(a) The angular acceleration is found from Eq. 8-9c.
$$\omega^2 = \omega_0^2 + 2\alpha\Delta\theta \ \rightarrow$$

$$\alpha = \frac{\omega^2 - \omega_0^2}{2\Delta\theta} = \frac{(v/r)^2 - 0}{2\Delta\theta} = \frac{\left[(28.0\,\text{m/s})/(1.20\,\text{m})\right]^2}{2(8\pi\,\text{rad})} = \boxed{10.8\,\text{rad/s}^2}$$

(b) The tangential acceleration is found from the angular acceleration and the radius.
$$a_{\text{tan}} = \alpha r = (10.8\,\text{rad/s}^2)(1.20\,\text{m}) = \boxed{13.0\,\text{m/s}^2}$$

(c) The centripetal acceleration is found from the speed and the radius.
$$a_{\text{rad}} = v^2/r = (28.0\,\text{m/s})^2/(1.20\,\text{m}) = \boxed{653\,\text{m/s}^2}$$

(d) The net force is the mass times the net acceleration. It is in the same direction as the net acceleration, also.
$$F_{\text{net}} = ma_{\text{net}} = m\sqrt{a_{\text{tan}}^2 + a_{\text{rad}}^2} = (7.30\,\text{kg})\sqrt{(13.0\,\text{m/s}^2)^2 + (653\,\text{m/s}^2)^2} = \boxed{4.77\times10^3\,\text{N}}$$

(e) Find the angle from the two acceleration vectors.
$$\theta = \tan^{-1}\frac{a_{\text{tan}}}{a_{\text{rad}}} = \tan^{-1}\frac{13.0\,\text{m/s}^2}{653\,\text{m/s}^2} = \boxed{1.14°}$$

43. The energy required to bring the rotor up to speed from rest is equal to the final rotational KE of the rotor.

$$KE_{\text{rot}} = \tfrac{1}{2}I\omega^2 = \tfrac{1}{2}(3.75\times10^{-2}\,\text{kg}\cdot\text{m}^2)\left[8250\frac{\text{rev}}{\text{min}}\left(\frac{2\pi\,\text{rad}}{1\,\text{rev}}\right)\left(\frac{1\,\text{min}}{60\,\text{s}}\right)\right]^2 = \boxed{1.40\times10^4\,\text{J}}$$

44. Work can be expressed in rotational quantities as $W = \tau\Delta\theta$, and so power can be expressed in

rotational quantities as $P = \dfrac{W}{\Delta t} = \tau\dfrac{\Delta\theta}{\Delta t} = \tau\omega$.

$$P = \tau\omega = (280\,\text{m}\cdot\text{N})\left(3800\frac{\text{rev}}{\text{min}}\right)\left(\frac{2\pi\,\text{rad}}{1\,\text{rev}}\right)\left(\frac{1\,\text{min}}{60\,\text{s}}\right) = 1.114\times10^5\,\text{W} \approx \boxed{1.1\times10^5\,\text{W}}$$

$$1.114\times10^5\,\text{W}\left(\frac{1\,\text{hp}}{746\,\text{W}}\right) = \boxed{1.5\times10^2\,\text{hp}}$$

45. The total kinetic energy is the sum of the translational and rotational kinetic energies. Since the ball is rolling without slipping, the angular velocity is given by $\omega = v/R$. The rotational inertia of a sphere about an axis through its center is $I = \frac{2}{5}mR^2$.

$$KE_{total} = KE_{trans} + KE_{rot} = \tfrac{1}{2}mv^2 + \tfrac{1}{2}I\omega^2 = \tfrac{1}{2}mv^2 + \tfrac{1}{2}\tfrac{2}{5}mR^2\frac{v^2}{R^2} = \tfrac{7}{10}mv^2$$

$$= 0.7(7.3 \text{ kg})(3.3 \text{ m/s})^2 = \boxed{56 \text{ J}}$$

46. (a) For the daily rotation about its axis, treat the Earth as a uniform sphere, with an angular frequency of one revolution per day.

$$KE_{daily} = \tfrac{1}{2}I\omega_{daily}^2 = \tfrac{1}{2}\left(\tfrac{2}{5}MR_{Earth}^2\right)\omega_{daily}^2$$

$$= \tfrac{1}{5}(6.0\times10^{24}\text{ kg})(6.4\times10^6\text{ m})^2\left[\left(\frac{2\pi \text{ rad}}{1 \text{ day}}\right)\left(\frac{1 \text{ day}}{86,400 \text{ s}}\right)\right]^2 = \boxed{2.6\times10^{29}\text{ J}}$$

(b) For the yearly revolution about the Sun, treat the Earth as a particle, with an angular frequency of one revolution per year.

$$KE_{yearly} = \tfrac{1}{2}I\omega_{yearly}^2 = \tfrac{1}{2}\left(MR_{Sun-Earth}^2\right)\omega_{yearly}^2$$

$$= \tfrac{1}{2}(6.0\times10^{24}\text{ kg})(1.5\times10^{11}\text{ m})^2\left[\left(\frac{2\pi \text{ rad}}{365 \text{ day}}\right)\left(\frac{1 \text{ day}}{86,400 \text{ s}}\right)\right]^2 = \boxed{2.7\times10^{33}\text{ J}}$$

Thus the total KE is $KE_{daily} + KE_{yearly} = 2.6\times10^{29}\text{ J} + 2.6\times10^{33}\text{ J} = \boxed{2.6\times10^{33}\text{ J}}$. The KE due to the daily motion is about 10,000 smaller than that due to the yearly motion.

47. The work required is the change in rotational kinetic energy. The initial angular velocity is 0.

$$W = \Delta KE_{rot} = \tfrac{1}{2}I\omega_f^2 - \tfrac{1}{2}I\omega_i^2 = \tfrac{1}{2}\tfrac{1}{2}MR^2\omega_f^2 = \tfrac{1}{4}(1640 \text{ kg})(7.50 \text{ m})^2\left(\frac{2\pi \text{ rad}}{8.00 \text{ s}}\right)^2 = \boxed{1.42\times10^4\text{ J}}$$

48. Apply conservation of energy to the sphere, as done in Example 8-13.
    (a) The work of Example 8-13 is exactly applicable here. The symbol d is to represent the distance the sphere rolls along the plane. The sphere is rolling without slipping, so $v_{CM} = \omega R$.

$$v_{CM} = \sqrt{\tfrac{10}{7}gh} = \sqrt{\tfrac{10}{7}gd\sin\theta} = \sqrt{\tfrac{10}{7}(9.80 \text{ m/s}^2)(10.0 \text{ m})(\sin 30.0°)} = 8.367$$

$$= \boxed{8.37 \text{ m/s}}$$

$$\omega = v_{CM}/R = 8.367 \text{ m/s}/(2.00\times10^{-1}\text{ m}) = \boxed{41.8 \text{ rad/s}}$$

(b) $\dfrac{KE_{trans}}{KE_{rot}} = \dfrac{\tfrac{1}{2}Mv_{CM}^2}{\tfrac{1}{2}I_{CM}\omega^2} = \dfrac{\tfrac{1}{2}Mv_{CM}^2}{\tfrac{1}{2}\left(\tfrac{2}{5}MR^2\right)\dfrac{v_{CM}^2}{R^2}} = \boxed{2.5}$

(c) Only the angular speed depends on the radius. $\boxed{\text{None of the results depend on the mass.}}$

49. The only force doing work in this system is gravity, so mechanical energy will be conserved. The initial state of the system is the configuration with m_1 on the ground and all objects at rest. The final state of the system has m_2 just reaching the ground, and all objects in motion. Call the zero level of gravitational potential energy to be the ground level. Both masses will have the same speed since they are connected by the rope. Assuming that the rope does not slip on the pulley, the angular speed of the pulley is related to the speed of the masses by $\omega = v/R$. All objects have an initial speed of 0.

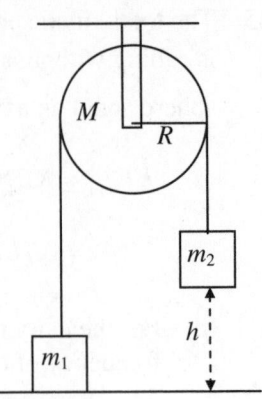

$$E_i = E_f$$

$$\tfrac{1}{2}m_1 v_i^2 + \tfrac{1}{2}m_2 v_i^2 + \tfrac{1}{2}I\omega_i^2 + m_1 g y_{1i} + m_2 g y_{2i} = \tfrac{1}{2}m_1 v_f^2 + \tfrac{1}{2}m_2 v_f^2 + \tfrac{1}{2}I\omega_f^2 + m_1 g y_{1f} + m_2 g y_{2f}$$

$$m_2 gh = \tfrac{1}{2}m_1 v_f^2 + \tfrac{1}{2}m_2 v_f^2 + \tfrac{1}{2}\left(\tfrac{1}{2}MR^2\right)\left(\frac{v_f^2}{R^2}\right) + m_1 gh$$

$$v_f = \sqrt{\frac{2(m_2 - m_1)gh}{\left(m_1 + m_2 + \tfrac{1}{2}M\right)}} = \sqrt{\frac{2(26.5\,\text{kg} - 18.0\,\text{kg})\left(9.80\,\text{m/s}^2\right)(3.00\,\text{m})}{\left(26.5\,\text{kg} + 18.0\,\text{kg} + \left(\tfrac{1}{2}\right)7.50\,\text{kg}\right)}} = \boxed{3.22\,\text{m/s}}$$

50. Since the lower end of the pole does not slip on the ground, the friction does no work, and so mechanical energy is conserved. The initial energy is the potential energy, treating all the mass as if it were at the CM. The final energy is rotational KE, for rotation about the point of contact with the ground. The linear velocity of the falling tip of the rod is its angular velocity divided by the length.

$$PE = KE \quad \rightarrow \quad mgh = \tfrac{1}{2}I\omega^2 \quad \rightarrow \quad mg\,L/2 = \tfrac{1}{2}\left(\tfrac{1}{3}mL^2\right)\left(v_{end}/L\right)^2 \quad \rightarrow$$

$$v_{end} = \sqrt{3gL} = \sqrt{3\left(9.80\,\text{m/s}^2\right)(2.30\,\text{m})} = \boxed{8.22\,\text{m/s}}$$

51. The angular momentum is given by Eq. 8-18.

$$L = I\omega = MR^2\omega = (0.210\,\text{kg})(1.10\,\text{m})^2(10.4\,\text{rad/s}) = \boxed{2.64\,\text{kg}\cdot\text{m}^2/\text{s}}$$

52. (a) The angular momentum is given by Eq. 8-18.

$$L = I\omega = \tfrac{1}{2}MR^2\omega = \tfrac{1}{2}(2.8\,\text{kg})(0.18\,\text{m})^2\left[\left(\frac{1500\,\text{rev}}{1\,\text{min}}\right)\left(\frac{2\pi\,\text{rad}}{1\,\text{rev}}\right)\left(\frac{1\,\text{min}}{60\,\text{s}}\right)\right]$$

$$= \boxed{7.1\,\text{kg}\cdot\text{m}^2/\text{s}}$$

(b) The torque required is the change in angular momentum per unit time. The final angular momentum is zero.

$$\tau = \frac{L - L_0}{\Delta t} = \frac{0 - 7.1\,\text{kg}\cdot\text{m}^2/\text{s}}{6.0\,\text{s}} = \boxed{-1.2\,\text{m}\cdot\text{N}}$$

The negative sign indicates that the torque is used to oppose the initial angular momentum.

53. (a) Consider the person and platform a system for angular momentum analysis. Since the force and torque to raise and/or lower the arms is internal to the system, the raising or lowering of the arms will cause no change in the total angular momentum of the system. However, the rotational inertia increases when the arms are raised. Since angular momentum is conserved, an increase in rotational inertia must be accompanied by a decrease in angular velocity.

(b) $L_i = L_f \rightarrow I_i\omega_i = I_f\omega_f \rightarrow I_f = I_i\dfrac{\omega_i}{\omega_f} = I_i\dfrac{1.30\,\text{rev/s}}{0.80\,\text{rev/s}} = 1.625\,I_i \approx 1.6\,I_i$

The rotational inertia has increased by a factor of $\boxed{1.6}$.

54. There is no net torque on the diver because the only external force (gravity) passes through the center of mass of the diver. Thus the angular momentum of the diver is conserved. Subscript 1 refers to the tuck position, and subscript 2 refers to the straight position.

$$L_1 = L_2 \rightarrow I_1\omega_1 = I_2\omega_2 \rightarrow \omega_2 = \omega_1\dfrac{I_1}{I_2} = \left(\dfrac{2\ \text{rev}}{1.5\ \text{sec}}\right)\left(\dfrac{1}{3.5}\right) = \boxed{0.38\ \text{rev/s}}$$

55. The skater's angular momentum is constant, since no external torques are applied to her.

$$L_i = L_f \rightarrow I_i\omega_i = I_f\omega_f \rightarrow I_f = I_i\dfrac{\omega_i}{\omega_f} = \left(4.6\ \text{kg}\cdot\text{m}^2\right)\dfrac{0.50\,\text{rev/s}}{3.0\,\text{rev/s}} = \boxed{0.77\ \text{kg}\cdot\text{m}^2}$$

She accomplishes this by starting with her arms extended (initial angular velocity) and then $\boxed{\text{pulling her arms in to the center of her body}}$ (final angular velocity).

56. Because there is no external torque applied to the wheel-clay system, the angular momentum will be conserved. We assume that the clay is thrown with no angular momentum so that its initial angular momentum is 0. This situation is a totally inelastic collision, in which the final angular velocity is the same for both the clay and the wheel. Subscript 1 represents before the clay is thrown, and subscript 2 represents after the clay is thrown.

$$L_1 = L_2 \rightarrow I_1\omega_1 = I_2\omega_2 \rightarrow$$

$$\omega_2 = \omega_1\dfrac{I_1}{I_2} = \dfrac{I_{\text{wheel}}}{I_{\text{wheel}} + I_{\text{clay}}} = \omega_1\left(\dfrac{\frac{1}{2}M_{\text{wheel}}R_{\text{wheel}}^2}{\frac{1}{2}M_{\text{wheel}}R_{\text{wheel}}^2 + \frac{1}{2}M_{\text{clay}}R_{\text{clay}}^2}\right)$$

$$= (1.5\,\text{rev/s})\left[\dfrac{(5.0\ \text{kg})(0.20\ \text{m})^2}{(5.0\ \text{kg})(0.20\ \text{m})^2 + (3.1\ \text{kg})(8.0\times10^{-2}\,\text{m})^2}\right] = 1.36\,\text{rev/s} \approx \boxed{1.4\,\text{rev/s}}$$

$\boxed{57.}$ (a) $L = I\omega = \frac{1}{2}MR^2\omega = \frac{1}{2}(55\ \text{kg})(0.15\ \text{m})^2\left(3.5\dfrac{\text{rev}}{\text{s}}\right)\left(\dfrac{2\pi\ \text{rad}}{1\ \text{rev}}\right) = \boxed{14\ \text{kg}\cdot\text{m}^2/\text{s}}$

(b) If the rotational inertia does not change, then the change in angular momentum is strictly due to a change in angular velocity.

$$\tau = \dfrac{\Delta L}{\Delta t} = \dfrac{0 - 14\ \text{kg}\cdot\text{m}^2/\text{s}}{5.0\ \text{s}} = \boxed{-2.7\,\text{m}\cdot\text{N}}$$

The negative sign indicates that the torque is in the opposite direction as the initial angular momentum.

58. (a) For the daily rotation about its axis, treat the Earth as a uniform sphere, with an angular frequency of one revolution per day.

$$L_{\text{daily}} = I\omega_{\text{daily}} = \left(\tfrac{2}{5}MR_{\text{Earth}}^2\right)\omega_{\text{daily}}$$

$$= \tfrac{2}{5}\left(6.0\times10^{24}\,\text{kg}\right)\left(6.4\times10^6\,\text{m}\right)^2\left[\left(\dfrac{2\pi\ \text{rad}}{1\ \text{day}}\right)\left(\dfrac{1\ \text{day}}{86,400\ \text{s}}\right)\right] = \boxed{7.1\times10^{33}\ \text{kg}\cdot\text{m}^2/\text{s}}$$

(*b*) For the yearly revolution about the Sun, treat the Earth as a particle, with an angular frequency of one revolution per year.

$$L_{daily} = I\omega_{daily} = \left(MR^2_{\substack{Sun-\\Earth}}\right)\omega_{daily}$$

$$= \left(6.0\times10^{24}\,kg\right)\left(1.5\times10^{11}\,m\right)^2\left[\left(\frac{2\pi\,rad}{365\,day}\right)\left(\frac{1\,day}{86{,}400\,s}\right)\right] = \boxed{2.7\times10^{40}\,kg{\cdot}m^2/s}$$

59. Since there are no external torques on the system, the angular momentum of the 2-disk system is conserved. The two disks have the same final angular velocity.

$$L_i = L_f \;\rightarrow\; I\omega + I(0) = 2I\omega_f \;\rightarrow\; \boxed{\omega_f = \tfrac{1}{2}\omega}$$

60. The angular momentum of the disk – rod combination will be conserved because there are no external torques on the combination. This situation is a totally inelastic collision, in which the final angular velocity is the same for both the disk and the rod. Subscript 1 represents before the collision, and subscript 2 represents after the collision. The rod has no initial angular momentum.

$$L_1 = L_2 \;\rightarrow\; I_1\omega_1 = I_2\omega_2 \;\rightarrow\;$$

$$\omega_2 = \omega_1\frac{I_1}{I_2} = \omega_1\frac{I_{disk}}{I_{disk}+I_{rod}} = \omega_1\left[\frac{\tfrac{1}{2}MR^2}{\tfrac{1}{2}MR^2+\tfrac{1}{12}M(2R)^2}\right] = \left(2.4\,rev/s\right)\left(\frac{3}{5}\right) = \boxed{1.4\,rev/s}$$

61. Since the person is walking radially, no torques will be exerted on the person-platform system, and so angular momentum will be conserved. The person will be treated as a point mass. Since the person is initially at the center, they have no initial rotational inertia.

(*a*) $$L_i = L_f \;\rightarrow\; I_{platform}\omega_i = \left(I_{platform}+I_{person}\right)\omega_f$$

$$\omega_f = \frac{I_{platform}}{I_{platform}+mR^2}\omega_i = \frac{920\,kg{\cdot}m^2}{920\,kg{\cdot}m^2+(75\,kg)(3.0\,m)^2}\left(2.0\,rad/s\right) = 1.154\,rad/s \approx \boxed{1.2\,rad/s}$$

(*b*) $$KE_i = \tfrac{1}{2}I_{platform}\omega_i^2 = \tfrac{1}{2}\left(920\,kg{\cdot}m^2\right)\left(2.0\,rad/s\right)^2 = \boxed{1.8\times10^3\,J}$$

$$KE_f = \tfrac{1}{2}\left(I_{platform}+I_{person}\right)\omega_f^2 = \tfrac{1}{2}\left(I_{platform}+m_{person}r_{person}^2\right)\omega_f^2$$

$$= \tfrac{1}{2}\left[920\,kg{\cdot}m^2+(75\,kg)(3.0\,m)^2\right]\left(1.154\,rad/s\right)^2 = 1062\,J \approx \boxed{1.1\times10^3\,J}$$

62. The angular momentum of the merry-go-round and people combination will be conserved because there are no external torques on the combination. This situation is a totally inelastic collision, in which the final angular velocity is the same for both the merry-go-round and the people. Subscript 1 represents before the collision, and subscript 2 represents after the collision. The people have no initial angular momentum.

$$L_1 = L_2 \;\rightarrow\; I_1\omega_1 = I_2\omega_2 \;\rightarrow\;$$

$$\omega_2 = \omega_1\frac{I_1}{I_2} = \omega_1\frac{I_{m\text{-}g\text{-}r}}{I_{m\text{-}g\text{-}r}+I_{people}} = \omega_1\left[\frac{I_{m\text{-}g\text{-}r}}{I_{m\text{-}g\text{-}r}+4M_{person}R^2}\right]$$

$$= \left(0.80\,rad/s\right)\left[\frac{1760\,kg{\cdot}m^2}{1760\,kg{\cdot}m^2+4(65\,kg)(2.1\,m)^2}\right] = \boxed{0.48\,rad/s}$$

If the people jump off the merry-go-round radially, then they exert no torque on the merry-go-round, and thus cannot change the angular momentum of the merry-go-round. The merry-go-round would continue to rotate at $\boxed{0.80\,\text{rad/s}}$.

63. Since the lost mass carries away no angular momentum, the angular momentum of the remaining mass will be the same as the initial angular momentum.

$$L_i = L_f \;\rightarrow\; I_i\omega_i = I_f\omega_f \;\rightarrow\; \frac{\omega_f}{\omega_i} = \frac{I_i}{I_f} = \frac{\frac{2}{5}M_iR_i^2}{\frac{2}{5}M_fR_f^2} = \frac{M_iR_i^2}{\left(0.5M_i\right)\left(0.01R_i\right)^2} = 2.0\times10^4$$

$$\omega_f = 2.0\times10^4\,\omega_i = 2.0\times10^4\left(\frac{2\pi\,\text{rad}}{30\,\text{day}}\right)\left(\frac{1\,\text{d}}{86400\,\text{s}}\right) = 4.848\times10^{-2}\;\text{rad/s} \approx \boxed{5\times10^{-2}\;\text{rad/s}}$$

The period would be a factor of 20,000 smaller, which would make it about 130 seconds. The ratio of angular kinetic energies of the spinning mass would be

$$\frac{KE_f}{KE_i} = \frac{\frac{1}{2}I_f\omega_f^2}{\frac{1}{2}I_i\omega_i^2} = \frac{\frac{1}{2}\left[\frac{2}{5}\left(0.5M_i\right)\left(0.01R_i\right)^2\right]\left(2.0\times10^4\,\omega_i\right)^2}{\frac{1}{2}\left(\frac{2}{5}M_iR_i^2\right)\omega_i^2} = 2.0\times10^4 \;\rightarrow\; \boxed{KE_f = 2\times10^4\,KE_i}$$

64. For our crude estimate, we model the hurricane as a rigid cylinder of air. Since the "cylinder" is rigid, each part of it has the same angular velocity. The mass of the air is the product of the density of air times the volume of the air cylinder.

$$M = \rho V = \rho\pi R^2 h = \left(1.3\,\text{kg/m}^3\right)\pi\left(1.00\times10^5\,\text{m}\right)^2\left(4.0\times10^3\,\text{m}\right) = 1.634\times10^{14}\,\text{kg}$$

(a) $$KE = \tfrac{1}{2}I\omega^2 = \tfrac{1}{2}\left(\tfrac{1}{2}MR^2\right)\left(v_{\text{edge}}/R\right)^2 = \tfrac{1}{4}Mv_{\text{edge}}^2$$

$$= \tfrac{1}{4}\left(1.634\times10^{14}\,\text{kg}\right)\left[\left(120\,\text{km/h}\right)\left(\frac{1\,\text{m/s}}{3.6\,\text{km/h}}\right)\right]^2 = 4.539\times10^{16}\,\text{J} \approx \boxed{5\times10^{16}\,\text{J}}$$

(b) $$L = I\omega = \left(\tfrac{1}{2}MR^2\right)\left(v_{\text{edge}}/R\right) = \tfrac{1}{2}MRv_{\text{edge}}$$

$$= \tfrac{1}{2}\left(1.634\times10^{14}\,\text{kg}\right)\left(1.00\times10^5\,\text{m}\right)\left[\left(120\,\text{km/h}\right)\left(\frac{1\,\text{m/s}}{3.6\,\text{km/h}}\right)\right] = 2.723\times10^{20}\;\text{kg}\cdot\text{m}^2/\text{s}$$

$$\approx \boxed{3\times10^{20}\;\text{kg}\cdot\text{m}^2/\text{s}}$$

65. Angular momentum will be conserved in the Earth – asteroid system, since all forces and torques are internal to the system. The initial angular velocity of the satellite, just before collision, can be found from $\omega_{\text{asteroid}} = v_{\text{asteroid}}/R_{\text{Earth}}$. Assuming the asteroid becomes imbedded in the Earth at the surface, the Earth and the asteroid will have the same angular velocity after the collision. We model the Earth as a uniform sphere, and the asteroid as a point mass.

$$L_i = L_f \;\rightarrow\; I_{\text{Earth}}\omega_{\text{Earth}} + I_{\text{asteroid}}\omega_{\text{asteroid}} = \left(I_{\text{Earth}} + I_{\text{asteroid}}\right)\omega_f$$

The moment of inertia of the satellite can be ignored relative to that of the Earth on the right side of the above equation, and so the percent change in Earth's angular velocity is found as follows.

$$I_{\text{Earth}}\omega_{\text{Earth}} + I_{\text{asteroid}}\omega_{\text{asteroid}} = I_{\text{Earth}}\omega_f \;\rightarrow\; \frac{\left(\omega_f - \omega_{\text{Earth}}\right)}{\omega_{\text{Earth}}} = \frac{I_{\text{asteroid}}}{I_{\text{Earth}}}\frac{\omega_{\text{asteroid}}}{\omega_{\text{Earth}}}$$

$$\% \text{ change} = \frac{\left(\omega_f - \omega_{\text{Earth}}\right)}{\omega_{\text{Earth}}}(100) = \frac{m_{\text{asteroid}} R_{\text{Earth}}^2 \overset{v_{\text{asteroid}}}{\overbrace{R_{\text{Earth}}}}}{\frac{2}{5} M_{\text{Earth}} R_{\text{Earth}}^2 \omega_{\text{Earth}}} = \frac{m_{\text{asteroid}}}{\frac{2}{5} M_{\text{Earth}}} \frac{v_{\text{asteroid}}}{\omega_{\text{Earth}} R_{\text{Earth}}}(100)$$

$$= \frac{\left(1.0 \times 10^5 \, \text{kg}\right)\left(3.0 \times 10^4 \, \text{m/s}\right)}{(0.4)\left(5.97 \times 10^{24} \, \text{kg}\right)\left(\dfrac{2\pi \, \text{rad}}{86400 \, \text{s}}\right)\left(6.38 \times 10^6 \, \text{m}\right)}(100) = \boxed{2.7 \times 10^{-16} \, \%}$$

66. When the person and the platform rotate, they do so about the vertical axis. Initially there is no angular momentum pointing along the vertical axis, and so any change that the person – wheel – platform undergoes must result in no net angular momentum along the vertical axis.

    (*a*) If the wheel is moved so that its angular momentum points upwards, then the person and platform must get an equal but opposite angular momentum, which will point downwards. Write the angular momentum conservation condition for the vertical direction to solve for the angular velocity of the platform.

$$L_i = L_f \quad \rightarrow \quad 0 = I_{\text{W}}\omega_{\text{W}} + I_{\text{P}}\omega_{\text{P}} \quad \rightarrow \quad \boxed{\omega_{\text{P}} = -\frac{I_{\text{W}}}{I_{\text{P}}}\omega_{\text{W}}}$$

    The negative sign means that the platform is rotating in the opposite direction of the wheel. If the wheel is spinning counterclockwise when viewed from above, the platform is spinning clockwise.

    (*b*) If the wheel is pointing at a 60° angle to the vertical, then the component of its angular momentum that is along the vertical direction is $I_{\text{W}}\omega_{\text{W}}\cos 60°$. See the diagram. Write the angular momentum conservation condition for the vertical direction to solve for the angular velocity of the platform.

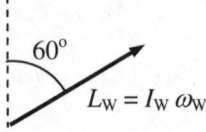

$$L_i = L_f \quad \rightarrow \quad 0 = I_{\text{W}}\omega_{\text{W}}\cos 60° + I_{\text{P}}\omega_{\text{P}} \quad \rightarrow \quad \boxed{\omega_{\text{P}} = -\frac{I_{\text{W}}}{2I_{\text{P}}}\omega_{\text{W}}}$$

    Again, the negative sign means that the platform is rotating in the opposite direction of the wheel.

    (*c*) If the wheel is moved so that its angular momentum points downwards, then the person and platform must get an equal but opposite angular momentum, which will point upwards. Write the angular momentum conservation condition for the vertical direction to solve for the angular velocity of the platform.

$$L_i = L_f \quad \rightarrow \quad 0 = -I_{\text{W}}\omega_{\text{W}} + I_{\text{P}}\omega_{\text{P}} \quad \rightarrow \quad \boxed{\omega_{\text{P}} = \omega_{\text{W}} I_{\text{W}}/I_{\text{P}}}$$

    The platform is rotating in the same direction as the wheel. If the wheel is spinning counterclockwise when viewed from above, the platform is also spinning counterclockwise.

    (*d*) Since the total angular momentum is 0, if the wheel is stopped from rotating, the platform will also stop. Thus $\boxed{\omega_{\text{P}} = 0}$.

67. The angular momentum of the person – turntable system will be conserved. Call the direction of the person's motion the positive rotation direction. Relative to the ground, the person's speed will be $v + v_{\text{T}}$, where v is the person's speed relative to the turntable, and v_{T} is the speed of the rim of the turntable with respect to the ground. The turntable's angular speed is $\omega_{\text{T}} = v_{\text{T}}/R$, and the person's

angular speed relative to the ground is $\omega_P = \dfrac{v + v_T}{R} = \dfrac{v}{R} + \omega_T$. The person is treated as a point particle for calculation of the moment of inertia.

$$L_i = L_f \quad \rightarrow \quad 0 = I_T \omega_T + I_P \omega_P = I_T \omega_T + mR^2 \left(\omega_T + \dfrac{v}{R} \right) \quad \rightarrow$$

$$\omega_T = -\dfrac{mRv}{I_T + mR^2} = -\dfrac{(55\text{ kg})(3.25\text{ m})(3.8\text{ m/s})}{1700\text{ kg} \cdot \text{m}^2 + (55\text{ kg})(3.25\text{ m})^2} = \boxed{-0.30\text{ rad/s}}$$

68. Since the spool rolls without slipping, each point on the edge of the spool moves with a speed of $v = r\omega = v_{CM}$ relative to the center of the spool, where v_{CM} is the speed of the center of the spool relative to the ground. Since the spool is moving to the right relative to the ground, and the top of the spool is moving to the right relative to the center of the spool, the top of the spool is moving with a speed of $2v_{CM}$ relative to the ground. This is the speed of the rope, assuming it is unrolling without slipping and is at the outer edge of the spool. The speed of the rope is the same as the speed of the person, since the person is holding the rope. So the person is walking with a speed of twice that of the center of the spool. Thus if the person moves forward a distance L, in the same time the center of the spool, traveling with half the speed, moves forward a distance $\boxed{L/2}$. The rope, to stay connected both to the person and to the spool, must therefore unwind by an amount $\boxed{L/2}$ also.

69. The spin angular momentum of the Moon can be calculated by $L_{spin} = I_{spin} \omega_{spin} = \frac{2}{5} MR_{Moon}^2 \omega_{spin}$. The orbital angular momentum can be calculated by $L_{orbit} = I_{orbit} \omega_{orbit} = MR_{orbit}^2 \omega_{orbit}$. Because the same side of the Moon always faces the Earth, $\omega_{spin} = \omega_{orbit}$.

$$\dfrac{L_{spin}}{L_{orbit}} = \dfrac{\frac{2}{5} MR_{Moon}^2 \omega_{spin}}{MR_{orbit}^2 \omega_{orbit}} = \dfrac{2}{5}\left(\dfrac{R_{Moon}}{R_{orbit}} \right)^2 = 0.4\left(\dfrac{1.74 \times 10^6\text{ m}}{3.84 \times 10^8\text{ m}} \right)^2 = \boxed{8.21 \times 10^{-6}}$$

70. As discussed in section 8-3, from the reference frame of the axle of the wheel, the points on the wheel are all moving with the same speed of $v = r\omega$, where v is the speed of the axle of the wheel relative to the ground. The top of the tire has a velocity of v to the right relative to the axle, so it has a velocity of $2v$ to the right relative to the ground.

$$\vec{\mathbf{v}}_{\substack{\text{top rel} \\ \text{ground}}} = \vec{\mathbf{v}}_{\substack{\text{top rel} \\ \text{center}}} + \vec{\mathbf{v}}_{\substack{\text{center rel} \\ \text{ground}}} = (v\text{ to the right}) + (v\text{ to the right}) = 2v\text{ to the right}$$

$$v_{\substack{\text{top rel} \\ \text{ground}}} = 2v = 2(v_0 + at) = 2at = 2(1.00\text{ m/s}^2)(3.0\text{ s}) = \boxed{6.0\text{ m/s}}$$

71. The torque is found from $\tau = I\alpha$. The angular acceleration can be found from $\omega = \omega_o + \alpha t$, with an initial angular velocity of 0. The rotational inertia is that of a cylinder.

$$\tau = I\alpha = \tfrac{1}{2}MR^2 \left(\dfrac{\omega - \omega_o}{t} \right) = 0.5(1.4\text{ kg})(0.20\text{ m})^2 \dfrac{(1800\text{ rev/s})(2\pi\text{ rad/rev})}{6.0\text{ s}} = \boxed{53\text{ m} \cdot \text{N}}$$

72. (*a*)   There are two forces on the yo-yo: gravity and the string tension. If we assume that the top of the string is held in a fixed position, then the tension does no work, and so mechanical energy is conserved. The initial gravitational PE is converted into rotational and translational KE. Since the yo-yo rolls without slipping at the point of contact of the string, the velocity of the CM is simply related to the angular velocity of the yo-yo: $v_{CM} = r\omega$, where r is the radius of the inner hub. Let m be the mass of the inner hub, and M and R be the mass and radius of each outer disk. Calculate the rotational inertia of the yo-yo about its CM, and then use conservation of energy to find the linear speed of the CM. We take the 0 of gravitational PE to be at the bottom of its fall.

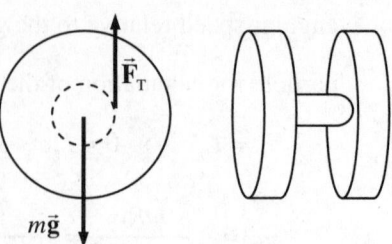

$$I_{CM} = \tfrac{1}{2}mr^2 + 2\left(\tfrac{1}{2}MR^2\right) = \tfrac{1}{2}mr^2 + MR^2$$

$$= \tfrac{1}{2}\left(5.0\times10^{-3}\,\text{kg}\right)\left(5.0\times10^{-3}\,\text{m}\right)^2 + \left(5.0\times10^{-2}\,\text{kg}\right)\left(3.75\times10^{-2}\,\text{m}\right)^2 = 7.038\times10^{-5}\,\text{kg}\cdot\text{m}^2$$

$$m_{total} = m + 2M = 5.0\times10^{-3}\,\text{kg} + 2\left(5.0\times10^{-2}\,\text{kg}\right) = 0.105\,\text{kg}$$

$$PE_i = KE_f \quad \rightarrow$$

$$m_{total}gh = \tfrac{1}{2}m_{total}v_{CM}^2 + \tfrac{1}{2}I_{CM}\omega^2 = \tfrac{1}{2}m_{total}v_{CM}^2 + \tfrac{1}{2}\frac{I_{CM}}{r^2}v_{CM}^2 = \left(\tfrac{1}{2}m_{total} + \tfrac{1}{2}\frac{I_{CM}}{r^2}\right)v_{CM}^2 \quad \rightarrow$$

$$v_{CM} = \sqrt{\frac{m_{total}gh}{\tfrac{1}{2}\left(m_{total} + \frac{I_{CM}}{r^2}\right)}} = \sqrt{\frac{\left(0.105\,\text{kg}\right)\left(9.80\,\text{m/s}^2\right)\left(1.0\,\text{m}\right)}{\tfrac{1}{2}\left[\left(0.105\,\text{kg}\right) + \frac{\left(7.038\times10^{-5}\,\text{kg}\cdot\text{m}^2\right)}{\left(5.0\times10^{-3}\,\text{m}\right)^2}\right]}} = 0.8395 = \boxed{0.84\,\text{m/s}}$$

(*b*)   Calculate the ratio KE_{rot}/KE_{tot}.

$$\frac{KE_{rot}}{KE_{tot}} = \frac{KE_{rot}}{PE_{tot}} = \frac{\tfrac{1}{2}I_{CM}\omega^2}{m_{total}gh} = \frac{\tfrac{1}{2}\frac{I_{CM}}{r^2}v_{CM}^2}{m_{total}gh} = \frac{I_{CM}v_{CM}^2}{2r^2 m_{total}gh}$$

$$= \frac{\left(7.038\times10^{-5}\,\text{kg}\cdot\text{m}^2\right)\left(0.8395\,\text{m/s}\right)^2}{2\left(5.0\times10^{-3}\,\text{m}\right)^2\left(0.105\,\text{kg}\right)\left(9.8\,\text{m/s}^2\right)\left(1.0\,\text{m}\right)} = 0.96 = \boxed{96\%}$$

73. (*a*)   The linear speed of the chain must be the same as it passes over both sprockets. The linear speed is related to the angular speed by $v = \omega R$, and so

$$\omega_R R_R = \omega_F R_F.$$

If the spacing of the teeth on the sprockets is a distance d, then the number of teeth on a sprocket times the spacing distance must give the circumference of the sprocket.

$$Nd = 2\pi R \text{ and so } R = \frac{Nd}{2\pi}. \text{ Thus } \omega_R\frac{N_R d}{2\pi} = \omega_F\frac{N_F d}{2\pi} \quad \rightarrow \quad \boxed{\frac{\omega_R}{\omega_F} = \frac{N_F}{N_R}}$$

(*b*) $\boxed{\omega_R/\omega_F = 52/13 = 4.0}$

(*c*) $\boxed{\omega_R/\omega_F = 42/28 = 1.5}$

74. Since the lost mass carries away no angular momentum, the angular momentum of the remaining mass will be the same as the initial angular momentum.

$$L_i = L_f \rightarrow I_i \omega_i = I_f \omega_f$$

$$\frac{\omega_f}{\omega_i} = \frac{I_i}{I_f} = \frac{\frac{2}{5} M_i R_i^2}{\frac{2}{5} M_f R_f^2} = \frac{(8.0 M_{Sun})(6.96 \times 10^8 \text{ m})^2}{(0.25)(8.0 M_{Sun})(1.1 \times 10^4 \text{ m})^2} = 1.601 \times 10^{10}$$

$$\omega_f = 1.601 \times 10^{10} \omega_i = 1.601 \times 10^{10} \left(\frac{1 \text{ rev}}{12 \text{ day}} \right) = 1.334 \times 10^9 \text{ rev/day}$$

$$\approx \boxed{1.3 \times 10^9 \text{ rev/day} = 1.5 \times 10^4 \text{ rev/s}}$$

75. (a) The initial energy of the flywheel is used for two purposes – to give the car translational kinetic energy 20 times, and to replace the energy lost due to friction, from air resistance and from braking. The statement of the problem leads us to ignore any gravitational potential energy changes.

$$W_{fr} = KE_{final} - KE_{initial} \rightarrow F_{fr} \Delta x \cos 180° = \frac{1}{2} M_{car} v_{car}^2 - KE_{flywheel}$$

$$KE_{flywheel} = F_{fr} \Delta x + \frac{1}{2} M_{car} v_{car}^2$$

$$= (450 \text{ N})(3.5 \times 10^5 \text{ m}) + (20)\frac{1}{2}(1400 \text{ kg}) \left[(95 \text{ km/h}) \left(\frac{1 \text{ m/s}}{3.6 \text{ km/h}} \right) \right]^2$$

$$= 1.672 \times 10^8 \text{ J} \approx \boxed{1.7 \times 10^8 \text{ J}}$$

(b) $KE_{flywheel} = \frac{1}{2} I \omega^2$

$$\omega = \sqrt{\frac{2 KE}{I}} = \sqrt{\frac{2 KE}{\frac{1}{2} M_{flywheel} R_{flywheel}^2}} = \sqrt{\frac{2(1.672 \times 10^8 \text{ J})}{\frac{1}{2}(240 \text{ kg})(0.75 \text{ m})^2}} = \boxed{2.2 \times 10^3 \text{ rad/s}}$$

(c) To find the time, use the relationship that $Power = \dfrac{Work}{t}$, where the work done by the motor will be equal to the kinetic energy of the flywheel.

$$P = \frac{W}{t} \rightarrow t = \frac{W}{P} = \frac{(1.672 \times 10^8 \text{ J})}{(150 \text{ hp})(746 \text{ W/hp})} = 1.494 \times 10^3 \text{ s} \approx \boxed{25 \text{ min}}$$

76. The mass of a hydrogen atom is 1.01 atomic mass units. The atomic mass unit is 1.66×10^{-27} kg. Since the axis passes through the oxygen atom, it will have no rotational inertia.

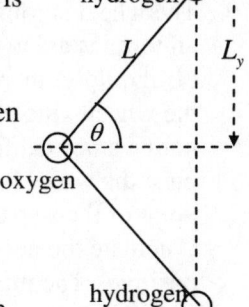

(a) If the axis is perpendicular to the plane of the molecule, then each hydrogen atom is a distance L from the axis of rotation.

$$I_{perp} = 2m_H L^2 = 2(1.01)(1.66 \times 10^{-27} \text{ kg})(0.96 \times 10^{-9} \text{ m})^2$$

$$= \boxed{3.1 \times 10^{-45} \text{ kg} \cdot \text{m}^2}$$

(b) If the axis is in the plane of the molecule, bisecting the H-O-H bonds, each hydrogen atom is a distance of $L_y = L \sin \theta = (9.6 \times 10^{-10} \text{ m}) \sin 52°$

$$= 7.564 \times 10^{-10} \text{ m}. \text{ Thus the moment of inertia is}$$

$$I_{\text{plane}} = 2m_H L_y^2 = 2(1.01)(1.66 \times 10^{-27} \text{ kg})(7.564 \times 10^{-10} \text{ m})^2 = \boxed{1.9 \times 10^{-45} \text{ kg} \cdot \text{m}^2}$$

77. (a) Assuming that there are no dissipative forces doing work,
    conservation of energy may be used to find the final height h of
    the hoop. Take the bottom of the incline to be the zero level of
    gravitational potential energy. We assume that the hoop is
    rolling without sliding, so that $\omega = v/R$. Relate the conditions
    at the bottom of the incline to the conditions at the top by conservation of energy. The hoop has
    both translational and rotational kinetic energy at the bottom, and the rotational inertia of the
    hoop is given by $I = mR^2$.

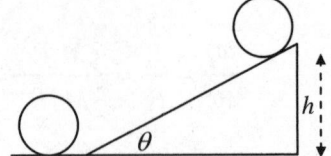

$$E_{\text{bottom}} = E_{\text{top}} \rightarrow \tfrac{1}{2}mv^2 + \tfrac{1}{2}I\omega^2 = mgh \rightarrow \tfrac{1}{2}mv^2 + \tfrac{1}{2}mR^2 \frac{v^2}{R^2} = mgh \rightarrow$$

$$h = \frac{v^2}{g} = \frac{(3.3 \text{ m/s})^2}{9.8 \text{ m/s}^2} = 1.111 \text{ m}$$

The distance along the plane is given by $d = \dfrac{h}{\sin\theta} = \dfrac{1.111 \text{ m}}{\sin 15^\circ} = 4.293 \text{ m} \approx \boxed{4.3 \text{ m}}$

(b) The time can be found from the constant accelerated linear motion. Use the relationship

$$\Delta x = \tfrac{1}{2}(v + v_o)t \rightarrow t = \frac{2\Delta x}{v + v_o} = \frac{2(4.293 \text{ m})}{0 + 3.3 \text{ m/s}} = 2.602 \text{ s}.$$

This is the time to go up the plane. The time to come back down the plane is the same, and so
the total time is $\boxed{5.2 \text{ s}}$.

78. (a) The force of gravity acting through the CM will cause a clockwise torque which produces an
    angular acceleration. At the moment of release, the force of gravity is perpendicular to the lever
    arm from the hinge to the CM.

$$\tau = I\alpha \rightarrow \alpha = \frac{\tau_{\text{gravity}}}{I_{\text{rod about end}}} = \frac{Mg\,L/2}{\tfrac{1}{3}ML^2} = \boxed{\frac{3g}{2L}}$$

(b) At the end of the rod, there is a tangential acceleration equal to the angular acceleration times
the distance from the hinge. There is no radial acceleration since at the moment of release, the
speed of the end of the rod is 0. Thus the tangential acceleration is the entire linear acceleration.

$$a_{\text{linear}} = a_{\text{tan}} = \alpha L = \boxed{\tfrac{3}{2}g}$$

79. The wheel is rolling about the point of contact with the step, and so
     all torques are to be taken about that point. As soon as the wheel is
     off the floor, there will be only two forces that can exert torques on
     the wheel – the pulling force and the force of gravity. There will
     not be a normal force of contact between the wheel and the floor
     once the wheel is off the floor, and any force on the wheel from the
     point of the step cannot exert a torque about that very point.
     Calculate the net torque on the wheel, with clockwise torques
     positive. The minimum force occurs when the net torque is 0.

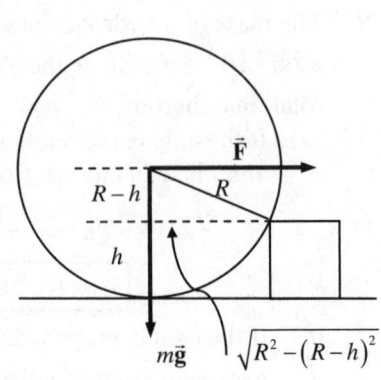

$$\sum \tau = F\left(R-h\right) - mg\sqrt{R^2 - \left(R-h\right)^2} = 0$$

$$F = \frac{Mg\sqrt{R^2 - \left(R-h\right)^2}}{R-h} = \boxed{\frac{Mg\sqrt{2Rh - h^2}}{R-h}}$$

80. (a) In order not to fall over, the net torque on the cyclist about an axis through the CM and parallel to the ground must be zero. Consider the free-body diagram shown. Sum torques about the CM, with counterclockwise as positive, and set the sum equal to zero.

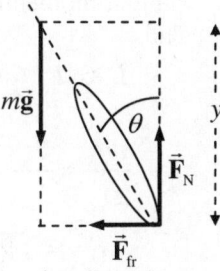

$$\sum \tau = F_N x - F_{fr} y = 0 \quad \rightarrow \quad \frac{F_{fr}}{F_N} = \frac{x}{y} = \tan\theta$$

(b) The cyclist is not accelerating vertically, so $F_N = mg$. The cyclist is accelerating horizontally, because he is traveling in a circle. Thus the frictional force must be supplying the centripetal force, so $F_{fr} = mv^2/r$.

$$\tan\theta = \frac{F_{fr}}{F_N} = \frac{mv^2/r}{mg} = \frac{v^2}{rg} \quad \rightarrow \quad \theta = \tan^{-1}\frac{v^2}{rg} = \tan^{-1}\frac{\left(4.2\,\text{m/s}\right)^2}{\left(6.4\,\text{m}\right)\left(9.8\,\text{m/s}^2\right)} = 15.71° \approx \boxed{16°}$$

(c) From $F_{fr} = mv^2/r$, the smallest turning radius results in the maximum force. The maximum static frictional force is $F_{fr} = \mu F_N$. Use this to calculate the radius.

$$mv^2/r_{min} = \mu F_N = \mu mg \quad \rightarrow \quad r_{min} = \frac{v^2}{\mu g} = \frac{\left(4.2\,\text{m/s}\right)^2}{\left(0.70\right)\left(9.8\,\text{m/s}^2\right)} = \boxed{2.6\,\text{m}}$$

81. Assume that the angular acceleration is uniform. Then the torque required to whirl the rock is the moment of inertia of the rock (treated as a particle) times the angular acceleration.

$$\tau = I\alpha = \left(mr^2\right)\left(\frac{\omega - \omega_0}{t}\right) = \frac{\left(0.50\,\text{kg}\right)\left(1.5\,\text{m}\right)^2}{5.0\,\text{s}}\left[\left(120\frac{\text{rev}}{\text{min}}\right)\left(\frac{2\pi\,\text{rad}}{\text{rev}}\right)\left(\frac{1\,\text{min}}{60\,\text{s}}\right)\right] = \boxed{2.8\,\text{m}\cdot\text{N}}$$

That torque comes from the arm swinging the sling, and so comes from the arm muscles.

82. Assume a mass of 50 kg, corresponding to a weight of about 110 lb. From Table 7-1, we find that the total arm and hand mass is about 12.5% of the total mass, and so the rest of the body is about 87.5% of the total mass. Model the skater as a cylinder of mass 44 kg, and model each arm as a thin rod of mass 3 kg. Estimate the body as 150 cm tall with a radius of 15 cm. Estimate the arm dimension as 50 cm long.

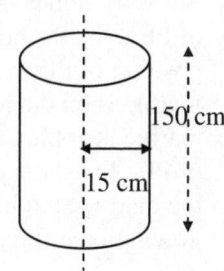

With the arms held tightly, we approximate that the arms are part of the body cylinder. A sketch of the skater in this configuration is then as shown in the first diagram. In this configuration, the rotational inertia is

$$I_{in} = I_{cylinder} = \tfrac{1}{2} M_{\substack{total \\ body}} R_{body}^2 .$$

With the arms extended, the configuration changes to the second diagram. In this configuration, the rotational inertia is

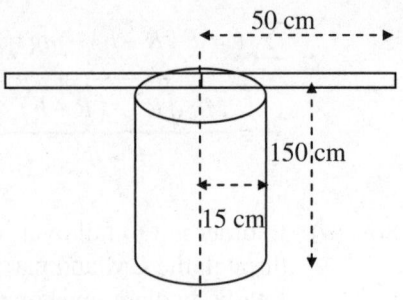

$$I_{out} = I_{body} + I_{arms} = \tfrac{1}{2}M_{body}R_{body}^2 + 2\tfrac{1}{3}M_{arm}L_{arm}^2$$

The forces and torques involved in changing the configuration of the skater are internal to the skater, and so the skater's angular momentum is conserved during a configuration change. Thus

$$L_{in} = L_{out} \quad \rightarrow \quad I_{in}\omega_{in} = I_{out}\omega_{out} \quad \rightarrow$$

$$\frac{\omega_{out}}{\omega_{in}} = \frac{I_{in}}{I_{out}} = \frac{\tfrac{1}{2}M_{total}R_{body}^2}{\tfrac{1}{2}M_{body}R_{body}^2 + 2\tfrac{1}{3}M_{arm}L_{arm}^2} = \frac{\tfrac{1}{2}(50\text{ kg})(0.15\text{ m})^2}{\tfrac{1}{2}(44\text{ kg})(0.15\text{ m})^2 + 2\tfrac{1}{3}(3\text{ kg})(0.50\text{ m})^2}$$

$$= 0.575 \approx \boxed{0.6}$$

83. (a) The angular momentum of M_A will be

$$L_A = I_A\omega_1 = \tfrac{1}{2}M_AR^2\omega_1 = \tfrac{1}{2}(6.0\text{ kg})(0.60\text{ m})^2(7.2\text{ rad/s}) = \boxed{7.8\text{ kg}\cdot\text{m}^2/\text{s}}.$$

   (b) The torque required to accelerate M_A will be

$$\tau = \frac{\Delta L}{\Delta t} = \frac{7.8\text{ kg}\cdot\text{m}^2/\text{s} - 0}{2.0\text{ s}} = \boxed{3.9\text{ m}\cdot\text{N}}$$

   (c) Since there are no torques external to the two plates, the angular momentum of the two plates will be conserved. Since the two plates stick together, they will have a common final angular velocity. This is a totally inelastic collision.

$$L_i = L_f \quad \rightarrow \quad I_A\omega_1 = (I_A + I_B)\omega_2 \quad \rightarrow$$

$$\omega_2 = \frac{I_A}{I_A + I_B}\omega_1 = \frac{\tfrac{1}{2}M_AR^2}{\tfrac{1}{2}M_AR^2 + \tfrac{1}{2}M_BR^2}\omega_1 = \frac{M_A}{M_A + M_B}\omega_1 = \left(\frac{6.0\text{ kg}}{15.0\text{ kg}}\right)(7.2\text{ rad/s})$$

$$= \boxed{2.9\text{ rad/s}}$$

84. Since frictional losses can be ignored, energy will be conserved for the marble. Define the 0 position of PE to be the bottom of the track, so that the bottom of the ball is initially a height h above the 0 position of PE. Since $r \ll R$, the marble's CM is very close to the surface of the track. While the marble is on the loop, we then approximate that it will be moving in a circle of radius R. When the marble is at the top of the loop, we approximate that its CM is a distance of $2R$ above the 0 position of PE. For the marble to just be on the verge of leaving the track means the normal force between the marble and the track is zero, and so the centripetal force at the top must be equal to the gravitational force on the marble.

$$\frac{mv^2_{\text{top of loop}}}{R} = mg \quad \rightarrow \quad v^2_{\text{top of loop}} = gR$$

We assume that the marble is rolling without slipping, and so $\omega = v/r$, and that the marble is released from rest. Use energy conservation to relate the release point to the point at the top of the loop. Note that the marble has both translational and rotational kinetic energy.

$$E_{\substack{\text{release}}} = E_{\substack{\text{top of}\\\text{loop}}} \quad \rightarrow \quad KE_{\substack{\text{release}}} + PE_{\substack{\text{release}}} = KE_{\substack{\text{top of}\\\text{loop}}} + PE_{\substack{\text{top of}\\\text{loop}}}$$

$$0 + mgh = \tfrac{1}{2}mv^2_{\substack{\text{top of}\\\text{loop}}} + \tfrac{1}{2}I\omega^2_{\substack{\text{top of}\\\text{loop}}} + mg\,2R = \tfrac{1}{2}mv^2_{\substack{\text{top of}\\\text{loop}}} + \tfrac{1}{2}\left(\tfrac{2}{5}mr^2\right)\frac{v^2_{\substack{\text{top of}\\\text{loop}}}}{r^2} + 2mgR$$

$$mgh = \tfrac{7}{10}mv^2_{\substack{\text{top of}\\\text{loop}}} + 2mgR = \tfrac{7}{10}mgR + 2mgR = 2.7mgR \quad \rightarrow \quad \boxed{h = 2.7R}$$

85. Since frictional losses can be ignored, energy will be conserved for the marble. Define the 0 position of PE to be bottom of the track, so that the bottom of the ball is initially a height h above the 0 position of PE. Since we are not to assume that $r \ll R$, then while the marble is on the loop portion of the track, it is moving in a circle of radius $R - r$, and when at the top of the loop, the bottom of the marble is a height of $2(R - r)$ above the 0 position of PE (see the diagram). For the marble to just be on the verge of leaving the track means the normal force between the marble and the track is zero, and so the centripetal force at the top must be equal to the gravitational force on the marble.

$$\frac{mv^2_{\substack{\text{top of}\\\text{loop}}}}{R - r} = mg \quad \rightarrow \quad v^2_{\substack{\text{top of}\\\text{loop}}} = g(R - r)$$

We assume that the marble is rolling without slipping and so $\omega = v/r$, and that the marble is released from rest. Use energy conservation to relate the release point to the point at the top of the loop. Note that the marble has both translational and rotational kinetic energy.

$$E_{\substack{\text{release}}} = E_{\substack{\text{top of}\\\text{loop}}} \quad \rightarrow \quad KE_{\substack{\text{release}}} + PE_{\substack{\text{release}}} = KE_{\substack{\text{top of}\\\text{loop}}} + PE_{\substack{\text{top of}\\\text{loop}}}$$

$$0 + mgh = \tfrac{1}{2}mv^2_{\substack{\text{top of}\\\text{loop}}} + \tfrac{1}{2}I\omega^2_{\substack{\text{top of}\\\text{loop}}} + mg\,2(R - r) = \tfrac{1}{2}mv^2_{\substack{\text{top of}\\\text{loop}}} + \tfrac{1}{2}\left(\tfrac{2}{5}mr^2\right)\frac{v^2_{\substack{\text{top of}\\\text{loop}}}}{r^2} + 2mg(R - r)$$

$$mgh = \tfrac{7}{10}mv^2_{\substack{\text{top of}\\\text{loop}}} + 2mg(R - r) = \tfrac{7}{10}mg(R - r) + 2mg(R - r) = 2.7mg(R - r)$$

$$\boxed{h = 2.7(R - r)}$$

86. (a) The angular acceleration can be found from $\omega^2 = \omega_o^2 + 2\alpha\theta$, with the angular velocities being given by $\omega = v/r$.

$$\alpha = \frac{\omega^2 - \omega_o^2}{2\theta} = \frac{(v^2 - v_o^2)}{2r^2\theta} = \frac{\left[(60.0\,\text{km/h})^2 - (90.0\,\text{km/h})^2\right]\left(\dfrac{1\,\text{m/s}}{3.6\,\text{km/h}}\right)^2}{2(0.45\,\text{m})^2(85\,\text{rev})(2\pi\,\text{rad/rev})}$$

$$= -1.6053\,\text{rad/s}^2 \approx \boxed{-1.61\,\text{rad/s}^2}$$

(b) The time to stop can be found from $\omega = \omega_o + \alpha t$, with a final angular velocity of 0.

$$t = \frac{\omega - \omega_o}{\alpha} = \frac{v - v_o}{r\alpha} = \frac{0 - (60.0\,\text{km/h})\left(\dfrac{1\,\text{m/s}}{3.6\,\text{km/h}}\right)}{(0.45\,\text{m})(-1.6053\,\text{rad/s}^2)} = \boxed{23\,\text{s}}$$

CHAPTER 9: Static Equilibrium; Elasticity and Fracture

Answers to Questions

1. If the object has a net force on it of zero, then its center of mass does not accelerate. But since it is not in equilibrium, it must have a net torque, and therefore have an angular acceleration. Some examples are:

   a) A compact disk in a player as it comes up to speed, after just being put in the player.
   b) A hard drive on a computer when the computer is first turned on.
   c) A window fan immediately after the power to it has been shut off.

2. The bungee jumper is not in equilibrium, because the net force on the jumper is not zero. If the jumper were at rest and the net force were zero, then the jumper would stay at rest by Newton's 1st law. The jumper has a net upward force when at the bottom of the dive, and that is why the jumper is then pulled back upwards.

3. If the fingers are not the same distance from the CG, the finger closer to the CG will support a larger fraction of the weight of the meter stick so that the net torque on the stick is zero. That larger vertical force means there will be more friction between the stick and that closer finger, and thus the finger further from the CG will be easier to move. The more distant finger will slide easier, and therefore move in closer to the CG. That finger, when it becomes the one closest to the CG, will then have more friction and will "stick". The other finger will then slide. You then repeat the process. Whichever finger is farther from the CG will slide closer to it, until the two fingers eventually meet at the CG.

4. Like almost any beam balance, the movable weights are connected to the fulcrum point by relatively long lever arms, while the platform on which you stand is connected to the fulcrum point by a very short lever arm. The scale "balances" when the torque provided by your weight (large mass, small lever arm) is equal to that provided by the sliding weights (small mass, large lever arm).

5. (a) If we assume that the pivot point of rotation is the lower left corner of the wall in the picture, then the gravity force acting through the CM provides the torque to keep the wall upright. Note that the gravity force would have a relatively small lever arm (about half the width of the wall) and so the sideways force would not have to be particularly large to start to move the wall.

   (b) With the horizontal extension, there are factors that make the wall less likely to overturn.
   - The mass of the second wall is larger, and so the torque caused by gravity (helping to keep the wall upright) will be larger for the second wall.
   - The center of gravity of the second wall is further to the right of the pivot point and so gravity exerts a larger torque to counteract the torque due to $\vec{F}$.
   - The weight of the ground above the new part of the wall provides a large clockwise torque that helps to counteract the torque due to $\vec{F}$.

6. For rotating the upper half body, the pivot point is near the waist and hips. In that position, the arms have a relatively small torque, even when extended, due to their smaller mass, and the more massive trunk–head combination has a very short lever arm, and so also has a relatively small torque. Thus the force of gravity on the upper body causes relatively little torque about the hips tending to rotate you forward, and so the back muscles need to produce little torque to keep you from rotating forward. The force on the upper half body due to the back muscles is small, and so the

(partially rightward) force at the base of the spinal column, to keep the spine in equilibrium, will be small.

When standing and bending over, the lever arm for the upper body is much larger than while sitting, and so causes a much larger torque. The CM of the arms is also further from the support point, and so causes more torque. The back muscles, assumed to act at the center of the back, do not have a very long lever arm. Thus the back muscles will have to exert a large force to cause a counter-torque that keeps you from falling over. And accordingly, there will have to be a large force (mostly to the right in the picture) at the base of the spine to keep the spine in equilibrium.

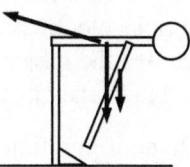

7. When the person stands near the top, the ladder is more likely to slip. In the accompanying diagram, the force of the person pushing down on the ladder $(M\vec{g})$ causes a clockwise torque about the contact point with the ground, with lever arm d_x. The only force causing a counterclockwise torque about that same point is the reaction force of the wall on the ladder, $\vec{F}_w$. While the ladder is in equilibrium, $\vec{F}_w$ will be the same magnitude as the frictional force at the ground, $\vec{F}_{Gx}$. Since $\vec{F}_{Gx}$ has a maximum value, $\vec{F}_w$ will have the same maximum value, and so $\vec{F}_w$ will have a maximum counterclockwise torque that it can exert. As the person climbs the ladder, their lever arm gets longer and so the torque due to their weight gets larger. Eventually, if the torque caused by the person is larger than the maximum torque caused by $\vec{F}_w$, the ladder will start to slip – it will not stay in equilibrium.

8. The mass of the meter stick is equal to that of the rock. For purposes of calculating torques, the meter stick can be treated as if all of its mass were at the 50 cm mark. Thus the CM of the meter stick is the same distance from the pivot point as the rock, and so their masses must be the same in order to exert the same torque.

9. If the sum of the forces on an object are not zero, then the CM of the object will accelerate in the direction of the net force. If the sum of the torques on the object are zero, then the object has no angular acceleration. Some examples are:
    a) A satellite in a circular orbit around the Earth.
    b) A block sliding down an inclined plane.
    c) An object that is in projectile motion but not rotating
    d) The startup motion of an elevator, changing from rest to having a non-zero velocity.

10.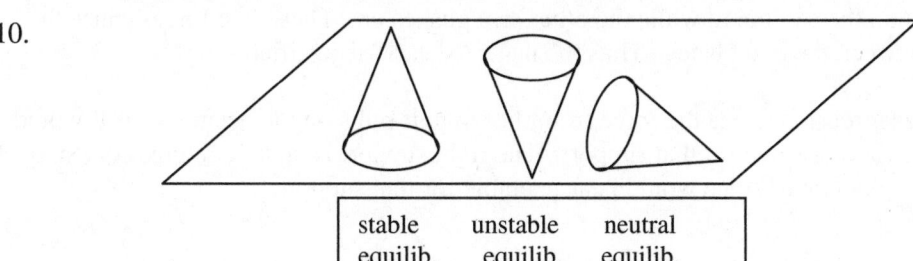

stable | unstable | neutral
equilib. | equilib. | equilib.

11. Configuration (b) is more likely to be stable. In configuration (a), the CG of the bottom brick is at the edge of the table, and the CG of the top brick is to the right of the edge of the table. Thus the CG of the two-brick system is not above the base of support, and so gravity will exert a torque to roll the bricks clockwise off the table. Another way to see this is that more than 50% of the brick mass is not above the base of support – 50% of the bottom brick and 75% of the top brick are to the right of the edge of the table. It is not in stable, neutral, or unstable equilibrium.

In configuration (b), exactly half of the mass (75% of the top brick and 25% of the bottom brick) is over the edge of the table. Thus the CG of the pair is at the edge of the table – it is in unstable equilibrium.

12. When walking, you must keep your CG over your feet. If you have a heavy load in your arms, your CG is shifted forward, and so you must lean backwards to realign your CG over your feet.

13. When you rise on your tiptoes, your CM shifts forward. Since you are already standing with your nose and abdomen against the door, your CM cannot shift forward. Thus gravity exerts a torque on you and you are unable to stay on your tiptoes – you will return to being flat-footed on the floor.

14. When you start to stand up from a normal sitting position, your CM is not over your point of support (your feet), and so gravity will exert a torque about your feet that rotates you back down into the chair. You must lean forward in order that your CM be over your feet so that you can stand up.

15. In the midst of doing a sit-up, the abdomen muscles provide a torque to rotate you up away from the floor, while the force of gravity on your upper half-body is tending to pull you back down to the floor, providing the difficulty for doing sit-ups. The force of gravity on your lower half-body provides a torque that opposes the torque caused by the force of gravity on your upper half-body, making the sit-up a little easier. With the legs bent, the lever arm for the lower half-body is shorter, and so less counter-torque is available.

16. Position "A" is unstable equilibrium, position "B" is stable equilibrium, and position "C" is neutral equilibrium.

17. The Young's modulus for a bungee cord is much smaller than that for ordinary rope. From its behavior, we know that the bungee cord stretches relatively easily, compared to ordinary rope. From Eq. 9-4, we have $E = \dfrac{F/A}{\Delta L/L_o}$. The value of Young's modulus is inversely proportional to the change in length of a material under a tension. Since the change in length of a bungee cord is much larger than that of an ordinary rope if other conditions are identical (stressing force, unstretched length, cross-sectional area of rope or cord), it must have a smaller Young's modulus.

18. An object under shear stress has equal and opposite forces applied across it. One blade of the scissors pushes down on the cardboard while the other arm pushes up. These two forces cause the cardboard to shear between the two blades. Thus the name "shears" is justified.

19. The left support is under tension, since the force from the support pulls on the beam. Thus it would not be wise to use concrete or stone for that support. The right support is under compression, since it pushes on the beam. Concrete or stone would be acceptable for that support.

Solutions to Problems

1. If the tree is not accelerating, then the net force in all directions is 0.

    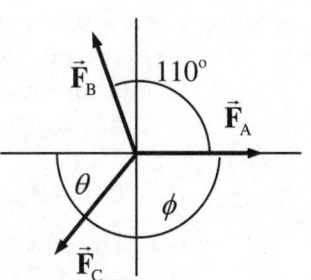

    $$\sum F_x = F_A + F_B \cos 110 + F_{Cx} = 0 \quad \rightarrow$$

    $$F_{Cx} = -F_A - F_B \cos 110 = -310 \text{ N} - (425 \text{ N}) \cos 110 = -164.6 \text{ N}$$

    $$\sum F_y = F_B \sin + F_{Cy} = 0 \quad \rightarrow$$

    $$F_{Cy} = -F_B \sin 110 = -(425 \text{ N}) \sin 110 = -399.4 \text{ N}$$

    $$F_C = \sqrt{F_{Cx}^2 + F_{Cy}^2} = \sqrt{(-164.6 \text{ N})^2 + (-399.4 \text{ N})^2} = 432.0 \text{ N} \approx \boxed{4.3 \times 10^2 \text{ N}}$$

    $$\theta = \tan^{-1} \frac{F_{Cy}}{F_{Cx}} = \tan^{-1} \frac{-399.4 \text{ N}}{-164.6 \text{ N}} = 67.6^\circ \ , \ \phi = 180^\circ - 67.6^\circ = 112.4^\circ \approx \boxed{112^\circ}$$

    And so $\vec{\mathbf{F}}_C$ is 430 N, at an angle of 112° clockwise from $\vec{\mathbf{F}}_A$.

2. The torque is the force times the lever arm.

    $$\tau = Fr = (58 \text{ kg})(9.8 \text{ m/s}^2)(3.0 \text{ m}) = \boxed{1.7 \times 10^3 \text{ m} \cdot \text{N , clockwise}}$$

3. Because the mass m is stationary, the tension in the rope pulling up on the sling must be mg, and so the force of the sling on the leg must be mg, upward. Calculate torques about the hip joint, with counterclockwise torque taken as positive. See the free-body diagram for the leg. Note that the forces on the leg exerted by the hip joint are not drawn, because they do not exert a torque about the hip joint.

    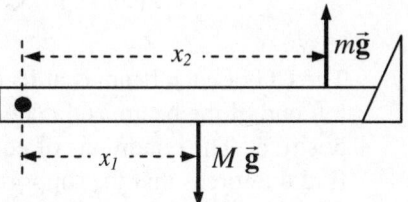

    $$\sum \tau = mgx_2 - Mgx_1 = 0 \quad \rightarrow \quad m = M \frac{x_1}{x_2} = (15.0 \text{ kg}) \frac{(35.0 \text{ cm})}{(80.5 \text{ cm})} = \boxed{6.52 \text{ kg}}$$

4. The torque is the force times the lever arm.

    $$\tau = Fr \quad \rightarrow \quad r = \frac{\tau}{F} = \frac{1100 \text{ m} \cdot \text{N}}{(58 \text{ kg})(9.8 \text{ m/s}^2)} = \boxed{1.9 \text{ m}}$$

5. Write Newton's 2nd law for the junction, in both the x and y directions.

    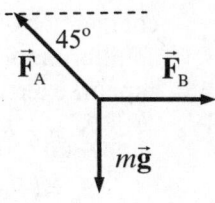

    $$\sum F_x = F_B - F_A \cos 45^\circ = 0$$

    From this, we see that $F_A > F_B$. Thus set $F_A = 1550 \text{ N}$.

    $$\sum F_y = F_A \sin 45^\circ - mg = 0$$

    $$mg = F_A \sin 45^\circ = (1550 \text{ N}) \sin 45^\circ = \boxed{1.1 \times 10^3 \text{ N}}$$

6. (*a*) Let $m = 0$. Calculate the net torque about the left end of the diving board, with counterclockwise torques positive. Since the board is in equilibrium, the net torque is zero.

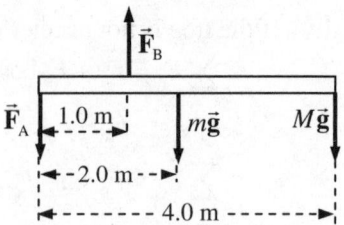

$$\sum \tau = F_B(1.0\ m) - Mg(4.0\ m) = 0 \quad \rightarrow$$

$$F_B = 4Mg = 4(58\ kg)(9.80\ m/s^2) = 2274\ N \approx \boxed{2.3 \times 10^3\ N}$$

Use Newton's 2nd law in the vertical direction to find F_A.

$$\sum F_y = F_B - Mg - F_A \quad \rightarrow$$

$$F_A = F_B - Mg = 4Mg - Mg = 3Mg = 3(58\ kg)(9.80\ m/s^2) = 1705\ N \approx \boxed{1.7 \times 10^3\ N}$$

(*b*) Repeat the basic process, but with $m = 35$ kg. The weight of the board will add more clockwise torque.

$$\sum \tau = F_B(1.0\ m) - mg(2.0\ m) - Mg(4.0\ m) = 0 \quad \rightarrow$$

$$F_B = 4Mg + 2mg = \left[4(58\ kg) + 2(35\ kg)\right](9.80\ m/s^2) = 2960\ N \approx \boxed{3.0 \times 10^3\ N}$$

$$\sum F_y = F_B - Mg - mg - F_A \quad \rightarrow$$

$$F_A = F_B - Mg - mg = 4Mg + 2mg - Mg - mg = 3Mg + mg$$

$$= \left[3(58\ kg) + 35\ kg\right](9.80\ m/s^2) = 2048\ N \approx \boxed{2.0 \times 10^3\ N}$$

7. The CG of each beam is at its center. Calculate torques about the left end of the beam, and take counterclockwise torques to be positive. The conditions of equilibrium for the beam are used to find the forces that the support exerts on the beam.

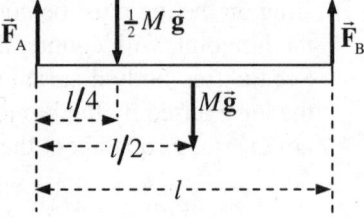

$$\sum \tau = F_B l - Mg(l/2) - \tfrac{1}{2}Mg(l/4) = 0 \quad \rightarrow$$

$$F_B = \tfrac{5}{8}Mg = \tfrac{5}{8}(940\ kg)(9.80\ m/s^2) = 5758\ N \approx \boxed{5.8 \times 10^3\ N}$$

$$\sum F_y = F_A + F_B - Mg - \tfrac{1}{2}Mg = 0 \quad \rightarrow$$

$$F_A = \tfrac{3}{2}Mg - F_B = \tfrac{7}{8}Mg = \tfrac{7}{8}(940\ kg)(9.80\ m/s^2) = 8061\ N \approx \boxed{8.1 \times 10^3\ N}$$

8. Let m be the mass of the beam, and M be the mass of the piano. Calculate torques about the left end of the beam, with counterclockwise torques positive. The conditions of equilibrium for the beam are used to find the forces that the support exerts on the beam.

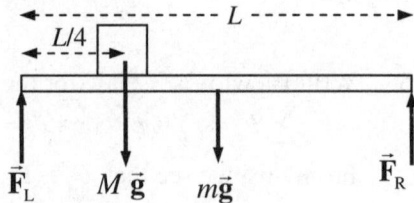

$$\sum \tau = F_R L - mg\left(\tfrac{1}{2}L\right) - Mg\left(\tfrac{1}{4}L\right) = 0$$

$$F_R = \left(\tfrac{1}{2}m + \tfrac{1}{4}M\right)g = \left[\tfrac{1}{2}(140\ kg) + \tfrac{1}{4}(320\ kg)\right](9.80\ m/s^2) = 1.47 \times 10^3\ N$$

$$\sum F_y = F_L + F_R - mg - Mg = 0$$

$$F_L = (m + M)g - F_R = (460\ kg)(9.80\ m/s^2) - 1.47 \times 10^3\ N = 3.04 \times 10^3\ N$$

The forces on the supports are equal in magnitude and opposite in direction to the above two results.

$$\boxed{F_R = 1.5 \times 10^3\ N\ \text{down}} \qquad \boxed{F_L = 3.0 \times 10^3\ N\ \text{down}}$$

9. The pivot should be placed so that the net torque on the board is zero. We calculate torques about the pivot point, with counterclockwise torques as positive. The upward force $\vec{F}_P$ at the pivot point is shown, but it exerts no torque about the pivot point. The mass of the board is m_B, and the CG is at the middle of the board.

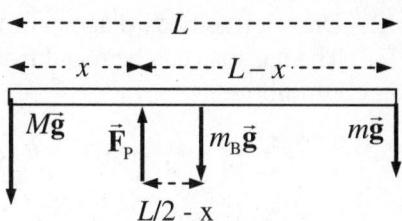

L/2 - x

(a) Ignore the force $m_B g$.

$$\sum \tau = Mgx - mg(L-x) = 0 \ \rightarrow$$

$$x = \frac{m}{m+M}L = \frac{(25\ \text{kg})}{(25\ \text{kg}+75\ \text{kg})}(9.0\ \text{m}) = 2.25\ \text{m} \approx \boxed{2.3\ \text{m from adult}}$$

(b) Include the force $m_B g$.

$$\sum \tau = Mgx - mg(L-x) - m_B g(L/2-x) = 0$$

$$x = \frac{(m+m_B/2)}{(M+m+m_B)}L = \frac{(25\ \text{kg}+7.5\ \text{kg})}{(75\ \text{kg}+25\ \text{kg}+15\ \text{kg})}(9.0\ \text{m}) = 2.54\ \text{m} \approx \boxed{2.5\ \text{m from adult}}$$

10. Calculate torques about the left end of the beam, with counterclockwise torques positive. The conditions of equilibrium for the beam are used to find the forces that the support exerts on the beam.

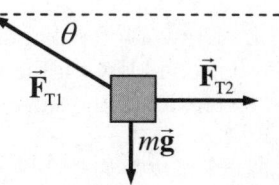

$$\sum \tau = F_2(20.0\ \text{m}) - mg(25.0\ \text{m}) = 0 \ \rightarrow$$

$$F_2 = \frac{25.0}{20.0}mg = (1.25)(1250\ \text{kg})(9.80\ \text{m/s}^2) = \boxed{1.53\times 10^4\ \text{N}}$$

$$\sum F_y = F_1 + F_2 - mg = 0$$

$$F_1 = mg - F_2 = mg - 1.25mg = -0.25mg = -(0.25)(1250\ \text{kg})(9.80\ \text{m/s}^2) = \boxed{-3.06\times 10^3\ \text{N}}$$

Notice that $\vec{F}_1$ points down.

11. Using the free-body diagram, write Newton's second law for both the horizontal and vertical directions, with net forces of zero.

$$\sum F_x = F_{T2} - F_{T1}\cos\theta = 0 \ \rightarrow \ F_{T2} = F_{T1}\cos\theta$$

$$\sum F_y = F_{T1}\sin\theta - mg = 0 \ \rightarrow \ F_{T1} = \frac{mg}{\sin\theta}$$

$$F_{T2} = F_{T1}\cos\theta = \frac{mg}{\sin\theta}\cos\theta = \frac{mg}{\tan\theta} = \frac{(170\ \text{kg})(9.80\ \text{m/s}^2)}{\tan 33°} = \boxed{2.6\times 10^3\ \text{N}}$$

$$F_{T1} = \frac{mg}{\sin\theta} = \frac{(170\ \text{kg})(9.80\ \text{m/s}^2)}{\sin 33°} = \boxed{3.1\times 10^3\ \text{N}}$$

12. Draw a free-body diagram of the junction of the three wires. The tensions can be found from the conditions for force equilibrium.

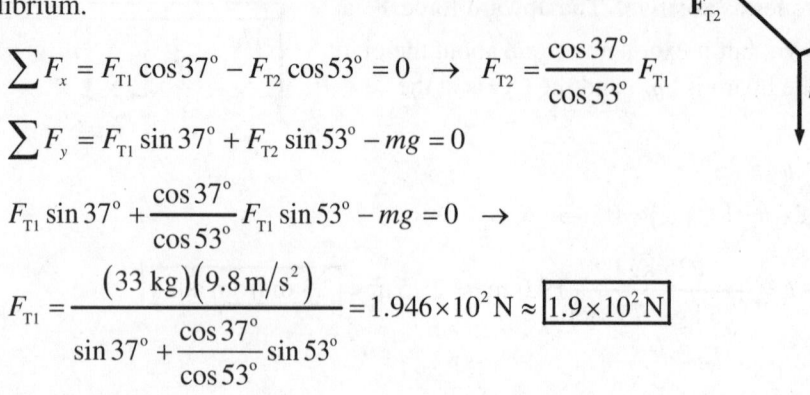

$$\sum F_x = F_{T1}\cos 37° - F_{T2}\cos 53° = 0 \quad \rightarrow \quad F_{T2} = \frac{\cos 37°}{\cos 53°}F_{T1}$$

$$\sum F_y = F_{T1}\sin 37° + F_{T2}\sin 53° - mg = 0$$

$$F_{T1}\sin 37° + \frac{\cos 37°}{\cos 53°}F_{T1}\sin 53° - mg = 0 \quad \rightarrow$$

$$F_{T1} = \frac{(33\text{ kg})(9.8\text{ m/s}^2)}{\sin 37° + \dfrac{\cos 37°}{\cos 53°}\sin 53°} = 1.946\times10^2\text{ N} \approx \boxed{1.9\times10^2\text{ N}}$$

$$F_{T2} = \frac{\cos 37°}{\cos 53°}F_{T1} = \frac{\cos 37°}{\cos 53°}(1.946\times10^2\text{ N}) = 2.583\times10^2\text{ N} \approx \boxed{2.6\times10^2\text{ N}}$$

13. The table is symmetric, so the person can sit near either edge and the same distance will result. We assume that the person (mass *M*) is on the right side of the table, and that the table (mass *m*) is on the verge of tipping, so that the left leg is on the verge of lifting off the floor. There will then be no normal force between the left leg of the table and the floor. Calculate torques about the right leg of the table, so that the normal force between the table and the floor causes no torque. Counterclockwise torques are taken to be positive. The conditions of equilibrium for the table are used to find the person's location.

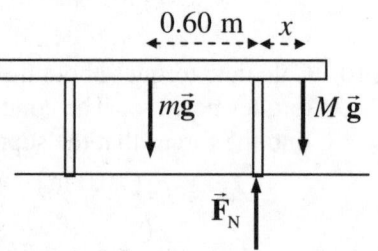

$$\sum \tau = mg(0.60\text{ m}) - Mgx = 0 \quad \rightarrow \quad x = (0.60\text{ m})\frac{m}{M} = (0.60\text{ m})\frac{20.0\text{ kg}}{66.0\text{ kg}} = 0.182\text{ m}$$

Thus the distance from the edge of the table is $0.50\text{ m} - 0.182\text{ m} = \boxed{0.32\text{ m}}$

14. Draw a force diagram for the sheet, and write Newton's second law for the vertical direction. Note that the tension is the same in both parts of the clothesline.

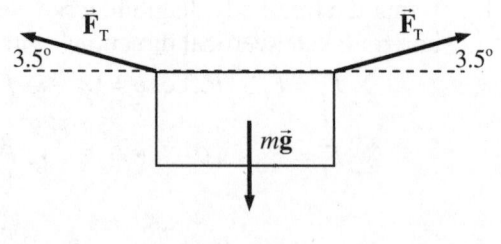

$$\sum F_y = F_T\sin 3.5° + F_T\sin 3.5° - mg = 0 \quad \rightarrow$$

$$F_T = \frac{mg}{2(\sin 3.5°)} = \frac{(0.60\text{ kg})(9.80\text{ m/s}^2)}{2(\sin 3.5°)} = \boxed{48\text{ N}}$$

The 48-N tension is much higher than the ~ 6-N weight of the sheet because of the angle. Only the vertical components of the tension are supporting the sheet, and since the angle is small, the tension has to be large to have a large enough vertical component.

15. The beam is in equilibrium, and so both the net torque and net force on it must be zero. From the free-body diagram, calculate the net torque about the center of the left support, with counterclockwise torques as positive. Calculate the net force, with upward as positive. Use those two equations to find F_A and F_B.

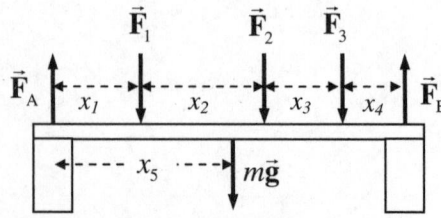

$$\sum \tau = F_{\text{B}}\left(x_1 + x_2 + x_3 + x_4\right) - F_1 x_1 - F_2\left(x_1 + x_2\right) - F_3\left(x_1 + x_2 + x_3\right) - mgx_5$$

$$F_{\text{B}} = \frac{F_1 x_1 + F_2\left(x_1 + x_2\right) + F_3\left(x_1 + x_2 + x_3\right) + mgx_5}{\left(x_1 + x_2 + x_3 + x_4\right)}$$

$$= \frac{\left(4300 \text{ N}\right)\left(2.0 \text{ m}\right) + \left(3100 \text{ N}\right)\left(6.0 \text{ m}\right) + \left(2200 \text{ N}\right)\left(9.0 \text{ m}\right) + \left(250 \text{ kg}\right)\left(9.8 \text{ m/s}^2\right)\left(5.0 \text{ m}\right)}{10.0 \text{ m}}$$

$$= 5925 \text{ N} \approx \boxed{5.9 \times 10^3 \text{ N}}$$

$$\sum F = F_{\text{A}} + F_{\text{B}} - F_1 - F_2 - F_3 - mg = 0$$

$$F_{\text{A}} = F_1 + F_2 + F_3 + mg - F_{\text{B}} = 9600 \text{ N} + \left(250 \text{ kg}\right)\left(9.8 \text{ m/s}^2\right) - 5925 \text{ N} = 6125 \text{ N} \approx \boxed{6.1 \times 10^3 \text{ N}}$$

16. From the free-body diagram, the conditions of equilibrium are used to find the location of the girl (mass m_{C}). The 50-kg boy is represented by m_{A}, and the 35-kg girl by m_{B}. Calculate torques about the center of the see-saw, and take counterclockwise torques to be positive. The upward force of the fulcrum on the see-saw $\left(\vec{\mathbf{F}}\right)$ causes no torque about the center.

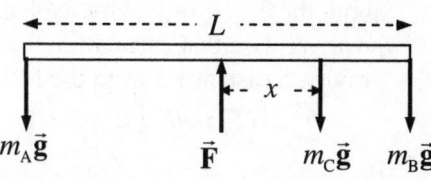

$$\sum \tau = m_{\text{A}} g\left(\tfrac{1}{2}L\right) - m_{\text{C}} gx - m_{\text{B}} g\left(\tfrac{1}{2}L\right) = 0$$

$$x = \frac{\left(m_{\text{A}} - m_{\text{B}}\right)}{m_{\text{C}}}\left(\tfrac{1}{2}L\right) = \frac{\left(50 \text{ kg} - 35 \text{ kg}\right)}{25 \text{ kg}}\tfrac{1}{2}\left(3.6 \text{ m}\right) = \boxed{1.1 \text{ m}}$$

17. Since each half of the forceps is in equilibrium, the net torque on each half of the forceps is zero. Calculate torques with respect to an axis perpendicular to the plane of the forceps, through point P, counterclockwise being positive. Consider a force diagram for one half of the forceps. $\vec{\mathbf{F}}_1$ is the force on the half-forceps due to the plastic rod, and force $\vec{\mathbf{F}}_{\text{P}}$ is the force on the half-forceps from the pin joint. $\vec{\mathbf{F}}_{\text{P}}$ does not exert any torque about point P.

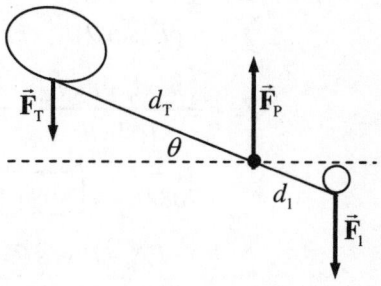

$$\sum \tau = F_{\text{T}} d_{\text{T}} \cos\theta - F_1 d_1 \cos\theta = 0 \quad \rightarrow \quad F_1 = F_{\text{T}}\frac{d_{\text{T}}}{d_1} = \left(11.0 \text{ N}\right)\frac{8.50 \text{ cm}}{2.70 \text{ cm}} = 34.6 \text{ N}$$

The force that the forceps exerts on the rod is the opposite of $\vec{\mathbf{F}}_1$, and so is also $\boxed{34.6 \text{ N}}$.

18. The beam is in equilibrium, and so the net force and net torque on the beam must be zero. From the free-body diagram for the beam, calculate the net torque (counterclockwise positive) about the wall support point to find $\vec{\mathbf{F}}_{\text{T}}$, and calculate the net force in both the x and y directions to find the components of $\vec{\mathbf{F}}_{\text{W}}$.

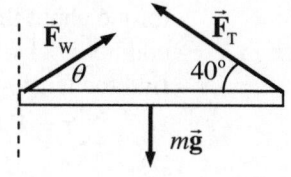

$$\sum \tau = F_{\text{T}} L \sin 40^\circ - mg \, L/2 = 0 \quad \rightarrow$$

$$F_{\text{T}} = \frac{mg}{2 \sin 40^\circ} = \frac{\left(27 \text{ kg}\right)\left(9.80 \text{ m/s}^2\right)}{2 \sin 40^\circ} = 205.8 \text{ N} \approx \boxed{2.1 \times 10^2 \text{ N}}$$

$$\sum F_x = F_{Wx} - F_T \cos 40° = 0 \quad \rightarrow \quad F_{Wx} = F_T \cos 40° = (205.8 \text{ N}) \cos 40° = 157.7 \text{ N}$$

$$\sum F_y = F_{Wy} + F_T \sin 40° - mg = 0 \quad \rightarrow$$

$$F_{Wy} = mg - F_T \sin 40° = (27 \text{ kg})(9.80 \text{ m/s}^2) - (205.8 \text{ N}) \sin 40° = 132.3 \text{ N}$$

$$F_W = \sqrt{F_{Wx}^2 + F_{Wx}^2} = \sqrt{(157.7 \text{ N})^2 + (132.3 \text{ N})^2} = 205.8 \text{ N} \approx \boxed{2.1 \times 10^2 \text{ N}}$$

$$\theta = \tan^{-1} \frac{F_{Wy}}{F_{Wx}} = \tan^{-1} \frac{132.3}{157.7} = \boxed{40°}$$

19. The person is in equilibrium, and so both the net torque and net force must be zero. From the free-body diagram, calculate the net torque about the center of gravity, with counterclockwise torques as positive. Use that calculation to find the location of the center of gravity, a distance x from the feet.

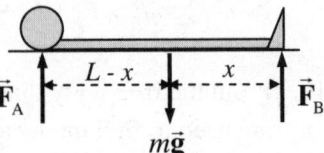

$$\sum \tau = F_B x - F_A (L - x) = 0$$

$$x = \frac{F_A}{F_A + F_B} L = \frac{m_A g}{m_A g + m_B g} L = \frac{m_A}{m_A + m_B} L = \frac{35.1 \text{ kg}}{31.6 \text{ kg} + 35.1 \text{ kg}} (1.72 \text{ m}) = \boxed{9.05 \times 10^{-1} \text{ m}}$$

The center of gravity is about 90.5 cm from the feet.

20. The beam is in equilibrium. Use the conditions of equilibrium to calculate the tension in the wire and the forces at the hinge. Calculate torques about the hinge, and take counterclockwise torques to be positive.

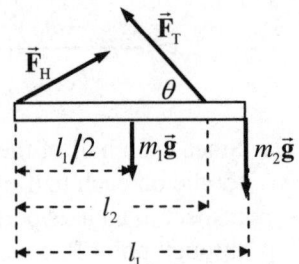

$$\sum \tau = (F_T \sin \theta) l_2 - m_1 g \, l_1 / 2 - m_2 g l_1 = 0 \quad \rightarrow$$

$$F_T = \frac{\frac{1}{2} m_1 g l_1 + m_2 g l_1}{l_2 \sin \theta} = \frac{\frac{1}{2}(155 \text{ N})(1.70 \text{ m}) + (245 \text{ N})(1.70 \text{ m})}{(1.35 \text{ m})(\sin 35.0°)}$$

$$= 708.0 \text{ N} \approx \boxed{7.08 \times 10^2 \text{ N}}$$

$$\sum F_x = F_{Hx} - F_T \cos \theta = 0 \quad \rightarrow \quad F_{Hx} = F_T \cos \theta = (708 \text{ N}) \cos 35.0° = 579.99 \text{ N} \approx \boxed{5.80 \times 10^2 \text{ N}}$$

$$\sum F_y = F_{Hy} + F_T \sin \theta - m_1 g - m_2 g = 0 \quad \rightarrow$$

$$F_{Hy} = m_1 g + m_2 g - F_T \sin \theta = 155 \text{ N} + 245 \text{ N} - (708 \text{ N}) \sin 35.0° = -6.092 \text{ N} \approx \boxed{-6 \text{ N (down)}}$$

21. (a) The pole is in equilibrium, and so the net torque on it must be zero. From the free-body diagram, calculate the net torque about the lower end of the pole, with counterclockwise torques as positive. Use that calculation to find the tension in the cable. The length of the pole is L.

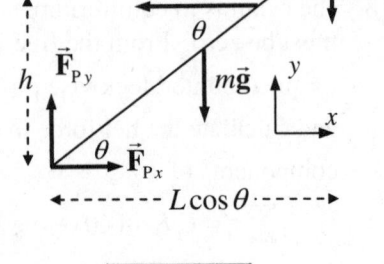

$$\sum \tau = F_T h - mg (L/2) \cos \theta - MgL \cos \theta = 0$$

$$F_T = \frac{(m/2 + M) gL \cos \theta}{h}$$

$$= \frac{(6.0 \text{ kg} + 21.5 \text{ kg})(9.80 \text{ m/s}^2)(7.50 \text{ m}) \cos 37°}{3.80 \text{ m}} = 424.8 \text{ N} \approx \boxed{4.25 \times 10^2 \text{ N}}$$

(*b*) The net force on the pole is also zero since it is in equilibrium. Write Newton's 2ⁿᵈ law in both the *x* and *y* directions to solve for the forces at the pivot.

$$\sum F_x = F_{Px} - F_T = 0 \rightarrow F_{Px} = F_T = \boxed{4.25 \times 10^2 \text{ N}}$$

$$\sum F_y = F_{Py} - mg - Mg = 0 \rightarrow F_{Py} = (m + M)g = (33.5 \text{ kg})(9.80 \text{ m/s}^2) = \boxed{3.28 \times 10^2 \text{ N}}$$

22. The man is in equilibrium, so the net force and the net torque on him are both zero. From the force diagram, write an expression for the net torque about a vertical axis through his right hand, with counterclockwise torques as positive. Also write an expression for the net force in the vertical direction.

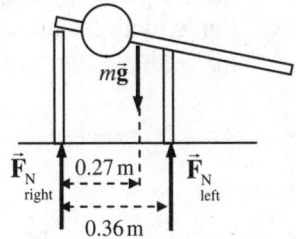

$$\sum \tau = F_{N_{\text{left}}} (0.36 \text{ m}) - mg(0.27 \text{ m}) = 0 \rightarrow$$

$$F_{N_{\text{left}}} = mg \frac{0.27}{0.36} = (72 \text{ kg})(9.80 \text{ m/s}^2) \frac{0.27}{0.36} = 529.2 \text{ N} \approx \boxed{5.3 \times 10^2 \text{ N}}$$

$$\sum F_y = F_{N_{\text{left}}} + F_{N_{\text{right}}} - mg = 0 \rightarrow$$

$$F_{N_{\text{right}}} = mg - F_{N_{\text{left}}} = (72 \text{ kg})(9.80 \text{ m/s}^2) - 529.2 \text{ N} = \boxed{1.8 \times 10^2 \text{ N}}$$

23. (*a*) The meter stick is in equilibrium, so the net torque and the net force are both zero. From the force diagram, write an expression for the net torque about the 90-cm mark, with counterclockwise torques as positive.

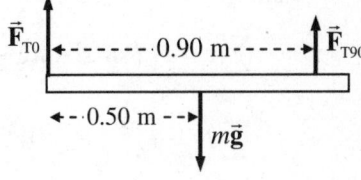

$$\sum \tau = mg(0.40 \text{ m}) - F_{T0}(0.90 \text{ m}) = 0 \rightarrow$$

$$F_{T0} = mg \frac{0.40}{0.90} = (0.180 \text{ kg})(9.80 \text{ m/s}^2) \frac{0.40}{0.90} = \boxed{0.78 \text{ N}}$$

(*b*) Write Newton's 2ⁿᵈ law for the vertical direction with a net force of 0 to find the other tension.

$$\sum F_y = F_{T0} + F_{T90} - mg = 0 \rightarrow$$

$$F_{T90} = mg - F_{T0} = (0.180 \text{ kg})(9.80 \text{ m/s}^2) - 0.78 \text{ N} = \boxed{0.98 \text{ N}}$$

24. Since the backpack is midway between the two trees, the angles in the diagram are equal. Write Newton's 2ⁿᵈ law for the vertical direction for the point at which the backpack is attached to the cord, with the weight of the backpack being the downward vertical force. The angle is determined by the distance between the trees and the amount of sag at the midpoint, as illustrated in the second diagram.

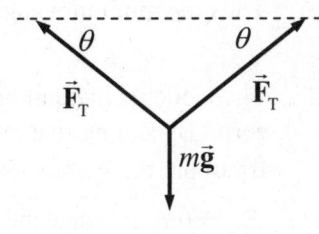

(*a*) $\theta = \tan^{-1} \dfrac{y}{L/2} = \tan^{-1} \dfrac{1.5 \text{ m}}{3.8 \text{ m}} = 21.5°$

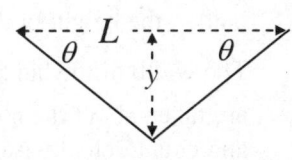

$$\sum F_y = 2F_T \sin \theta_1 - mg = 0 \rightarrow$$

$$F_T = \frac{mg}{2 \sin \theta_1} = \frac{(19 \text{ kg})(9.80 \text{ m/s}^2)}{2 \sin 21.5°} = \boxed{2.5 \times 10^2 \text{ N}}$$

(b) $\theta = \tan^{-1} \dfrac{y}{L/2} = \tan^{-1} \dfrac{0.15\,\text{m}}{3.8\,\text{m}} = 2.26°$ $F_{\text{T}} = \dfrac{mg}{2 \sin \theta_1} = \dfrac{(19\,\text{kg})(9.80\,\text{m/s}^2)}{2 \sin 2.26°} = \boxed{2.4 \times 10^3\,\text{N}}$

25. The forces on the door are due to gravity and the hinges. Since the door is in equilibrium, the net torque and net force must be zero. Write the three equations of equilibrium. Calculate torques about the bottom hinge, with counterclockwise torques as positive. From the statement of the problem, $F_{Ay} = F_{By} = \frac{1}{2}mg$.

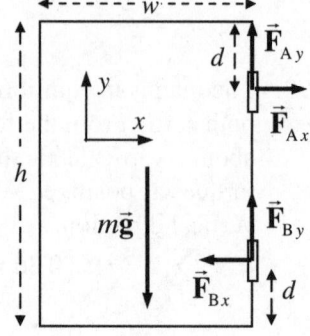

$$\sum \tau = mg\frac{w}{2} - F_{Ax}(h - 2d) = 0$$

$$F_{Ax} = \frac{mgw}{2(h - 2d)} = \frac{(13.0\,\text{kg})(9.80\,\text{m/s}^2)(1.30\,\text{m})}{2(2.30\,\text{m} - 0.80\,\text{m})} = \boxed{55.2\,\text{N}}$$

$$\sum F_x = F_{Ax} - F_{Bx} = 0 \;\rightarrow\; F_{Bx} = F_{Ax} = \boxed{55.2\,\text{N}}$$

$$\sum F_y = F_{Ay} + F_{By} - mg = 0 \;\rightarrow\; F_{Ay} = F_{By} = \tfrac{1}{2}mg = \tfrac{1}{2}(13.0\,\text{kg})(9.8\,\text{m/s}^2) = \boxed{63.7\,\text{N}}$$

26. Write the conditions of equilibrium for the ladder, with torques taken about the bottom of the ladder, and counterclockwise torques as positive.

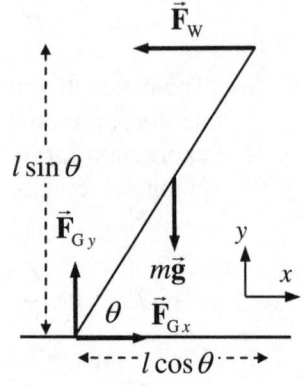

$$\sum \tau = F_{\text{W}}\, l \sin \theta - mg\frac{l}{2}\cos \theta = 0 \;\rightarrow\; F_{\text{W}} = \tfrac{1}{2}\frac{mg}{\tan \theta}$$

$$\sum F_x = F_{Gx} - F_{\text{W}} = 0 \;\rightarrow\; F_{Gx} = F_{\text{W}} = \tfrac{1}{2}\frac{mg}{\tan \theta}$$

$$\sum F_y = F_{Gy} - mg = 0 \;\rightarrow\; F_{Gy} = mg$$

For the ladder to not slip, the force at the ground F_{Gx} must be less than or equal to the maximum force of static friction.

$$F_{Gx} \le \mu F_{\text{N}} = \mu F_{Gy} \;\rightarrow\; \tfrac{1}{2}\frac{mg}{\tan \theta} \le \mu mg \;\rightarrow\; \frac{1}{2\mu} \le \tan \theta \;\rightarrow\; \theta \ge \tan^{-1}(1/2\mu)$$

Thus the minimum angle is $\boxed{\theta_{\min} = \tan^{-1}(1/2\mu)}$.

27. The ladder is in equilibrium, so the net torque and net force must be zero. By stating that the ladder is on the verge of slipping, the static frictional force at the ground, F_{Cx} is at its maximum value and so $F_{Cx} = \mu_s F_{Cy}$. Since the person is standing 70% of the way up the ladder, the height of the ladder is $L_y = d_y/0.7 = 2.8\,\text{m}/0.7 = 4.0\,\text{m}$. The width of the ladder is $L_x = d_x/0.7 = 2.1\,\text{m}/0.7 = 3.0\,\text{m}$. Torques are taken about the point of contact of the ladder with the ground, and counterclockwise torques are taken as positive. The three conditions of equilibrium are as follows.

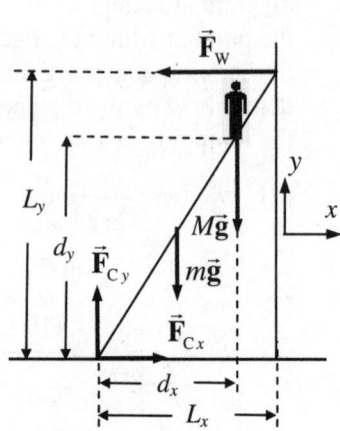

$$\sum F_x = F_{Cx} - F_{\text{W}} = 0 \;\rightarrow\; F_{Cx} = F_{\text{W}}$$

$$\sum F_y = F_{Gy} - Mg - mg = 0 \quad \rightarrow$$

$$F_{Gy} = (M + m)g = (67.0 \text{ kg})(9.80 \text{ m/s}^2) = 656.6 \text{ N}$$

$$\sum \tau = F_W L_y - mg\left(\tfrac{1}{2}L_x\right) - Mgd_x = 0$$

Solving the torque equation gives

$$F_W = \frac{\tfrac{1}{2}mL_x + Md_x}{L_y}g = \frac{\tfrac{1}{2}(12.0 \text{ kg})(3.0 \text{ m}) + (55.0 \text{ kg})(2.1 \text{ m})}{4.0 \text{ m}}(9.80 \text{ m/s}^2) = 327.1 \text{ N}.$$

The coefficient of friction then is found to be

$$\mu_s = \frac{F_{Gx}}{F_{Gy}} = \frac{327.1 \text{ N}}{656.6 \text{ N}} = \boxed{0.50}.$$

28. If the lamp is just at the point of tipping, then the normal force will be acting at the edge of the base, 12 cm from the lamp stand pole. We assume the lamp is in equilibrium and just on the verge of tipping, and is being pushed sideways at a constant speed. Take torques about the center of the base, with counterclockwise torques positive. Also write Newton's 2nd law for both the vertical and horizontal directions.

$$\sum F_y = F_N - mg = 0 \quad \rightarrow \quad F_N = mg \qquad \sum F_x = F_P - F_{fr} = 0 \quad \rightarrow \quad F_P = F_{fr} = \mu F_N = \mu mg$$

$$\sum \tau = F_N(0.12 \text{ m}) - F_P x = 0 \quad \rightarrow \quad x = \frac{F_N}{F_P}(0.12 \text{ m}) = \frac{mg}{\mu mg}(0.12 \text{ m}) = \frac{0.12 \text{ m}}{0.20} = \boxed{0.60 \text{ m}}$$

29. First consider the triangle made by the pole and one of the wires (first diagram). It has a vertical leg of 2.6 m, and a horizontal leg of 2.0 m. The angle that the tension (along the wire) makes with the vertical is

$$\theta = \tan^{-1}\frac{2.0}{2.6} = 37.6°. \text{ The part of the tension that is parallel to the ground is}$$

therefore $F_{Th} = F_T \sin\theta$. Now consider a top view of the pole, showing only

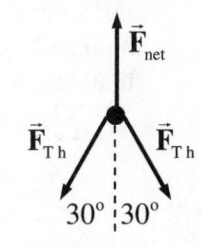

force parallel to the ground (second diagram). The horizontal parts of the tension lie as the sides of an equilateral triangle, and so each make a 30° angle with the tension force of the net. Write the equilibrium equation for the forces along the direction of the tension in the net.

$$\sum F = F_{net} - 2F_{Th}\cos 30° = 0 \quad \rightarrow$$

$$F_{net} = 2F_T \sin\theta\cos 30° = 2(95 \text{ N})\sin 37.6°\cos 30° = \boxed{1.0 \times 10^2 \text{ N}}$$

30. The arm is in equilibrium. Take torques about the elbow joint (the dot in the free-body diagram), so that the force at the elbow joint does not enter the calculation. Counterclockwise torques are positive. The mass of the lower arm is $m = 2.0 \text{ kg}$, and the mass of the load is M. It is given that $F_M = 450 \text{ N}$.

$$\sum \tau = F_M d_1 - mgd_2 - Mgd_3 = 0 \quad \rightarrow$$

$$M = \frac{F_M d_1 - mgd_2}{gd_3} = \frac{(450 \text{ N})(0.060 \text{ m}) - (2.0 \text{ kg})(9.80 \text{ m/s}^2)(0.15 \text{ m})}{(9.80 \text{ m/s}^2)(0.35 \text{ m})} = \boxed{7.0 \text{ kg}}$$

31. Calculate the torques about the elbow joint (the dot in the free body diagram). The arm is in equilibrium. Counterclockwise torques are positive.

$$\sum \tau = F_M d - mgD - MgL = 0$$

$$F_M = \frac{mD + ML}{d}g = \frac{(2.8\text{ kg})(0.12\text{ m}) + (7.3\text{ kg})(0.300\text{ m})}{0.025\text{ m}}(9.8\text{ m/s}^2) = \boxed{9.9 \times 10^2\text{ N}}$$

32. (*a*) Calculate the torques about the elbow joint (the dot in the free-body diagram). The arm is in equilibrium. Take counterclockwise torques as positive.

$$\sum \tau = (F_M \sin \theta)d - mgD = 0 \quad \rightarrow$$

$$F_M = \frac{mgD}{d \sin \theta} = \frac{(3.3\text{ kg})(9.80\text{ m/s}^2)(0.24\text{ m})}{(0.12\text{ m})\sin 15°} = \boxed{2.5 \times 10^2\text{ N}}$$

(*b*) To find the components of F_J, write Newton's 2nd law for both the *x* and *y* directions. Then combine them to find the magnitude.

$$\sum F_x = F_{Jx} - F_M \cos \theta = 0 \quad \rightarrow \quad F_{Jx} = F_M \cos \theta = (250\text{ N})\cos 15° = 241\text{ N}$$

$$\sum F_y = F_M \sin \theta - mg - F_{Jy} = 0 \quad \rightarrow$$

$$F_{Jy} = F_M \sin \theta - mg = (250\text{ N})\sin 15° - (3.3\text{ kg})(9.80\text{ m/s}^2) = 32\text{ N}$$

$$F_J = \sqrt{F_{Jx}^2 + F_{Jy}^2} = \sqrt{(241\text{ N})^2 + (32\text{ N})^2} = 243.5\text{ N} \approx \boxed{2.4 \times 10^2\text{ N}}$$

33. Calculate the torques about the shoulder joint, which is at the left end of the free-body diagram of the arm. Since the arm is in equilibrium, the sum of the torques will be zero. Take counterclockwise torques to be positive. The force due to the shoulder joint is drawn, but it does not exert any torque about the shoulder joint.

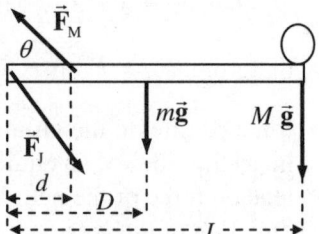

$$\sum \tau = F_m d \sin \theta - mgD - MgL = 0$$

$$F_m = \frac{mD + ML}{d \sin \theta}g = \frac{(3.3\text{ kg})(0.24\text{ cm}) + (15\text{ kg})(0.52\text{ m})}{(0.12\text{ m})\sin 15°}(9.8\text{ m/s}^2) = \boxed{2.7 \times 10^3\text{ N}}$$

34. There will be a normal force upwards at the ball of the foot, equal to the person's weight $(F_N = mg)$. Calculate torques about a point on the floor directly below the leg bone (and so in line with the leg bone force, $\vec{F}_B$). Since the foot is in equilibrium, the sum of the torques will be zero. Take counterclockwise torques as positive.

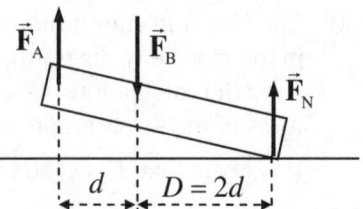

$$\sum \tau = F_N(2d) - F_A d = 0 \quad \rightarrow$$

$$F_A = 2F_N = 2mg = 2(72\text{ kg})(9.80\text{ m/s}^2) = \boxed{1.4 \times 10^3\text{ N}}$$

The net force in the *y* direction must be zero. Use that to find F_B.

$$\sum F_y = F_N + F_A - F_B = 0 \quad \rightarrow \quad F_B = F_N + F_A = 2mg + mg = 3mg = \boxed{2.1 \times 10^3 \, \text{N}}$$

35. Figures 9-14 (b) and (c) are redrawn here with the person 45° from the horizontal, instead of the original 30°. The distances are all the same as in the original problem. We still assume that the back muscles pull at a 12° angle to the spine. The 18° angle from the original problem becomes 33°. Torques are taken about the same point at the base of the spine, with counterclockwise torques as positive.

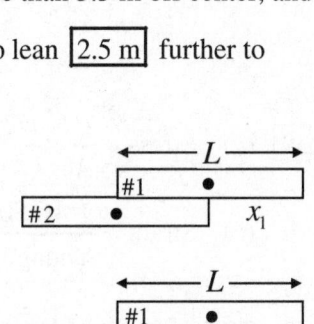

$$\sum \tau = (0.48 \text{ m}) F_M \sin 12° - (0.72 \text{ m})(w_H) \sin 45°$$
$$- (0.48 \text{ m})(w_A) \sin 45° - (0.36 \text{ m})(w_T) \sin 45° = 0$$

As in the original problem, $w_H = 0.07w$, $w_A = 0.12w$, $w_T = 0.46w$. With this, the torque equation gives the following result.

$$F_M = \frac{\left[(0.72 \text{ m})(0.07) + (0.48 \text{ m})(0.12) + (0.36 \text{ m})(0.46)\right]}{(0.48 \text{ m}) \sin 12°} w \sin 45° = 1.94w$$

Take the sum of the forces in the vertical direction, set equal to zero.

$$\sum F_y = F_{Vy} - F_M \sin 33° - 0.07w - 0.12w - 0.46w = 0 \quad \rightarrow \quad F_{Vy} = 1.71w$$

Take the sum of the forces in the horizontal direction, set equal to zero.

$$\sum F_x = F_{Vx} - F_M \cos 33° = 0 \quad \rightarrow \quad F_{Vy} = 1.63w$$

The final result is

$$F_V = \sqrt{F_{Vx}^2 + F_{Vy}^2} = \boxed{2.4w}$$

This compares to 2.5w for the more bent position.

36. From Section 9-4: "An object whose CG is above its base of support will be stable if a vertical line projected downward from the CG falls within the base of support." For the tower, the base of support is a circle of radius 3.5 m. If the top is 4.5 m off center, then the CG will be 2.25 m off center, and a vertical line downward from the CG will be 2.25 m from the center of the base. Thus the tower is in $\boxed{\text{stable equilibrium}}$. To be unstable, the CG has to be more than 3.5 m off center, and thus the top must be more than 7.0 m off center. Thus the top will have to lean $\boxed{2.5 \text{ m}}$ further to reach the verge of instability.

37. (*a*) The maximum distance for brick #1 to remain on brick #2 will be reached when the CM of brick #1 is directly over the edge of brick #2. Thus brick #1 will overhang brick #2 by $x_1 = L/2$.

   The maximum distance for the top two bricks to remain on brick #3 will be reached when the center of mass of the top two bricks is directly over the edge of brick #3. The CM of the top two bricks is (obviously) at the point labeled x on brick #2, a distance of $L/4$ from the right edge of brick #2. Thus $x_2 = L/4$.

   The maximum distance for the top three bricks to remain on brick #4 will be reached when the center of mass of the top three bricks is directly over the edge of brick #4. The CM of the top three bricks is at the point labeled x on brick #3, and is found relative to the center of brick # 3 by

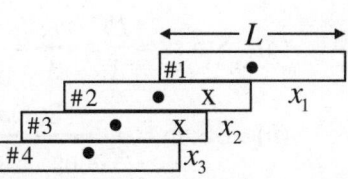

$$CM = \frac{m(0) + 2m(L/2)}{3m} = L/3, \text{ or } L/6 \text{ from the right edge of brick #3. Thus } x_3 = L/6.$$

The maximum distance for the four bricks to remain on a tabletop will be reached when the center of mass of the four bricks is directly over the edge of the table. The CM of all four bricks is at the point labeled x on brick #4, and is found relative to the center of brick #4 by

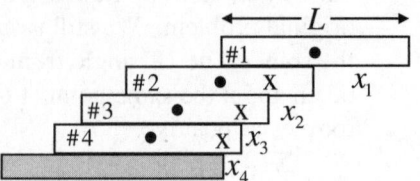

$$CM = \frac{m(0) + 3m(L/2)}{4m} = 3L/8, \text{ or } L/8 \text{ from the right}$$

edge of brick #4. Thus $x_4 = L/8$.

(b) From the last diagram, the distance from the edge of the tabletop to the right edge of brick #1 is

$$x_4 + x_3 + x_2 + x_1 = (L/8) + (L/6) + (L/4) + (L/2) = 25L/24 > L$$

Since this distance is greater than L, the answer is $\boxed{\text{yes}}$, the first brick is completely beyond the edge of the table.

(c) From the work in part (a), we see that the general formula for the total distance spanned by n bricks is

$$x_1 + x_2 + x_3 + \cdots x_n = (L/2) + (L/4) + (L/6) + \cdots + (L/2n) = \boxed{\sum_{i=1}^{n} \frac{L}{2i}}$$

(d) The arch is to span 1.0 m, so the span from one side will be 0.50 m. Thus we must solve

$$\sum_{i=1}^{n} \frac{0.30\,\text{m}}{2i} \geq 0.50\,\text{m}.$$ Evaluation of this expression for various values of n shows that 15 bricks

will span a distance of 0.498 m, and that 16 bricks will span a distance of 0.507 m. Thus it takes 16 bricks for each half-span, plus 1 brick on top and 1 brick as the base on each side (as in Fig. 9-67(b)), for a total of $\boxed{35 \text{ bricks}}$.

38. The amount of stretch can be found using the elastic modulus in Eq. 9-4.

$$\Delta L = \frac{1}{E}\frac{F}{A}L_0 = \frac{1}{5 \times 10^9\,\text{N/m}^2} \frac{275\,\text{N}}{\pi(5.00 \times 10^{-4})^2}(0.300\,\text{m}) = \boxed{2.10 \times 10^{-2}\,\text{m}}$$

$\boxed{39.}$ (a) Stress $= \dfrac{F}{A} = \dfrac{mg}{A} = \dfrac{(25000\,\text{kg})(9.8\,\text{m/s}^2)}{1.2\,\text{m}^2} = 2.042 \times 10^5\,\text{N/m}^2 \approx \boxed{2.0 \times 10^5\,\text{N/m}^2}$

(b) Strain $= \dfrac{\text{Stress}}{\text{Young's Modulus}} = \dfrac{2.042 \times 10^5\,\text{N/m}^2}{50 \times 10^9\,\text{N/m}^2} = \boxed{4.1 \times 10^{-6}}$

40. The change in length is found from the strain.

$$\text{Strain} = \frac{\Delta L}{L_0} \rightarrow \Delta L = L_0(\text{Strain}) = (9.6\,\text{m})(4.1 \times 10^{-6}) = \boxed{3.9 \times 10^{-5}\,\text{m}}$$

41. (a) Stress $= \dfrac{F}{A} = \dfrac{mg}{A} = \dfrac{(2100\,\text{kg})(9.8\,\text{m/s}^2)}{0.15\,\text{m}^2} = 1.372 \times 10^5\,\text{N/m}^2 \approx \boxed{1.4 \times 10^5\,\text{N/m}^2}$

(b) Strain $= \dfrac{\text{Stress}}{\text{Young's Modulus}} = \dfrac{1.372 \times 10^5\,\text{N/m}^2}{200 \times 10^9\,\text{N/m}^2} = 6.86 \times 10^{-7} \approx \boxed{6.9 \times 10^{-7}}$

(c) $\Delta L = (\text{Strain})(L_o) = (6.86 \times 10^{-7})(9.50 \text{ m}) = \boxed{6.5 \times 10^{-6} \text{ m}}$

42. The change in volume is given by Eq. 9-7. We assume the original pressure is atmospheric pressure, $1.0 \times 10^5 \text{ N/m}^2$.

$$\Delta V = -V_0 \frac{\Delta P}{B} = -(1000 \text{ cm}^3) \frac{(2.6 \times 10^6 \text{ N/m}^2 - 1.0 \times 10^5 \text{ N/m}^2)}{1.0 \times 10^9 \text{ N/m}^2} = -2.5 \text{ cm}^3$$

$$V = V_0 + \Delta V = 1000 \text{ cm}^3 - 2.5 \text{ cm}^3 = \boxed{997 \text{ cm}^3}$$

43. The Young's Modulus is the stress divided by the strain.

$$\text{Young's Modulus} = \frac{\text{Stress}}{\text{Strain}} = \frac{F/A}{\Delta L/L_o} = \frac{(13.4 \text{ N}) / \left[\pi \left(\frac{1}{2} \times 8.5 \times 10^{-3} \text{ m} \right)^2 \right]}{(3.7 \times 10^{-3} \text{ m}) / (15 \times 10^{-2} \text{ m})} = \boxed{9.6 \times 10^6 \text{ N/m}^2}$$

44. The relationship between pressure change and volume change is given by Eq. 9-7.

$$\Delta V = -V_0 \frac{\Delta P}{B} \rightarrow \Delta P = -\frac{\Delta V}{V_0} B = -(0.10 \times 10^{-2})(90 \times 10^9 \text{ N/m}^2) = \boxed{9.0 \times 10^7 \text{ N/m}^2}$$

$$\frac{\Delta P}{P_{\text{atm}}} = \frac{9.0 \times 10^7 \text{ N/m}^2}{1.0 \times 10^5 \text{ N/m}^2} = \boxed{9.0 \times 10^2}$$

45. The percentage change in volume is found by multiplying the relative change in volume by 100. The change in pressure is 199 times atmospheric pressure, since it increases from atmospheric pressure to 200 times atmospheric pressure.

$$100 \frac{\Delta V}{V_o} = -100 \frac{\Delta P}{B} = -100 \frac{199(1.0 \times 10^5 \text{ N/m}^2)}{90 \times 10^9 \text{ N/m}^2} = \boxed{-2 \times 10^{-2} \%}$$

The negative sign indicates that the interior space got smaller.

46. Elastic potential energy is given by $PE_{\text{elastic}} = \frac{1}{2} k (\Delta x)^2 = \frac{1}{2} F \Delta x$. The force is found from Eq. 9-4, using ΔL as Δx.

$$PE_{\text{elastic}} = \frac{1}{2} F \Delta x = \frac{1}{2} \left(\frac{EA}{L_0} \Delta L \right) \Delta L = \frac{1}{2} \frac{(2.0 \times 10^6 \text{ N/m}^2)(0.50 \times 10^{-4} \text{ m}^2)}{(3.0 \times 10^{-3} \text{ m})} (1.0 \times 10^{-3} \text{ m})^2$$

$$= \boxed{1.7 \times 10^{-2} \text{ J}}$$

47. (a)   The torque due to the sign is the product of the weight of the sign and the distance of the sign from the wall.

$$\tau = mgd = (5.1 \text{ kg})(9.80 \text{ m/s}^2)(2.2 \text{ m}) = \boxed{1.1 \times 10^2 \text{ m} \cdot \text{N , clockwise}}$$

(b)   Since the wall is the only other object that can put force on the pole (ignoring the weight of the pole), then the wall must put a torque on the pole. The torque due to the sign is clockwise, so the torque due to the wall must be counterclockwise. See the diagram. Also note that the wall must put an upward force on the pole as well, so that the net force on the pole will be zero.

(*c*) The torque on the rod can be considered as the wall pulling horizontally to the left on the top left corner of the rod and pushing horizontally to the right at the bottom left corner of the rod. The reaction forces to these put a shear on the wall at the point of contact. Also, since the wall is pulling upwards on the rod, the rod is pulling down on the wall at the top surface of contact, causing tension. Likewise the rod is pushing down on the wall at the bottom surface of contact, causing compression. Thus all three are present .

48. Set the compressive strength of the bone equal to the stress of the bone.

$$\text{Compressive Strength} = \frac{F_{max}}{A} \rightarrow F_{max} = \left(170 \times 10^6 \text{ N/m}^2\right)\left(3.0 \times 10^{-4} \text{ m}^2\right) = \boxed{5.1 \times 10^4 \text{ N}}$$

49. (*a*) The maximum tension can be found from the ultimate tensile strength of the material.

$$\text{Tensile Strength} = \frac{F_{max}}{A} \rightarrow$$

$$F_{max} = \left(\text{Tensile Strength}\right) A = \left(500 \times 10^6 \text{ N/m}^2\right)\pi\left(5.00 \times 10^{-4}\text{ m}\right)^2 = \boxed{393 \text{ N}}$$

(*b*) To prevent breakage, thicker strings should be used, which will increase the cross-sectional area of the strings, and thus increase the maximum force. Breakage occurs because when the strings are hit by the ball, they stretch, increasing the tension. The strings are reasonably tight in the normal racket configuration, so when the tension is increased by a particularly hard hit, the tension may exceed the maximum force.

50. (*a*) Compare the stress on the bone to the compressive strength to see if the bone breaks.

$$\text{Stress} = \frac{F}{A} = \frac{3.6 \times 10^4 \text{ N}}{3.6 \times 10^{-4} \text{ m}^2} = 1.0 \times 10^8 \text{ N/m}^2 < \text{Compressive Strength of bone}$$

The bone will not break.

(*b*) The change in length is calculated from Eq. 9-4.

$$\Delta L = \frac{L_0}{E} \frac{F}{A} = \left(\frac{0.22 \text{ m}}{15 \times 10^9 \text{ N/m}^2}\right)\left(1.0 \times 10^8 \text{ N/m}^2\right) = \boxed{1.5 \times 10^{-3} \text{ m}}$$

51. (*a*) The area can be found from the ultimate tensile strength of the material.

$$\frac{\text{Tensile Strength}}{\text{Safety Factor}} = \frac{F}{A}$$

$$A = F\left(\frac{\text{Safety Factor}}{\text{Tensile Strength}}\right) = \left(320 \text{ kg}\right)\left(9.8 \text{ m/s}^2\right)\frac{7.0}{500 \times 10^6 \text{ N/m}^2} = \boxed{4.4 \times 10^{-5} \text{ m}^2}$$

(*b*) The change in length can be found from the stress-strain relationship, equation (9-5).

$$\frac{F}{A} = E\frac{\Delta L}{L_0} \rightarrow \Delta L = \frac{L_0 F}{AE} = \frac{\left(7.5 \text{ m}\right)\left(320 \text{ kg}\right)\left(9.8 \text{ m/s}^2\right)}{\left(4.4 \times 10^{-5} \text{ m}^2\right)\left(200 \times 10^9 \text{ N/m}^2\right)} = \boxed{2.7 \times 10^{-3} \text{ m}}$$

52. For each support, to find the minimum cross-sectional area with a safety factor means that $\dfrac{F}{A} = \dfrac{\text{Strength}}{\text{Safety Factor}}$, where either the tensile or compressive strength is used, as appropriate for each force. To find the force on each support, use the conditions of equilibrium for the beam. Take torques about the left end of the beam, calling counterclockwise

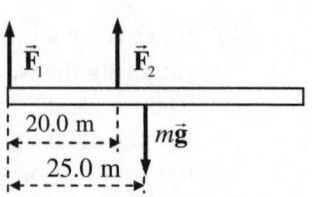

torques positive, and also sum the vertical forces, taking upward forces as positive.

$$\sum \tau = F_2 (20.0 \text{ m}) - mg (25.0 \text{ m}) = 0 \quad \rightarrow \quad F_2 = \tfrac{25.0}{20.0} mg = 1.25mg$$

$$\sum F_y = F_1 + F_2 - mg = 0 \quad \rightarrow \quad F_1 = mg - F_2 = mg - 1.25mg = -0.25mg$$

Notice that the forces on the supports are the opposite of $\vec{F}_1$ and $\vec{F}_2$. So the force on support # 1 is directed upwards, which means that support # 1 is in tension. The force on support # 2 is directed downwards, so support # 2 is in compression.

$$\frac{F_1}{A_1} = \frac{\text{Tensile Strength}}{8.5} \quad \rightarrow$$

$$A_1 = 8.5 \frac{(0.25mg)}{\text{Tensile Strength}} = 8.5 \frac{(0.25)(2.6 \times 10^3 \text{ kg})(9.80 \text{ m/s}^2)}{40 \times 10^6 \text{ N/m}^2} = \boxed{1.4 \times 10^{-3} \text{ m}^2}$$

$$\frac{F_2}{A_2} = \frac{\text{Compressive Strength}}{8.5} \quad \rightarrow$$

$$A_1 = 8.5 \frac{(1.25mg)}{\text{Compressive Strength}} = 8.5 \frac{(1.25)(2.6 \times 10^3 \text{ kg})(9.80 \text{ m/s}^2)}{35 \times 10^6 \text{ N/m}^2} = \boxed{7.7 \times 10^{-3} \text{ m}^2}$$

53. The diameter can be found from the ultimate shear strength of the material.

$$\frac{\text{Shear Strength}}{\text{Safety Factor}} = \frac{F}{A} = \frac{F}{\pi (d/2)^2}$$

$$d = \sqrt{\frac{4F}{\pi} \left(\frac{\text{Safety Factor}}{\text{Shear Strength}} \right)} = \sqrt{\frac{4(3200 \text{ N})}{\pi} \frac{6.0}{170 \times 10^6 \text{ N/m}^2}} = \boxed{1.2 \times 10^{-2} \text{ m}}$$

54. See the free-body diagram. The largest tension will occur when the elevator has an upward acceleration. Use that with the maximum tension to calculate the diameter of the bolt, d. Write Newton's second law for the elevator to find the tension.

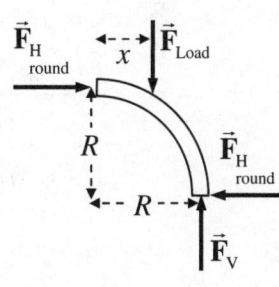

$$\sum F_y = F_T - mg = ma \quad \rightarrow$$

$$F_T = mg + ma = m(g + a) = m(9.8 \text{ m/s}^2 + 1.2 \text{ m/s}^2) = 11.0m$$

$$\frac{F_T}{A} = \frac{F_T}{\pi (d/2)^2} = \tfrac{1}{7} (\text{Tensile strength}) \quad \rightarrow$$

$$d = \sqrt{\frac{28 F_T}{\pi (\text{Tensile strength})}} = \sqrt{\frac{28(11.0)(3.1 \times 10^3 \text{ kg})}{\pi (500 \times 10^6 \text{ N/m}^2)}} = \boxed{2.5 \times 10^{-2} \text{ m}}$$

55. Draw free-body diagrams similar to Figures 9-31(a) and 9-31(b) for the forces on the right half of a round arch and a pointed arch. The load force is placed at the same horizontal position on each arch. For each half-arch, take torques about the lower right hand corner, with counterclockwise as positive.

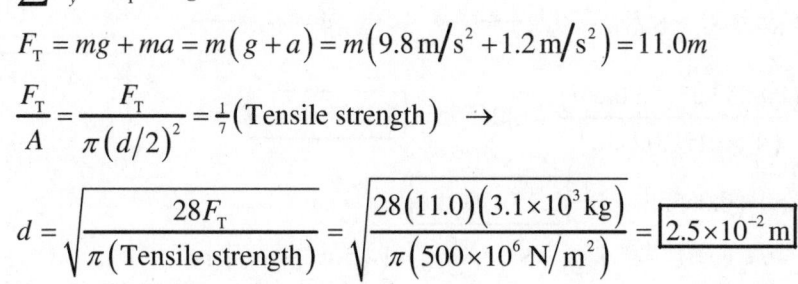

For the round arch:

$$\sum \tau = F_{\text{Load}} (R - x) - F_{\substack{\text{H} \\ \text{round}}} R = 0 \quad \rightarrow \quad F_{\substack{\text{H} \\ \text{round}}} = F_{\text{Load}} \frac{R - x}{R}$$

For the pointed arch:

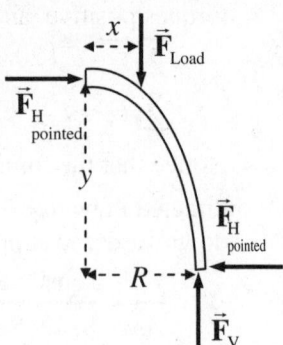

$$\sum \tau = F_{\text{Load}}\left(R-x\right) - F_{\text{H}_{\text{pointed}}} \; y = 0 \;\rightarrow\; F_{\text{H}_{\text{pointed}}} = F_{\text{Load}}\frac{R-x}{y}$$

Solve for y, given that $F_{\text{H}_{\text{pointed}}} = \frac{1}{3}F_{\text{H}_{\text{round}}}$.

$$F_{\text{H}_{\text{pointed}}} = \frac{1}{3}F_{\text{H}_{\text{round}}} \;\rightarrow\; F_{\text{Load}}\frac{R-x}{y} = \frac{1}{3}F_{\text{Load}}\frac{R-x}{R} \;\rightarrow$$

$$y = 3R = 3\left(\tfrac{1}{2}8.0 \text{ m}\right) = \boxed{12 \text{ m}}$$

56. Write Newton's 2nd law for the horizontal direction.

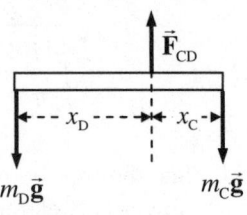

$$\sum F_x = F_2 \cos\theta - F_1 \cos\theta = 0 \;\rightarrow\; F_2 = F_1$$

Thus the two forces are the same size. Now write Newton's 2nd law for the vertical direction.

$$\sum F_y = F_1\sin\theta + F_1\sin\theta - F_{\text{butress}} = 0 \;\rightarrow\; F_1 = \frac{F_{\text{butress}}}{2\sin\theta} = \frac{4.3\times10^5 \text{ N}}{2\left(\sin 5^\circ\right)} = \boxed{2.5\times10^6 \text{ N}}$$

57. Each crossbar in the mobile is in equilibrium, and so the net torque about the suspension point for each crossbar must be 0. Counterclockwise torques will be taken as positive. The suspension point is used so that the tension in the suspension string need not be known initially. The net vertical force must also be 0.

The bottom bar:

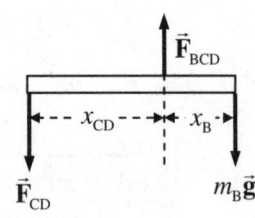

$$\sum \tau = m_{\text{D}}gx_{\text{D}} - m_{\text{C}}gx_{\text{C}} = 0 \;\rightarrow$$

$$m_{\text{C}} = m_{\text{D}}\frac{x_{\text{D}}}{x_{\text{C}}} = m_{\text{D}}\frac{17.50 \text{ cm}}{5.00 \text{ cm}} = 3.50m_{\text{D}}$$

$$\sum F_y = F_{\text{CD}} - m_{\text{C}}g - m_{\text{D}}g = 0 \;\rightarrow\; F_{\text{CD}} = \left(m_{\text{C}} + m_{\text{D}}\right)g = 4.50m_{\text{D}}g$$

The middle bar:

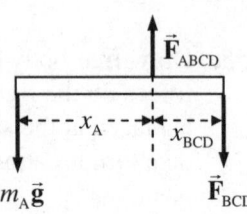

$$\sum \tau = F_{\text{CD}}x_{\text{CD}} - m_{\text{B}}gx_{\text{B}} = 0 \;\rightarrow\; F_{\text{CD}} = m_{\text{B}}g\frac{x_{\text{B}}}{x_{\text{CD}}} \;\rightarrow\; 4.50m_{\text{D}}g = m_{\text{B}}g\frac{x_{\text{B}}}{x_{\text{CD}}}$$

$$m_{\text{D}} = \frac{m_{\text{B}}}{4.50}\frac{x_{\text{B}}}{x_{\text{CD}}} = \frac{\left(0.885 \text{ kg}\right)\left(5.00 \text{ cm}\right)}{\left(4.50\right)\left(15.00 \text{ cm}\right)} = 0.06555 \approx \boxed{6.56\times10^{-2} \text{ kg}}$$

$$m_{\text{C}} = 3.50m_{\text{D}} = \left(3.50\right)\left(0.06555 \text{ kg}\right) = \boxed{2.29\times10^{-1} \text{ kg}}$$

$$\sum F_y = F_{\text{BCD}} - F_{\text{CD}} - m_{\text{B}}g = 0 \;\rightarrow\; F_{\text{BCD}} = F_{\text{CD}} + m_{\text{B}}g = \left(4.50m_{\text{D}} + m_{\text{B}}\right)g$$

The top bar:

$$\sum \tau = m_{\text{A}}gx_{\text{A}} - F_{\text{BCD}}x_{\text{BCD}} = 0 \;\rightarrow$$

$$m_{\text{A}} = \frac{\left(4.50m_{\text{D}} + m_{\text{B}}\right)gx_{\text{BCD}}}{gx_{\text{A}}} = \left(4.50m_{\text{D}} + m_{\text{B}}\right)\frac{x_{\text{BCD}}}{x_{\text{A}}}$$

$$= \left[\left(4.50\right)\left(0.06555 \text{ kg}\right) + 0.885 \text{ kg}\right]\frac{7.50 \text{ cm}}{30.00 \text{ cm}} = \boxed{2.94\times10^{-1} \text{ kg}}$$

58. From the free-body diagram (not to scale), write the
    force equilibrium condition for the vertical direction.

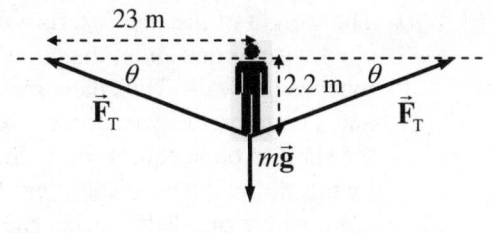

$$\sum F_y = 2T\sin\theta - mg = 0$$

$$T = \frac{mg}{2\sin\theta} = \frac{(60.0\,\text{kg})(9.80\,\text{m/s}^2)}{2\left(\dfrac{2.2\,\text{m}}{23\,\text{m}}\right)} = \boxed{3.1\times10^3\,\text{N}}$$

 $\boxed{\text{It is not possible to increase the tension so that there is no sag.}}$ There must always be a vertical
component of the tension to balance the gravity force. The larger the tension gets, the smaller the
sag angle will be, however.

59. (*a*) If the wheel is just lifted off the lowest level, then the only
    forces on the wheel are the horizontal pull, its weight, and the
    contact force $\vec{\mathbf{F}}_N$ at the corner. Take torques about the corner
    point, for the wheel just barely off the ground, being held in
    equilibrium. The contact force at the corner exerts no torque
    and so does not enter the calculation. The pulling force has a
    lever arm of $R + R - h = 2R - h$, and gravity has a lever arm of
    x, found from the triangle shown.

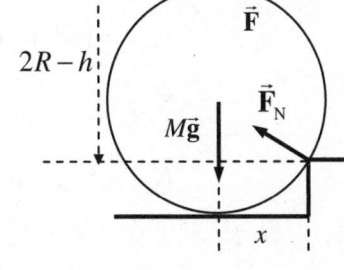

$$x = \sqrt{R^2 - (R-h)^2} = \sqrt{h(2R-h)}$$
$$\sum\tau = Mgx - F(2R-h) = 0 \quad\rightarrow$$

$$F = \frac{Mgx}{2R-h} = Mg\frac{\sqrt{h(2R-h)}}{2R-h} = \boxed{Mg\sqrt{\frac{h}{2R-h}}}$$

. (*b*) The only difference is that now the pulling force has a lever arm
    of $R - h$.

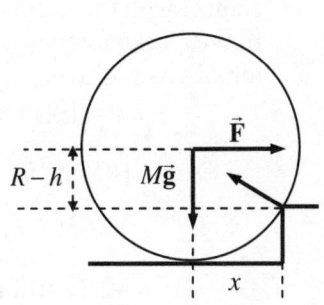

$$\sum\tau = Mgx - F(R-h) = 0 \quad\rightarrow$$

$$F = \frac{Mgx}{R-h} = \boxed{Mg\frac{\sqrt{h(2R-h)}}{R-h}}$$

60. The mass is to be placed symmetrically between two legs of the table.
    When enough mass is added, the table will rise up off of the third leg,
    and then the normal force on the table will all be on just two legs.
    Since the table legs are equally spaced, the angle marked in the
    diagram is 30°. Take torques about a line connecting the two legs that
    remain on the floor, so that the normal forces cause no torque. It is
    seen from the second diagram (a portion of the first diagram but
    enlarged) that the two forces are equidistant from the line joining the
    two legs on the floor. Since the lever arms are equal, then the torques will be
    equal if the forces are equal. Thus, to be in equilibrium, the two forces must
    be the same. If the force on the edge of the table is any bigger than the
    weight of the table, it will tip. Thus $\boxed{M > 25\,\text{kg}}$ will cause the table to tip.

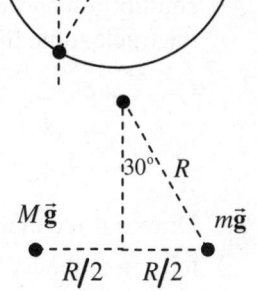

61. (*a*) The weight of the shelf exerts a downward force and a
clockwise torque about the point where the shelf
touches the wall. Thus there must be an upward force
and a counterclockwise torque exerted by the slot for
the shelf to be in equilibrium. Since any force exerted
by the slot will have a short lever arm relative to the
point where the shelf touches the wall, the upward force
must be larger than the gravity force. Accordingly, there then must be a downward force
exerted by the slot at its left edge, exerting no torque, but balancing the vertical forces.

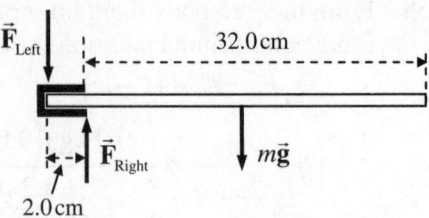

(*b*) Calculate the values of the three forces by first taking torques about the left end of the shelf,
with the net torque being zero, and then sum the vertical forces, with the sum being zero.

$$\sum \tau = F_{\text{Right}} \left(2.0 \times 10^{-2}\,\text{m}\right) - mg\left(17.0 \times 10^{-2}\,\text{m}\right) = 0 \quad \rightarrow$$

$$F_{\text{Right}} = \left(5.0\,\text{kg}\right)\left(9.80\,\text{m/s}^2\right)\left(\frac{17.0 \times 10^{-2}\,\text{m}}{2.0 \times 10^{-2}\,\text{m}}\right) = 416.5\,\text{N} \approx \boxed{4.2 \times 10^{2}\,\text{N}}$$

$$\sum F_y = F_{\text{Right}} - F_{\text{Left}} - mg \quad \rightarrow$$

$$F_{\text{Left}} = F_{\text{Right}} - mg = 416.5\,\text{N} - \left(5.0\,\text{kg}\right)\left(9.80\,\text{m/s}^2\right) = \boxed{3.7 \times 10^{2}\,\text{N}}$$

(*c*) The torque exerted by the support about the left end of the rod is

$$\tau = F_{\text{Right}}\left(2.0 \times 10^{-2}\,\text{m}\right) = \left(416.5\,\text{N}\right)\left(2.0 \times 10^{-2}\,\text{m}\right) = \boxed{8.3\,\text{m}\cdot\text{N}}$$

62. Assume that the building has just begun to tip, so that it is
essentially vertical, but that all of the force on the building due to
contact with the Earth is at the lower left corner, as shown in the
figure. Take torques about that corner, with counterclockwise
torques as positive.

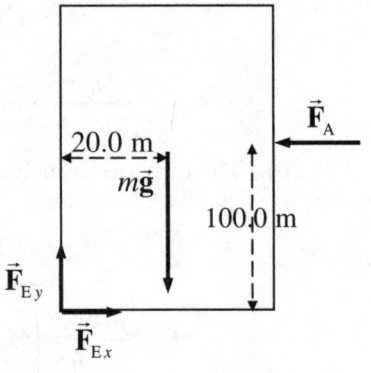

$$\sum \tau = F_A\left(100.0\,\text{m}\right) - mg\left(20.0\,\text{m}\right)$$

$$= \left(950\,\text{N/m}^2\right)\left(200.0\,\text{m}\right)\left(70.0\,\text{m}\right)\left(100.0\,\text{m}\right)$$

$$-\left(1.8 \times 10^{7}\,\text{kg}\right)\left(9.80\,\text{m/s}^2\right)\left(20.0\,\text{m}\right)$$

$$= -2.2 \times 10^{9}\,\text{m}\cdot\text{N}$$

Since this is a negative torque, the building will tend to rotate clockwise, which means it will rotate
back down to the ground. Thus $\boxed{\text{the building will not topple}}$.

63. The truck will not tip as long as a vertical line down from the CG is between
the wheels. When that vertical line is at the wheel, it is in unstable
equilibrium and will tip if the road is inclined any more. See the diagram for
the truck at the tipping angle, showing the truck's weight vector.

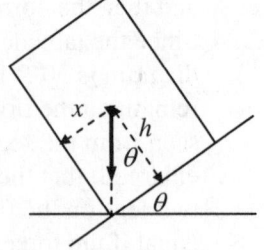

$$\tan \theta = \frac{x}{h} \quad \rightarrow \quad \theta = \tan^{-1}\frac{x}{h} = \tan^{-1}\frac{1.2\,\text{m}}{2.2\,\text{m}} = \boxed{29^\circ}$$

64. Draw a force diagram for the cable that is supporting the right-hand section. The forces will be the
tension at the left end, $\vec{\mathbf{F}}_{T2}$, the tension at the right end, $\vec{\mathbf{F}}_{T1}$, and the weight of the section, $m\vec{\mathbf{g}}$. The
weight acts at the midpoint of the horizontal span of the cable. The system is in equilibrium. Write
Newton's 2nd law in both the *x* and *y* directions to find the tensions.

$$\sum F_x = F_{T1} \cos 19° - F_{T2} \sin 60° = 0 \quad \rightarrow$$

$$F_{T2} = F_{T1} \frac{\cos 19°}{\sin 60°}$$

$$\sum F_y = F_{T2} \cos 60° - F_{T1} \sin 19° - mg = 0 \quad \rightarrow$$

$$F_{T1} = \frac{F_{T2} \cos 60° - mg}{\sin 19°} = \frac{F_{T1} \dfrac{\cos 19°}{\sin 60°} \cos 60° - mg}{\sin 19°} \quad \rightarrow$$

$$F_{T1} = mg \frac{\sin 60°}{\left(\cos 19° \cos 60° - \sin 19° \sin 60° \right)} = 4.539 \, mg \approx \boxed{4.5 \, mg}$$

$$F_{T2} = F_{T1} \frac{\cos 19°}{\sin 60°} = 4.539 \frac{\cos 19°}{\sin 60°} mg = 4.956 \, mg \approx \boxed{5.0 \, mg}$$

To find the height of the tower, take torques about the point where the roadway meets the ground, at the right side of the roadway. Note that then $\vec{F}_{T1}$ will exert no torque. Take counterclockwise torques as positive. For purposes of calculating the torque due to $\vec{F}_{T2}$, split it into x and y components.

$$\sum \tau = mg \left(\tfrac{1}{2} d_1 \right) + F_{T2x} h - F_{T2y} d_1 = 0 \quad \rightarrow$$

$$h = \frac{\left(F_{T2y} - \tfrac{1}{2} mg \right)}{F_{T2x}} d_1 = \frac{\left(F_{T2} \cos 60° - \tfrac{1}{2} mg \right)}{F_{T2} \sin 60°} d_1 = \frac{\left(4.956 \, mg \cos 60° - 0.50 \, mg \right)}{4.956 \, mg \sin 60°} (343 \text{ m})$$

$$= \boxed{158 \text{ m}}$$

65. The radius of the wire can be determined from the relationship between stress and strain, expressed by equation (9-5).

$$\frac{F}{A} = E \frac{\Delta L}{L_0} \quad \rightarrow \quad A = \frac{FL_0}{E \Delta L} = \pi r^2 \quad \rightarrow \quad r = \sqrt{\frac{1}{\pi} \frac{F}{E} \frac{L_0}{\Delta L}}$$

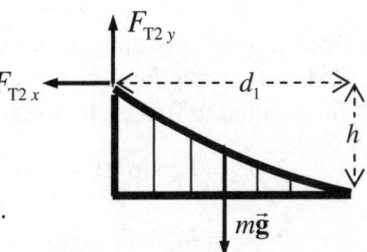

Use the free-body diagram for the point of connection of the mass to the wire to determine the tension force in the wire.

$$\sum F_y = 2 F_T \sin \theta - mg = 0 \quad \rightarrow \quad F_T = \frac{mg}{2 \sin \theta} = \frac{(25 \text{ kg})(9.8 \text{ m/s}^2)}{2 \sin 12°} = 589.2 \text{ N}$$

The fractional change in the length of the wire can be found from the geometry of the problem.

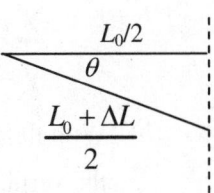

$$\cos \theta = \frac{L_0/2}{\dfrac{L_0 + \Delta L}{2}} \quad \rightarrow \quad \frac{\Delta L}{L_0} = \frac{1}{\cos \theta} - 1 = \frac{1}{\cos 12°} - 1 = 2.234 \times 10^{-2}$$

Thus the radius is

$$r = \sqrt{\frac{1}{\pi} \frac{F_T}{E} \frac{L_0}{\Delta L}} = \sqrt{\frac{1}{\pi} \frac{589.2 \text{ N}}{70 \times 10^9 \text{ N/m}^2} \left(2.234 \times 10^{-2} \right)} = \boxed{7.7 \times 10^{-6} \text{ m}}$$

66. The airplane is in equilibrium, and so the net force in each direction and the net torque are all equal to zero. First write Newton's 2nd law for both the horizontal and vertical directions, to find the values of the forces.

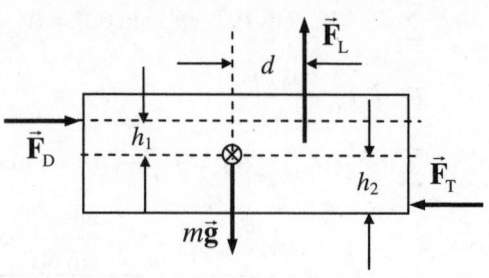

$$\sum F_x = F_D - F_T = 0 \quad \rightarrow \quad F_D = F_T = \boxed{5.0 \times 10^5 \, \text{N}}$$

$$\sum F_y = F_L - mg = 0$$

$$F_L = mg = (6.7 \times 10^4 \, \text{kg})(9.8 \, \text{m/s}^2) = \boxed{6.6 \times 10^5 \, \text{N}}$$

Calculate the torques about the CM, calling counterclockwise torques positive.

$$\sum \tau = F_L d - F_D h_1 - F_T h_2 = 0$$

$$h_1 = \frac{F_L d - F_T h_2}{F_D} = \frac{(6.6 \times 10^5 \, \text{N})(3.2 \, \text{m}) - (5.0 \times 10^5 \, \text{N})(1.6 \, \text{m})}{(5.0 \times 10^5 \, \text{N})} = \boxed{2.6 \, \text{m}}$$

67. Draw a free-body diagram for half of the cable. Write Newton's 2nd law for both the vertical and horizontal directions, with the net force equal to 0 in each direction.

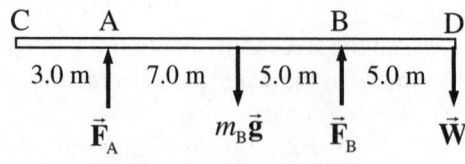

$$\sum F_y = F_{T1} \sin 60° - \tfrac{1}{2} mg = 0 \quad \rightarrow \quad F_{T1} = \tfrac{1}{2} \frac{mg}{\sin 60°} = 0.58 mg$$

$$\sum F_x = F_{T2} - F_{T1} \cos 60° = 0 \quad \rightarrow \quad F_{T2} = 0.58 mg (\cos 60°) = 0.29 mg$$

So the results are:

(a) $F_{T2} = \boxed{0.29 mg}$

(b) $F_{T1} = \boxed{0.58 mg}$

(c) The direction of the tension force is tangent to the cable at all points on the cable. Thus the direction of the tension force is $\boxed{\text{horizontal at the lowest point}}$, and is

$\boxed{60° \text{ above the horizontal at the attachment point}}$.

68. (a) For the extreme case of the beam being ready to tip, there would be no normal force at point A from the support. Use the free-body diagram to write the equation of rotational equilibrium under that condition to find the weight of the person, with $F_A = 0$. Take torques about the location of support

B, and call counterclockwise torques positive. $\vec{\mathbf{W}}$ is the weight of the person.

$$\sum \tau = m_B g (5.0 \, \text{m}) - W (5.0 \, \text{m}) = 0 \quad \rightarrow$$

$$W = m_B g = \boxed{550 \, \text{N}}$$

(b) With the person standing at point D, we have already assumed that $\boxed{F_A = 0}$. The net force in the vertical direction must also be zero.

$$\sum F_y = F_A + F_B - m_B g - W = 0 \quad \rightarrow \quad F_B = m_B g + W = 550 \, \text{N} + 550 \, \text{N} = \boxed{1100 \, \text{N}}$$

(c) Now the person moves to a different spot, so the free-body diagram changes as shown. Again use the net torque about support B and then use the net vertical force.

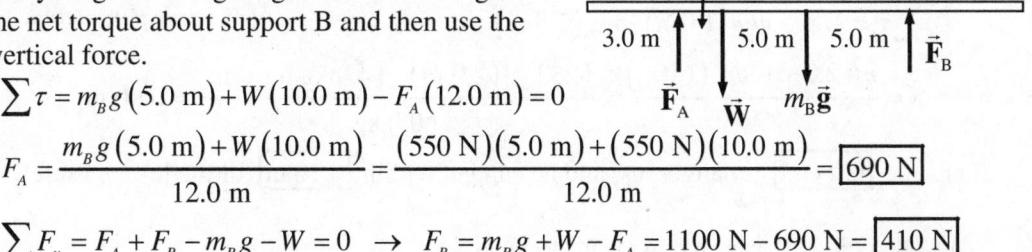

$$\sum \tau = m_B g\left(5.0\ \text{m}\right) - W\left(2.0\ \text{m}\right) - F_A\left(12.0\ \text{m}\right) = 0$$

$$F_A = \frac{m_B g\left(5.0\ \text{m}\right) - W\left(2.0\ \text{m}\right)}{12.0\ \text{m}} = \frac{\left(550\ \text{N}\right)\left(3.0\ \text{m}\right)}{12.0\ \text{m}}$$

$$= \boxed{140\ \text{N}}$$

$$\sum F_y = F_A + F_B - m_B g - W = 0 \ \rightarrow \ F_B = m_B g + W - F_A = 1100\ \text{N} - 140\ \text{N} = \boxed{960\ \text{N}}$$

(d) Again the person moves to a different spot, so the free-body diagram changes again as shown. Again use the net torque about support B and then use the net vertical force.

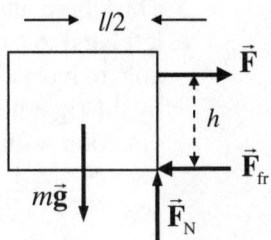

$$\sum \tau = m_B g\left(5.0\ \text{m}\right) + W\left(10.0\ \text{m}\right) - F_A\left(12.0\ \text{m}\right) = 0$$

$$F_A = \frac{m_B g\left(5.0\ \text{m}\right) + W\left(10.0\ \text{m}\right)}{12.0\ \text{m}} = \frac{\left(550\ \text{N}\right)\left(5.0\ \text{m}\right) + \left(550\ \text{N}\right)\left(10.0\ \text{m}\right)}{12.0\ \text{m}} = \boxed{690\ \text{N}}$$

$$\sum F_y = F_A + F_B - m_B g - W = 0 \ \rightarrow \ F_B = m_B g + W - F_A = 1100\ \text{N} - 690\ \text{N} = \boxed{410\ \text{N}}$$

69. If the block is on the verge of tipping, the normal force will be acting at the lower right corner of the block, as shown in the free-body diagram. The block will begin to rotate when the torque caused by the pulling force is larger than the torque caused by gravity. For the block to be able to slide, the pulling force must be as large as the maximum static frictional force. Write the equations of equilibrium for forces in the x and y directions and for torque with the conditions as stated above.

$$\sum F_y = F_N - mg = 0 \ \rightarrow \ F_N = mg$$

$$\sum F_x = F - F_{fr} = 0 \ \rightarrow \ F = F_{fr} = \mu_s F_N = \mu_s mg$$

$$\sum \tau = mg \frac{l}{2} - Fh = 0 \ \rightarrow \ \frac{mgl}{2} = Fh = \mu_s mgh$$

Solve for the coefficient of friction in this limiting case, to find $\mu_s = \dfrac{l}{2h}$.

(a) If $\boxed{\mu_s < l/2h}$, then sliding will happen before tipping.

(b) If $\boxed{\mu_s > l/2h}$, then tipping will happen before sliding.

70. The limiting condition for the safety of the painter is the tension in the ropes. The ropes can only exert an upward tension on the scaffold. The tension will be least in the rope that is farther from the painter. The mass of the pail is m_p, the mass of the scaffold is m, and the mass of the painter is M.

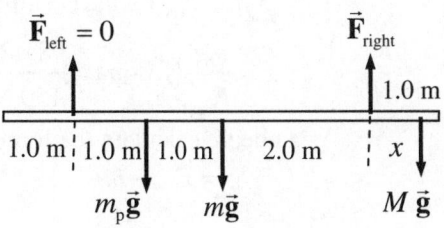

Find the distance to the right that the painter can walk before the tension in the left rope becomes zero. Take torques about the point where the right-side tension is attached to the scaffold, so that its value need not be known. Take counterclockwise torques as positive.

$$\sum \tau = mg\left(2.0\,\text{m}\right) + m_p g\left(3.0\,\text{m}\right) - Mgx = 0 \quad \rightarrow$$

$$x = \frac{m\left(2.0\,\text{m}\right) + m_p\left(3.0\,\text{m}\right)}{M} = \frac{\left(25\,\text{kg}\right)\left(2.0\,\text{m}\right) + \left(4.0\,\text{kg}\right)\left(3.0\,\text{m}\right)}{60.0\,\text{kg}} = 1.03\,\text{m}$$

Since the maximum value for x is 1.0 m, the painter can walk to the right edge of the scaffold safely.

Now find the distance to the left that the painter can walk before the tension in the right rope becomes zero. Take torques about the point where the left-side tension is attached to the scaffold, so that its value need not be known. Take counterclockwise torques as positive.

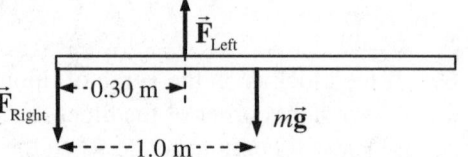

$$\sum \tau = Mgx - m_p g\left(1.0\,\text{m}\right) - mg\left(2.0\,\text{m}\right) = 0 \quad \rightarrow$$

$$x = \frac{m\left(2.0\,\text{m}\right) + m_p\left(1.0\,\text{m}\right)}{M} = \frac{\left(25\,\text{kg}\right)\left(2.0\,\text{m}\right) + \left(4.0\,\text{kg}\right)\left(1.0\,\text{m}\right)}{60.0\,\text{kg}} = 0.90\,\text{m}$$

Thus the $\boxed{\text{left end}}$ is dangerous, and he can get within $\boxed{0.10\,\text{m}}$ of the left end safely.

71. (*a*) The pole will exert a downward force and a clockwise torque about the woman's right hand. Thus there must be an upward force exerted by the left hand to cause a counterclockwise torque for the pole to have a net torque of zero. The force exerted by the right hand is then of such a magnitude and direction for the net vertical force on the pole to be zero.

$$\sum \tau = F_{\text{Left}}\left(0.30\,\text{m}\right) - mg\left(1.0\,\text{m}\right) = 0 \quad \rightarrow$$

$$F_{\text{Left}} = mg\left(\frac{1.0\,\text{m}}{0.30\,\text{m}}\right) = \frac{\left(10.0\,\text{kg}\right)\left(9.80\,\text{m/s}^2\right)}{0.30} = 326.7\,\text{N} \approx \boxed{3.3 \times 10^2\,\text{N, upward}}$$

$$\sum F_y = F_{\text{Left}} - F_{\text{Right}} - mg = 0 \quad \rightarrow$$

$$F_{\text{Right}} = F_{\text{Left}} - mg = 326.7\,\text{N} - \left(10.0\,\text{kg}\right)\left(9.80\,\text{m/s}^2\right) = 228.7\,\text{N} \approx \boxed{2.3 \times 10^2\,\text{N, downward}}$$

(*b*) We see that the force due to the left hand is larger than the force due to the right hand, since both the right hand and gravity are downward. Set the left hand force equal to 150 N and calculate the location of the left hand, by setting the net torque equal to zero.

$$\sum \tau = F_{\text{Left}}x - mg\left(1.0\,\text{m}\right) = 0 \quad \rightarrow$$

$$x = \frac{mg}{F_{\text{Left}}}\left(1.0\,\text{m}\right) = \frac{98.0\,\text{N}}{150\,\text{N}}\left(1.0\,\text{m}\right) = \boxed{0.65\,\text{m}}$$

As a check, calculate the force due to the right hand.

$$F_{\text{Right}} = F_{\text{Left}} - mg = 150\,\text{N} - 98.0\,\text{N} = 52\,\text{N} \quad \text{OK}$$

(c)   Follow the same procedure, setting the left hand force equal to 85 N.

$$\sum \tau = F_{Left}x - mg(1.0\ m) = 0 \quad \rightarrow \quad x = \frac{mg}{F_{Left}}(1.0\ m) = \frac{98.0\ N}{85\ N}(1.0\ m) = 1.153\ m \approx \boxed{1.2\ m}$$

$$F_{Right} = F_{Left} - mg = 85\ N - 98.0\ N = -13\ N \quad OK$$

Note that now the force due to the right hand must be pulling upwards.

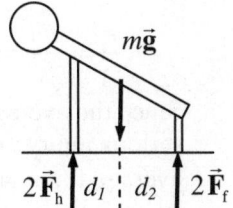

72. The man is in equilibrium, so the net force and the net torque on him must be zero. We represent the force on the hands as twice the force on one hand, and the force on the feet as twice the force on one foot. Take torques about the point where his hands touch the ground, with counterclockwise as positive.

$$\sum \tau = 2F_f(d_1 + d_2) - mgd_1 = 0$$

$$F_f = \frac{mgd_1}{2(d_1 + d_2)} = \frac{(75\ kg)(9.8\ m/s^2)(0.40\ m)}{2(1.35\ m)} = 109\ N \approx \boxed{1.1 \times 10^2\ N}$$

$$\sum F_y = 2F_h + 2F_f - mg = 0$$

$$F_h = \tfrac{1}{2}mg - F_f = \tfrac{1}{2}(75\ kg)(9.8\ m/s^2) - 109\ N = 259\ N \approx \boxed{2.6 \times 10^2\ N}$$

73. The force on the sphere from each plane will be normal to the sphere, and so perpendicular to the plane at the point of contact. Use Newton's 2nd law in both the horizontal and vertical directions to determine the magnitudes of the forces.

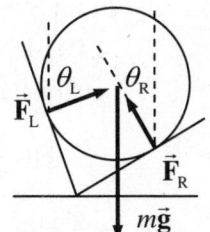

$$\sum F_x = F_L \sin\theta_L - F_R \sin\theta_R = 0 \quad \rightarrow \quad F_R = F_L \frac{\sin\theta_L}{\sin\theta_R} = F_L \frac{\sin 70°}{\sin 30°}$$

$$\sum F_y = F_L \cos\theta_L + F_R \cos\theta_R - mg = 0 \quad \rightarrow \quad F_L\left(\cos 70° + \frac{\sin 70°}{\sin 30°}\cos 30°\right) = mg$$

$$F_L = \frac{mg}{\left(\cos 70° - \dfrac{\sin 70°}{\sin 30°}\cos 30°\right)} = \frac{(20\ kg)(9.80\ m/s^2)}{\left(\cos 70° - \dfrac{\sin 70°}{\sin 30°}\cos 30°\right)} = 99.51\ N \approx \boxed{1.0 \times 10^2\ N}$$

$$F_R = F_L \frac{\sin 70°}{\sin 30°} = (99.51\ N)\frac{\sin 70°}{\sin 30°} = 187.0\ N \approx \boxed{1.9 \times 10^2\ N}$$

74. To find the normal force exerted on the road by the trailer tires, take the torques about point B, with counterclockwise torques as positive.

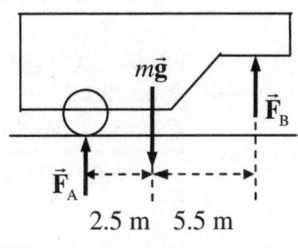

$$\sum \tau = mg(5.5\ m) - F_A(8.0\ m) = 0 \quad \rightarrow$$

$$F_A = mg\left(\frac{5.5\ m}{8.0\ m}\right) = (2200\ kg)(9.80\ m/s^2)\left(\frac{5.5\ m}{8.0\ m}\right) = 14,823\ N$$

$$\approx \boxed{1.5 \times 10^4\ N}$$

The net force in the vertical direction must be zero.

$$\sum F_y = F_B + F_A - mg = 0 \quad \rightarrow \quad F_B = mg - F_A = (2200\ kg)(9.80\ m/s^2) - 14,823\ N = \boxed{6.7 \times 10^3\ N}$$

75. Assume a constant acceleration as the person is brought to rest, with up as the positive direction. Use Eq. 2-11c to find the acceleration. From the acceleration, find the average force of the snow on the person, and compare the force per area to the strength of body tissue.

$$v^2 = v_0^2 - 2a(x - x_0) \quad \rightarrow \quad a = \frac{v^2 - v_0^2}{2(x - x_0)} = \frac{0 - (60\,\text{m/s})^2}{2(-1.0\,\text{m})} = 1800\,\text{m/s}^2$$

$$\frac{F}{A} = \frac{ma}{A} = \frac{(75\,\text{kg})(1800\,\text{m/s}^2)}{0.30\,\text{m}^2} = 4.5 \times 10^5 \,\text{N/m}^2 < \text{Tissue strength} = 5 \times 10^5 \,\text{N/m}^2$$

Since the average force on the person is less than the strength of body tissue, the person may escape serious injury. Certain parts of the body, such as the legs if landing feet first, may get more than the average force, though, and so still sustain injury.

76. The mass can be calculated from the equation for the relationship between stress and strain. The force causing the strain is the weight of the mass suspended from the wire.

$$\frac{\Delta L}{L_0} = \frac{1}{E}\frac{F}{A} = \frac{mg}{EA} \quad \rightarrow \quad m = \frac{EA}{g}\frac{\Delta L}{L_0} = (200 \times 10^9 \,\text{N/m}^2)\frac{\pi(1.0 \times 10^{-3}\,\text{m})^2}{(9.80\,\text{m/s}^2)}\frac{0.030}{100} = \boxed{19\,\text{kg}}$$

77. (a) From Example 7-6, the total force of the ground on one leg for a "stiff-legged landing" is $2.1 \times 10^5 \,\text{N}/2 = 1.05 \times 10^5 \,\text{N}$. The stress in the tibia bone is the force divided by the cross-sectional area of the bone.

$$\text{Stress} = \frac{F}{A} = \frac{1.05 \times 10^5 \,\text{N}}{3.0 \times 10^{-4} \,\text{m}^2} = \boxed{3.5 \times 10^8 \,\text{N/m}^2}$$

(b) Since the stress from above is greater than the compressive strength of bone $(1.7 \times 10^8 \,\text{N/m}^2)$, the $\boxed{\text{bone will break}}$.

(c) From Example 7-6, the total force of the ground on one leg for a "bent-legged landing" is $4.9 \times 10^3 \,\text{N}/2 = 2.45 \times 10^3 \,\text{N}$. The stress in the tibia bone is the force divided by the cross-sectional area of the bone.

$$\text{Stress} = \frac{F}{A} = \frac{2.45 \times 10^3 \,\text{N}}{3.0 \times 10^{-4} \,\text{m}^2} = \boxed{8.2 \times 10^6 \,\text{N/m}^2}$$

Since the stress from above is less than the compressive strength of bone $(1.7 \times 10^8 \,\text{N/m}^2)$, the $\boxed{\text{bone will not break}}$.

78. The number of supports can be found from the compressive strength of the wood. Since the wood will be oriented longitudinally, the stress will be parallel to the grain.

$$\frac{\text{Compressive Strength}}{\text{Safety Factor}} = \frac{\text{Load force on supports}}{\text{Area of supports}} = \frac{\text{Weight of roof}}{(\#\,\text{supports})(\text{area per support})}$$

$$(\#\,\text{supports}) = \frac{\text{Weight of roof}}{(\text{area per support})}\frac{\text{Safety Factor}}{\text{Compressive Strength}}$$

$$= \frac{(1.26 \times 10^4 \,\text{kg})(9.80\,\text{m/s}^2)}{(0.040\,\text{m})(0.090\,\text{m})}\frac{12}{(35 \times 10^6 \,\text{N/m}^2)} = 12 \,\text{supports}$$

Since there are to be 12 supports, there will be $\boxed{\text{6 supports on each side}}$. That means there will be 5

gaps on each side between the supports, and so $\text{Spacing} = \dfrac{10.0\,\text{m}}{5\,\text{gaps}} = \boxed{2.0\,\text{m/gap}}$.

79. The tension in the string when it breaks is found from the ultimate strength of nylon under tension, from Table 9-2.

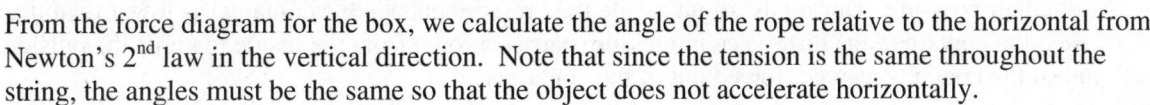

$\dfrac{F_T}{A} = \text{Tensile Strength} \ \rightarrow$

$F_T = A\left(\text{Tensile Strength}\right)$

$\qquad = \pi\left(5.00\times10^{-4}\,\text{m}\right)^2\left(500\times10^6\,\text{N/m}^2\right) = 392.7\,\text{N}$

From the force diagram for the box, we calculate the angle of the rope relative to the horizontal from Newton's 2ⁿᵈ law in the vertical direction. Note that since the tension is the same throughout the string, the angles must be the same so that the object does not accelerate horizontally.

$\sum F_y = 2F_T\sin\theta - mg = 0 \ \rightarrow$

$\theta = \sin^{-1}\dfrac{mg}{2F_T} = \sin^{-1}\dfrac{\left(25\,\text{kg}\right)\left(9.80\,\text{m/s}^2\right)}{2\left(392.7\,\text{N}\right)} = 18.18°$

To find the height above the ground, consider the second diagram.

$\tan\theta = \dfrac{3.00\,\text{m} - h}{2.00\,\text{m}} \ \rightarrow \ h = 3.00\,\text{m} - 2.00\,\text{m}\left(\tan\theta\right) = 3.00\,\text{m} - 2.00\,\text{m}\left(\tan 18.18°\right) = \boxed{2.34\,\text{m}}$

80. The maximum compressive force in a column will occur at the bottom. The bottom layer supports the entire weight of the column, and so the compressive force on that layer is mg. For the column to be on the verge of buckling, the weight divided by the area of the column will be the compressive strength of the material. The mass of the column is its volume (area x height) times its density.

$\dfrac{mg}{A} = \text{Compressive Strength} = \dfrac{hA\rho g}{A} \ \rightarrow \ h = \dfrac{\text{Compressive Strength}}{\rho g}$

Note that the area of the column cancels out of the expression, and so the height does not depend on the cross-sectional area of the column.

(a) $h_{\text{steel}} = \dfrac{\text{Compressive Strength}}{\rho g} = \dfrac{500\times10^6\,\text{N/m}^2}{\left(7.8\times10^3\,\text{kg/m}^3\right)\left(9.80\,\text{m/s}^2\right)} = \boxed{6.5\times10^3\,\text{m}}$

(b) $h_{\text{granite}} = \dfrac{\text{Compressive Strength}}{\rho g} = \dfrac{170\times10^6\,\text{N/m}^2}{\left(2.7\times10^3\,\text{kg/m}^3\right)\left(9.80\,\text{m/s}^2\right)} = \boxed{6.4\times10^3\,\text{m}}$

CHAPTER 10: Fluids

Answers to Questions

1. Density is the ratio of mass to volume. A high density may mean that lighter molecules are packed more closely together and thus a given amount of mass is occupying a smaller volume, making a higher density. An atom of gold weighs less than an atom of lead, because gold has a lower atomic mass, but the density of gold is higher than that of lead.

2. The air pressure inside the cabin of an airplane is lower than normal sea-level air pressure, evidenced by the sensation in the ears as the plane descends and the cabin reaches normal air pressure. If the container was opened at normal air pressure before the flight, then the pressure inside the container is normal air pressure. During the flight, while the pressure outside the container is lower than that inside the container, the difference in pressure causes a force from the inside towards the outside, and so the contents may get forced out of the container.

3. Let the first container have a mass of water M_1. The force of gravity on the water, acting downward, is thus $M_1 g$. The side walls only exert a force perpendicular to the walls, which is horizontal for the first container. Thus there must also be a net upward force of $F_{up} = M_1 g$ on the water to keep it at rest. This is the normal force from the bottom of the container. This upward force is the pressure at the bottom of the container times the area of the container, and is the same for all three containers. The second container has more water, and so has a larger downward force of gravity on it $(M_2 g > F_{up})$, but the same upward force from the bottom of the container. Thus there must be additional upward force on the water. That upward force comes from the normal force of the slanted sides of the container pushing on the water. That force has an upward component – just enough to add to the normal force and balance the force of gravity. Similarly, the third container has less water, and so has a smaller downward force of gravity $(M_3 g < F_{up})$. With the same upward normal force from the bottom, there must be more downward force on the water for it to be at rest. That downward force comes from the normal force of the slanted sides of the container pushing on the water. That force has a downward component – just enough to add to the gravity force and balance the force. The key to this problem is that the force on a container due to the hydrostatic pressure is always perpendicular to the surface of the water. According to Newton's 3rd law, the container will push back on the water in the exact opposite direction, also perpendicular to the surface of the container.

4. The sharp end of the pin (with a smaller area) will pierce the skin when pushed with a certain minimum force, while the same force applied in pushing the blunt end of the pen (with a larger area) into the skin does not pierce the skin. Thus it is pressure (force per unit area) that determines whether or not the skin is pierced.

5. The boiling water makes a relatively large quantity of steam inside the can. The gas inside the can (including the steam) will be at atmospheric pressure, but will be much warmer than the surroundings. When the gas in the sealed can cools, the steam condenses and the pressure drops greatly. This lowering of pressure on the inside means that the outside air pressure is higher than the pressure in the can, and thus the outside air pressure crushes the can.

From a microscopic viewpoint, the water molecules are moving very fast when boiled to a vapor. Many of the water molecules escape the can, but the remaining ones can hold the can in its original shape because their high speeds mean they hit the walls with a large force and balance the force caused by the outside air pressure. After the lid is put on and the can is cooled, the water vapor molecules slow down (some will condense), and no gas can enter from outside the can. The slow molecules are not moving as fast and so put less force on the inside walls. The greater force from the outside air pressure then crushes the can.

6. The blood pressure exerted by the heart is to be measured. If the blood pressure is measured at a location h lower than the heart, the blood pressure will be higher than the pressure at the heart, due to the effects of gravity, by an amount $\rho g h$. Likewise, if the blood pressure is measured at a location h higher than the heart, the blood pressure will be lower than the pressure at the heart, again due to the effects of gravity, by an amount $\rho g h$.

7. Since the ice floats, the density of ice must be less than that of the water. The mass of the ice displaces a water volume equal to its weight, whether it is solid or liquid. Thus as the ice melts, the level in the glass stays the same. The ice displaces its melted volume.

8. The density of ice is greater than that of alcohol, so the ice cube will not float in a glass of alcohol. The ice cube will sink in the alcohol.

9. Both products have gas dissolved in them (the carbonation process), making their density lower than that of water. The Coke has a significant amount of sugar dissolved in it, increasing its density and making it greater than that of water. The Diet Coke does not have the dissolved sugar, and so its density remains less than that of water . Thus the Coke sinks, and the Diet Coke floats.

10. Iron ships are not solid iron. If they were, then they would sink. But the ships have quite a bit of open space in their volume (the volume between the deck and the hull, for instance), making their overall density less than that of water. The total mass of iron divided by the total volume of the boat is less than the density of water, and so the boat floats.

11. Refer to the diagram in the textbook. The pressure at the surface of both containers of liquid is atmospheric pressure. The pressure in each tube would thus be atmospheric pressure at the level of the surface of the liquid in each container. The pressure in each tube will decrease with height by an amount $\rho g h$. Since the portion of the tube going into the lower container is longer than the portion of the tube going into the higher container, the pressure at the highest point on the right side is lower than the pressure at the highest point on the left side. This pressure difference causes liquid to flow from the left side of the tube to the right side of the tube. And as noted in the question, the tube must be filled with liquid before this argument can be made.

12. Since sand is denser than water, adding a given volume of sand (equal to the area of the barge times the depth of added sand) to the barge will require that an even greater volume of water be displaced to support the added weight. Thus the extra height of the barge caused by adding the sand will be more than compensated for by the extra depth to which the barge has to be submerged in order to float. Removing sand would have the opposite effect – the barge would get higher.

13. If you assume that the air is incompressible, then the answer is yes. The full balloon will have more weight (more downward force), due to the mass of the air in the balloon. The full balloon will also have an upward buoyant force on it, equal to the weight of the air displaced by the balloon. Since the balloon is both containing air and floating in air, the weight of the air inside the balloon is the same magnitude as the buoyant force. Thus the empty balloon will have the same apparent weight as the filled balloon.

    However, the air inside the balloon is compressed slightly compared to the outside air, and so has a higher density. This higher density means that the weight of the air inside the balloon is higher than the weight of the air it displaces, and so the filled balloon has a higher apparent weight than the empty balloon.

14. As the balloon rises, the air pressure outside the balloon will decrease and be lower than the pressure inside the balloon. The excess inside air pressure will cause the balloon to expand, lowering the pressure inside but stretching the balloon in the process. If, at launch, the material of the balloon were already stretched to the limit, the expansion of the balloon due to the decreasing outside air pressure would cause the balloon to burst. Thus the balloon is only filled to a fraction of the maximum volume.

15. (a) The boat displaces enough water to equal the weight of the boat. If the boat is removed from the water, the water will no longer be displaced and thus the water level will lower.
    (b) While the anchor is in the boat, the water displaced has a weight equal to that of the boat and the anchor together. If the anchor is placed on the shore, then less water will need to be displaced, and the water level will lower.
    (c) While the anchor is in the boat, the water displaced has a weight equal to that of the boat and the anchor together. If the anchor is dropped into the pool, the water displaced is equal to the weight of the boat (which will float) and the weight of a volume of water equal to the volume of the anchor (which will sink). Since the anchor is more dense than the water, it takes more water displacement to hold up the anchor (while in the boat) than is displaced when the anchor is in the water. Thus the water level will lower when the anchor is thrown overboard.

16. Salt water has a higher density than fresh water. Thus you have to displace less salt water to equal your weight than you do in fresh water. You then float "higher" in the salt water.

17. The papers will move toward each other. Bernoulli's principle says that as the speed of the gas flow increases, the pressure decreases (when there is no appreciable change in height). So as the air passes between the papers, the air pressure between the papers is lowered. The air pressure on the outside of the papers is then greater than that between the papers, and so the papers are pushed together.

18. As the car drives through the air, the air inside the car is stationary with respect to the top, but the outside air is moving with respect to the top. There is no appreciable change in height between the two sides of the canvas top. By Bernoulli's principle, the outside air pressure near the canvas top will be less than the inside air pressure. That difference in pressure results in a force that makes the top bulge outward.

19. The roofs are actually pushed off from the inside. By Bernoulli's principle, the fast moving winds of the tornado or hurricane cause the air pressure above the roof to be quite low, but the pressure inside the house is still near normal levels. There is no appreciable change in height between the two sides of the roof. This pressure difference, combined with the large surface area of the roof, gives a very large force which can push the roof off the house. That is why it is advised to open some windows if

a tornado is imminent, so that the pressure inside the house can somewhat equalize with the outside pressure.

20. It is possible. Due to viscosity, some of the air near the train will be pulled along at a speed approximately that of the train. By Bernoulli's principle, that air will be at a lower pressure than air further away from the train. That difference in pressure results in a force towards the train, which could push a lightweight child towards the train.

21. Water will not flow from the holes when the cup and water are in free fall. The acceleration due to gravity is the same for all falling objects (ignoring friction), and so the cup and water would fall together. For the water to flow out of the holes while falling would mean that the water would have an acceleration larger than the acceleration due to gravity. Another way to consider the situation is that there will no longer be a pressure difference between the top and bottom of the cup of water, since the lower water molecules don't need to hold up the upper water molecules.

22. The lift generated by a wind depends on the speed of the air relative to the wing. For example, a model in a wind tunnel will have lift even though the model isn't moving relative to the ground. By taking off into the wind, the speed of the air relative to the wing is the sum of the plane's speed and the wind speed. This allows the plane to take off at a lower ground speed, requiring a shorter runway.

23. As the stream of water falls, its vertical speed is faster away from the faucet than close to it, due to the acceleration caused by gravity. Since the water is essentially incompressible, Eq. 10-4b applies, which says that a faster flow has a smaller cross-sectional area. Thus the faster moving water has a narrower stream.

24. When the two ships are moving parallel to each other, water between them starts to move with them due to viscosity. There will be more water moving along with the ships in between them then on their outside sides. According to Bernoulli's principle, this moving water is at a lower pressure than stationary water, further away from the ship. Each ship will thus experience a net force towards the other ship and be drawn in towards the other ship. Thus they risk colliding.

Solutions to Problems

1. The mass is found from the density of granite and the volume of granite.
    $$m = \rho V = \left(2.7 \times 10^3 \text{ kg/m}^3\right)\left(10^8 \text{ m}^3\right) = 2.7 \times 10^{11} \text{ kg} \approx \boxed{3 \times 10^{11} \text{ kg}}$$

2. The mass is found from the density of air and the volume of air.
    $$m = \rho V = \left(1.29 \text{ kg/m}^3\right)\left(4.8 \text{ m}\right)\left(3.8 \text{ m}\right)\left(2.8 \text{ m}\right) = \boxed{66 \text{ kg}}$$

3. The mass is found from the density of gold and the volume of gold.
    $$m = \rho V = \left(19.3 \times 10^3 \text{ kg/m}^3\right)\left(0.60 \text{ m}\right)\left(0.28 \text{ m}\right)\left(0.18 \text{ m}\right) = \boxed{5.8 \times 10^2 \text{ kg}} \quad (\sim 1300 \text{ lb})$$

4. Assume that your density is that of water, and that your mass is 75 kg.
    $$V = \frac{m}{\rho} = \frac{75 \text{ kg}}{1.00 \times 10^3 \text{ kg/m}^3} = \boxed{7.5 \times 10^{-2} \text{ m}^3} = 75 \text{ L}$$

5. To find the specific gravity of the fluid, take the ratio of the density of the fluid to that of water, noting that the same volume is used for both liquids.

$$SJ_{fluid} = \frac{\rho_{fluid}}{\rho_{water}} = \frac{(m/V)_{fluid}}{(m/V)_{water}} = \frac{m_{fluid}}{m_{water}} = \frac{88.78 \text{ g} - 35.00 \text{ g}}{98.44 \text{ g} - 35.00 \text{ g}} = \boxed{0.8477}$$

6. The specific gravity of the mixture is the ratio of the density of the mixture to that of water. To find the density of the mixture, the mass of antifreeze and the mass of water must be known.

$$m_{antifreeze} = \rho_{antifreeze} V_{antifreeze} = SG_{antifreeze} \rho_{water} V_{antifreeze} \qquad m_{water} = \rho_{water} V_{water}$$

$$SG_{mixture} = \frac{\rho_{mixture}}{\rho_{water}} = \frac{m_{mixture}/V_{mixture}}{\rho_{water}} = \frac{m_{antifreeze} + m_{water}}{\rho_{water} V_{mixture}} = \frac{SG_{antifreeze} \rho_{water} V_{antifreeze} + \rho_{water} V_{water}}{\rho_{water} V_{mixture}}$$

$$= \frac{SG_{antifreeze} V_{antifreeze} + V_{water}}{V_{mixture}} = \frac{(0.80)(5.0 \text{ L}) + 4.0 \text{ L}}{9.0 \text{ L}} = \boxed{0.89}$$

7. (a) The pressure exerted on the floor by the chair leg is caused by the leg pushing down on the floor. That downward push is the reaction to the normal force of the floor on the leg, and the normal forced is equal to the weight of the leg. Thus the pressure is

$$P_{chair} = \frac{W_{leg}}{A} = \frac{\frac{1}{4}(60 \text{ kg})(9.8 \text{ m/s}^2)}{(0.020 \text{ cm}^2)\left(\dfrac{1 \text{ m}}{100 \text{ cm}}\right)^2} = 7.35 \times 10^7 \text{ N/m}^2 \approx \boxed{7 \times 10^7 \text{ N/m}^2}.$$

(b) The pressure exerted by the elephant is

$$P_{elephant} = \frac{W_{elephant}}{A} = \frac{(1500 \text{ kg})(9.8 \text{ m/s}^2)}{(800 \text{ cm}^2)\left(\dfrac{1 \text{ m}}{100 \text{ cm}}\right)^2} = 1.84 \times 10^5 \text{ N/m}^2 \approx \boxed{2 \times 10^5 \text{ N/m}^2}.$$

Note that the chair pressure is larger than the elephant pressure by a factor of about 400.

8. From Equation 10-3b, the pressure difference is

$$\Delta P = \rho g \Delta h = (1.05 \times 10^3 \text{ kg/m}^3)(9.80 \text{ m/s}^2)(1.60 \text{ m}) = 1.646 \times 10^4 \text{ N/m}^2 \left(\frac{1 \text{ mm-Hg}}{133 \text{ N/m}^2}\right)$$

$$= \boxed{124 \text{ mm-Hg}}$$

9. (a) The total force of the atmosphere on the table will be the air pressure times the area of the table.

$$F = PA = (1.013 \times 10^5 \text{ N/m}^2)(1.6 \text{ m})(2.9 \text{ m}) = \boxed{4.7 \times 10^5 \text{ N}}$$

(b) Since the atmospheric pressure is the same on the underside of the table (the height difference is minimal), the upward force of air pressure is the same as the downward force of air on the top of the table, $\boxed{4.7 \times 10^5 \text{ N}}$.

10. The pressure difference on the lungs is the pressure change from the depth of water

$$\Delta P = \rho g \Delta h \quad \rightarrow \quad \Delta h = \frac{\Delta P}{\rho g} = \frac{(85 \text{ mm-Hg})\left(\dfrac{133 \text{ N/m}^2}{1 \text{ mm-Hg}}\right)}{(1.00 \times 10^3 \text{ kg/m}^3)(9.80 \text{ m/s}^2)} = 1.154 \text{ m} \approx \boxed{1.2 \text{ m}}$$

11. The sum of the force exerted by the pressure in each tire is equal to the weight of the car.

$$mg = 4PA \rightarrow m = \frac{4PA}{g} = \frac{4(2.40 \times 10^5 \text{ N/m}^2)(220 \text{ cm}^2)\left(\frac{1 \text{ m}^2}{10^4 \text{ cm}^2}\right)}{(9.80 \text{ m/s}^2)} = \boxed{2.2 \times 10^3 \text{ kg}}$$

12. The force exerted by the gauge pressure will be equal to the weight of the vehicle.

$$mg = PA = P(\pi r^2) \rightarrow$$

$$m = \frac{P \pi r^2}{g} = \frac{\pi(17.0 \text{ atm})\left(\frac{1.013 \times 10^5 \text{ N/m}^2}{1 \text{ atm}}\right)(0.140 \text{ m})^2}{(9.80 \text{ m/s}^2)} = \boxed{1.08 \times 10^4 \text{ kg}}$$

13. The height is found from Eq. 10-3a, using normal atmospheric pressure.

$$P = \rho g h \rightarrow h = \frac{P}{\rho g} = \frac{1.013 \times 10^5 \text{ N/m}^2}{(0.79 \times 10^3 \text{ kg/m}^3)(9.80 \text{ m/s}^2)} = \boxed{13 \text{ m}}$$

14. (a) The absolute pressure is given by Eq. 10-3c, and the total force is the absolute pressure times the area of the bottom of the pool.

$$P = P_0 + \rho g h = 1.013 \times 10^5 \text{ N/m}^2 + (1.00 \times 10^3 \text{ kg/m}^3)(9.80 \text{ m/s}^2)(2.0 \text{ m})$$

$$= \boxed{1.21 \times 10^5 \text{ N/m}^2}$$

$$F = PA = (1.21 \times 10^5 \text{ N/m}^2)(22.0 \text{ m})(8.5 \text{ m}) = \boxed{2.3 \times 10^7 \text{ N}}$$

(b) The pressure against the side of the pool, near the bottom, will be the same as the pressure at the bottom, $P = \boxed{1.21 \times 10^5 \text{ N/m}^2}$

15. If the atmosphere were of uniform density, then the pressure at any height h would be $P = P_0 - \rho g h$. At the top of the uniform atmosphere, the pressure would be 0. Thus solve for the height at which the pressure becomes 0, using a density of half of sea-level atmospheric density.

$$P = P_0 - \rho g h = 0 \rightarrow h = \frac{P_0}{\rho g} = \frac{(1.013 \times 10^5 \text{ N/m}^2)}{\frac{1}{2}(1.29 \text{ kg/m}^3)(9.80 \text{ m/s}^2)} = \boxed{1.60 \times 10^4 \text{ m}}$$

16. The pressure at points a and b are equal since they are the same height in the same fluid. If they were unequal, the fluid would flow. Calculate the pressure at both a and b, starting with atmospheric pressure at the top surface of each liquid, and then equate those pressures.

$$P_a = P_b \rightarrow P_0 + \rho_{oil} g h_{oil} = P_0 + \rho_{water} g h_{water} \rightarrow \rho_{oil} h_{oil} = \rho_{water} h_{water} \rightarrow$$

$$\rho_{oil} = \frac{\rho_{water} h_{water}}{h_{oil}} = \frac{(1.00 \times 10^3 \text{ kg/m}^3)(0.272 \text{ m} - 0.0941 \text{ m})}{(0.272 \text{ m})} = \boxed{6.54 \times 10^2 \text{ kg/m}^3}$$

17. (a) The gauge pressure is given by Eq. 10-3a. The height is the height from the bottom of the hill to the top of the water tank.

$$P_G = \rho g h = (1.00 \times 10^3 \text{ kg/m}^3)(9.80 \text{ m/s}^2)[5.0 \text{ m} + (110 \text{ m}) \sin 58°] = \boxed{9.6 \times 10^5 \text{ N/m}^2}$$

(*b*)   The water would be able to shoot up to the top of the tank (ignoring any friction).

$$h = 5.0 \text{ m} + (110 \text{ m})\sin 58° = \boxed{98 \text{ m}}$$

18.   The minimum gauge pressure would cause the water to come out of the faucet with very little speed. This means the gauge pressure needed must be enough to hold the water at this elevation. Use Eq. 10-3a.

$$P_G = \rho g h = (1.00 \times 10^3 \text{ kg/m}^3)(9.80 \text{ m/s}^2)(38 \text{ m}) = \boxed{3.7 \times 10^5 \text{ N/m}^2}$$

19.   The pressure in the tank is atmospheric pressure plus the pressure difference due to the column of mercury, as given in Eq. 10-3c.

(*a*) $P = P_0 + \rho g h = 1.04 \text{ bar} + \rho_{\text{Hg}} g h$

$$= (1.04 \text{ bar})\left(\frac{1.00 \times 10^5 \text{ N/m}^2}{1 \text{ bar}}\right) + (13.6 \times 10^3 \text{ kg/m}^3)(9.80 \text{ m/s}^2)(0.280 \text{ m}) = \boxed{1.41 \times 10^5 \text{ N/m}^2}$$

(*b*) $P = (1.04 \text{ bar})\left(\dfrac{1.00 \times 10^5 \text{ N/m}^2}{1 \text{ bar}}\right) + (13.6 \times 10^3 \text{ kg/m}^3)(9.80 \text{ m/s}^2)(-0.042 \text{ m}) = \boxed{9.84 \times 10^4 \text{ N/m}^2}$

20.   (*a*)   The mass of water in the tube is the volume of the tube times the density of water.

$$m = \rho V = \rho \pi r^2 h = (1.00 \times 10^3 \text{ kg/m}^3)\pi (0.30 \times 10^{-2} \text{ m})^2 (12 \text{ m}) = 0.3393 \text{ kg} \approx \boxed{0.34 \text{ kg}}$$

(*b*)   The net force exerted on the lid is the gauge pressure of the water times the area of the lid. The gauge pressure is found from Eq. 10-3b.

$$F = P_{\text{gauge}} A = \rho g h \pi R^2 = (1.00 \times 10^3 \text{ kg/m}^3)(9.80 \text{ m/s}^2)(12 \text{ m})\pi (0.21 \text{ m})^2 = \boxed{1.6 \times 10^4 \text{ N}}$$

21.   From section 9-5, the change in volume due to pressure change is $\dfrac{\Delta V}{V_0} = -\dfrac{\Delta P}{B}$, where *B* is the bulk

modulus of the water, given in Table 9-1. The pressure increase with depth for a fluid of constant density is given by $\Delta P = \rho g \Delta h$, where Δh is the depth of descent. If the density change is small, then we can use the initial value of the density to calculate the pressure change, and so $\Delta P \cong \rho_0 g \Delta h$. Finally, consider a constant mass of water. That constant mass will relate the volume and density at the two locations by $M = \rho V = \rho_0 V_0$. Combine these relationships and solve for the density deep in the sea, ρ.

$$\rho V = \rho_0 V_0 \rightarrow$$

$$\rho = \frac{\rho_0 V_0}{V} = \frac{\rho_0 V_0}{V_0 + \Delta V} = \frac{\rho_0 V_0}{V_0 + \left(-V_0 \dfrac{\Delta P}{B}\right)} = \frac{\rho_0}{1 - \dfrac{\rho_0 g h}{B}} = \frac{1025 \text{ kg/m}^3}{1 - \dfrac{(1025 \text{ kg/m}^3)(9.80 \text{ m/s}^2)(6.0 \times 10^3 \text{ m})}{2.0 \times 10^9 \text{ N/m}^2}}$$

$$= 1057 \text{ kg/m}^3 \approx \boxed{1.06 \times 10^3 \text{ kg/m}^3}$$

$$\rho / \rho_0 = \frac{1057}{1025} = 1.03$$

The density at the 6 km depth is about $\boxed{3\% \text{ larger}}$ than the density at the surface.

22. The difference in the actual mass and the apparent mass is the mass of the water displaced by the rock. The mass of the water displaced is the volume of the rock times the density of water, and the volume of the rock is the mass of the rock divided by its density. Combining these relationships yields an expression for the density of the rock.

$$m_{actual} - m_{apparent} = \Delta m = \rho_{water} V_{rock} = \rho_{water} \frac{m_{rock}}{\rho_{rock}} \rightarrow$$

$$\rho_{rock} = \rho_{water} \frac{m_{rock}}{\Delta m} = \left(1.00 \times 10^3 \text{ kg/m}^3\right) \frac{9.28 \text{ kg}}{9.28 \text{ kg} - 6.18 \text{ kg}} = \boxed{2.99 \times 10^3 \text{ kg/m}^3}$$

23. If the aluminum is floating, then the net force on it is zero. The buoyant force on the aluminum must be equal to its weight. The buoyant force is equal to the weight of the mercury displaced by the submerged aluminum.

$$F_{buoyant} = m_{Al} g \rightarrow \rho_{Hg} g V_{submerged} = \rho_{Al} g V_{total} \rightarrow$$

$$\frac{V_{submerged}}{V_{total}} = \frac{\rho_{Al}}{\rho_{Hg}} = \frac{2.70 \times 10^3 \text{ kg/m}^3}{13.6 \times 10^3 \text{ kg/m}^3} = \boxed{0.199} \approx 20\%$$

24. (*a*) When the hull is submerged, both the buoyant force and the tension force act upward on the hull, and so their sum is equal to the weight of the hull. The buoyant force is the weight of the water displaced.

$$T + F_{buoyant} = mg \rightarrow$$

$$T = mg - F_{buoyant} = m_{hull} g - \rho_{water} V_{sub} g = m_{hull} g - \rho_{water} \frac{m_{hull}}{\rho_{hull}} g = m_{hull} g \left(1 - \frac{\rho_{water}}{\rho_{hull}}\right)$$

$$= \left(1.8 \times 10^4 \text{ kg}\right)\left(9.80 \text{ m/s}^2\right)\left(1 - \frac{1.00 \times 10^3 \text{ kg/m}^3}{7.8 \times 10^3 \text{ kg/m}^3}\right) = 1.538 \times 10^5 \text{ N} \approx \boxed{1.5 \times 10^5 \text{ N}}$$

(*b*) When the hull is completely out of the water, the tension in the crane's cable must be equal to the weight of the hull.

$$T = mg = \left(1.8 \times 10^4 \text{ kg}\right)\left(9.80 \text{ m/s}^2\right) = 1.764 \times 10^5 \text{ N} \approx \boxed{1.8 \times 10^5 \text{ N}}$$

25. The buoyant force of the balloon must equal the weight of the balloon plus the weight of the helium in the balloon plus the weight of the load. For calculating the weight of the helium, we assume it is at 0°C and 1 atm pressure. The buoyant force is the weight of the air displaced by the volume of the balloon.

$$F_{buoyant} = \rho_{air} V_{balloon} g = m_{He} g + m_{balloon} g + m_{cargo} g \rightarrow$$

$$m_{cargo} = \rho_{air} V_{balloon} - m_{He} - m_{balloon} = \rho_{air} V_{balloon} - \rho_{He} V_{balloon} - m_{balloon} = \left(\rho_{air} - \rho_{He}\right) V_{balloon} - m_{balloon}$$

$$= \left(1.29 \text{ kg/m}^3 - 0.179 \text{ kg/m}^3\right) \tfrac{4}{3} \pi \left(7.35 \text{ m}\right)^3 - 930 \text{ kg} = \boxed{920 \text{ kg}} = 9.0 \times 10^3 \text{ N}$$

26. The difference in the actual mass and the apparent mass is the mass of the water displaced by the legs. The mass of the water displaced is the volume of the legs times the density of water, and the volume of the legs is the mass of the legs divided by their density. The density of the legs is assumed to be the same as that of water. Combining these relationships yields an expression for the mass of the legs.

$$m_{actual} - m_{apparent} = \Delta m = \rho_{water} V_{legs} = \rho_{water} \frac{m_{legs}}{\rho_{legs}} = 2m_{leg} \rightarrow$$

$$m_{leg} = \frac{\Delta m}{2} = \frac{(78 \text{ kg} - 54 \text{ kg})}{2} = \boxed{12 \text{ kg}}$$

27. The apparent weight is the actual weight minus the buoyant force. The buoyant force is weight of a mass of water occupying the volume of the metal sample.

$$m_{apparent} g = m_{metal} g - F_B = m_{metal} g - V_{metal} \rho_{H_2O} g = m_{metal} g - \frac{m_{metal}}{\rho_{metal}} \rho_{H_2O} g \rightarrow$$

$$m_{apparent} = m_{metal} - \frac{m_{metal}}{\rho_{metal}} \rho_{H_2O} \rightarrow$$

$$\rho_{metal} = \frac{m_{metal}}{(m_{metal} - m_{apparent})} \rho_{H_2O} = \frac{63.5 \text{ g}}{(63.5 \text{ g} - 55.4 \text{ g})} (1000 \text{ kg/m}^3) = 7840 \text{ kg/m}^3$$

Based on the density value, the metal is probably $\boxed{\text{iron or steel}}$.

28. The difference in the actual mass and the apparent mass of the aluminum is the mass of the air displaced by the aluminum. The mass of the air displaced is the volume of the aluminum times the density of air, and the volume of the aluminum is the actual mass of the aluminum divided by the density of aluminum. Combining these relationships yields an expression for the actual mass.

$$m_{actual} - m_{apparent} = \rho_{air} V_{Al} = \rho_{air} \frac{m_{actual}}{\rho_{Al}} \rightarrow$$

$$m_{actual} = \frac{m_{apparent}}{1 - \frac{\rho_{air}}{\rho_{Al}}} = \frac{2.0000 \text{ kg}}{1 - \frac{1.29 \text{ kg/m}^3}{2.70 \times 10^3 \text{ kg/m}^3}} = \boxed{2.0010 \text{ kg}}$$

29. There are three forces on the chamber: the weight of the chamber, the tension in the cable, and the buoyant force. See the free-body diagram.
    (a) The buoyant force is the weight of water displaced by the chamber.

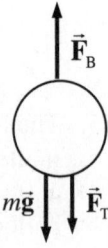

$$F_{buoyant} = \rho_{H_2O} V_{chamber} g = \rho_{H_2O} \tfrac{4}{3} \pi R_{chamber}^3 g$$

$$= (1.025 \times 10^3 \text{ kg/m}^3) \tfrac{4}{3} \pi (2.60 \text{ m})^3 (9.80 \text{ m/s}^2)$$

$$= 7.3953 \times 10^5 \text{ N} \approx \boxed{7.40 \times 10^5 \text{ N}}$$

    (b) To find the tension, use Newton's 2nd law for the stationary chamber.

$$F_{buoyant} = mg + F_T \rightarrow$$

$$F_T = F_{buoyant} - mg = 7.3953 \times 10^5 \text{ N} - (7.44 \times 10^4 \text{ kg})(9.80 \text{ m/s}^2) = \boxed{1.04 \times 10^4 \text{ N}}$$

30. (a) The buoyant force is the weight of the water displaced, using the density of sea water.

$$F_{buoyant} = m_{water \atop displaced} g = \rho_{water} V_{displaced} g$$

$$= (1.025 \times 10^3 \text{ kg/m}^3)(65.0 \text{ L}) \left(\frac{1 \times 10^{-3} \text{ m}^3}{1 \text{ L}} \right) (9.80 \text{ m/s}^2) = \boxed{653 \text{ N}}$$

(*b*)   The weight of the diver is $m_{\text{diver}}\, g = (68.0\ \text{kg})(9.80\ \text{m/s}^2) = 666\ \text{N}$. Since the buoyant

force is not as large as her weight, $\boxed{\text{she will sink}}$, although it will be very gradual since the two forces are almost the same.

31.   (*a*)   The difference in the actual mass and the apparent mass of the aluminum ball is the mass of the liquid displaced by the ball. The mass of the liquid displaced is the volume of the ball times the density of the liquid, and the volume of the ball is the mass of the ball divided by its density. Combining these relationships yields an expression for the density of the liquid.

$$m_{\text{actual}} - m_{\text{apparent}} = \Delta m = \rho_{\text{liquid}} V_{\text{ball}} = \rho_{\text{liquid}} \frac{m_{\text{ball}}}{\rho_{\text{Al}}} \quad \rightarrow$$

$$\rho_{\text{liquid}} = \frac{\Delta m}{m_{\text{ball}}} \rho_{\text{Al}} = \frac{(3.40\ \text{kg} - 2.10\ \text{kg})}{3.40\ \text{kg}}\left(2.70\times10^3\ \text{kg/m}^3\right) = \boxed{1.03\times10^3\ \text{kg/m}^3}$$

(*b*)   Generalizing the relation from above, we have $\boxed{\rho_{\text{liquid}} = \dfrac{m_{\text{object}} - m_{\text{apparent}}}{m_{\text{object}}} \rho_{\text{object}}}$

32.   The difference in the actual mass and the apparent mass is the mass of the alcohol displaced by the wood. The mass of the alcohol displaced is the volume of the wood times the density of the alcohol, the volume of the wood is the mass of the wood divided by the density of the wood, and the density of the alcohol is its specific gravity times the density of water.

$$m_{\text{actual}} - m_{\text{apparent}} = \rho_{\text{alc}} V_{\text{wood}} = \rho_{\text{alc}} \frac{m_{\text{actual}}}{\rho_{\text{wood}}} = \text{SG}_{\text{alc}} \rho_{\text{H}_2\text{O}} \frac{m_{\text{actual}}}{\rho_{\text{wood}}} \quad \rightarrow$$

$$\frac{\rho_{\text{wood}}}{\rho_{\text{H}_2\text{O}}} = \text{SG}_{\text{wood}} = \text{SG}_{\text{alc}} \frac{m_{\text{actual}}}{\left(m_{\text{actual}} - m_{\text{apparent}}\right)} = (0.79)\frac{0.48\ \text{kg}}{(0.48\ \text{kg} - 0.047\ \text{kg})} = \boxed{0.88}$$

33.   The buoyant force on the ice is equal to the weight of the ice, since it floats.

$$F_{\text{buoyant}} = W_{\text{ice}} \quad \rightarrow \quad m_{\substack{\text{seawater}\\ \text{submerged}}} g = m_{\text{ice}} g \quad \rightarrow \quad m_{\substack{\text{seawater}\\ \text{submerged}}} = m_{\text{ice}} \quad \rightarrow$$

$$\rho_{\text{seawater}} V_{\text{seawater}} = \rho_{\text{ice}} V_{\text{ice}} \quad \rightarrow \quad (SG)_{\text{seawater}} \rho_{\text{water}} V_{\substack{\text{submerged}\\ \text{ice}}} = (SG)_{\text{ice}} \rho_{\text{water}} V_{\text{ice}} \quad \rightarrow$$

$$(SG)_{\text{seawater}} V_{\substack{\text{submerged}\\ \text{ice}}} = (SG)_{\text{ice}} V_{\text{ice}} \quad \rightarrow$$

$$V_{\substack{\text{submerged}\\ \text{ice}}} = \frac{(SG)_{\text{ice}}}{(SG)_{\text{seawater}}} V_{\text{ice}} = \frac{0.917}{1.025} V_{\text{ice}} = 0.895\, V_{\text{ice}}$$

Thus the fraction above the water is $V_{\text{above}} = V_{\text{ice}} - V_{\text{submerged}} = 0.105\ V_{\text{ice}}$ or $\boxed{10.5\%}$

34.   For the combination to just barely sink, the total weight of the wood and lead must be equal to the total buoyant force on the wood and the lead.

$$F_{\text{weight}} = F_{\text{buoyant}} \quad \rightarrow \quad m_{\text{wood}} g + m_{\text{Pb}} g = V_{\text{wood}} \rho_{\text{water}} g + V_{\text{Pb}} \rho_{\text{water}} g \quad \rightarrow$$

$$m_{\text{wood}} + m_{\text{Pb}} = \frac{m_{\text{wood}}}{\rho_{\text{wood}}} \rho_{\text{water}} + \frac{m_{\text{Pb}}}{\rho_{\text{Pb}}} \rho_{\text{water}} \quad \rightarrow \quad m_{\text{Pb}}\left(1 - \frac{\rho_{\text{water}}}{\rho_{\text{Pb}}}\right) = m_{\text{wood}}\left(\frac{\rho_{\text{water}}}{\rho_{\text{wood}}} - 1\right) \quad \rightarrow$$

$$m_{Pb} = m_{wood} \frac{\left(\dfrac{\rho_{water}}{\rho_{wood}} - 1\right)}{\left(1 - \dfrac{\rho_{water}}{\rho_{Pb}}\right)} = m_{wood} \frac{\left(\dfrac{1}{SG_{wood}} - 1\right)}{\left(1 - \dfrac{1}{SG_{Pb}}\right)} = (5.25\,\text{kg}) \frac{\left(\dfrac{1}{0.50} - 1\right)}{\left(1 - \dfrac{1}{11.3}\right)} = \boxed{5.76\,\text{kg}}$$

35. Use Eq. 10-4b, the equation of continuity for an incompressible fluid, to compare blood flow in the aorta and in the major arteries.

$$\left(Av\right)_{aorta} = \left(Av\right)_{arteries} \quad \rightarrow$$

$$v_{arteries} = \frac{A_{aorta}}{A_{arteries}} v_{aorta} = \frac{\pi\left(1.2\,\text{cm}\right)^2}{2.0\,\text{cm}^2}\left(40\,\text{cm/s}\right) = 90.5\,\text{cm/s} \approx \boxed{0.9\,\text{m/s}}$$

36. We apply the equation of continuity at constant density, Eq. 10-4b.
    Flow rate out of duct = Flow rate into room

$$A_{duct}v_{duct} = \pi r^2 v_{duct} = \frac{V_{room}}{t_{to\,fill \atop room}} \quad \rightarrow \quad v_{duct} = \frac{V_{room}}{\pi r^2 t_{to\,fill \atop room}} = \frac{\left(9.2\,\text{m}\right)\left(5.0\,\text{m}\right)\left(4.5\,\text{m}\right)}{\pi\left(0.15\,\text{m}\right)^2\left(16\,\text{min}\right)\left(\dfrac{60\,\text{s}}{1\,\text{min}}\right)} = \boxed{3.1\,\text{m/s}}$$

37. Bernoulli's equation is evaluated with $v_1 = v_2 = 0$. Let point 1 be the initial point, and point 2 be the final point.

$$P_1 + \tfrac{1}{2}\rho v_1^2 + \rho g y_1 = P_2 + \tfrac{1}{2}\rho v_2^2 + \rho g y_2 \quad \rightarrow \quad P_1 + \rho g y_1 = P_2 + \rho g y_2 \quad \rightarrow$$

$$P_2 - P_1 = \rho g\left(y_1 - y_2\right) \quad \rightarrow \quad \Delta P = -\rho g \Delta y$$

But a change in y coordinate is the opposite of the change in depth which is what is represented in Eq. 10-3b. So our final result is $\Delta P = \rho g \Delta h$, Eq. 10-3b.

38. We may apply Torricelli's theorem., Eq. 10-6.

$$v_1 = \sqrt{2g\left(y_2 - y_1\right)} = \sqrt{2\left(9.80\,\text{m/s}^2\right)\left(4.6\,\text{m}\right)} = \boxed{9.5\,\text{m/s}}$$

39. The volume flow rate of water from the hose, multiplied times the time of filling, must equal the volume of the pool.

$$\left(Av\right)_{hose} = \frac{V_{pool}}{t} \quad \rightarrow \quad t = \frac{V_{pool}}{A_{hose}v_{hose}} = \frac{\pi\left(3.05\,\text{m}\right)^2\left(1.2\,\text{m}\right)}{\pi\left[\tfrac{1}{2}\left(\tfrac{5}{8}\right)''\left(\dfrac{1\,\text{m}}{39.37''}\right)\right]^2\left(0.40\,\text{m/s}\right)} = 4.429 \times 10^5\,\text{s}$$

$$4.429 \times 10^5\,\text{s}\left(\frac{1\,\text{day}}{60 \times 60 \times 24\,\text{s}}\right) = \boxed{5.1\,\text{days}}$$

40. Apply Bernoulli's equation with point 1 being the water main, and point 2 being the top of the spray. The velocity of the water will be zero at both points. The pressure at point 2 will be atmospheric pressure. Measure heights from the level of point 1.

$$P_1 + \tfrac{1}{2}\rho v_1^2 + \rho g y_1 = P_2 + \tfrac{1}{2}\rho v_2^2 + \rho g y_2 \quad \rightarrow$$

$$P_1 - P_{atm} = \rho g y_2 = \left(1.00 \times 10^3\,\text{kg/m}^3\right)\left(9.8\,\text{m/s}^2\right)\left(15\,\text{m}\right) = \boxed{1.5 \times 10^5\,\text{N/m}^2}$$

41. Use the equation of continuity (Eq. 10-4) to relate the volume flow of water at the two locations, and use Bernoulli's equation (Eq. 10-5) to relate the pressure conditions at the two locations. We assume that the two locations are at the same height. Express the pressures as atmospheric pressure plus gauge pressure. We use subscript "1" for the larger diameter, and subscript "2" for the smaller diameter.

$$A_1 v_1 = A_2 v_2 \quad \rightarrow \quad v_2 = v_1 \frac{A_1}{A_2} = v_1 \frac{\pi r_1^2}{\pi r_2^2} = v_1 \frac{r_1^2}{r_2^2}$$

$$P_0 + P_1 + \tfrac{1}{2}\rho v_1^2 + \rho g y_1 = P_0 + P_2 + \tfrac{1}{2}\rho v_2^2 + \rho g y_2 \quad \rightarrow$$

$$P_1 + \tfrac{1}{2}\rho v_1^2 = P_2 + \tfrac{1}{2}\rho v_2^2 = P_2 + \tfrac{1}{2}\rho v_1^2 \frac{r_1^4}{r_2^4} \quad \rightarrow \quad v_1 = \sqrt{\frac{2(P_1 - P_2)}{\rho\left(\frac{r_1^4}{r_2^4} - 1\right)}} \quad \rightarrow$$

$$A_1 v_1 = \pi r_1^2 \sqrt{\frac{2(P_1 - P_2)}{\rho\left(\frac{r_1^4}{r_2^4} - 1\right)}} = \pi \left(3.0\times10^{-2}\,\text{m}\right)^2 \sqrt{\frac{2\left(32.0\times10^3\,\text{Pa} - 24.0\times10^3\,\text{Pa}\right)}{\left(1.0\times10^3\,\text{kg/m}^3\right)\left(\frac{\left(3.0\times10^{-2}\,\text{m}\right)^4}{\left(2.0\times10^{-2}\,\text{m}\right)^4} - 1\right)}}$$

$$= \boxed{5.6\times10^{-3}\,\text{m}^3/\text{s}}$$

42. The pressure head can be interpreted as an initial height for the water, with a speed of 0 and atmospheric pressure. Apply Bernoulli's equation to the faucet location and the pressure head location to find the speed of the water at the faucet, and then calculate the volume flow rate. Since the faucet is open, the pressure there will be atmospheric as well.

$$P_{\text{faucet}} + \tfrac{1}{2}\rho v_{\text{faucet}}^2 + \rho g y_{\text{faucet}} = P_{\text{head}} + \tfrac{1}{2}\rho v_{\text{head}}^2 + \rho g y_{\text{head}} \quad \rightarrow$$

$$v_{\text{faucet}}^2 = \frac{2}{\rho}\left(P_{\text{head}} - P_{\text{faucet}}\right) + v_{\text{head}}^2 + 2g\left(y_{\text{head}} - y_{\text{faucet}}\right) = 2g y_{\text{head}} \quad \rightarrow$$

$$v_{\text{faucet}} = \sqrt{2g y_{\text{head}}}$$

Volume flow rate $= Av = \pi r^2 \sqrt{2g y_{\text{head}}} = \pi \left[\tfrac{1}{2}\left(1.85\times10^{-2}\,\text{m}\right)\right]^2 \sqrt{2\left(9.80\,\text{m/s}^2\right)\left(15.0\,\text{m}\right)}$

$$= \boxed{4.6\times10^{-3}\,\text{m}^3/\text{s}}$$

43. We assume that there is no appreciable height difference between the two sides of the roof. Then the net force on the roof due to the air is the difference in pressure on the two sides of the roof, times the area of the roof. The difference in pressure can be found from Bernoulli's equation.

$$P_{\text{inside}} + \tfrac{1}{2}\rho v_{\text{inside}}^2 + \rho g y_{\text{inside}} = P_{\text{outside}} + \tfrac{1}{2}\rho v_{\text{outside}}^2 + \rho g y_{\text{outside}} \quad \rightarrow$$

$$P_{\text{inside}} - P_{\text{outside}} = \tfrac{1}{2}\rho_{\text{air}} v_{\text{outside}}^2 = \frac{F_{\text{air}}}{A_{\text{roof}}} \quad \rightarrow$$

$$F_{\text{air}} = \tfrac{1}{2}\rho_{\text{air}} v_{\text{outside}}^2 A_{\text{roof}} = \tfrac{1}{2}\left(1.29\,\text{kg/m}^3\right)\left(35\,\text{m/s}\right)^2\left(240\,\text{m}^2\right) = \boxed{1.9\times10^5\,\text{N}}$$

44. The lift force would be the difference in pressure between the two wing surfaces, times the area of the wing surface. The difference in pressure can be found from Bernoulli's equation. We consider the two surfaces of the wing to be at the same height above the ground. Call the bottom surface of the wing point 1, and the top surface point 2.

$$P_1 + \tfrac{1}{2}\rho v_1^2 + \rho g y_1 = P_2 + \tfrac{1}{2}\rho v_2^2 + \rho g y_2 \;\rightarrow\; P_1 - P_2 = \tfrac{1}{2}\rho\left(v_2^2 - v_1^2\right)$$

$$F_{\text{lift}} = \left(P_1 - P_2\right)\left(\text{Area of wing}\right) = \tfrac{1}{2}\rho\left(v_2^2 - v_1^2\right)A$$

$$= \tfrac{1}{2}\left(1.29\,\text{kg/m}^3\right)\left[\left(260\,\text{m/s}\right)^2 - \left(150\,\text{m/s}\right)^2\right]\left(78\,\text{m}^2\right) = \boxed{2.3\times10^6\,\text{N}}$$

45. The air pressure inside the hurricane can be estimated using Bernoulli's equation. Assume the pressure outside the hurricane is air pressure, the speed of the wind outside the hurricane is 0, and that the two pressure measurements are made at the same height.

$$P_{\text{inside}} + \tfrac{1}{2}\rho v_{\text{inside}}^2 + \rho g y_{\text{inside}} = P_{\text{outside}} + \tfrac{1}{2}\rho v_{\text{outside}}^2 + \rho g y_{\text{outside}} \;\rightarrow$$

$$P_{\text{inside}} = P_{\text{outside}} - \tfrac{1}{2}\rho_{\text{air}} v_{\text{inside}}^2$$

$$= 1.013\times10^5\,\text{Pa} - \tfrac{1}{2}\left(1.29\,\text{kg/m}^3\right)\left[\left(300\,\text{km/h}\right)\left(\frac{1000\,\text{m}}{\text{km}}\right)\left(\frac{1\,\text{h}}{3600\,\text{s}}\right)\right]^2$$

$$= \boxed{9.7\times10^4\,\text{Pa}} \approx 0.96\,\text{atm}$$

46. Use the equation of continuity (Eq. 10-4) to relate the volume flow of water at the two locations, and use Bernoulli's equation (Eq. 10-5) to relate the conditions at the street to those at the top floor. Express the pressures as atmospheric pressure plus gauge pressure.

$$A_{\text{street}} v_{\text{street}} = A_{\text{top}} v_{\text{top}} \;\rightarrow$$

$$v_{\text{top}} = v_{\text{street}}\frac{A_{\text{street}}}{A_{\text{top}}} = \left(0.60\,\text{m/s}\right)\frac{\pi\left(5.0\times10^{-2}\,\text{m}\right)^2}{\pi\left(2.6\times10^{-2}\,\text{m}\right)^2} = 2.219\,\text{m/s} \approx \boxed{2.2\,\text{m/s}}$$

$$P_0 + P_{\text{gauge}\atop\text{street}} + \tfrac{1}{2}\rho v_{\text{street}}^2 + \rho g y_{\text{street}} = P_0 + P_{\text{gauge}\atop\text{top}} + \tfrac{1}{2}\rho v_{\text{top}}^2 + \rho g y_{\text{top}} \;\rightarrow$$

$$P_{\text{gauge}\atop\text{top}} = P_{\text{gauge}\atop\text{street}} + \tfrac{1}{2}\rho\left(v_{\text{street}}^2 - v_{\text{top}}^2\right) + \rho g y\left(y_{\text{street}} - y_{\text{top}}\right)$$

$$= \left(3.8\,\text{atm}\right)\left(\frac{1.013\times10^5\,\text{Pa}}{\text{atm}}\right) + \tfrac{1}{2}\left(1.00\times10^3\,\text{kg/m}^3\right)\left[\left(0.60\,\text{m/s}\right)^2 - \left(2.219\,\text{m/s}\right)^2\right]$$

$$+ \left(1.00\times10^3\,\text{kg/m}^3\right)\left(9.8\,\text{m/s}^2\right)\left(-18\,\text{m}\right)$$

$$= 2.063\times10^5\,\text{Pa}\left(\frac{1\,\text{atm}}{1.013\times10^5\,\text{Pa}}\right) \approx \boxed{2.0\,\text{atm}}$$

47. (*a*) Apply the equation of continuity and Bernoulli's equation at the same height to the wide and narrow portions of the tube.

$$A_2 v_2 = A_1 v_1 \;\rightarrow\; v_2 = v_1\frac{A_1}{A_2}$$

$$P_1 + \tfrac{1}{2}\rho v_1^2 = P_2 + \tfrac{1}{2}\rho v_2^2 \;\rightarrow\; \frac{2\left(P_1 - P_2\right)}{\rho} = v_2^2 - v_1^2 \;\rightarrow$$

$$\left(v_1\frac{A_1}{A_2}\right)^2 - v_1^2 = \frac{2\left(P_1 - P_2\right)}{\rho} \;\rightarrow\; v_1^2\left(\frac{A_1^2}{A_2^2} - \frac{A_2^2}{A_2^2}\right) = \frac{2\left(P_1 - P_2\right)}{\rho} \;\rightarrow$$

$$v_1^2 = \frac{2A_2^2 (P_1 - P_2)}{\rho (A_1^2 - A_2^2)} \quad \rightarrow \quad \boxed{v_1 = A_2 \sqrt{\frac{2(P_1 - P_2)}{\rho (A_1^2 - A_2^2)}}}$$

(b) $v_1 = A_2 \sqrt{\dfrac{2(P_1 - P_2)}{\rho (A_1^2 - A_2^2)}}$

$$= \pi \left[\tfrac{1}{2}(0.010\,\mathrm{m})\right]^2 \sqrt{\frac{2(18\,\mathrm{mm\,Hg})\left(\dfrac{133\,\mathrm{N/m}^2}{\mathrm{mm\,Hg}}\right)}{(1000\,\mathrm{kg/m}^3)\left(\pi^2 \left[\tfrac{1}{2}(0.030\,\mathrm{m})\right]^4 - \pi^2 \left[\tfrac{1}{2}(0.010\,\mathrm{m})\right]^4\right)}} = \boxed{0.24\,\mathrm{m/s}}$$

48. Apply both Bernoulli's equation and the equation of continuity between the two openings of the tank. Note that the pressure at each opening will be atmospheric pressure.

$$A_2 v_2 = A_1 v_1 \quad \rightarrow \quad v_2 = v_1 \frac{A_1}{A_2}$$

$$P_1 + \tfrac{1}{2}\rho v_1^2 + \rho g y_1 = P_2 + \tfrac{1}{2}\rho v_2^2 + \rho g y_2 \quad \rightarrow \quad v_2^2 - v_1^2 = 2g(y_2 - y_1) = 2gh$$

$$v_1^2 - \left(v_1 \frac{A_1}{A_2}\right) = 2gh \quad \rightarrow \quad v_1^2 \left(1 - \frac{A_1^2}{A_2^2}\right) = 2gh \quad \rightarrow \quad \boxed{v_1 = \sqrt{\frac{2gh}{\left(1 - A_1^2 / A_2^2\right)}}}$$

49. Use Bernoulli's equation to find the speed of the liquid as it leaves the opening, assuming that the speed of the liquid at the top is 0, and that the pressure at each opening is air pressure.

$$P_1 + \tfrac{1}{2}\rho v_1^2 + \rho g y_1 = P_2 + \tfrac{1}{2}\rho v_2^2 + \rho g y_2 \quad \rightarrow \quad v_1 = \sqrt{2g(h_2 - h_1)}$$

(a)   Since the liquid is launched horizontally, the initial vertical speed is zero. Use Eq. 2-11(a) for constant acceleration to find the time of fall, with upward as the positive direction. Then multiply the time of fall times v_1, the (constant) horizontal speed.

$$y = y_0 + v_{0y}t + \tfrac{1}{2}a_y t^2 \quad \rightarrow \quad 0 = h_1 + 0 - \tfrac{1}{2}gt^2 \quad \rightarrow \quad t = \sqrt{\frac{2h_1}{g}}$$

$$\Delta x = v_1 t = \sqrt{2g(h_2 - h_1)}\sqrt{\frac{2h_1}{g}} = \boxed{2\sqrt{(h_2 - h_1)h_1}}$$

(b)   We seek some height h_1' such that $2\sqrt{(h_2 - h_1)h_1} = 2\sqrt{(h_2 - h_1')h_1'}$.

$$2\sqrt{(h_2 - h_1)h_1} = 2\sqrt{(h_2 - h_1')h_1'} \quad \rightarrow \quad (h_2 - h_1)h_1 = (h_2 - h_1')h_1' \quad \rightarrow$$

$$h_1'^2 - h_2 h_1' + (h_2 - h_1)h_1 = 0 \quad \rightarrow$$

$$h_1' = \frac{h_2 \pm \sqrt{h_2^2 - 4(h_2 - h_1)h_1}}{2} = \frac{h_2 \pm \sqrt{h_2^2 - 4h_1 h_2 + 4h_1^2}}{2} = \frac{h_2 \pm (h_2 - 2h_1)}{2} = \frac{2h_2 - 2h_1}{2}, \frac{2h_1}{2}$$

$$\boxed{h_1' = h_2 - h_1}$$

50. Apply Eq. 10-8. Use the average radius to calculate the plate area.

$$F = \eta A \frac{v}{l} \quad \rightarrow \quad \eta = \frac{Fl}{Av} = \frac{\left(\dfrac{\tau}{r_{inner}}\right)\left(r_{outer} - r_{inner}\right)}{\left(2\pi r_{avg} h\right)\left(\omega r_{inner}\right)}$$

$$= \frac{\left(\dfrac{0.024\,\text{m}\cdot\text{N}}{0.0510\,\text{m}}\right)\left(0.20\times10^{-2}\,\text{m}\right)}{2\pi\left(0.0520\,\text{m}\right)\left(0.120\,\text{m}\right)\left(62\dfrac{\text{rev}}{\text{min}}\times\dfrac{2\pi\,\text{rad}}{\text{rev}}\times\dfrac{1\,\text{min}}{60\,\text{s}}\right)\left(0.0510\,\text{m}\right)} = \boxed{7.2\times10^{-2}\,\text{Pa}\cdot\text{s}}$$

51. From Poiseuille's equation, the volume flow rate Q is proportional to R^4 if all other factors are the same. Thus $Q/R^4 = \dfrac{V}{t}\dfrac{1}{R^4}$ is constant. If the volume of water used to water the garden is to be same in both cases, then tR^4 is constant.

$$t_1 R_1^4 = t_2 R_2^4 \quad \rightarrow \quad t_2 = t_1\left(\frac{R_1}{R_2}\right)^4 = t_1\left(\frac{3/8}{5/8}\right)^4 = 0.13 t_1$$

Thus the $\boxed{\text{time has been cut by 87\%}}$.

52. Use Poiseuille's equation to find the pressure difference.

$$Q = \frac{\pi R^4 \left(P_2 - P_1\right)}{8\eta L} \quad \rightarrow$$

$$\left(P_2 - P_1\right) = \frac{8Q\eta L}{\pi R^4} = \frac{8\left[5.6\times10^{-3}\dfrac{\text{L}}{\text{min}}\times\dfrac{1\,\text{min}}{60\,\text{s}}\times\dfrac{1\times10^{-3}\,\text{m}^3}{1\,\text{L}}\right]\left(0.2\,\text{Pa}\cdot\text{s}\right)\left(5.5\times10^{-2}\,\text{m}\right)}{\pi\left(0.9\times10^{-3}\,\text{m}\right)^4}$$

$$= \boxed{4.0\times10^{3}\,\text{Pa}}$$

53. Use Poiseuille's equation to find the pressure difference.

$$Q = \frac{\pi R^4 \left(P_2 - P_1\right)}{8\eta L} \quad \rightarrow$$

$$\left(P_2 - P_1\right) = \frac{8Q\eta L}{\pi R^4} = \frac{8\left(450\,\text{cm}^3/\text{s}\right)\left(10^{-6}\,\text{m}^3/\text{cm}^3\right)\left(0.20\,\text{Pa}\cdot\text{s}\right)\left(1.9\times10^{3}\,\text{m}\right)}{\pi\left(0.145\,\text{m}\right)^4} = 985.1\,\text{Pa} \approx \boxed{990\,\text{Pa}}$$

54. Use Poiseuille's equation to find the radius, and then double the radius to the diameter.

$$Q = \frac{\pi R^4 \left(P_2 - P_1\right)}{8\eta L} \quad \rightarrow$$

$$d = 2R = 2\left[\frac{8\eta L Q}{\pi\left(P_2 - P_1\right)}\right]^{1/4} = 2\left[\frac{8\left(1.8\times10^{-5}\,\text{Pa}\cdot\text{s}\right)\left(21.0\,\text{m}\right)\left(\dfrac{9.0\times12.0\times4.0\,\text{m}^3}{600\,\text{s}}\right)}{\pi\left(0.71\times10^{-3}\,\text{atm}\right)\left(1.013\times10^{5}\,\text{Pa}/\text{atm}\right)}\right]^{1/4} = \boxed{0.11\,\text{m}}$$

55. The pressure drop per cm can be found from Poiseuille's equation, using a length of 1 cm. The volume flow rate is area of the aorta times the speed of the moving blood.

$$Q = \frac{\pi R^4 (P_2 - P_1)}{8\eta L} \rightarrow$$

$$\frac{(P_2 - P_1)}{L} = \frac{8\eta Q}{\pi R^4} = \frac{8\eta \pi R^2 v}{\pi R^4} = \frac{8\eta v}{R^2} = \frac{8(4 \times 10^{-3} \, \text{Pa} \cdot \text{s})(0.4 \, \text{m/s})}{(1.2 \times 10^{-2} \, \text{m})^2} = 88.9 \, \text{Pa/m} = \boxed{0.89 \, \text{Pa/cm}}$$

56. From Poiseuille's equation, the volume flow rate Q is proportional to R^4 if all other factors are the same. Thus Q/R^4 is constant.

$$\frac{Q_{\text{final}}}{R_{\text{final}}^4} = \frac{Q_{\text{initial}}}{R_{\text{initial}}^4} \rightarrow R_{\text{final}} = \left(\frac{Q_{\text{final}}}{Q_{\text{initial}}}\right)^{1/4} R_{\text{initial}} = (0.25)^{1/4} R_{\text{initial}} = 0.707 R_{\text{initial}}$$

Thus the radius has been reduced by about $\boxed{29\%}$.

57. (a) $Re = \frac{2\bar{v}r\rho}{\eta} = \frac{2(0.40 \, \text{cm/s})(1.2 \times 10^{-2} \, \text{m})(1.05 \times 10^3 \, \text{kg/m}^3)}{4 \times 10^{-3} \, \text{Pa} \cdot \text{s}} = 2520$

The flow is $\boxed{\text{turbulent}}$ at this speed.

(b) Since the velocity is doubled the Reynolds number will double to 5040. The flow is $\boxed{\text{turbulent}}$ at this speed.

58. The fluid pressure must be 18 torr higher than air pressure as it exits the needle, so that the blood will enter the vein. The pressure at the entrance to the needle must be higher than 18 torr, due to the viscosity of the blood. To produce that excess pressure, the blood reservoir is placed above the level of the needle. Use Poiseuille's equation to calculate the excess pressure needed due to the viscosity, and then use Eq. 10-3b to find the height of the blood reservoir necessary to produce that excess pressure.

$$Q = \frac{\pi R^4 (P_2 - P_1)}{8\eta_{\text{blood}} L} \rightarrow P_2 = P_1 + \frac{8\eta_{\text{blood}} LQ}{\pi R^4} = \rho_{\text{blood}} g \Delta h \rightarrow$$

$$\Delta h = \frac{1}{\rho_{\text{blood}} g}\left(P_1 + \frac{8\eta_{\text{blood}} LQ}{\pi R^4}\right)$$

$$= \frac{1}{\left(1.05 \times 10^3 \, \frac{\text{kg}}{\text{m}^3}\right)(9.80 \, \text{m/s}^2)}\left(\frac{(18 \, \text{mm-Hg})\left(\frac{133 \, \text{N/m}^2}{1 \, \text{mm-Hg}}\right) +}{\frac{8(4 \times 10^{-3} \, \text{Pa} \cdot \text{s})(4.0 \times 10^{-2} \, \text{m})\left(\frac{4.0 \times 10^{-6} \, \text{m}^3}{60 \, \text{s}}\right)}{\pi (0.20 \times 10^{-3} \, \text{m})^4}}\right)$$

$$= \boxed{1.8 \, \text{m}}$$

59. In Figure 10-35, we have $\gamma = F/2L$. Use this to calculate the force.

$$\gamma = \frac{F}{2L} = \frac{5.1 \times 10^{-3} \, \text{N}}{2(0.070 \, \text{m})} = \boxed{3.6 \times 10^{-2} \, \text{N/m}}$$

60. As in Figure 10-35, there are 2 surfaces being increased, and so $\gamma = F/2L$. Use this relationship to calculate the force.

$$\gamma = F/2L \quad \rightarrow \quad F = 2\gamma L = 2(0.025\,\text{N/m})(0.182\,\text{m}) = \boxed{9.1\times10^{-3}\,\text{N}}$$

61. From Example 10-14, we have that $2\pi r\gamma \cos\theta = \tfrac{1}{6}mg$. The maximum mass will occur at $\theta = 0°$.

$$2\pi r\gamma \cos\theta = \tfrac{1}{6}mg \quad \rightarrow \quad m_{max} = \frac{12\pi r\gamma}{g} = \frac{12\pi\left(3.0\times10^{-5}\,\text{m}\right)(0.072\,\text{N/m})}{9.80\,\text{m/s}^2} = 8.3\times10^{-6}\,\text{kg}$$

This is much less than the insect's mass, and so $\boxed{\text{the insect will not remain on top of the water}}$.

62. (*a*) We assume that the weight of the platinum ring is negligible. Then the surface tension is the force to lift the ring, divided by the length of surface that is being pulled. Surface tension will act at both edges of the ring, as in Figure 10-35 (b). Thus $\boxed{\gamma = \dfrac{F}{2(2\pi r)} = \dfrac{F}{4\pi r}}$

(*b*) $\quad \gamma = \dfrac{F}{4\pi r} = \dfrac{8.40\times10^{-3}\,\text{N}}{4\pi\left(2.8\times10^{-2}\,\text{m}\right)} = \boxed{2.4\times10^{-2}\,\text{N/m}}$

63. The pressures for parts (*a*) and (*b*) stated in this problem are gauge pressures, relative to atmospheric pressure. The pressure change due to depth in a fluid is given by Eq. 10-3b, $\Delta P = \rho g\Delta h$.

(*a*) $\quad \Delta h = \dfrac{\Delta P}{\rho g} = \dfrac{(55\,\text{mm-Hg})\left(\dfrac{133\,\text{N/m}^2}{1\,\text{mm-Hg}}\right)}{\left(1.00\dfrac{\text{g}}{\text{cm}^3}\times\dfrac{1\,\text{kg}}{1000\,\text{g}}\times\dfrac{10^6\,\text{cm}^3}{1\,\text{m}^3}\right)(9.80\,\text{m/s}^2)} = \boxed{0.75\,\text{m}}$

(*b*) $\quad \Delta h = \dfrac{\Delta P}{\rho g} = \dfrac{(650\,\text{mm-H}_2\text{O})\left(\dfrac{9.81\,\text{N/m}^2}{1\,\text{mm-H}_2\text{O}}\right)}{\left(1.00\dfrac{\text{g}}{\text{cm}^3}\times\dfrac{1\,\text{kg}}{1000\,\text{g}}\times\dfrac{10^6\,\text{cm}^3}{1\,\text{m}^3}\right)(9.80\,\text{m/s}^2)} = \boxed{0.65\,\text{m}}$

(*c*) For the fluid to just barely enter the vein, the fluid pressure must be the same as the blood pressure.

$$\Delta h = \dfrac{\Delta P}{\rho g} = \dfrac{(18\,\text{mm-Hg})\left(\dfrac{133\,\text{N/m}^2}{1\,\text{mm-Hg}}\right)}{\left(1.00\dfrac{\text{g}}{\text{cm}^3}\times\dfrac{1\,\text{kg}}{1000\,\text{g}}\times\dfrac{10^6\,\text{cm}^3}{1\,\text{m}^3}\right)(9.80\,\text{m/s}^2)} = \boxed{0.24\,\text{m}}$$

64. (*a*) The fluid in the needle is confined, and so Pascal's principle may be applied.

$$P_{plunger} = P_{needle} \quad \rightarrow \quad \frac{F_{plunger}}{A_{plunger}} = \frac{F_{needle}}{A_{needle}} \quad \rightarrow \quad F_{needle} = F_{plunger}\frac{A_{needle}}{A_{plunger}} = F_{plunger}\frac{\pi r_{needle}^2}{\pi r_{plunger}^2} = F_{plunger}\frac{r_{needle}^2}{r_{plunger}^2}$$

$$= (2.4\,\text{N})\frac{\left(0.10\times10^{-3}\,\text{m}\right)^2}{\left(0.65\times10^{-2}\,\text{m}\right)^2} = \boxed{5.7\times10^{-4}\,\text{N}}$$

(b) $F_{plunger} = P_{plunger}A_{plunger}$ $(18\,\text{mm-Hg})\left(\dfrac{133\,\text{N}/\text{m}^2}{1\,\text{mm-Hg}}\right)\pi\left(0.65\times10^{-2}\,\text{m}\right)^2 = \boxed{0.32\,\text{N}}$

65. The force can be found by multiplying the pressure times the area of the pump cylinder.

$$F_i = P_iA = \left(2.10\times10^5\,\text{N}/\text{m}^2\right)\pi\left(0.015\,\text{m}\right)^2 = 1.5\times10^2\,\text{N}$$

$$F_f = P_fA = \left(3.10\times10^5\,\text{N}/\text{m}^2\right)\pi\left(0.015\,\text{m}\right)^2 = 2.2\times10^2\,\text{N}$$

The range of forces is $\boxed{1.5\times10^2\,\text{N} \le F \le 2.2\times10^2\,\text{N}}$

66. The pressure would be the weight of the ice divided by the area covered by the ice. The volume of the ice is represented by V, and its thickness by d. The volume is also the mass of the ice divided by the density of the ice.

$$P = \frac{F}{A} = \frac{mg}{V/d} = \frac{mgd}{V} = \frac{mgd}{m/\rho} = gd\rho = \left(9.80\,\text{m}/\text{s}^2\right)\left(3000\,\text{m}\right)\left(917\,\text{kg}/\text{m}^3\right) = \boxed{2.7\times10^7\,\text{Pa}}$$

$$= 2.7\times10^7\,\text{Pa}\left(\frac{1\,\text{atm}}{1.013\times10^5\,\text{Pa}}\right) \approx \boxed{270\,\text{atm}}$$

67. The change in pressure with height is given by Eq. 10-3b.

$$\Delta P = \rho g\Delta h \ \rightarrow \ \frac{\Delta P}{P_0} = \frac{\rho g\Delta h}{P_0} = \frac{\left(1.29\,\text{kg}/\text{m}^3\right)\left(9.80\,\text{m}/\text{s}^2\right)\left(380\,\text{m}\right)}{1.013\times10^5\,\text{Pa}} = 0.047 \ \rightarrow$$

$$\boxed{\Delta P = 0.047\,\text{atm}}$$

68. (a) The input pressure is equal to the output pressure.

$$P_{input} = P_{output} \ \rightarrow \ \frac{F_{input}}{A_{input}} = \frac{F_{output}}{A_{output}} \ \rightarrow$$

$$A_{input} = A_{output}\frac{F_{input}}{F_{output}} = \pi\left(9.0\times10^{-2}\,\text{m}\right)^2\frac{250\,\text{N}}{\left(970\,\text{kg}\right)\left(9.80\,\text{m}/\text{s}^2\right)} = \boxed{6.7\times10^{-4}\,\text{m}^2}$$

(b) The work is the force needed to lift the car (its weight) times the vertical distance lifted.

$$W = mgh = \left(970\,\text{kg}\right)\left(9.80\,\text{m}/\text{s}^2\right)\left(0.12\,\text{m}\right) = 1.141\times10^3\,\text{J} \approx \boxed{1.1\times10^3\,\text{J}}$$

(c) The work done by the input piston is equal to the work done in lifting the car.

$$W_{input} = W_{output} \ \rightarrow \ F_{input}d_{input} = F_{output}d_{output} = mgh \ \rightarrow$$

$$h = \frac{F_{input}d_{input}}{mg} = \frac{\left(250\,\text{N}\right)\left(0.13\,\text{m}\right)}{\left(970\,\text{kg}\right)\left(9.80\,\text{m}/\text{s}^2\right)} = 3.419\times10^{-3}\,\text{m} \approx \boxed{3.4\times10^{-3}\,\text{m}}$$

(d) The number of strokes is the full distance divided by the distance per stroke.

$$h_{full} = Nh_{stroke} \ \rightarrow \ N = \frac{h_{full}}{h_{stroke}} = \frac{0.12\,\text{m}}{3.419\times10^{-3}\,\text{m}} = \boxed{35\,\text{strokes}}$$

(e) The work input is the input force times the total distance moved by the input piston.

$$W_{input} = NF_{input}d_{input} \ \rightarrow \ 35\left(250\,\text{N}\right)\left(0.13\,\text{m}\right) = \boxed{1.1\times10^3\,\text{J}}$$

Since the work input is equal to the work output, energy is conserved.

69. The change in pressure with height is given by Eq. 10-3b.

$$\Delta P = \rho g \Delta h \quad \rightarrow \quad \frac{\Delta P}{P_0} = \frac{\rho g \Delta h}{P_0} = \frac{\left(1.05 \times 10^3 \, \text{kg/m}^3\right)\left(9.80 \, \text{m/s}^2\right)\left(6 \, \text{m}\right)}{1.013 \times 10^5 \, \text{Pa}} = 0.609 \quad \rightarrow$$

$$\boxed{\Delta P = 0.6 \, \text{atm}}$$

70. The pressure change due to a change in height is given by Eq. 10-3b. That pressure is the excess force on the eardrum, divided by the area of the eardrum.

$$\Delta P = \rho g \Delta h = \frac{F}{A} \quad \rightarrow$$

$$F = \rho g \Delta h A = \left(1.29 \, \text{kg/m}^3\right)\left(9.80 \, \text{m/s}^2\right)\left(950 \, \text{m}\right)\left(0.50 \times 10^{-4} \, \text{m}^2\right) = \boxed{0.60 \, \text{N}}$$

71. The pressure at the top of each liquid will be atmospheric pressure, and the pressure at the place where the two fluids meet must be the same if the fluid is to be stationary. In the diagram, the darker color represents the water, and the lighter color represents the alcohol. Write the expression for the pressure at a depth for both liquids, starting at the top of each liquid with atmospheric pressure.

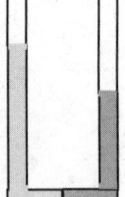

$$P_{\text{alcohol}} = P_0 + \rho_{\text{alcohol}} g \Delta h_{\text{alcohol}} = P_{\text{water}} = P_0 + \rho_{\text{water}} g \Delta h_{\text{water}} \quad \rightarrow$$

$$\rho_{\text{alcohol}} \Delta h_{\text{alcohol}} = \rho_{\text{water}} \Delta h_{\text{water}} \quad \rightarrow$$

$$\Delta h_{\text{water}} = \Delta h_{\text{alcohol}} \frac{\rho_{\text{alcohol}}}{\rho_{\text{water}}} = 18.0 \, \text{cm} \left(0.79\right) = \boxed{14.2 \, \text{cm}}$$

72. The buoyant force, equal to the weight of mantle displaced, must be equal to the weight of the continent. Let h represent the full height of the continent, and y represent the height of the continent above the surrounding rock.

$$W_{\text{continent}} = W_{\substack{\text{displaced} \\ \text{mantle}}} \quad \rightarrow \quad A h \rho_{\text{continent}} g = A \left(h - y\right) \rho_{\text{mantle}} g \quad \rightarrow$$

$$y = h \left(1 - \frac{\rho_{\text{continent}}}{\rho_{\text{mantle}}}\right) = \left(35 \, \text{km}\right)\left(1 - \frac{2800 \, \text{kg/m}^3}{3300 \, \text{kg/m}^3}\right) = \boxed{5.3 \, \text{km}}$$

73. The force is the pressure times the surface area.

$$F = PA = \left(120 \, \text{mm-Hg}\right)\left(\frac{133 \, \text{N/m}^2}{1 \, \text{mm-Hg}}\right)\left(82 \times 10^{-4} \, \text{m}^2\right) = 130.9 \, \text{N} \approx \boxed{130 \, \text{N}}$$

74. We assume that the air pressure is due to the weight of the atmosphere, with the area equal to the surface area of the Earth.

$$P = \frac{F}{A} \quad \rightarrow \quad F = PA = mg \quad \rightarrow$$

$$m = \frac{PA}{g} = \frac{4\pi R_{\text{Earth}}^2 P}{g} = \frac{4\pi \left(6.38 \times 10^6 \, \text{m}\right)^2 \left(1.013 \times 10^5 \, \text{N/m}^2\right)}{9.80 \, \text{m/s}^2} = \boxed{5.29 \times 10^{18} \, \text{kg}}$$

75. The pressure difference due to the lungs is the pressure change in the column of water.

$$\Delta P = \rho g \Delta h \quad \rightarrow \quad \Delta h = \frac{\Delta P}{\rho g} = \frac{(80\,\text{mm-Hg})\left(\dfrac{133\,\text{N}/\text{m}^2}{1\,\text{mm-Hg}}\right)}{\left(1.00 \times 10^3\,\text{kg}/\text{m}^3\right)\left(9.80\,\text{m}/\text{s}^2\right)} = 1.086\,\text{m} \approx \boxed{1.1\,\text{m}}$$

76. The buoyant force due to the fresh water must be the weight of displaced seawater, and would be the volume of the displacement times the density of sea water times the acceleration due to gravity. But the buoyant force on the ship is also the weight of displaced sea water.

$$F_{\text{buoyant}} = V_{\text{displaced}}\,\rho_{\substack{\text{sea}\\ \text{water}}}\,g = m_{\text{fresh}}\,g \quad \rightarrow \quad m_{\text{fresh}} = \left(2650\,\text{m}^2\right)\left(8.50\,\text{m}\right)\left(1025\,\text{kg}/\text{m}^3\right) = \boxed{2.31 \times 10^7\,\text{kg}}$$

This can also be expressed as a volume.

$$V_{\text{fresh}} = \frac{m_{\text{fresh}}}{\rho_{\text{fresh}}} = \frac{2.31 \times 10^7\,\text{kg}}{1.00 \times 10^3\,\text{kg}/\text{m}^3} = \boxed{2.31 \times 10^4\,\text{m}^3} = \boxed{2.31 \times 10^7\,\text{L}}$$

77. The buoyant force on the block of wood must be equal to the combined weight of the wood and copper.

$$\left(m_{\text{wood}} + m_{\text{Cu}}\right)g = V_{\text{wood}}\,\rho_{\text{water}}\,g = \frac{m_{\text{wood}}}{\rho_{\text{wood}}}\rho_{\text{water}}\,g \quad \rightarrow \quad m_{\text{wood}} + m_{\text{Cu}} = \frac{m_{\text{wood}}}{\rho_{\text{wood}}}\rho_{\text{water}} \quad \rightarrow$$

$$m_{\text{Cu}} = m_{\text{wood}}\left(\frac{\rho_{\text{water}}}{\rho_{\text{wood}}} - 1\right) = \left(0.50\,\text{kg}\right)\left(\frac{1000\,\text{kg}/\text{m}^3}{600\,\text{kg}/\text{m}^3} - 1\right) = \boxed{0.33\,\text{kg}}$$

78. The buoyant force must be equal to the weight of the water displaced by the full volume of the logs, and must also be equal to the full weight of the raft plus the passengers. Let N represent the number of passengers.

weight of water displaced by logs = weight of people + weight of logs

$$10V_{\text{log}}\,\rho_{\text{water}}\,g = Nm_{\text{person}}\,g + 10V_{\text{log}}\,\rho_{\text{log}}\,g \quad \rightarrow$$

$$N = \frac{10V_{\text{log}}\left(\rho_{\text{water}} - \rho_{\text{log}}\right)}{m_{\text{person}}} = \frac{10\pi r_{\text{log}}^2 l_{\text{log}}\left(\rho_{\text{water}} - SG_{\text{log}}\rho_{\text{water}}\right)}{m_{\text{person}}} = \frac{10\pi r_{\text{log}}^2 l_{\text{log}}\rho_{\text{water}}\left(1 - SG_{\text{log}}\right)}{m_{\text{person}}}$$

$$= \frac{10\pi\left(0.28\,\text{m}\right)^2\left(6.1\,\text{m}\right)\left(1000\,\text{kg}/\text{m}^3\right)\left(1 - 0.60\right)}{68\,\text{kg}} = 88.37$$

Thus $\boxed{88}$ people can stand on the raft without getting wet. When the 89th person gets on, the raft will sink.

79. The work done during each heartbeat is the force on the fluid times the distance that the fluid moves in the direction of the force.

$$W = F\Delta l = PA\Delta l = PV \quad \rightarrow$$

$$\text{Power} = \frac{W}{t} = \frac{PV}{t} = \frac{\left(105\,\text{mm-Hg}\right)\left(\dfrac{133\,\text{N}/\text{m}^2}{1\,\text{mm-Hg}}\right)\left(70 \times 10^{-6}\,\text{m}^3\right)}{\left(\dfrac{1}{70}\,\text{min}\right)\left(\dfrac{60\,\text{s}}{\text{min}}\right)} = \boxed{1.1\,\text{W}}$$

80. The buoyant force on the rock is the force that would be on a mass of water with the same volume as the rock. Since the equivalent mass of water is accelerating upward, that same acceleration must be taken into account in the calculation of the buoyant force.

$$F_{buoyant} - m_{water}g = m_{water}a \rightarrow$$

$$F_{buoyant}^{\cdot} = m_{water}(g+a) = V_{water}\rho_{water}(g+a) = V_{rock}\rho_{water}(g+a)$$

$$= \frac{m_{rock}}{\rho_{rock}}\rho_{water}(g+a) = \frac{m_{rock}}{SG_{rock}}(g+a) = \frac{(3.0\,\text{kg})3.4(9.80\,\text{m/s}^2)}{2.7} = \boxed{37\,\text{N}}$$

For the rock to not sink, the upward buoyant force on the rock minus the weight of the rock must be equal to the net force on the rock.

$$F_{buoyant} - m_{rock}g = m_{rock}a \rightarrow F_{buoyant} = m_{rock}(g+a) = (3.0\,\text{kg})3.4(9.80\,\text{m/s}^2) = 100\,\text{N}$$

$\boxed{\text{The rock will sink}}$, because the buoyant force is not large enough to "float" the rock.

81. The pressure head can be interpreted as an initial height for the water, with a speed of 0 and atmospheric pressure. Apply Bernoulli's equation to the faucet location and the pressure head location to find the speed of the water at the faucet. Since the faucet is open, the pressure there will be atmospheric as well.

$$P_{faucet} + \tfrac{1}{2}\rho v_{faucet}^2 + \rho g y_{faucet} = P_{head} + \tfrac{1}{2}\rho v_{head}^2 + \rho g y_{head} \rightarrow$$

$$y_{head} = \frac{v_{faucet}^2}{2g} = \frac{(9.5\,\text{m/s})^2}{2(9.80\,\text{m/s}^2)} = \boxed{4.6\,\text{m}}$$

82. Apply both Bernoulli's equation and the equation of continuity at the two locations of the stream, with the faucet being location 0 and the lower position being location 1. The pressure will be air pressure at both locations. The lower location has $y_1 = 0$ and the faucet is at height $y_0 = y$.

$$A_0 v_0 = A_1 v_1 \rightarrow v_1 = v_0 \frac{A_0}{A_1} = v_0 \frac{\pi(d_0/2)^2}{\pi(d_1/2)^2} = v_0 \frac{d_0^2}{d_1^2} \rightarrow$$

$$P_0 + \tfrac{1}{2}\rho v_0^2 + \rho g y_0 = P_1 + \tfrac{1}{2}\rho v_1^2 + \rho g y_1 \rightarrow v_0^2 + 2gy = v_1^2 = v_0^2 \frac{d_0^4}{d_1^4} \rightarrow$$

$$\boxed{d_1 = d_0 \left(\frac{v_0^2}{v_0^2 + 2gy}\right)^{1/4}}$$

83. (*a*) We assume that the water is launched at ground level. Since it also lands at ground level, the level range formula from chapter 4 may be used.

$$R = \frac{v_0^2 \sin 2\theta}{g} \rightarrow v_0 = \sqrt{\frac{Rg}{\sin 2\theta}} = \sqrt{\frac{(8.0\,\text{m})(9.80\,\text{m/s}^2)}{\sin 70^\circ}} = 9.134\,\text{m/s} \approx \boxed{9.1\,\text{m/s}}$$

(*b*) The volume rate of flow is the area of the flow times the speed of the flow. Multiply by 4 for the 4 heads.

$$\text{Volume flow rate} = Av = 4\pi r^2 v = 4\pi(1.5 \times 10^{-3}\,\text{m})^2 (9.134\,\text{m/s})$$

$$= 2.583 \times 10^{-4}\,\text{m}^3/\text{s}\left(\frac{1\,\text{L}}{1.0 \times 10^{-3}\,\text{m}^3}\right) \approx \boxed{0.26\,\text{L/s}}$$

(*c*) Use the equation of continuity to calculate the flow rate in the supply pipe.

$$(Av)_{supply} = (Av)_{heads} \rightarrow v_{supply} = \frac{(Av)_{heads}}{A_{supply}} = \frac{2.583 \times 10^{-4} \text{ m}^3/\text{s}}{\pi (0.95 \times 10^{-2} \text{ m})^2} = \boxed{0.91 \text{ m/s}}$$

84. (*a*) We assume that the tube in the pail is about 4.0 cm below the surface of the liquid in the pail so that the pressure at that two tube ends is approximately the same. Apply Bernoulli's equation between the two ends of the tube.

$$P_{sink} + \tfrac{1}{2}\rho v_{sink}^2 + \rho g y_{sink} = P_{pail} + \tfrac{1}{2}\rho v_{pail}^2 + \rho g y_{pail} \rightarrow$$

$$v_{pail} = \sqrt{2g(y_{sink} - y_{pail})} = \sqrt{2(9.80 \text{ m/s}^2)(0.50 \text{ m})} = 3.130 \text{ m/s} \approx \boxed{3.1 \text{ m/s}}$$

(*b*) The volume flow rate (at the pail end of the tube) times the time must equal the volume of water in the sink.

$$(Av)_{pail} t = V_{sink} \rightarrow t = \frac{V_{sink}}{(Av)_{pail}} = \frac{(0.48 \text{ m}^2)(4.0 \times 10^{-2} \text{ m})}{\pi (1.0 \times 10^{-2} \text{ m})^2 (3.13 \text{ m/s})} = \boxed{20 \text{ s}}$$

85. We assume that the speed of the water at the entry point to the siphon tube is zero, and we assume that the pressure at both ends of the siphon hose is the same.

$$P_{top} + \tfrac{1}{2}\rho v_{top}^2 + \rho g y_{top} = P_{bottom} + \tfrac{1}{2}\rho v_{bottom}^2 + \rho g y_{bottom} \rightarrow v_{bottom} = \sqrt{2g(y_{top} - y_{bottom})}$$

$$Av = \pi r_{tube}^2 v_{bottom} = \pi r_{tube}^2 \sqrt{2g(y_{top} - y_{bottom})} = \pi (0.60 \times 10^{-2} \text{ m})^2 \sqrt{2(9.80 \text{ m/s}^2)(0.64 \text{ m})}$$

$$= \boxed{4.0 \times 10^{-4} \text{ m}^3/\text{s}}$$

86. The upward force due to air pressure on the bottom of the wing must be equal to the weight of the airplane plus the downward force due to air pressure on the top of the wing. Bernoulli's equation can be used to relate the forces due to air pressure. We assume that there is no appreciable height difference between the top and the bottom of the wing.

$$P_{top}A + mg = P_{bottom}A \rightarrow (P_{bottom} - P_{top}) = \frac{mg}{A}$$

$$P_0 + P_{bottom} + \tfrac{1}{2}\rho v_{bottom}^2 + \rho g y_{bottom} = P_0 + P_{top} + \tfrac{1}{2}\rho v_{top}^2 + \rho g y_{top}$$

$$v_{top}^2 = \frac{2(P_{bottom} - P_{top})}{\rho} + v_{bottom}^2 \rightarrow$$

$$v_{top} = \sqrt{\frac{2(P_{bottom} - P_{top})}{\rho} + v_{bottom}^2} = \sqrt{\frac{2mg}{\rho A} + v_{bottom}^2} = \sqrt{\frac{2(2.0 \times 10^6 \text{ kg})(9.80 \text{ m/s}^2)}{(1.29 \text{ kg/m}^3)(1200 \text{ m}^2)} + (95 \text{ m/s})^2}$$

$$= 185.3 \text{ m/s} \approx \boxed{190 \text{ m/s}}$$

87. From Poiseuille's equation, the viscosity can be found from the volume flow rate, the geometry of the tube, and the pressure difference. The pressure difference over the length of the tube is the same as the pressure difference due to the height of the reservoir, assuming that the open end of the needle is at atmospheric pressure.

$$Q = \frac{\pi R^4 (P_2 - P_1)}{8\eta L} \quad ; \quad P_2 - P_1 = \rho_{blood} gh \rightarrow$$

$$\eta = \frac{\pi R^4 (P_2 - P_1)}{8QL} = \frac{\pi R^4 \rho_{blood} gh}{8QL} = \frac{\pi (0.20 \times 10^{-3}\,\text{m})^4 (1.05 \times 10^3\,\text{kg/m}^3)(9.80\,\text{m/s}^2)(1.70\,\text{m})}{8\left[4.1\dfrac{\text{cm}^3}{\text{min}} \times \dfrac{1\,\text{min}}{60\,\text{s}} \times \dfrac{10^{-6}\,\text{m}^3}{\text{cm}^3}\right](3.8 \times 10^{-2}\,\text{m})}$$

$$= \boxed{4.2 \times 10^{-3}\,\text{Pa} \cdot \text{s}}$$

88. From Poiseuille's equation, the volume flow rate Q is proportional to R^4 if all other factors are the same. Thus Q/R^4 is constant. Also, if the diameter is reduced by 15%, so is the radius.

$$\frac{Q_{final}}{R_{final}^4} = \frac{Q_{initial}}{R_{initial}^4} \quad \rightarrow \quad \frac{Q_{final}}{Q_{initial}} = \frac{R_{final}^4}{R_{initial}^4} = (0.85)^4 = 0.52$$

$\boxed{\text{The flow rate is 52\% of the original value.}}$

CHAPTER 11: Vibrations and Waves

Answers to Questions

1. The blades in an electric shaver vibrate, approximately in SHM.
    The speakers in a stereo system vibrate, but usually in a very complicated way since many notes are being sounded at the same time.
    A piano string vibrates when struck, in approximately SHM.
    The pistons in a car engine oscillate, in approximately SHM.
    The free end of a diving board oscillates after a diver jumps, in approximately SHM.

2. The acceleration of a simple harmonic oscillator is zero whenever the oscillating object is at the equilibrium position.

3. The motion of the piston can be approximated as simple harmonic. First of all, the piston will have a constant period while the engine is running at a constant speed. The speed of the piston will be zero at the extremes of its motion – the top and bottom of the stroke – which is the same as in simple harmonic motion. There is a large force exerted on the piston at one extreme of its motion – the combustion of the fuel mixture – and simple harmonic motion has the largest force at the extremes of the motion. Also, as the crankshaft moves in a circle, its component of motion in one dimension is transferred to the piston. It is similar to Fig. 11-6.

4. Since the real spring has mass, the mass that is moving is greater than the mass at the end of the spring. Since $f = \dfrac{1}{2\pi}\sqrt{\dfrac{k}{m}}$, a larger mass means a smaller frequency. Thus the true frequency will be smaller than the "massless spring" approximation. And since the true frequency is smaller, the true period will be larger than the "massless spring" approximation. About 1/3 the mass of the spring contributes to the total mass value.

5. The maximum speed is given by $v_{max} = A\sqrt{k/m}$. Various combinations of changing A, k, and/or m can result in a doubling of the maximum speed. For example, if k and m are kept constant, then doubling the amplitude will double the maximum speed. Or, if A and k are kept constant, then reducing the mass to one-fourth its original value will double the maximum speed. Note that changing either k or m will also change the frequency of the oscillator, since $f = \dfrac{1}{2\pi}\sqrt{\dfrac{k}{m}}$.

6. The scale reading will oscillate with damped oscillations about an equilibrium reading of 5.0 kg, with an initial amplitude of 5.0 kg (so the range of readings is initially from 0.0 kg and 10.0 kg). Due to friction in the spring and scale mechanism, the oscillation amplitude will decrease over time, eventually coming to rest at the 5.0 kg mark.

7. The period of a pendulum clock is inversely proportional to the square root of g, by Equation 11-11a, $T = 2\pi\sqrt{L/g}$. When taken to high altitude, the value of g will decrease (by a small amount), which means the period will increase. If the period is too long, the clock is running slow and so will lose time.

8.   The tire swing approximates a simple pendulum. With a stopwatch, you can measure the period T of

the tire swing, and then solve Equation 11-11a for the length, $L = \dfrac{gT^2}{4\pi^2}$.

9.   To make the water "slosh", you must shake the water (and the pan) at the natural frequency for water waves in the pan. The water then is in resonance, or in a standing wave pattern, and the amplitude of oscillation gets large. That natural frequency is determined by the size of the pan – smaller pans will slosh at higher frequencies, corresponding to shorter wavelengths for the standing waves. The period of the shaking must be the same as the time it takes a water wave to make a "round trip" in the pan.

10.   Some examples of resonance:
         Pushing a child on a playground swing – you always push at the frequency of the swing.
         Seeing a stop sign oscillating back and forth on a windy day.
         When singing in the shower, certain notes will sound much louder than others.
         Utility lines along the roadside can have a large amplitude due to the wind.
         Rubbing your finger on a wineglass and making it "sing".
         Blowing across the top of a bottle.
         A rattle in a car (see Question 11).

11.   A rattle in a car is very often a resonance phenomenon. The car itself vibrates in many pieces, because there are many periodic motions occurring in the car – wheels rotating, pistons moving up and down, valves opening and closing, transmission gears spinning, driveshaft spinning, etc. There are also vibrations caused by irregularities in the road surface as the car is driven, such as hitting a hole in the road. If there is a loose part, and its natural frequency is close to one of the frequencies already occurring in the car's normal operation, then that part will have a larger than usual amplitude of oscillation, and it will rattle. This is why some rattles only occur at certain speeds when driving.

12.   The frequency of a simple periodic wave is equal to the frequency of its source. The wave is created by the source moving the wave medium that is in contact with the source. If you have one end of a taut string in your hand, and you move your hand with a frequency of 2 Hz, then the end of the string in your hand will be moving at 2 Hz, because it is in contact with your hand. Then those parts of the medium that you are moving exert forces on adjacent parts of the medium and cause them to oscillate. Since those two portions of the medium stay in contact with each other, they also must be moving with the same frequency. That can be repeated all along the medium, and so the entire wave throughout the medium has the same frequency as the source.

13.   The speed of the transverse wave is measuring how fast the wave disturbance moves along the cord. For a uniform cord, that speed is constant, and depends on the tension in the cord and the mass density of the cord. The speed of a tiny piece of the cord is measuring how fast the piece of cord moves perpendicularly to the cord, as the disturbance passes by. That speed is not constant – if a sinusoidal wave is traveling on the cord, the speed of each piece of the cord will be given by the speed relationship of a simple harmonic oscillator (Equation 11-9), which depends on the amplitude of the wave, the frequency of the wave, and the specific time of observation.

14.   From Equation 11-19b, the fundamental frequency of oscillation for a string with both ends fixed is

$f_1 = \dfrac{v}{2L}$. The speed of waves on the string is given by Equation 11-13, $v = \sqrt{\dfrac{F_T}{m/L}}$. Combining these two relationships gives $f_1 = \frac{1}{2}\sqrt{\dfrac{F_T}{mL}}$. By wrapping the string with wire, the mass of the string can be greatly increased without changing the length or the tension of the string, and thus the string has a low fundamental frequency.

15. If you strike the horizontal rod vertically, you will create primarily transverse waves. If you strike the rod parallel to its length, you will create primarily longitudinal waves.

16. From Equation 11-14b, the speed of waves in a gas is given by $v = \sqrt{B/\rho}$. A decrease in the density due to a temperature increase therefore leads to a higher speed of sound. We expect the speed of sound to increase as temperature increases.

17. (a) Similar to the discussion in section 11-9 for spherical waves, as a circular wave expands, the circumference of the wave increases. For the energy in the wave to be conserved, as the circumference increases, the intensity has to decrease. The intensity of the wave is proportional to the square of the amplitude
    (b) The water waves will decrease in amplitude due to dissipation of energy from viscosity in the water (dissipative or frictional energy loss).

18. Assuming the two waves are in the same medium, then they will both have the same speed. Since $v = f\lambda$, the wave with the smaller wavelength will have twice the frequency of the other wave. From Equation 11-18, the intensity of wave is proportional to the square of the frequency of the wave. Thus the wave with the shorter wavelength will transmit 4 times as much energy as the other wave.

19. The frequency must stay the same because the media is continuous – the end of one section of cord is physically tied to the other section of cord. If the end of the first section of cord is vibrating up and down with a given frequency, then since it is attached to the other section of cord, the other section must vibrate at the same frequency. If the two pieces of cord did not move at the same frequency, they would not stay connected, and then the waves would not pass from one section to another.

20. The string could be touched at the location of a node without disturbing the motion, because the nodes do not move. A string vibrating in three segments has 2 nodes in addition to the ones at the ends. See the diagram.

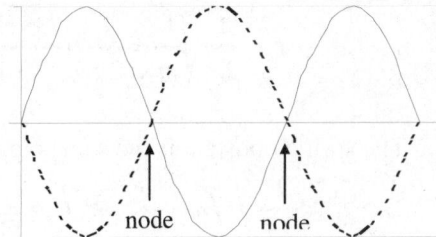

21. The energy of a wave is not localized at one point, because the wave is not localized at one point, and so to talk about the energy "at a node" being zero is not really a meaningful statement. Due to the interference of the waves the total energy of the medium particles at the nodes points is zero, but the energy of the medium is not zero at points of the medium that are not nodes. In fact, the anti-node points have more energy than they would have if only one of the two waves were present.

22. A major distinction between energy transfer by particles and energy transfer by waves is that particles must travel in a straight line from one place to another in order to transfer energy, but waves can diffract around obstacles. For instance, sound can be heard around a corner, while you cannot throw a ball around a corner. So if a barrier is placed between the source of the energy and the

location where the energy is being received, and energy is still received in spite of the barrier, it is a good indication that the energy is being carried by waves. If the placement of the barrier stops the energy transfer, it could be that the energy transfer is being carried out by particles. It could also be that the energy transfer is being carried out with waves whose wavelength is much smaller than the dimensions of the barrier.

Solutions to Problems

1. The particle would travel four times the amplitude: from $x = A$ to $x = 0$ to $x = -A$ to $x = 0$ to $x = A$. So the total distance $= 4A = 4(0.18 \text{ m}) = \boxed{0.72 \text{ m}}$.

2. The spring constant is the ratio of applied force to displacement.

    $$k = \frac{F}{x} = \frac{180 \text{ N} - 75 \text{ N}}{0.85 \text{ m} - 0.65 \text{ m}} = \frac{105 \text{ N}}{0.20 \text{ m}} = \boxed{5.3 \times 10^2 \text{ N/m}}$$

3. The spring constant is found from the ratio of applied force to displacement.

    $$k = \frac{F}{x} = \frac{mg}{x} = \frac{(68 \text{ kg})(9.8 \text{ m/s}^2)}{5 \times 10^{-3} \text{ m}} = 1.333 \times 10^5 \text{ N/m}$$

    The frequency of oscillation is found from the total mass and the spring constant.

    $$f = \frac{1}{2\pi}\sqrt{\frac{k}{m}} = \frac{1}{2\pi}\sqrt{\frac{1.333 \times 10^5 \text{ N/m}}{1568 \text{ kg}}} = 1.467 \text{ Hz} \approx \boxed{1.5 \text{ Hz}}$$

4. (*a*) The spring constant is found from the ratio of applied force to displacement.

    $$k = \frac{F}{x} = \frac{mg}{x} = \frac{(2.7 \text{ kg})(9.80 \text{ m/s}^2)}{3.6 \times 10^{-2} \text{ m}} = 735 \text{ N/m} \approx \boxed{7.4 \times 10^2 \text{ N/m}}$$

    (*b*) The amplitude is the distance pulled down from equilibrium, so $A = \boxed{2.5 \times 10^{-2} \text{ m}}$
    The frequency of oscillation is found from the total mass and the spring constant.

    $$f = \frac{1}{2\pi}\sqrt{\frac{k}{m}} = \frac{1}{2\pi}\sqrt{\frac{735 \text{ N/m}}{2.7 \text{ kg}}} = 2.626 \text{ Hz} \approx \boxed{2.6 \text{ Hz}}$$

5. The spring constant is the same regardless of what mass is hung from the spring.

    $$f = \frac{1}{2\pi}\sqrt{k/m} \;\rightarrow\; \sqrt{k}/2\pi = f\sqrt{m} = \text{constant} \;\rightarrow\; f_1\sqrt{m_1} = f_2\sqrt{m_2} \;\rightarrow$$

    $$f_2 = f_1\sqrt{m_1/m_2} = (3.0 \text{ Hz})\sqrt{0.60 \text{ kg}/0.38 \text{ kg}} = \boxed{3.8 \text{ Hz}}$$

6. The table of data is shown, along with the smoothed graph. Every quarter of a period, the mass moves from an extreme point to the

time	position
0	- A
T /4	0
T/2	A
3T/4	0
T	- A
5T/4	0

    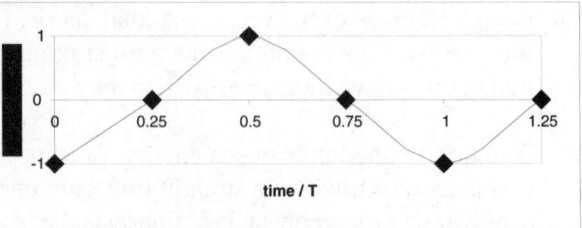

    equilibrium. The graph resembles a cosine wave (actually, the opposite of a cosine wave).

7. The relationship between frequency, mass, and spring constant is $f = \dfrac{1}{2\pi}\sqrt{\dfrac{k}{m}}$.

    (a) $f = \dfrac{1}{2\pi}\sqrt{\dfrac{k}{m}} \rightarrow k = 4\pi^2 f^2 m = 4\pi^2 (4.0\text{ Hz})^2 (2.5\times10^{-4}\text{ kg}) = 0.1579\text{ N/m} \approx \boxed{0.16\text{ N/m}}$

    (b) $f = \dfrac{1}{2\pi}\sqrt{\dfrac{k}{m}} = \dfrac{1}{2\pi}\sqrt{\dfrac{0.1579\text{ N/m}}{5.0\times10^{-4}\text{ kg}}} = \boxed{2.8\text{ Hz}}$

8. The spring constant is the same regardless of what mass is attached to the spring.

    $f = \dfrac{1}{2\pi}\sqrt{\dfrac{k}{m}} \rightarrow \dfrac{k}{4\pi^2} = mf^2 = \text{constant} \rightarrow m_1 f_1^2 = m_2 f_1^2 \rightarrow$

    $(m\text{ kg})(0.88\text{ Hz})^2 = (m\text{ kg} + 0.68\text{ kg})(0.60\text{ Hz})^2 \rightarrow m = \dfrac{(0.68\text{ kg})(0.60\text{ Hz})^2}{(0.88\text{ Hz})^2 - (0.60\text{ Hz})^2} = \boxed{0.59\text{ kg}}$

9. (a) At equilibrium, the velocity is its maximum.

    $v_{max} = \sqrt{\dfrac{k}{m}}A = \omega A = 2\pi f A = 2\pi(3\text{ Hz})(0.13\text{ m}) = 2.450\text{ m/s} \approx \boxed{2.5\text{ m/s}}$

    (b) From Equation (11-5), we find the velocity at any position.

    $v = \pm v_{max}\sqrt{1 - \dfrac{x^2}{A^2}} = \pm(2.45\text{ m/s})\sqrt{1 - \dfrac{(0.10\text{ m})^2}{(0.13\text{ m})^2}} = \pm 1.565\text{ m/s} \approx \boxed{\pm 1.6\text{ m/s}}$

    (c) $E_{total} = \tfrac{1}{2}mv_{max}^2 = \tfrac{1}{2}(0.60\text{ kg})(2.45\text{ m/s})^2 = 1.801\text{ J} \approx \boxed{1.8\text{ J}}$

    (d) Since the object has a maximum displacement at $t = 0$, the position will be described by the cosine function.

    $x = (0.13\text{ m})\cos(2\pi(3.0\text{ Hz})t) \rightarrow \boxed{x = (0.13\text{ m})\cos(6.0\pi t)}$

10. The relationship between the velocity and the position of a SHO is given by Equation (11-5). Set that expression equal to half the maximum speed, and solve for the displacement.

    $v = \pm v_{max}\sqrt{1 - x^2/A^2} = \tfrac{1}{2}v_{max} \rightarrow \pm\sqrt{1 - x^2/A^2} = \tfrac{1}{2} \rightarrow 1 - x^2/A^2 = \tfrac{1}{4} \rightarrow x^2/A^2 = \tfrac{3}{4} \rightarrow$

    $\boxed{x = \pm\sqrt{3}A/2 \approx 0.866A}$

11. Since $F = -kx = ma$ for an object attached to a spring, the acceleration is proportional to the displacement (although in the opposite direction), as $a = -xk/m$. Thus the acceleration will have half its maximum value where the displacement has half its maximum value, at $\boxed{\pm\tfrac{1}{2}x_0}$

12. The spring constant can be found from the stretch distance corresponding to the weight suspended on the spring.

    $k = \dfrac{F}{x} = \dfrac{mg}{x} = \dfrac{(2.62\text{ kg})(9.80\text{ m/s}^2)}{0.315\text{ m}} = 81.5\text{ N/m}$

    After being stretched further and released, the mass will oscillate. It takes one-quarter of a period for the mass to move from the maximum displacement to the equilibrium position.

$$\tfrac{1}{4}T = \tfrac{1}{4}2\pi\sqrt{m/k} = \frac{\pi}{2}\sqrt{\frac{2.62\text{ kg}}{81.5\text{ N/m}}} = \boxed{0.282\text{ s}}$$

13. (a) The total energy of an object in SHM is constant. When the position is at the amplitude, the speed is zero. Use that relationship to find the amplitude.

$$E_{\text{tot}} = \tfrac{1}{2}mv^2 + \tfrac{1}{2}kx^2 = \tfrac{1}{2}kA^2 \;\rightarrow$$

$$A = \sqrt{\frac{m}{k}v^2 + x^2} = \sqrt{\frac{3.0\text{ kg}}{280\text{ N/m}}(0.55\text{ m/s})^2 + (0.020\text{ m})^2} = 6.034\times10^{-2}\text{ m} \approx \boxed{6.0\times10^{-2}\text{ m}}$$

(b) Again use conservation of energy. The energy is all kinetic energy when the object has its maximum velocity.

$$E_{\text{tot}} = \tfrac{1}{2}mv^2 + \tfrac{1}{2}kx^2 = \tfrac{1}{2}kA^2 = \tfrac{1}{2}mv_{\text{max}}^2 \;\rightarrow$$

$$v_{\text{max}} = A\sqrt{\frac{k}{m}} = (6.034\times10^{-2}\text{ m})\sqrt{\frac{280\text{ N/m}}{3.0\text{ kg}}} = 0.5829\text{ m/s} \approx \boxed{0.58\text{ m/s}}$$

14. The spring constant is found from the ratio of applied force to displacement.

$$k = \frac{F}{x} = \frac{80.0\text{ N}}{0.200\text{ m}} = 4.00\times10^2\text{ N/m}$$

Assuming that there are no dissipative forces acting on the ball, the elastic potential energy in the loaded position will become kinetic energy of the ball.

$$E_i = E_f \;\rightarrow\; \tfrac{1}{2}kx_{\text{max}}^2 = \tfrac{1}{2}mv_{\text{max}}^2 \;\rightarrow\; v_{\text{max}} = x_{\text{max}}\sqrt{\frac{k}{m}} = (0.200\text{ m})\sqrt{\frac{4.00\times10^2\text{ N/m}}{0.180\text{ kg}}} = \boxed{9.43\text{ m/s}}$$

15. (a) The work done to compress a spring is stored as potential energy.

$$W = \tfrac{1}{2}kx^2 \;\rightarrow\; k = \frac{2W}{x^2} = \frac{2(3.0\text{ J})}{(0.12\text{ m})^2} = 416.7\text{ N/m} \approx \boxed{4.2\times10^2\text{ N/m}}$$

(b) The distance that the spring was compressed becomes the amplitude of its motion. The maximum acceleration is given by $a_{\text{max}} = \dfrac{k}{m}A$. Solve this for the mass.

$$a_{\text{max}} = \frac{k}{m}A \;\rightarrow\; m = \frac{k}{a_{\text{max}}}A = \left(\frac{4.167\times10^2\text{ N/m}}{15\text{ m/s}^2}\right)(0.12\text{ m}) = 3.333\text{ kg} \approx \boxed{3.3\text{ kg}}$$

16. The general form of the motion is $x = A\cos\omega t = 0.45\cos 6.40t$.

(a) The amplitude is $A = x_{\text{max}} = \boxed{0.45\text{ m}}$.

(b) The frequency is found by $\omega = 2\pi f = 6.40\text{ s}^{-1} \;\rightarrow\; f = \dfrac{6.40\text{ s}^{-1}}{2\pi} = 1.019\text{ Hz} \approx \boxed{1.02\text{ Hz}}$

(c) The total energy is given by

$$E_{\text{total}} = \tfrac{1}{2}mv_{\text{max}}^2 = \tfrac{1}{2}m(\omega A)^2 = \tfrac{1}{2}(0.60\text{ kg})\left[(6.40\text{ s}^{-1})(0.45\text{ m})\right]^2 = 2.488\text{ J} \approx \boxed{2.5\text{ J}}$$

(d) The potential energy is given by

$$E_{\text{potential}} = \tfrac{1}{2}kx^2 = \tfrac{1}{2}m\omega^2 x^2 = \tfrac{1}{2}(0.60\text{ kg})(6.40\text{ s}^{-1})^2(0.30\text{ m})^2 = 1.111\text{ J} \approx \boxed{1.1\text{ J}}$$

The kinetic energy is given by

$$E_{kinetic} = E_{total} - E_{potential} = 2.488\ J - 1.111\ J = 1.377\ J \approx \boxed{1.4\ J}$$

17. If the energy of the SHO is half potential and half kinetic, then the potential energy is half the total energy. The total energy is the potential energy when the displacement has the value of the amplitude.

$$E_{pot} = \tfrac{1}{2}E_{tot} \quad \rightarrow \quad \tfrac{1}{2}kx^2 = \tfrac{1}{2}\left(\tfrac{1}{2}kA^2\right) \quad \rightarrow \quad \boxed{x = \pm\frac{1}{\sqrt{2}}A \approx \pm 0.707A}$$

18. If the frequencies and masses are the same, then the spring constants for the two vibrations are the same. The total energy is given by the maximum potential energy.

$$\frac{E_1}{E_2} = \frac{\tfrac{1}{2}kA_1^2}{\tfrac{1}{2}kA_2^2} = \left(\frac{A_1}{A_2}\right)^2 = 7.0 \quad \rightarrow \quad \frac{A_1}{A_2} = \sqrt{7.0} = \boxed{2.6}$$

19. (a) The general equation for SHM is Equation (11-8c), $y = A\cos\left(2\pi t/T\right)$. For the pumpkin,

$$\boxed{y = \left(0.18\ \text{m}\right)\cos\left(\frac{2\pi t}{0.65\ \text{s}}\right)}.$$

(b) The time to return back to the equilibrium position is one-quarter of a period.

$$t = \tfrac{1}{4}T = \tfrac{1}{4}\left(0.65\ \text{s}\right) = \boxed{0.16\ \text{s}}$$

(c) The maximum speed is given by the angular frequency times the amplitude.

$$v_{max} = \omega A = \frac{2\pi}{T}A = \frac{2\pi}{0.65\ \text{s}}\left(0.18\ \text{m}\right) = \boxed{1.7\ \text{m/s}}$$

(d) The maximum acceleration is given by

$$a_{max} = \omega^2 A = \left(\frac{2\pi}{T}\right)^2 A = \frac{4\pi^2}{\left(0.65\ \text{s}\right)^2}\left(0.18\ \text{m}\right) = \boxed{17\ \text{m/s}^2}.$$

The maximum acceleration is first attained at the release point of the pumpkin.

20. Consider the first free-body diagram for the block while it is at equilibrium, so that the net force is zero. Newton's 2nd law for vertical forces, choosing up as positive, gives this.

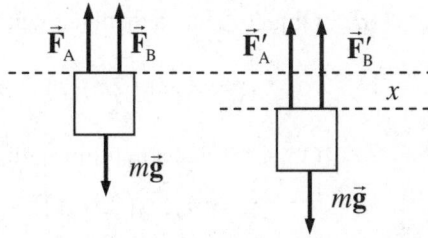

$$\sum F_y = F_A + F_B - mg = 0 \quad \rightarrow \quad F_A + F_B = mg$$

Now consider the second free-body diagram, in which the block is displaced a distance x from the equilibrium point. Each upward force will have increased by an amount $-kx$, since $x < 0$. Again write Newton's 2nd law for vertical forces.

$$\sum F_y = F_{net} = F_A' + F_B' - mg = F_A - kx + F_B - kx - mg = -2kx + \left(F_A + F_B - mg\right) = -2kx$$

This is the general form of a restoring force that produces SHM, with an effective spring constant of $2k$. Thus the frequency of vibration is as follows.

$$f = \frac{1}{2\pi}\sqrt{k_{effective}/m} = \boxed{\frac{1}{2\pi}\sqrt{\frac{2k}{m}}}$$

21. The equation of motion is $x = 0.38\sin 6.50t = A\sin\omega t$.

   (a) The amplitude is $A = x_{max} = \boxed{0.38\text{ m}}$.

   (b) The frequency is found by $\omega = 2\pi f = 6.50\text{ s}^{-1}$ → $f = \dfrac{6.50\text{ s}^{-1}}{2\pi} = \boxed{1.03\text{ Hz}}$

   (c) The period is the reciprocal of the frequency. $T = 1/f = 1/1.03\text{ Hz} = \boxed{0.967\text{ s}}$.

   (d) The total energy is given by
   $$E_{total} = \tfrac{1}{2}mv_{max}^2 = \tfrac{1}{2}m(\omega A)^2 = \tfrac{1}{2}(0.300\text{ kg})\left[(6.50\text{ s}^{-1})(0.38\text{ m})\right]^2 = 0.9151\text{ J} \approx \boxed{0.92\text{ J}}.$$

   (e) The potential energy is given by
   $$E_{potential} = \tfrac{1}{2}kx^2 = \tfrac{1}{2}m\omega^2 x^2 = \tfrac{1}{2}(0.300\text{ kg})(6.50\text{ s}^{-1})^2(0.090\text{m})^2 = 0.0513\text{ J} \approx \boxed{5.1\times10^{-2}\text{ J}}.$$

   The kinetic energy is given by
   $$E_{kinetic} = E_{total} - E_{potential} = 0.9151\text{ J} - 0.0513\text{ J} = 0.8638\text{ J} \approx \boxed{0.86\text{ J}}.$$

   (f)

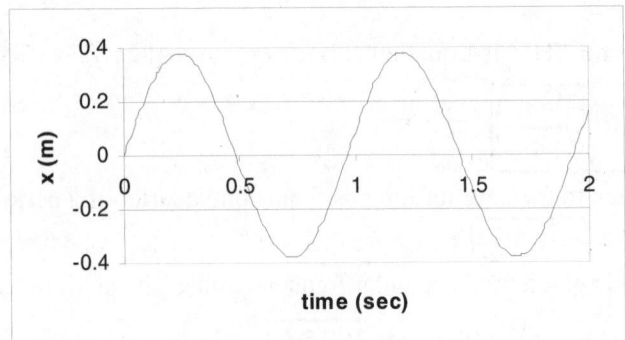

22. (a) For A, the amplitude is $A_A = \boxed{2.5\text{ m}}$. For B, the amplitude is $A_B = \boxed{3.5\text{ m}}$.

   (b) For A, the frequency is 1 cycle every 4.0 seconds, so $f_A = \boxed{0.25\text{ Hz}}$. For B, the frequency is 1 cycle every 2.0 seconds, so $f_B = \boxed{0.50\text{ Hz}}$.

   (c) For C, the period is $T_A = \boxed{4.0\text{ s}}$. For B, the period is $T_B = \boxed{2.0\text{ s}}$

   (d) Object A has a displacement of 0 when $t = 0$, so it is a sine function.
   $$x_A = A_A\sin(2\pi f_A t) \rightarrow \boxed{x_A = (2.5\text{ m})\sin\left(\frac{\pi}{2}t\right)}$$

   Object B has a maximum displacement when $t = 0$, so it is a cosine function.
   $$x_B = A_B\cos(2\pi f_B t) \rightarrow \boxed{x_B = (3.5\text{ m})\cos(\pi t)}$$

23. (a) Find the period and frequency from the mass and the spring constant.
   $$T = 2\pi\sqrt{m/k} = 2\pi\sqrt{0.755\text{ kg}/(124\text{ N/m})} = \boxed{0.490\text{ s}} \qquad f = 1/T = 1/(0.490\text{ s}) = \boxed{2.04\text{ Hz}}$$

   (b) The initial speed is the maximum speed, and that can be used to find the amplitude.
   $$v_{max} = A\sqrt{k/m} \rightarrow A = v_{max}\sqrt{m/k} = (2.96\text{ m/s})\sqrt{0.755\text{ kg}/(124\text{ N/m})} = \boxed{0.231\text{ m}}$$

   (c) The maximum acceleration can be found from the mass, spring constant, and amplitude
   $$a_{max} = Ak/m = (0.231\text{ m})(124\text{ N/m})/(0.755\text{ kg}) = \boxed{37.9\text{ m/s}^2}$$

(*d*) Because the mass started at the equilibrium position of $x = 0$, the position function will be proportional to the sine function.

$$x = (0.231 \text{ m})\sin[2\pi(2.04 \text{ Hz})t] \quad \rightarrow \quad \boxed{x = (0.231 \text{ m})\sin(4.08\pi t)}$$

(*e*) The maximum energy is the kinetic energy that the object has when at the equilibrium position.

$$E = \tfrac{1}{2}mv_{max}^2 = \tfrac{1}{2}(0.755 \text{ kg})(2.96 \text{ m/s})^2 = \boxed{3.31 \text{ J}}$$

24. We assume that downward is the positive direction of motion. For this motion, we have

$k = 305 \text{ N/m}$, $A = 0.280 \text{ m}$, $m = 0.260 \text{ kg}$ and $\omega = \sqrt{k/m} = \sqrt{305 \text{ N/m}/0.260 \text{ kg}} = 34.250 \text{ rad/s}$.

(*a*) Since the mass has a zero displacement and a positive velocity at $t = 0$, the equation is a sine function.

$$\boxed{y(t) = (0.280 \text{ m})\sin[(34.3 \text{ rad/s})t]}$$

(*b*) The period of oscillation is given by $T = \dfrac{2\pi}{\omega} = \dfrac{2\pi}{34.25 \text{ rad/s}} = 0.18345 \text{ s}$. The spring will have

its maximum extension at times given by the following.

$$t_{max} = \frac{T}{4} + nT = \boxed{4.59 \times 10^{-2} \text{ s} + n(0.183 \text{ s}), \, n = 0, 1, 2, \cdots}$$

The spring will have its minimum extension at times given by the following.

$$t_{min} = \frac{3T}{4} + nT = \boxed{1.38 \times 10^{-1} \text{ s} + n(0.183 \text{ s}), \, n = 0, 1, 2, \cdots}$$

25. If the block is displaced a distance x to the right in the diagram, then spring # 1 will exert a force $F_1 = -k_1 x$, in the opposite direction to x. Likewise, spring # 2 will exert a force $F_2 = -k_2 x$, in the same direction as F_1. Thus the net force on the block is $F = F_1 + F_2 = -k_1 x - k_2 x = -(k_1 + k_2)x$. The

effective spring constant is thus $k = k_1 + k_2$, and the period is given by $T = 2\pi\sqrt{\dfrac{m}{k}} = \boxed{2\pi\sqrt{\dfrac{m}{k_1 + k_2}}}$.

26. The energy of the oscillator will be conserved after the collision. Thus

$$E = \tfrac{1}{2}kA^2 = \tfrac{1}{2}(m+M)v_{max}^2 \quad \rightarrow \quad v_{max} = A\sqrt{k/(m+M)}$$

This speed is the speed that the block and bullet have immediately after the collision. Linear momentum in one dimension will have been conserved during the collision, and so the initial speed of the bullet can be found.

$$P_{before} = P_{after} \quad \rightarrow \quad mv_o = (m+M)v_{max}$$

$$v_o = \frac{m+M}{m}A\sqrt{\frac{k}{m+M}} = \frac{6.25 \times 10^{-1} \text{ kg}}{2.5 \times 10^{-2} \text{ kg}}(2.15 \times 10^{-1} \text{ m})\sqrt{\frac{7.70 \times 10^3 \text{ N/m}}{6.25 \times 10^{-1} \text{ kg}}} = \boxed{597 \text{ m/s}}$$

27. The period of the jumper's motion is $T = \dfrac{38.0 \text{ s}}{8 \text{ cycles}} = 4.75 \text{ s}$. The spring constant can then be found

from the period and the jumper's mass.

$$T = 2\pi\sqrt{\frac{m}{k}} \quad \rightarrow \quad k = \frac{4\pi^2 m}{T^2} = \frac{4\pi^2(65.0 \text{ kg})}{(4.75 \text{ s})^2} = 113.73 \text{ N/m} \approx \boxed{114 \text{ N/m}}$$

The stretch of the bungee cord needs to provide a force equal to the weight of the jumper when he is at the equilibrium point.

$$k\Delta x = mg \quad \rightarrow \quad \Delta x = \frac{mg}{k} = \frac{(65.0\,\text{kg})(9.80\,\text{m/s}^2)}{113.73\,\text{N/m}} = 5.60\,\text{m}$$

Thus the unstretched bungee cord must be $25.0\,\text{m} - 5.60\,\text{m} = \boxed{19.4\,\text{m}}$

28. (*a*) The period is given by $T = \dfrac{60\,\text{s}}{36\,\text{cycles}} = \boxed{1.7\,\text{s/cycle}}$.

    (*b*) The frequency is given by $f = \dfrac{36\,\text{cycles}}{60\,\text{s}} = \boxed{0.60\,\text{Hz}}$.

29. The period of a pendulum is given by $T = 2\pi\sqrt{L/g}$. Solve for the length using a period of 2.0 seconds.

$$T = 2\pi\sqrt{L/g} \quad \rightarrow \quad L = \frac{T^2 g}{4\pi^2} = \frac{(2.0\,\text{s})^2(9.8\,\text{m/s}^2)}{4\pi^2} = \boxed{0.99\,\text{m}}$$

30. The period of a pendulum is given by $T = 2\pi\sqrt{L/g}$. The length is assumed to be the same for the pendulum both on Mars and on Earth.

$$T = 2\pi\sqrt{L/g} \quad \rightarrow \quad \frac{T_{\text{Mars}}}{T_{\text{Earth}}} = \frac{2\pi\sqrt{L/g_{\text{Mars}}}}{2\pi\sqrt{L/g_{\text{Earth}}}} = \sqrt{\frac{g_{\text{Earth}}}{g_{\text{Mars}}}} \quad \rightarrow$$

$$T_{\text{Mars}} = T_{\text{Earth}}\sqrt{\frac{g_{\text{Earth}}}{g_{\text{Mars}}}} = (0.80\,\text{s})\sqrt{\frac{1}{0.37}} = \boxed{1.3\,\text{s}}$$

31. The period of a pendulum is given by $T = 2\pi\sqrt{L/g}$.

    (*a*) $T = 2\pi\sqrt{L/g} = 2\pi\sqrt{\dfrac{0.80\,\text{m}}{9.8\,\text{m/s}^2}} = \boxed{1.8\,\text{s}}$

    (*b*) If the pendulum is in free fall, there is no tension in the string supporting the pendulum bob, and so no restoring force to cause oscillations. Thus there will be no period – the pendulum will not oscillate and so no period can be defined.

32. (*a*) The frequency can be found from the length of the pendulum, and the acceleration due to gravity.

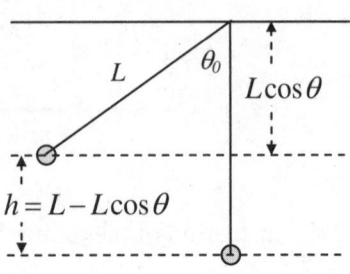

$$f = \frac{1}{2\pi}\sqrt{\frac{g}{L}} = \frac{1}{2\pi}\sqrt{\frac{9.80\,\text{m/s}^2}{0.760\,\text{m}}} = 0.57151\,\text{Hz} \approx \boxed{0.572\,\text{Hz}}$$

    (*b*) To find the speed at the lowest point, use the conservation of energy relating the lowest point to the release point of the pendulum. Take the lowest point to be the zero level of gravitational potential energy.

$$E_{\text{top}} = E_{\text{bottom}} \quad \rightarrow \quad KE_{\text{top}} + PE_{\text{top}} = KE_{\text{bottom}} + PE_{\text{bottom}}$$

$$0 + mg(L - L\cos\theta_{\text{o}}) = \tfrac{1}{2}mv_{\text{bottom}}^2 + 0$$

$$v_{\text{bottom}} = \sqrt{2gL(1-\cos\theta_o)} = \sqrt{2(9.80\,\text{m/s}^2)(0.760\,\text{m})(1-\cos 12.0°)} = \boxed{0.571\,\text{m/s}}$$

(c) The total energy can be found from the kinetic energy at the bottom of the motion.

$$E_{\text{total}} = \tfrac{1}{2}mv_{\text{bottom}}^2 = \tfrac{1}{2}(0.365\,\text{kg})(0.571\,\text{m/s})^2 = \boxed{5.95\times10^{-2}\,\text{J}}$$

33. There are $(24\,\text{h})(60\,\text{min/h})(60\,\text{s/min}) = 86,400\,\text{s}$ in a day. The clock should make one cycle in exactly two seconds (a "tick" and a "tock"), and so the clock should make 43,200 cycles per day. After one day, the clock in question is 30 seconds slow, which means that it has made 15 less cycles than required for precise timekeeping. Thus the clock is only making 43,185 cycles in a day.

Accordingly, the period of the clock must be decreased by a factor $\dfrac{43,185}{43,200}$.

$$T_{\text{new}} = \frac{43,185}{43,200}T_{\text{old}} \;\rightarrow\; 2\pi\sqrt{L_{\text{new}}/g} = \left(\frac{43,185}{43,200}\right)2\pi\sqrt{L_{\text{old}}/g} \;\rightarrow$$

$$L_{\text{new}} = \left(\frac{43,185}{43,200}\right)^2 L_{\text{old}} = \left(\frac{43,185}{43,200}\right)^2 (0.9930\,\text{m}) = 0.9923\,\text{m}$$

Thus the pendulum should be $\boxed{\text{shortened by 0.7 mm}}$.

34. Use energy conservation to relate the potential energy at the maximum height of the pendulum to the kinetic energy at the lowest point of the swing. Take the lowest point to be the zero location for gravitational potential energy. See the diagram.

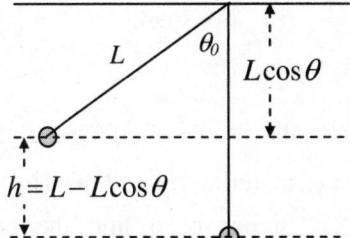

$$E_{\text{top}} = E_{\text{bottom}} \;\rightarrow\; KE_{\text{top}} + PE_{\text{top}} = KE_{\text{bottom}} + PE_{\text{bottom}} \;\rightarrow$$

$$0 + mgh = \tfrac{1}{2}mv_{\text{max}}^2 \;\rightarrow\; v_{\text{max}} = \sqrt{2gh} = \boxed{\sqrt{2gL(1-\cos\theta_o)}}$$

35. The equation of motion for an object in SHM that has the maximum displacement at $t=0$ is given by $x = A\cos(2\pi f t)$. For a pendulum, $x = L\theta$ and so $x_{\text{max}} = A = L\theta_{\text{max}}$, where θ must be measured in radians. Thus the equation for the pendulum's angular displacement is

$$L\theta = L\theta_{\text{max}}\cos(2\pi f t) \;\rightarrow\; \theta = \theta_{\text{max}}\cos(2\pi f t)$$

If both sides of the equation are multiplied by $180°/\pi$ rad, then the angles can be measured in degrees. Thus the angular displacement of the pendulum can be written as below. Please note that the argument of the cosine function is still in radians.

$$\theta° = \theta_{\text{max}}°\cos(2\pi ft) = 15°\cos(5.0\pi t)$$

(a) $\theta°(t=0.25\,\text{s}) = 15°\cos(5.0\pi(0.25)) = \boxed{-11°}$

(b) $\theta°(t=1.6\,\text{s}) = 15°\cos(5.0\pi(1.6)) = \boxed{15°}$ (here the time is exactly 4 periods)

(c) $\theta°(t=500\,\text{s}) = 15°\cos(5.0\pi(500)) = \boxed{15°}$ (here the time is exactly 1250 periods)

36. The wave speed is given by $v = \lambda f$. The period is 3.0 seconds, and the wavelength is 6.5 m.

$$v = \lambda f = \lambda/T = (6.5\,\text{m})/(3.0\,\text{s}) = \boxed{2.2\,\text{m/s}}$$

37. The distance between wave crests is the wavelength of the wave.

$$\lambda = v/f = 343\,\text{m/s}/262\,\text{Hz} = \boxed{1.31\,\text{m}}$$

38. To find the wavelength, use $\lambda = v/f$.

AM: $\quad \lambda_1 = \dfrac{v}{f_1} = \dfrac{3.00\times10^8\,\text{m/s}}{550\times10^3\,\text{Hz}} = 545\,\text{m} \qquad \lambda_2 = \dfrac{v}{f_2} = \dfrac{3.00\times10^8\,\text{m/s}}{1600\times10^3\,\text{Hz}} = 188\,\text{m} \qquad \boxed{\text{AM: 190 m to 550 m}}$

FM: $\quad \lambda_1 = \dfrac{v}{f_1} = \dfrac{3.00\times10^8\,\text{m/s}}{88.0\times10^6\,\text{Hz}} = 3.41\,\text{m} \qquad \lambda_2 = \dfrac{v}{f_2} = \dfrac{3.00\times10^8\,\text{m/s}}{108\times10^6\,\text{Hz}} = 2.78\,\text{m} \qquad \boxed{\text{FM: 2.78 m to 3.41 m}}$

39. The elastic and bulk moduli are taken from Table 9-1 in chapter 9. The densities are taken from Table 10-1 in chapter 10.

    (a) For water: $\quad v = \sqrt{B/\rho} = \sqrt{\dfrac{2.0\times10^9\,\text{N}/\text{m}^2}{1.00\times10^3\,\text{kg}/\text{m}^3}} = \boxed{1.4\times10^3\,\text{m/s}}$

    (b) For granite: $\quad v = \sqrt{E/\rho} = \sqrt{\dfrac{45\times10^9\,\text{N}/\text{m}^2}{2.7\times10^3\,\text{kg}/\text{m}^3}} = \boxed{4.1\times10^3\,\text{m/s}}$

    (c) For steel: $\quad v = \sqrt{E/\rho} = \sqrt{\dfrac{200\times10^9\,\text{N}/\text{m}^2}{7.8\times10^3\,\text{kg}/\text{m}^3}} = \boxed{5.1\times10^3\,\text{m/s}}$

40. The speed of a longitudinal wave in a solid is given by $v = \sqrt{E/\rho}$. Call the density of the less dense material ρ_1, and the density of the more dense material ρ_2. The less dense material will have the higher speed, since the speed is inversely proportional to the square root of the density.

$$\frac{v_1}{v_2} = \frac{\sqrt{E/\rho_1}}{\sqrt{E/\rho_2}} = \sqrt{\frac{\rho_2}{\rho_1}} = \sqrt{2} = \boxed{1.41}$$

41. To find the time for a pulse to travel from one end of the cord to the other, the velocity of the pulse on the cord must be known. For a cord under tension, we have $v = \sqrt{\dfrac{F_T}{m/L}}$.

$$v = \frac{\Delta x}{\Delta t} = \sqrt{\frac{F_T}{m/L}} \quad \rightarrow \quad \Delta t = \frac{\Delta x}{\sqrt{\dfrac{F_T}{m/L}}} = \frac{28\,\text{m}}{\sqrt{\dfrac{150\,\text{N}}{(0.65\,\text{kg})/(28\,\text{m})}}} = \boxed{0.35\,\text{s}}$$

42. (a) The speed of the pulse is given by

$$v = \frac{\Delta x}{\Delta t} = \frac{2(620\,\text{m})}{16\,\text{s}} = 77.5\,\text{m/s} \approx \boxed{78\,\text{m/s}}$$

    (b) The tension is related to the speed of the pulse by $v = \sqrt{\dfrac{F_T}{m/L}}$. The mass per unit length of the cable can be found from its volume and density.

$$\rho = \frac{m}{V} = \frac{m}{\pi(d/2)^2 L} \quad \rightarrow \quad \frac{m}{L} = \pi\rho\left(\frac{d}{2}\right)^2 = \pi\left(7.8\times10^3\,\text{kg/m}^3\right)\left(\frac{1.5\times10^{-2}\,\text{m}}{2}\right)^2 = 1.378\,\text{kg/m}$$

$$v = \sqrt{\frac{F_T}{m/L}} \quad \rightarrow \quad F_T = v^2\frac{m}{L} = \left(77.5\,\text{m/s}\right)^2\left(1.378\,\text{kg/m}\right) = \boxed{8.3\times10^3\,\text{N}}$$

43. The speed of the water wave is given by $v = \sqrt{B/\rho}$, where B is the bulk modulus of water, from Table 9-1, and ρ is the density of sea water, from Table 10-1. The wave travels twice the depth of the ocean during the elapsed time.

$$v = \frac{2L}{t} \quad \rightarrow \quad L = \frac{vt}{2} = \frac{t}{2}\sqrt{\frac{B}{\rho}} = \frac{3.0\,\text{s}}{2}\sqrt{\frac{2.0\times10^9\,\text{N/m}^2}{1.025\times10^3\,\text{kg/m}^3}} = \boxed{2.1\times10^3\,\text{m}}$$

44. (a) Both waves travel the same distance, so $\Delta x = v_1 t_1 = v_2 t_2$. We let the smaller speed be v_1, and the larger speed be v_2. The slower wave will take longer to arrive, and so t_1 is more than t_2.

$$t_1 = t_2 + 2.0\,\text{min} = t_2 + 120\,\text{s} \quad \rightarrow \quad v_1\left(t_2 + 120\,\text{s}\right) = v_2 t_2 \quad \rightarrow$$

$$t_2 = \frac{v_1}{v_2 - v_1}\left(120\,\text{s}\right) = \frac{5.5\,\text{km/s}}{8.5\,\text{km/s} - 5.5\,\text{km/s}}\left(120\,\text{s}\right) = 220\,\text{s}$$

$$\Delta x = v_2 t_2 = \left(8.5\,\text{km/s}\right)\left(220\,\text{s}\right) = \boxed{1.9\times10^3\,\text{km}}$$

(b) This is not enough information to determine the epicenter. All that is known is the distance of the epicenter from the seismic station. The direction is not known, so the epicenter lies on a circle of radius $1.9\times10^3\,\text{km}$ from the seismic station. Readings from at least two other seismic stations are needed to determine the epicenter's position.

45. We assume that the earthquake wave is moving the ground vertically, since it is a transverse wave. An object sitting on the ground will then be moving with SHM, due to the two forces on it – the normal force upwards from the ground and the weight downwards due to gravity. If the object loses contact with the ground, then the normal force will be zero, and the only force on the object will be its weight. If the only force is the weight, then the object will have an acceleration of g downwards. Thus the limiting condition for beginning to lose contact with the ground is when the maximum acceleration caused by the wave is greater than g. Any larger downward acceleration and the ground would "fall" quicker than the object. The maximum acceleration is related to the amplitude and the frequency as follows.

$$a_{max} = \omega^2 A > g \quad \rightarrow \quad A > \frac{g}{\omega^2} = \frac{g}{4\pi^2 f^2} = \frac{9.8\,\text{m/s}^2}{4\pi^2\left(0.50\,\text{Hz}\right)^2} = \boxed{0.99\,\text{m}}$$

46. (a) Assume that the earthquake waves spread out spherically from the source. Under those conditions, Eq. (11-16b) applies, stating that intensity is inversely proportional to the square of the distance from the source of the wave.

$$I_{20\,\text{km}}/I_{10\,\text{km}} = \left(10\,\text{km}\right)^2\big/\left(20\,\text{km}\right)^2 = \boxed{0.25}$$

(b) The intensity is proportional to the square of the amplitude, and so the amplitude is inversely proportional to the distance from the source of the wave.

$$A_{20\,\text{km}}/A_{10\,\text{km}} = 10\,\text{km}/20\,\text{km} = \boxed{0.50}$$

47. (*a*) Assuming spherically symmetric waves, the intensity will be inversely proportional to the square of the distance from the source. Thus Ir^2 will be constant.

$$I_{near}r_{near}^2 = I_{far}r_{far}^2 \quad \rightarrow$$

$$I_{near} = I_{far}\frac{r_{far}^2}{r_{near}^2} = \left(2.0\times10^6 \text{ W/m}^2\right)\frac{\left(48 \text{ km}\right)^2}{\left(1 \text{ km}\right)^2} = 4.608\times10^9 \text{ W/m}^2 \approx \boxed{4.6\times10^9 \text{ W/m}^2}$$

(*b*) The power passing through an area is the intensity times the area.

$$P = IA = \left(4.608\times10^9 \text{ W/m}^2\right)\left(5.0\,\text{m}^2\right) = \boxed{2.3\times10^{10}\,\text{W}}$$

48. From Equation (11-18), if the speed, medium density, and frequency of the two waves are the same, then the intensity is proportional to the square of the amplitude.

$$I_2/I_1 = E_2/E_1 = A_2^2/A_1^2 = 2 \quad \rightarrow \quad A_2/A_1 = \sqrt{2} = \boxed{1.41}$$

The more energetic wave has the larger amplitude.

49. From Equation (11-18), if the speed, medium density, and frequency of the two waves are the same, then the intensity is proportional to the square of the amplitude.

$$I_2/I_1 = P_2/P_1 = A_2^2/A_1^2 = 3 \quad \rightarrow \quad A_2/A_1 = \sqrt{3} = \boxed{1.73}$$

The more energetic wave has the larger amplitude.

50. The bug moves in SHM as the wave passes. The maximum KE of a particle in SHM is the total energy, which is given by $E_{total} = \frac{1}{2}kA^2$. Compare the two KE maxima.

$$\frac{KE_2}{KE_1} = \frac{\frac{1}{2}kA_2^2}{\frac{1}{2}kA_1^2} = \left(\frac{A_2}{A_1}\right)^2 = \left(\frac{2.25 \text{ cm}}{3.0 \text{ cm}}\right)^2 = \boxed{0.56}$$

51. (*a*)   (*b*)

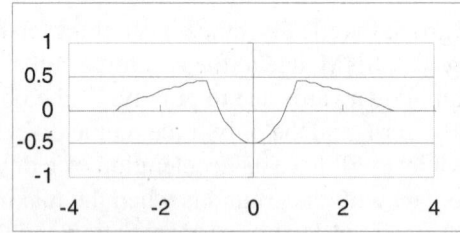   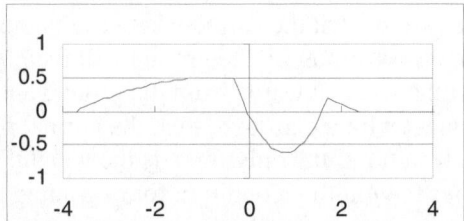

(*c*) The energy is all kinetic energy at the moment when the string has no displacement. There is no elastic potential energy at that moment. Each piece of the string has speed but no displacement.

52. The frequencies of the harmonics of a string that is fixed at both ends are given by $f_n = nf_1$, and so the first four harmonics are $\boxed{f_1 = 440 \text{ Hz}, f_2 = 880 \text{ Hz}, f_3 = 1320 \text{ Hz}, f_4 = 1760 \text{ Hz}}$.

53. The fundamental frequency of the full string is given by $f_{unfingered} = \dfrac{v}{2L} = 294 \text{ Hz}$. If the length is reduced to 2/3 of its current value, and the velocity of waves on the string is not changed, then the new frequency will be

$$f_{\text{fingered}} = \frac{v}{2\left(\frac{2}{3}L\right)} = \frac{3}{2}\frac{v}{2L} = \left(\frac{3}{2}\right)f_{\text{unfingered}} = \left(\frac{3}{2}\right)294\text{ Hz} = \boxed{441\text{ Hz}}$$

54. Four loops is the standing wave pattern for the 4th harmonic, with a frequency given by $f_4 = 4f_1 = 280$ Hz. Thus $\boxed{f_1 = 70\text{ Hz}, f_2 = 140\text{ Hz}, f_3 = 210\text{ Hz and } f_5 = 350\text{ Hz}}$ are all other resonant frequencies.

55. Adjacent nodes are separated by a half-wavelength, as examination of Figure 11-40 will show.
$$\lambda = \frac{v}{f} \rightarrow \Delta x_{\text{node}} = \tfrac{1}{2}\lambda = \frac{v}{2f} = \frac{92\text{ m/s}}{2(475\text{ Hz})} = \boxed{9.7 \times 10^{-2}\text{ m}}$$

56. Since $f_n = nf_1$, two successive overtones differ by the fundamental frequency, as shown below.
$$\Delta f = f_{n+1} - f_n = (n+1)f_1 - nf_1 = f_1 = 350\text{ Hz} - 280\text{ Hz} = \boxed{70\text{ Hz}}$$

$\boxed{57.}$ The speed of waves on the string is given by equation (11-13), $v = \sqrt{\dfrac{F_T}{m/L}}$. The resonant frequencies

of a string with both ends fixed are given by equation (11-19b), $f_n = \dfrac{nv}{2L_{\text{vib}}}$, where L_{vib} is the length

of the portion that is actually vibrating. Combining these relationships allows the frequencies to be calculated.

$$f_n = \frac{n}{2L_{\text{vib}}}\sqrt{\frac{F_T}{m/L}} \qquad f_1 = \frac{1}{2(0.62\text{ m})}\sqrt{\frac{520\text{ N}}{(3.6 \times 10^{-3}\text{ kg})/(0.90\text{ m})}} = 290.77\text{ Hz}$$

$$f_2 = 2f_1 = 581.54\text{ Hz} \qquad f_3 = 3f_1 = 872.31\text{ Hz}$$

So the three frequencies are $\boxed{290\text{ Hz}, 580\text{ Hz}, 870\text{ Hz}}$, to 2 significant figures.

58. From Equation (11-19b), $f_n = \dfrac{nv}{2L}$, we see that the frequency is proportional to the wave speed on

the stretched string. From equation (11-13), $v = \sqrt{\dfrac{F_T}{m/L}}$, we see that the wave speed is proportional

to the square root of the tension. Thus the frequency is proportional to the square root of the tension.

$$\sqrt{\frac{F_{T2}}{F_{T1}}} = \frac{f_2}{f_1} \rightarrow F_{T2} = \left(\frac{f_2}{f_1}\right)^2 F_{T1} = \left(\frac{200\text{ Hz}}{205\text{ Hz}}\right)^2 F_{T1} = 0.952\,F_{T1}$$

Thus the tension should be $\boxed{\text{decreased by 4.8\%}}$.

59. The string must vibrate in a standing wave pattern to have a certain number of loops. The frequency of the standing waves will all be 60 Hz, the same as the vibrator. That frequency is also expressed

by Equation (11-19b), $f_n = \dfrac{nv}{2L}$. The speed of waves on the string is given by Equation (11-13),

$v = \sqrt{\dfrac{F_T}{m/L}}$. The tension in the string will be the same as the weight of the masses hung from the end

of the string, $F_T = mg$. Combining these relationships gives an expression for the masses hung from the end of the string.

(a) $f_n = \dfrac{nv}{2L} = \dfrac{n}{2L}\sqrt{\dfrac{F_T}{m/L}} = \dfrac{n}{2L}\sqrt{\dfrac{mg}{(m/L)}} \rightarrow m = \dfrac{4L^2 f_n^2 (m/L)}{n^2 g}$

$m_1 = \dfrac{4(1.50\,\text{m})^2 (60\,\text{Hz})^2 (3.9\times10^{-4}\,\text{kg/m})}{1^2 (9.80\,\text{m/s}^2)} = 1.289\,\text{kg} \approx \boxed{1.3\,\text{kg}}$

(b) $m_2 = \dfrac{m_1}{2^2} = \dfrac{1.289\,\text{kg}}{4} = \boxed{0.32\,\text{kg}}$

(c) $m_5 = \dfrac{m_1}{5^2} = \dfrac{1.289\,\text{kg}}{25} = \boxed{5.2\times10^{-2}\,\text{kg}}$

60. The tension in the string is the weight of the hanging mass, $F_T = mg$. The speed of waves on the

string can be found by $v = \sqrt{\dfrac{F_T}{m/L}} = \sqrt{\dfrac{mg}{(m/L)}}$, and the frequency is given as $f = 60\,\text{Hz}$. The

wavelength of waves created on the string will thus be given by

$\lambda = \dfrac{v}{f} = \dfrac{1}{f}\sqrt{\dfrac{mg}{(m/L)}} = \dfrac{1}{60\,\text{Hz}}\sqrt{\dfrac{(0.080\,\text{kg})(9.80\,\text{m/s}^2)}{(3.9\times10^{-4}\,\text{kg/m})}} = 0.7473\,\text{m}$.

The length of the string must be an integer multiple of half of the wavelength for there to be nodes at both ends and thus form a standing wave. Thus $L = \lambda/2,\ \lambda,\ 3\lambda/2,\ \cdots$, and so on. This gives

$L = 0.37\,\text{m}$, $0.75\,\text{m}$, $1.12\,\text{m}$, $1.49\,\text{m}$ as the possible lengths, and so there are $\boxed{4}$ standing wave patterns that may be achieved.

61. From the description of the water's behavior, there is an anti-node at each end of the tub, and a node in the middle. Thus one wavelength is twice the tube length.

$v = \lambda f = (2L_{\text{tub}}) f = 2(0.65\,\text{m})(0.85\,\text{Hz}) = \boxed{1.1\,\text{m/s}}$

62. The speed in the second medium can be found from the law of refraction, Equation (11-20).

$\dfrac{\sin\theta_2}{\sin\theta_1} = \dfrac{v_2}{v_1} \rightarrow v_2 = v_1\dfrac{\sin\theta_2}{\sin\theta_1} = (8.0\,\text{km/s})\left(\dfrac{\sin 35°}{\sin 47°}\right) = \boxed{6.3\,\text{km/s}}$

63. The angle of refraction can be found from the law of refraction, Equation (11-20).

$\dfrac{\sin\theta_2}{\sin\theta_1} = \dfrac{v_2}{v_1} \rightarrow \sin\theta_2 = \sin\theta_1\dfrac{v_2}{v_1} = \sin 34°\dfrac{2.1\,\text{m/s}}{2.8\,\text{m/s}} = 0.419 \rightarrow \theta_2 = \sin^{-1} 0.419 = \boxed{25°}$

64. The angle of refraction can be found from the law of refraction, Equation (11-20). The relative velocities can be found from the relationship given in the problem.

$$\frac{\sin\theta_2}{\sin\theta_1}=\frac{v_2}{v_1}=\frac{331+0.60T_2}{331+0.60T_1} \quad\rightarrow\quad \sin\theta_2=\sin 25°\frac{331+0.60(-10)}{331+0.60(10)}=\sin 25°\frac{325}{337}=0.4076$$

$$\theta_2=\sin^{-1}0.4076=\boxed{24°}$$

65. The angle of refraction can be found from the law of refraction, Equation (11-20). The relative velocities can be found from Equation (11-14a).

$$\frac{\sin\theta_2}{\sin\theta_1}=\frac{v_2}{v_1}=\frac{\sqrt{E/\rho_2}}{\sqrt{E/\rho_1}}=\sqrt{\frac{\rho_1}{\rho_2}}=\sqrt{\frac{SG_1\rho_{water}}{SG_2\rho_{water}}}=\sqrt{\frac{SG_1}{SG_2}}$$

$$\sin\theta_2=\sin\theta_1\sqrt{\frac{SG_1}{SG_2}}=\sin 38°\sqrt{\frac{3.6}{2.8}}=0.70 \quad\rightarrow\quad \theta_2=\sin^{-1}0.70=\boxed{44°}$$

66. The error of $2°$ is allowed due to diffraction of the waves. If the waves are incident at the "edge" of the dish, they can still diffract into the dish if the relationship $\theta\approx\lambda/L$ is satisfied.

$$\theta\approx\frac{\lambda}{L} \quad\rightarrow\quad \lambda=L\theta=(0.5\text{ m})\left(2°\times\frac{\pi\text{ rad}}{180°}\right)=1.745\times10^{-2}\text{ m}\approx\boxed{2\times10^{-2}\text{ m}}$$

If the wavelength is longer than that, there will not be much diffraction, but "shadowing" instead.

67. The unusual decrease of water corresponds to a trough in Figure 11-24. The crest or peak of the wave is then one-half wavelength distant. The peak is 125 km away, traveling at 750 km/hr.

$$\Delta x=vt \quad\rightarrow\quad t=\frac{\Delta x}{v}=\frac{125\text{ km}}{750\text{ km/hr}}\left(\frac{60\text{ min}}{1\text{ hr}}\right)=\boxed{10\text{ min}}$$

68. Apply the conservation of mechanical energy to the car, calling condition # 1 to be before the collision and condition # 2 to be after the collision. Assume that all of the kinetic energy of the car is converted to potential energy stored in the bumper. We know that $x_1=0$ and $v_2=0$.

$$E_1=E_2 \quad\rightarrow\quad \tfrac{1}{2}mv_1^2+\tfrac{1}{2}kx_1^2=\tfrac{1}{2}mv_2^2+\tfrac{1}{2}kx_2^2 \quad\rightarrow\quad \tfrac{1}{2}mv_1^2=\tfrac{1}{2}kx_2^2 \quad\rightarrow$$

$$x_2=\sqrt{\frac{m}{k}}v_1=\sqrt{\frac{1500\text{ kg}}{550\times10^3\text{ N/m}}}(2.2\text{ m/s})=\boxed{0.11\text{ m}}$$

69. Consider the conservation of energy for the person. Call the unstretched position of the fire net the zero location for both elastic potential energy and gravitational potential energy. The amount of stretch of the fire net is given by x, measured positively in the downward direction. The vertical displacement for gravitational potential energy is given by the variable y, measured positively for the upward direction. Calculate the spring constant by conserving energy between the window height and the lowest location of the person. The person has no kinetic energy at either location.

$$E_{top}=E_{bottom} \quad\rightarrow\quad mgy_{top}=mgy_{bottom}+\tfrac{1}{2}kx_{bottom}^2$$

$$k=2mg\frac{\left(y_{top}-y_{bottom}\right)}{x_{bottom}^2}=2(65\text{ kg})(9.8\text{ m/s}^2)\frac{[18\text{ m}-(-1.1\text{ m})]}{(1.1\text{ m})^2}=2.011\times10^4\text{ N/m}$$

(a) If the person were to lie on the fire net, they would stretch the net an amount such that the upward force of the net would be equal to their weight.

$$F = kx = mg \quad \rightarrow \quad x = \frac{mg}{k} = \frac{(65 \text{ kg})(9.8 \text{ m/s}^2)}{2.011 \times 10^4 \text{ N/m}} = \boxed{3.2 \times 10^{-2} \text{ m}}$$

(b) To find the amount of stretch given a starting height of 35 m, again use conservation of energy. Note that $y_{\text{bottom}} = -x$, and there is no kinetic energy at the top or bottom positions.

$$E_{\text{top}} = E_{\text{bottom}} \quad \rightarrow \quad mgy_{\text{top}} = mgy_{\text{bottom}} + \tfrac{1}{2}kx^2 \quad \rightarrow \quad x^2 - 2\frac{mg}{k}x - 2\frac{mg}{k}y_{\text{top}} = 0$$

$$x^2 - 2\frac{(65 \text{ kg})(9.8 \text{ m/s}^2)}{2.011 \times 10^4 \text{ N/m}}x - 2\frac{(65 \text{ kg})(9.8 \text{ m/s}^2)}{2.011 \times 10^4 \text{ N/m}}(35 \text{ m}) = 0 \quad \rightarrow$$

$$x^2 - 0.06335x - 2.2173 = 0 \quad \rightarrow \quad x = 1.5211 \text{ m}, \; -1.458 \text{ m}$$

This is a quadratic equation. The solution is the positive root, since the net must be below the unstretched position. The result is $\boxed{1.5 \text{ m}}$.

70. Consider energy conservation for the mass over the range of motion from "letting go" (the highest point) to the lowest point. The mass falls the same distance that the spring is stretched, and has no KE at either endpoint. Call the lowest point the zero of gravitational potential energy. The variable "x" represents the amount that the spring is stretched from the equilibrium position.

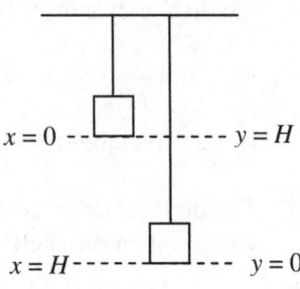

$$E_{\text{top}} = E_{\text{bottom}}$$

$$\tfrac{1}{2}mv_{\text{top}}^2 + mgy_{\text{top}} + \tfrac{1}{2}kx_{\text{top}}^2 = \tfrac{1}{2}mv_{\text{bottom}}^2 + mgy_{\text{bottom}} + \tfrac{1}{2}kx_{\text{bottom}}^2$$

$$0 + mgH + 0 = 0 + 0 + \tfrac{1}{2}kH^2 \quad \rightarrow \quad \frac{k}{m} = \frac{2g}{H} = \omega^2 \quad \rightarrow \quad \omega = \sqrt{\frac{2g}{H}}$$

$$f = \frac{\omega}{2\pi} = \frac{1}{2\pi}\sqrt{\frac{2g}{H}} = \frac{1}{2\pi}\sqrt{\frac{2(9.8 \text{ m/s}^2)}{0.33 \text{ m}}} = \boxed{1.2 \text{ Hz}}$$

71. (a) From conservation of energy, the initial kinetic energy of the car will all be changed into elastic potential energy by compressing the spring.

$$E_1 = E_2 \quad \rightarrow \quad \tfrac{1}{2}mv_1^2 + \tfrac{1}{2}kx_1^2 = \tfrac{1}{2}mv_2^2 + \tfrac{1}{2}kx_2^2 \quad \rightarrow \quad \tfrac{1}{2}mv_1^2 = \tfrac{1}{2}kx_2^2 \quad \rightarrow$$

$$k = m\frac{v_1^2}{x_2^2} = (950 \text{ kg})\frac{(22 \text{ m/s})^2}{(5.0 \text{ m})^2} = 1.8392 \times 10^4 \text{ N/m} \approx \boxed{1.8 \times 10^4 \text{ N/m}}$$

(b) The car will be in contact with the spring for half a period, as it moves from the equilibrium location to maximum displacement and back to equilibrium.

$$\tfrac{1}{2}T = \tfrac{1}{2}2\pi\sqrt{\frac{m}{k}} = \pi\sqrt{\frac{(950 \text{ kg})}{1.8392 \times 10^4 \text{ N/m}}} = \boxed{0.71 \text{ s}}$$

72. The frequency at which the water is being shaken is about 1 Hz. The sloshing coffee is in a standing wave mode, with anti-nodes at each edge of the cup. The cup diameter is thus a half-wavelength, or $\lambda = 16 \text{ cm}$. The wave speed can be calculated from the frequency and the wavelength.

$$v = \lambda f = (16 \text{ cm})(1 \text{ Hz}) = \boxed{16 \text{ cm/s}}$$

73. Relative to the fixed needle position, the ripples are moving with a linear velocity given by

$$v = \left(33\frac{\text{rev}}{\text{min}}\right)\left(\frac{1\,\text{min}}{60\,\text{s}}\right)\left(\frac{2\pi(0.108\,\text{m})}{1\,\text{rev}}\right) = 0.373\,\text{m/s}$$

This speed is the speed of the ripple waves moving past the needle. The frequency of the waves is

$$f = \frac{v}{\lambda} = \frac{0.373\,\text{m/s}}{1.70\times10^{-3}\,\text{m}} = \boxed{220\,\text{Hz}}$$

74. The equation of motion is $x = 0.650\cos 7.40t = A\cos\omega t$.

(a) The amplitude is $A = \boxed{0.650\,\text{m}}$

(b) The frequency is given by $\omega = 2\pi f = 7.40\,\text{rad/s} \rightarrow f = \frac{7.40\,\text{rad/s}}{2\pi\,\text{rad}} = 1.177\,\text{Hz} \approx \boxed{1.18\,\text{Hz}}$

(c) The total energy is given by
$$E_{\text{total}} = \tfrac{1}{2}kA^2 = \tfrac{1}{2}m\omega^2 A^2 = \tfrac{1}{2}(2.00\,\text{kg})(7.40\,\text{rad/s})^2(0.650\,\text{m})^2 = 23.136\,\text{J} \approx \boxed{23.1\,\text{J}}.$$

(d) The potential energy is found by
$$PE = \tfrac{1}{2}kx^2 = \tfrac{1}{2}m\omega^2 x^2 = \tfrac{1}{2}(2.00\,\text{kg})(7.40\,\text{rad/s})^2(0.260\,\text{m})^2 = 3.702\,\text{J} \approx \boxed{3.70\,\text{J}}.$$
The kinetic energy is found by
$$KE = E_{\text{total}} - PE = 23.136\,\text{J} - 3.702\,\text{J} = \boxed{19.4\,\text{J}}.$$

75. The frequency of a simple pendulum is given by $f = \frac{1}{2\pi}\sqrt{\frac{g}{L}}$. The pendulum is accelerating vertically which is equivalent to increasing (or decreasing) the acceleration due to gravity by the acceleration of the pendulum.

(a) $f_{\text{new}} = \frac{1}{2\pi}\sqrt{\frac{g+a}{L}} = \frac{1}{2\pi}\sqrt{\frac{1.50g}{L}} = \sqrt{1.50}\frac{1}{2\pi}\sqrt{\frac{g}{L}} = \sqrt{1.50}f = \boxed{1.22f}$

(b) $f_{\text{new}} = \frac{1}{2\pi}\sqrt{\frac{g+a}{L}} = \frac{1}{2\pi}\sqrt{\frac{0.5g}{L}} = \sqrt{0.5}\frac{1}{2\pi}\sqrt{\frac{g}{L}} = \sqrt{0.5}f = \boxed{0.71f}$

76. The force of the man's weight causes the raft to sink, and that causes the water to put a larger upward force on the raft. This extra buoyant force is a restoring force, because it is in the opposite direction of the force put on the raft by the man. This is analogous to pulling down on a mass-spring system that is in equilibrium, by applying an extra force. Then when the man steps off, the restoring force pushes upward on the raft, and thus the raft – water system acts like a spring, with a spring constant found as follows.

$$k = \frac{F}{x} = \frac{(75\,\text{kg})(9.8\,\text{m/s}^2)}{4.0\times10^{-2}\,\text{m}} = 1.8375\times10^4\,\text{N/m}$$

(a) The frequency of vibration is determined by the spring constant and the mass of the raft.

$$f_n = \frac{1}{2\pi}\sqrt{\frac{k}{m}} = \frac{1}{2\pi}\sqrt{\frac{1.8375\times10^4\,\text{N/m}}{220\,\text{kg}}} = 1.455\,\text{Hz} \approx \boxed{1.5\,\text{Hz}}$$

(b) As explained in the text, for a vertical spring the gravitational potential energy can be ignored if the displacement is measured from the oscillator's equilibrium position. The total energy is thus

$$E_{\text{total}} = \tfrac{1}{2}kA^2 = \tfrac{1}{2}(1.8375\times10^4\,\text{N/m})(4.0\times10^{-2}\,\text{m})^2 = 14.7\,\text{J} \approx \boxed{15\,\text{J}}.$$

77. (a) The overtones are given by $f_n = nf_1, n = 2, 3, 4 \dots$

   G: $f_2 = 2(392 \text{ Hz}) = \boxed{784 \text{ Hz}}$ $f_3 = 3(392 \text{ Hz}) = \boxed{1180 \text{ Hz}}$

   A: $f_2 = 2(440 \text{ Hz}) = \boxed{880 \text{ Hz}}$ $f_3 = 3(440 \text{ Hz}) = \boxed{1320 \text{ Hz}}$

   (b) If the two strings have the same length, they have the same wavelength. The frequency difference is then due to a difference in wave speed caused by different masses for the strings.

$$\frac{f_G}{f_A} = \frac{v_G/\lambda}{v_A/\lambda} = \frac{v_G}{v_A} = \frac{\sqrt{\dfrac{F_T}{m_G/L}}}{\sqrt{\dfrac{F_T}{m_A/L}}} = \sqrt{\frac{m_A}{m_G}} \rightarrow \frac{m_G}{m_A} = \left(\frac{f_A}{f_G}\right)^2 = \left(\frac{440}{392}\right)^2 = \boxed{1.26}$$

   (c) If the two strings have the same mass per unit length and the same tension, then the wave speed on both strings is the same. The frequency difference is then due to a difference in wavelength. For the fundamental, the wavelength is twice the length of the string.

$$\frac{f_G}{f_A} = \frac{v/\lambda_G}{v/\lambda_A} = \frac{\lambda_A}{\lambda_G} = \frac{2L_A}{2L_G} \rightarrow \frac{L_G}{L_A} = \frac{f_A}{f_G} = \frac{440}{392} = \boxed{1.12}$$

   (d) If the two strings have the same length, they have the same wavelength. The frequency difference is then due to a difference in wave speed caused by different tensions for the strings.

$$\frac{f_G}{f_A} = \frac{v_G/\lambda}{v_A/\lambda} = \frac{v_G}{v_A} = \frac{\sqrt{\dfrac{F_{TG}}{m/L}}}{\sqrt{\dfrac{F_{TA}}{m/L}}} = \sqrt{\frac{F_{TG}}{F_{TA}}} \rightarrow \frac{F_{TG}}{F_{TAA}} = \left(\frac{f_G}{f_A}\right)^2 = \left(\frac{392}{440}\right)^2 = \boxed{0.794}$$

78. (a) Since the cord is not accelerating to the left or right, the tension in the cord must be the same everywhere. Thus the tension is the same in the two parts of the cord. The speed difference will then be due to the different mass densities of the two parts of the cord. Let the symbol μ represent the mass per unit length of each part of the cord.

$$\frac{v_H}{v_L} = \frac{\left(\sqrt{F_T/\mu}\right)_H}{\left(\sqrt{F_T/\mu}\right)_L} = \boxed{\sqrt{\frac{\mu_L}{\mu_H}}}$$

   (b) The wavelength ratio is found as follows.

$$\frac{\lambda_H}{\lambda_L} = \frac{(v/f)_H}{(v/f)_L} = \frac{v_H}{v_L} = \boxed{\sqrt{\frac{\mu_L}{\mu_H}}}$$

   The two frequencies must be the same for the cord to remain continuous at the boundary. If the two parts of the cord oscillate at different frequencies, the cord cannot stay in one piece, because the two parts would be out of phase with each other at various times.

   (c) Since $\mu_H > \mu_L$, we see that $\lambda_H < \lambda_L$, and so the wavelength is greater in the $\boxed{\text{lighter cord}}$.

79. (a) The maximum speed is given by

$$v_{max} = 2\pi f A = 2\pi (264 \text{ Hz})(1.8 \times 10^{-3} \text{ m}) = \boxed{3.0 \text{ m/s}}.$$

   (b) The maximum acceleration is given by

$$a_{max} = 4\pi^2 f^2 A = 4\pi^2 (264 \text{ Hz})^2 (1.8 \times 10^{-3} \text{ m}) = \boxed{5.0 \times 10^3 \text{ m/s}^2}.$$

80. For the pebble to lose contact with the board means that there is no normal force of the board on the pebble. If there is no normal force on the pebble, then the only force on the pebble is the force of gravity, and the acceleration of the pebble will be g downward, the acceleration due to gravity. This is the maximum downward acceleration that the pebble can have. Thus if the board's downward acceleration exceeds g, then the pebble will lose contact. The maximum acceleration and the amplitude are related by $a_{max} = 4\pi^2 f^2 A$.

$$a_{max} = 4\pi^2 f^2 A \le g \quad \rightarrow \quad A \le \frac{g}{4\pi^2 f^2} \le \frac{9.8\,\text{m/s}^2}{4\pi^2 (1.5\,\text{Hz})^2} \le \boxed{1.1 \times 10^{-1}\,\text{m}}$$

81. For a resonant condition, the free end of the string will be an antinode, and the fixed end of the string will be a node. The minimum distance from a node to an antinode is $\lambda/4$. Other wave patterns that fit the boundary conditions of a node at one end and an antinode at the other end include $3\lambda/4$, $5\lambda/4$, ... See the diagrams. The general relationship is $L = (2n-1)\lambda/4$, $n = 1, 2, 3, \cdots$.

Solving for the wavelength gives $\boxed{\lambda = \dfrac{4L}{2n-1}, \ n = 1, 2, 3, \cdots}$

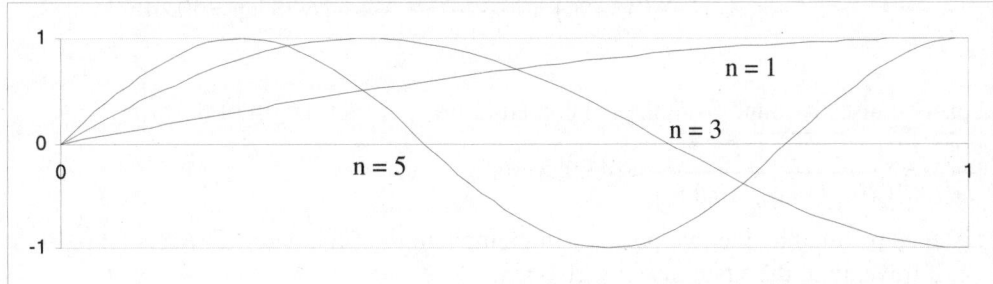

82. The period of a pendulum is given by $T = 2\pi\sqrt{L/g}$, and so the length is $L = \dfrac{T^2 g}{4\pi^2}$.

(a) $L_{\text{Austin}} = \dfrac{T^2 g_{\text{Austin}}}{4\pi^2} = \dfrac{(2.000\,\text{s})^2 (9.793\,\text{m/s}^2)}{4\pi^2} = \boxed{0.9922\,\text{m}}$

(b) $L_{\text{Paris}} = \dfrac{T^2 g_{\text{Paris}}}{4\pi^2} = \dfrac{(2.000\,\text{s})^2 (9.809\,\text{m/s}^2)}{4\pi^2} = 0.9939\,\text{m}$

$L_{\text{Paris}} - L_{\text{Austin}} = 0.9939\,\text{m} - 0.9922\,\text{m} = 0.0016\,\text{m} = \boxed{1.6\,\text{mm}}$

(c) $L_{\text{Moon}} = \dfrac{T^2 g_{\text{Moon}}}{4\pi^2} = \dfrac{(2.00\,\text{s})^2 (1.62\,\text{m/s}^2)}{4\pi^2} = \boxed{0.164\,\text{m}}$

83. The spring, originally of length l_0, will be stretched downward to a new equilibrium length L when the mass is hung on it. The amount of downward stretch $L - l_0$ is found from setting the spring force upward on the mass equal to the weight of the mass: $k(L - l_0) = mg \quad \rightarrow \quad L = l_0 + mg/k$. The length of the pendulum is then $L = l_0 + mg/k$. The period of the vertical oscillations is given by $T_{\text{ver}} = 2\pi\sqrt{m/k}$, while the period of the pendulum oscillations is given by $T_{\text{pen}} = 2\pi\sqrt{L/g}$. Now compare the periods of the two motions.

$$\frac{T_{pen}}{T_{ver}} = \frac{2\pi\sqrt{(l_0 + mg/k)/g}}{2\pi\sqrt{m/k}} = \sqrt{\frac{l_0 + mg/k}{mg/k}} = \sqrt{1 + \frac{l_0 k}{mg}} > 1 \rightarrow$$

$$\boxed{T_{pen} > T_{ver}, \text{ by a factor of } \sqrt{1 + \frac{l_0 k}{mg}}}$$

84. Block m stays on top of block M (executing SHM relative to the ground) without slipping due to static friction. The maximum static frictional force on m is $F_{fr_{max}} = \mu_s mg$. This frictional force causes block m to accelerate, so $ma_{max} = \mu_s mg \rightarrow a_{max} = \mu_s g$. Thus for the blocks to stay in contact without slipping, the maximum acceleration of block M is also $a_{max} = \mu_s g$. But an object in SHM has a maximum acceleration given by $a_{max} = \omega^2 A = \dfrac{k}{M_{total}} A$. Equate these two expressions for the maximum acceleration.

$$a_{max} = \frac{k}{M_{total}} A = \mu_s g \rightarrow A = \frac{\mu_s g}{k}(M + m) = \frac{(0.30)(9.8\,\text{m/s}^2)}{130\,\text{N/m}}(6.25\,\text{kg}) = \boxed{0.14\,\text{m}}$$

85. The speed of the pulses is found from the tension and mass per unit length of the wire.

$$v = \sqrt{\frac{F_T}{m/L}} = \sqrt{\frac{255\,\text{N}}{(0.123\,\text{kg})/(10.0\,\text{m})}} = 143.985\,\text{m/s}$$

The total distance traveled by the two pulses will be the length of the wire. The second pulse has a shorter time of travel than the first pulse, by 20.0 ms.

$$L = d_1 + d_2 = vt_1 + vt_2 = vt_1 + v(t_1 - 2.00 \times 10^{-2})$$

$$t_1 = \frac{L + 2.00 \times 10^{-2} v}{2v} = \frac{(10.0\,\text{m}) + 2.00 \times 10^{-2}(143.985\,\text{m/s})}{2(143.985\,\text{m/s})} = 4.4726 \times 10^{-2}\,\text{s}$$

$$d_1 = vt_1 = (143.985\,\text{m/s})(4.4726 \times 10^{-2}\,\text{s}) = 6.44\,\text{m}$$

The two pulses meet $\boxed{6.44\,\text{m}}$ from the end where the first pulse originated.

86. For the penny to stay on the block at all times means that there will be a normal force on the penny from the block, exerted upward. If down is taken to be the positive direction, then the net force on the penny is $F_{net} = mg - F_N = ma$. Solving for the magnitude of the normal force gives $F_N = mg - ma$. This expression is always positive if the acceleration is upwards ($a < 0$), and so there is no possibility of the penny losing contact while accelerating upwards. But if a downward acceleration were to be larger than g, then the normal force would go to zero, since the normal force cannot switch directions $(F_N > 0)$. Thus the limiting condition is $a_{down} = g$. This is the maximum value for the acceleration.

For SHM, we also know that $a_{max} = \omega^2 A = \dfrac{k}{M + m} A \approx \dfrac{k}{M} A$. Equate these two values for the acceleration.

$$a_{max} = \frac{k}{M} A = g \rightarrow \boxed{A = \frac{Mg}{k}}$$

87. The car on the end of the cable produces tension in the cable, and stretches the cable according to Equation (9-4), $\Delta L = \dfrac{1}{E}\dfrac{F}{A}L_o$, where E is Young's modulus. Rearrange this equation to see that the tension force is proportional to the amount of stretch, $F = \dfrac{EA}{L_o}\Delta L$, and so the effective spring constant is $k = \dfrac{EA}{L_o}$. The period of the bouncing can be found from the spring constant and the mass on the end of the cable.

$$T = 2\pi\sqrt{\frac{m}{k}} = 2\pi\sqrt{\frac{mL_o}{EA}} = 2\pi\sqrt{\frac{(1200\ \text{kg})(22\ \text{m})}{(200\times10^9\ \text{N/m}^2)\pi(3.2\times10^{-3}\ \text{m})^2}} = \boxed{0.40\ \text{s}}$$

88. From Equation (9-6) and Figure (9-22c), the restoring force on the top of the Jell-O is $F = \dfrac{GA}{L_o}\Delta L$, and is in the opposite direction to the displacement of the top from the equilibrium condition. Thus the "spring constant" for the restoring force is $k = \dfrac{GA}{L_o}$. If you were to look at a layer of Jell-O closer to the base, the displacement would be less, but so would the restoring force in proportion, and so we estimate all of the Jell-O as having the same spring constant. The frequency of vibration can be determined from the spring constant and the mass of the Jell-O.

$$f = \frac{1}{2\pi}\sqrt{\frac{k}{m}} = \frac{1}{2\pi}\sqrt{\frac{GA/L_o}{\rho V}} = \frac{1}{2\pi}\sqrt{\frac{GA/L_o}{\rho A L_o}} = \frac{1}{2\pi}\sqrt{\frac{G}{\rho L_o^2}}$$

$$= \frac{1}{2\pi}\sqrt{\frac{520\ \text{N/m}^2}{(1300\ \text{kg/m}^3)(4.0\times10^{-2}\ \text{m})^2}} = \boxed{2.5\ \text{Hz}}$$

CHAPTER 12: Sound

Answers to Questions

1. Sound exhibits several phenomena that give evidence that it is a wave. The phenomenon of interference is a wave phenomenon, and sound produces interference (such as beats). The phenomenon of diffraction is a wave phenomenon, and sound can be diffracted (such as sound being heard around corners). Refraction is a wave phenomenon, and sound exhibits refraction when passing obliquely from one medium to another.

2. Evidence that sound is a form of energy is found in the fact that sound can do work. A sound wave created in one location can cause the mechanical vibration of an object at a different location. For example, sound can set eardrums in motion, make windows rattle, or shatter a glass.

3. The child speaking into a cup creates sound waves which cause the bottom of the cup to vibrate. Since the string is tightly attached to the bottom of the cup, the vibrations of the cup are transmitted to longitudinal waves in the string. These longitudinal waves travel down the string, and cause the bottom of the receiver cup to vibrate. This relatively large vibrating surface moves the adjacent air, and generates sound waves from the bottom of the cup, traveling up into the cup. These waves are incident on the receiver's ear, and they hear the sound from the speaker.

4. If the frequency were to change, the two media could not stay in contact with each other. If one medium vibrates with a certain frequency, and the other medium vibrates with a different frequency, then particles from the two media initially in contact could not stay in contact with each other. But particles must be in contact in order for the wave to be transmitted from one medium to the other, and so the frequency does not change. Since the wave speed changes in passing from air into water, and the frequency does not change, we expect the wavelength to change. The wave travels about four times faster in water, so we expect the wavelength in water to be about four times longer than it is in air.

5. Listening to music while seated far away from the source of sound gives evidence that the speed of sound in air does not depend on frequency. If the speed were highly frequency dependent, then high and low sounds created at the same time at the source would arrive at your location at different times, and the music would sound very disjointed. The fact that the music "stays together" is evidence that the speed is independent of frequency.

6. The sound-production anatomy of a person includes various resonating cavities, such as the throat. The relatively fixed geometry of these cavities will determine the relatively fixed wavelengths of sound that a person can produce. Those wavelengths will have associated frequencies given by $f = v/\lambda$. The speed of sound is determined by the gas that is filling the resonant cavities. If the person has inhaled helium, then the speed of sound will be much higher than normal, since the speed of sound waves in helium is about 3 times that in air. Thus the person's frequencies will go up about a factor of 3. This is about a 1.5 octave shift, and so the person sounds very high pitched.

7. The basic equation determining the pitch of the organ pipe is either $f_{closed} = \dfrac{nv}{4L}, n = \text{odd integer}$, for a closed pipe, or $f_{open} = \dfrac{nv}{2L}, n = \text{integer}$, for an open pipe. In each case, the frequency is proportional to the speed of sound in air. Since the speed is a function of temperature, and the length of any

particular pipe is fixed, the frequency is also a function of temperature. Thus when the temperature changes, the resonant frequencies of the organ pipes change as well. Since the speed of sound increases with temperature, as the temperature increases, the pitch of the pipes increases as well.

8.   A tube of a given length will resonate (permit standing waves) at certain frequencies. When a mix of frequencies is input to the tube, only those frequencies close to resonant frequencies will produce sound that persists, because standing waves are created for those frequencies. Frequencies far from resonant frequencies will not persist very long at all – they will "die out" quickly. If, for example, two adjacent resonances of a tube are at 100 Hz and 200 Hz, then sound input near one of those frequencies will persist and sound relatively loud. A sound input near 150 Hz would fade out quickly, and so have a reduced amplitude as compared to the resonant frequencies. The length of the tube can be chosen to thus "filter" certain frequencies, if those filtered frequencies are not close to resonant frequencies.

9.   For a string with fixed ends, the fundamental frequency is given by $f = \dfrac{v}{2L}$ and so the length of

string for a given frequency is $L = \dfrac{v}{2f}$. For a string, if the tension is not changed while fretting, the

speed of sound waves will be constant. Thus for two frequencies $f_1 < f_2$, the spacing between the frets corresponding to those frequencies is given as follows.

$$L_1 - L_2 = \frac{v}{2f_1} - \frac{v}{2f_2} = \frac{v}{2}\left(\frac{1}{f_1} - \frac{1}{f_2}\right)$$

Now see table 12-3. Each note there would correspond to one fret on the guitar neck. Notice that as the adjacent frequencies get higher, the inter-frequency spacing also increases. The change from C to C# is 15 Hz, while the change from G to G# is 23 Hz. Thus their reciprocals get closer together, and so from the above formula, the length spacing gets closer together. Consider a numeric example.

$$L_C - L_{C\#} = \frac{v}{2}\left(\frac{1}{262} - \frac{1}{277}\right) = \frac{v}{2}\left(2.07\times10^{-4}\right) \qquad L_G - L_{G\#} = \frac{v}{2}\left(\frac{1}{392} - \frac{1}{415}\right) = \frac{v}{2}\left(1.41\times10^{-4}\right)$$

$$\frac{L_G - L_{G\#}}{L_C - L_{C\#}} = 0.68$$

The G to G# spacing is only about 68% of the C to C# spacing.

10.   When you first hear the truck, you cannot see it. There is no straight line path from the truck to you. The sound waves that you are hearing are therefore arriving at your location due to diffraction. Long wavelengths are diffracted more than short wavelengths, and so you are initially only hearing sound with long wavelengths, which are low-frequency sounds. After you can see the truck, you are able to receive all frequencies being emitted by the truck, not just the lower frequencies. Thus the sound "brightens" due to your hearing more high frequency components.

11.   The wave pattern created by standing waves does not "travel" from one place to another. The node locations are fixed in space. Any one point in the medium has the same amplitude at all times. Thus the interference can be described as "interference in space" – moving the observation point from one location to another changes the interference from constructive (anti-node) to destructive (node). To experience the full range from node to anti-node, the position of observation must change, but all observations could be made at the same time by a group of observers.

The wave pattern created by beats does travel from one place to another. Any one point in the medium will at one time have a 0 amplitude (node) and half a beat period later, have a maximum amplitude (anti-node). Thus the interference can be described as "interference in time". To experience the full range from constructive interference to destructive interference, the time of observation must change, but all observations could be made at the same position.

12. If the frequency of the speakers is lowered, then the wavelength will be increased. Each circle in the diagram will be larger, and so the points C and D will move farther apart.

13. So-called *active noise reduction* devices work on the principle of interference. If the electronics are fast enough to detect the noise, invert it, and create the opposite wave (180° out of phase with the original) in significantly less time than one period of the components of the noise, then the original noise and the created noise will be approximately in a destructive interference relationship. The person wearing the headphones will hear a net sound signal that is very low in intensity.

14. From the two waves shown, it is seen that the frequency of beating is higher in Figure (a) – the beats occur more frequently. The beat frequency is the difference between the two component frequencies, and so since (a) has a higher beat frequency, the component frequencies are further apart in (a).

15. There is no Doppler shift if the source and observer move in the same direction, with the same velocity. Doppler shift is caused by relative motion between source and observer, and if both source and observer move in the same direction with the same velocity, there is no relative motion.

16. If the wind is blowing but the listener is at rest with respect to the source, the listener will not hear a Doppler effect. We analyze the case of the wind blowing from the source towards the listener. The moving air (wind) has the same effect as if the speed of sound had been increased by an amount equal to the wind speed. The wavelength of the sound waves (distance that a wave travels during one period of time) will be increased by the same percentage that the wind speed is relative to the still-air speed of sound. Since the frequency is the speed divided by the wavelength, the frequency does not change, and so there is no Doppler effect to hear. Alternatively, the wind has the same effect as if the air were not moving but the source and listener were moving at the same speed in the same direction. See question 15 for a discussion of that situation.

17. The highest frequency of sound will be heard at position C, while the child is swinging forward. Assuming the child is moving with SHM, then the highest speed is at the equilibrium point, point C. And to have an increased pitch, the relative motion of the source and detector must be towards each other. The child would also hear the lowest frequency of sound at point C, while swinging backwards.

Solutions to Problems

In solving these problems, the authors did not always follow the rules of significant figures rigidly. We tended to take quoted frequencies as correct to the number of digits shown, especially where other values might indicate that. For example, in problem 42, values of 350 Hz and 355 Hz are used. We took both of those values to have 3 significant figures. We treated the decibel values similarly. For example, in problem 11, we treated the value of 120 dB as having three significant figures.

1. The round trip time for sound is 2.0 seconds, so the time for sound to travel the length of the lake is 1.0 seconds. Use the time and the speed of sound to determine the length of the lake.

$$d = vt = (343 \,\text{m/s})(1.0 \,\text{s}) = 343 \text{ m} \approx \boxed{3.4 \times 10^2 \,\text{m}}$$

2. The round trip time for sound is 2.5 seconds, so the time for sound to travel the length of the lake is 1.25 seconds. Use the time and the speed of sound in water to determine the depth of the lake.

$$d = vt = (1560 \text{ m/s})(1.25 \text{ s}) = 1950 \text{ m} = \boxed{2.0 \times 10^3 \text{ m}}$$

3. (a) $\lambda_{20 \text{ Hz}} = \dfrac{v}{f} = \dfrac{343 \text{ m/s}}{20 \text{ Hz}} = \boxed{17 \text{ m}}$ $\lambda_{20 \text{ kHz}} = \dfrac{v}{f} = \dfrac{343 \text{ m/s}}{2.0 \times 10^4 \text{ Hz}} = \boxed{1.7 \times 10^{-2} \text{ m}}$

So the range is from 17 cm to 17 m.

(b) $\lambda = \dfrac{v}{f} = \dfrac{343 \text{ m/s}}{10 \times 10^6 \text{ Hz}} = \boxed{3.4 \times 10^{-5} \text{ m}}$

4. (a) For the fish, the speed of sound in seawater must be used.

$$d = vt \rightarrow t = \frac{d}{v} = \frac{1.0 \times 10^3 \text{ m}}{1560 \text{ m/s}} = \boxed{0.64 \text{ s}}$$

(b) For the fishermen, the speed of sound in air must be used.

$$d = vt \rightarrow t = \frac{d}{v} = \frac{1.0 \times 10^3 \text{ m}}{343 \text{ m/s}} = \boxed{2.9 \text{ s}}$$

5. The total time T is the time for the stone to fall $\left(t_{\text{down}}\right)$ plus the time for the sound to come back to the top of the cliff $\left(t_{\text{up}}\right)$: $T = t_{\text{up}} + t_{\text{down}}$. Use constant acceleration relationships for an object dropped from rest that falls a distance h in order to find t_{down}, with down as the positive direction. Use the constant speed of sound to find t_{up} for the sound to travel a distance h.

$$\text{down: } y = y_0 + v_0 t_{\text{down}} + \tfrac{1}{2} a t_{\text{down}}^2 \rightarrow h = \tfrac{1}{2} g t_{\text{down}}^2 \qquad \text{up: } h = v_{\text{snd}} t_{\text{up}} \rightarrow t_{\text{up}} = \frac{h}{v_{\text{snd}}}$$

$$h = \tfrac{1}{2} g t_{\text{down}}^2 = \tfrac{1}{2} g \left(T - t_{\text{up}}\right)^2 = \tfrac{1}{2} g \left(T - \frac{h}{v_{\text{snd}}}\right)^2 \rightarrow h^2 - 2 v_{\text{snd}} \left(\frac{v_{\text{snd}}}{g} + T\right) h + T^2 v_{\text{snd}}^2 = 0$$

This is a quadratic equation for the height. This can be solved with the quadratic formula, but be sure to keep several significant digits in the calculations.

$$h^2 - 2(343 \text{ m/s})\left(\frac{343 \text{ m/s}}{9.80 \text{ m/s}^2} + 3.5 \text{ s}\right) h + (3.5 \text{ s})^2 (343 \text{ m/s})^2 = 0 \rightarrow$$

$$h^2 - (26411 \text{ m}) h + 1.4412 \times 10^6 \text{ m}^2 = 0 \rightarrow h = 26356 \text{ m}, 55 \text{ m}$$

The larger root is impossible since it takes more than 3.5 sec for the rock to fall that distance, so the correct result is $h = \boxed{55 \text{ m}}$.

6. The two sound waves travel the same distance. The sound will travel faster in the concrete, and thus take a shorter time.

$$d = v_{\text{air}} t_{\text{air}} = v_{\text{concrete}} t_{\text{concrete}} = v_{\text{concrete}} \left(t_{\text{air}} - 1.1 \text{ s}\right) \rightarrow t_{\text{air}} = \frac{v_{\text{concrete}}}{v_{\text{concrete}} - v_{\text{air}}} 1.1 \text{ s}$$

$$d = v_{\text{air}} t_{\text{air}} = v_{\text{air}} \left(\frac{v_{\text{concrete}}}{v_{\text{concrete}} - v_{\text{air}}} 1.1 \text{ s}\right)$$

The speed of sound in concrete is obtained from Equation (11-14a), Table (9-1), and Table (10-1).

$$v_{concrete} = \sqrt{\frac{E}{\rho}} = \sqrt{\frac{20 \times 10^9 \text{ N/m}^2}{2.3 \times 10^3 \text{ kg/m}^3}} = 2949 \text{ m/s}$$

$$d = v_{air} t_{air} = (343 \text{ m/s}) \left(\frac{2949 \text{ m/s}}{2949 \text{ m/s} - 343 \text{ m/s}} 1.1 \text{ s} \right) = 427 \text{ m} \approx \boxed{4.3 \times 10^2 \text{ m}}$$

7. The "5 second rule" says that for every 5 seconds between seeing a lightning strike and hearing the associated sound, the lightning is 1 mile distant. We assume that there are 5 seconds between seeing the lightning and hearing the sound.

(*a*) At 30°C, the speed of sound is $[331 + 0.60(30)]$ m/s $= 349$ m/s . The actual distance to the lightning is therefore $d = vt = (349 \text{ m/s})(5 \text{ s}) = 1745$ m. A mile is 1610 m.

$$\% \text{ error} = \frac{1745 - 1610}{1745}(100) \approx \boxed{8\%}$$

(*b*) At 10°C, the speed of sound is $[331 + 0.60(10)]$ m/s $= 337$ m/s . The actual distance to the lightning is therefore $d = vt = (337 \text{ m/s})(5 \text{ s}) = 1685$ m. A mile is 1610 m.

$$\% \text{ error} = \frac{1685 - 1610}{1685}(100) \approx \boxed{4\%}$$

$\boxed{8.}$ $120 \text{ dB} = 10 \log \dfrac{I_{120}}{I_0} \rightarrow I_{120} = 10^{12} I_0 = 10^{12} (1.0 \times 10^{-12} \text{ W/m}^2) = \boxed{1.0 \text{ W/m}^2}$

$20 \text{ dB} = 10 \log \dfrac{I_{20}}{I_0} \rightarrow I_{20} = 10^2 I_0 = 10^2 (1.0 \times 10^{-12} \text{ W/m}^2) = \boxed{1.0 \times 10^{-10} \text{ W/m}^2}$

The pain level is 10^{10} times more intense than the whisper.

9. $\beta = 10 \log \dfrac{I}{I_0} = 10 \log \dfrac{2.0 \times 10^{-6} \text{ W/m}^2}{1.0 \times 10^{-12} \text{ W/m}^2} = \boxed{63 \text{ dB}}$

10. From Example 12-4, we see that a sound level decrease of 3 dB corresponds to a halving of intensity. Thus the sound level for one firecracker will be 95 dB $-$ 3 dB $= \boxed{92 \text{ dB}}$.

11. From Example 12-4, we see that a sound level decrease of 3 dB corresponds to a halving of intensity. Thus, if two engines are shut down, the intensity will be cut in half, and the sound level will be 117 dB. Then, if one more engine is shut down, the intensity will be cut in half again, and the sound level will drop by 3 more dB, to a final value of $\boxed{114 \text{ dB}}$.

12. $58 \text{ dB} = 10 \log \left(I_{Signal} / I_{Noise} \right)_{tape} \rightarrow \left(I_{Signal} / I_{Noise} \right)_{tape} = 10^{5.8} = \boxed{6.3 \times 10^5}$

$95 \text{ dB} = 10 \log \left(I_{Signal} / I_{Noise} \right)_{tape} \rightarrow \left(I_{Signal} / I_{Noise} \right)_{tape} = 10^{9.5} = \boxed{3.2 \times 10^9}$

13. (*a*) According to Table 12-2, the intensity in normal conversation, when about 50 cm from the speaker, is about 3×10^{-6} W/m^2. The intensity is the power output per unit area, and so the power output can be found. The area is that of a sphere.

$$I = \frac{P}{A} \quad \rightarrow \quad P = IA = I\left(4\pi r^2\right) = \left(3 \times 10^{-6}\text{ W/m}^2\right)4\pi\left(0.50\text{ m}\right)^2 = 9.425 \times 10^{-6}\text{ W} \approx \boxed{9 \times 10^{-6}\text{ W}}$$

(*b*) $100\text{ W}\left(\dfrac{1\text{ person}}{9.425 \times 10^{-6}\text{ W}}\right) = 1.06 \times 10^7 \approx \boxed{1 \times 10^7\text{ people}}$

14. (*a*) The energy absorbed per second is the power of the wave, which is the intensity times the area.

$$50\text{ dB} = 10\log\frac{I}{I_0} \quad \rightarrow \quad I = 10^5 I_0 = 10^5\left(1.0 \times 10^{-12}\text{ W/m}^2\right) = 1.0 \times 10^{-7}\text{ W/m}^2$$

$$P = IA = \left(1.0 \times 10^{-7}\text{ W/m}^2\right)\left(5.0 \times 10^{-5}\text{ m}^2\right) = \boxed{5.0 \times 10^{-12}\text{ W}}$$

(*b*) $1\text{ J}\left(\dfrac{1\text{ s}}{5.0 \times 10^{-12}\text{ J}}\right)\left(\dfrac{1\text{ yr}}{3.16 \times 10^7\text{ s}}\right) = \boxed{6.3 \times 10^3\text{ yr}}$

15. The intensity of the sound is defined to be the power per unit area. We assume that the sound spreads out spherically from the loudspeaker.

(*a*) $I_{250} = \dfrac{250\text{ W}}{4\pi\left(3.5\text{m}\right)^2} = 1.6\text{ W/m}^2 \qquad \beta_{250} = 10\log\dfrac{I_{250}}{I_0} = 10\log\dfrac{1.6\text{ W/m}^2}{1.0 \times 10^{-12}\text{ W/m}^2} = \boxed{122\text{ dB}}$

$I_{40} = \dfrac{40\text{ W}}{4\pi\left(3.5\text{m}\right)^2} = 0.26\text{ W/m}^2 \qquad \beta_{40} = 10\log\dfrac{I_{40}}{I_0} = 10\log\dfrac{0.26\text{ W/m}^2}{1.0 \times 10^{-12}\text{ W/m}^2} = \boxed{114\text{ dB}}$

(*b*) According to the textbook, for a sound to be perceived as twice as loud as another means that the intensities need to differ by a factor of 10. That is not the case here – they differ only by a

factor of $\dfrac{1.6}{0.26} \approx 6$. $\boxed{\text{The expensive amp will not sound twice as loud as the cheaper one.}}$

16. (*a*) Find the intensity from the 130 dB value, and then find the power output corresponding to that intensity at that distance from the speaker.

$$\beta = 130\text{ dB} = 10\log\frac{I_{2.8\text{m}}}{I_0} \quad \rightarrow \quad I_{2.8\text{m}} = 10^{13}I_0 = 10^{13}\left(1.0 \times 10^{-12}\text{ W/m}^2\right) = 10\text{ W/m}^2$$

$$P = IA = 4\pi r^2 I = 4\pi\left(2.8\text{ m}\right)^2\left(10\text{ W/m}^2\right) = 985\text{ W} \approx \boxed{9.9 \times 10^2\text{ W}}$$

(*b*) Find the intensity from the 90 dB value, and then from the power output, find the distance corresponding to that intensity.

$$\beta = 90\text{ dB} = 10\log\frac{I}{I_0} \quad \rightarrow \quad I = 10^9 I_0 = 10^9\left(1.0 \times 10^{-12}\text{ W/m}^2\right) = 1.0 \times 10^{-3}\text{ W/m}^2$$

$$P = 4\pi r^2 I \quad \rightarrow \quad r = \sqrt{\frac{P}{4\pi I}} = \sqrt{\frac{985\text{ W}}{4\pi\left(1.0 \times 10^{-3}\text{ W/m}^2\right)}} = \boxed{2.8 \times 10^2\text{ m}}$$

17. The intensity is proportional to the square of the amplitude.

$$2.0 \text{ dB} = 10\log\frac{I_{2.0}}{I_0} = 10\log\frac{A_{2.0}^2}{A_0^2} = 20\log\frac{A_{2.0}}{A_0} \rightarrow \frac{A_{2.0}}{A_0} = 10^{0.1} = 1.259 \approx \boxed{1.3}$$

18. (*a*) The intensity is proportional to the square of the amplitude, so if the amplitude is tripled, the intensity will $\boxed{\text{increase by a factor of 9}}$.

(*b*) $\beta = 10\log I/I_0 = 10\log 9 = \boxed{9.5\text{ dB}}$

19. The intensity is given by $I = 2\rho v \pi^2 f^2 A^2$. If the only difference in two sound waves is their frequencies, then the ratio of the intensities is the ratio of the square of the frequencies.

$$\frac{I_{2f}}{I_f} = \frac{(2f)^2}{f^2} = \boxed{4}$$

$\boxed{20.}$ The intensity is given by $I = 2\rho v \pi^2 f^2 A^2$, using the density of air and the speed of sound in air.

$$I = 2\rho v \pi^2 f^2 A^2 = 2(1.29\text{ kg/m}^3)(343\text{ m/s})\pi^2(300\text{ Hz})^2(1.3\times10^{-4}\text{ m})^2 = 13.28\text{ W/m}^2$$

$$\beta = 10\log\frac{I}{I_0} = 10\log\frac{13.28\text{ W/m}^2}{1.0\times10^{-12}\text{ W/m}^2} = 131.2\text{ dB} \approx \boxed{130\text{ dB}}$$

Note that this is above the threshold of pain.

21. From Figure 12-6, a 100-Hz tone at 50 dB has a loudness of about 20 phons. At 6000 Hz, 20 phons corresponds to about $\boxed{25\text{ dB}}$. Answers may vary due to estimation in the reading of the graph.

22. From Figure 12-6, at 30 dB the low frequency threshold of hearing is about $\boxed{150\text{ Hz}}$. There is no intersection of the threshold of hearing with the 30 dB level on the high frequency side of the chart, and so a 30 dB signal can be heard all the way up to the highest frequency that a human can hear, $\boxed{20,000\text{ Hz}}$.

23. (*a*) From Figure 12-6, at 100 Hz, the threshold of hearing (the lowest detectable intensity by the ear) is approximately $5\times10^{-9}\text{ W/m}^2$. The threshold of pain is about 5 W/m^2. The ratio of highest to lowest intensity is thus $\dfrac{5\text{ W/m}^2}{5\times10^{-9}\text{ W/m}^2} = \boxed{10^9}$.

(*b*) At 5000 Hz, the threshold of hearing is about 10^{-13} W/m^2, and the threshold of pain is about 10^{-1} W/m^2. The ratio of highest to lowest intensity is $\dfrac{10^{-1}\text{ W/m}^2}{10^{-13}\text{ W/m}^2} = \boxed{10^{12}}$.

Answers may vary due to estimation in the reading of the graph.

24. For a vibrating string, the frequency of the fundamental mode is given by $f = \dfrac{v}{2L} = \dfrac{1}{2L}\sqrt{\dfrac{F_T}{m/L}}$.

$$f = \frac{1}{2L}\sqrt{\frac{F_T}{m/L}} \rightarrow F_T = 4Lf^2m = 4(0.32\,\text{m})(440\,\text{Hz})^2(3.5\times10^{-4}\,\text{kg}) = \boxed{87\,\text{N}}$$

25. (a) If the pipe is closed at one end, only the odd harmonic frequencies are present, and are given by

$$f_n = \frac{nv}{4L} = nf_1, n = 1, 3, 5\cdots.$$

$$f_1 = \frac{v}{4L} = \frac{343\,\text{m/s}}{4(1.12\,\text{m})} = \boxed{76.6\,\text{Hz}}$$

$$f_3 = 3f_1 = \boxed{230\,\text{Hz}} \quad f_5 = 5f_1 = \boxed{383\,\text{Hz}} \quad f_7 = 7f_1 = \boxed{536\,\text{Hz}}$$

(b) If the pipe is open at both ends, all the harmonic frequencies are present, and are given by

$$f_n = \frac{nv}{2L} = nf_1.$$

$$f_1 = \frac{v}{2L} = \frac{343\,\text{m/s}}{2(1.12\,\text{m})} = \boxed{153\,\text{Hz}}$$

$$f_2 = 2f_1 = \boxed{306\,\text{Hz}} \quad f_3 = 3f_1 = \boxed{459\,\text{Hz}} \quad f_4 = 4f_1 = \boxed{612\,\text{Hz}}$$

26. (a) The length of the tube is one-fourth of a wavelength for this (one end closed) tube, and so the wavelength is four times the length of the tube.

$$f = \frac{v}{\lambda} = \frac{343\,\text{m/s}}{4(0.18\,\text{m})} = \boxed{480\,\text{Hz}}$$

(b) If the bottle is one-third full, then the effective length of the air column is reduced to 12 cm.

$$f = \frac{v}{\lambda} = \frac{343\,\text{m/s}}{4(0.12\,\text{m})} = \boxed{710\,\text{Hz}}$$

27. For a pipe open at both ends, the fundamental frequency is given by $f_1 = \dfrac{v}{2L}$, and so the length for a

given fundamental frequency is $L = \dfrac{v}{2f_1}$.

$$L_{20\,\text{Hz}} = \frac{343\,\text{m/s}}{2(20\,\text{Hz})} = \boxed{8.6\,\text{m}} \qquad L_{20\,\text{kHz}} = \frac{343\,\text{m/s}}{2(20,000\,\text{Hz})} = \boxed{8.6\times10^{-3}\,\text{m}}$$

28. For a fixed string, the frequency of the nth harmonic is given by $f_n = nf_1$. Thus the fundamental for this string is $f_1 = f_3/3 = 540\,\text{Hz}/3 = 180\,\text{Hz}$. When the string is fingered, it has a new length of 60% of the original length. The fundamental frequency of the vibrating string is also given by

$f_1 = \dfrac{v}{2L}$, and v is a constant for the string, assuming its tension is not changed.

$$f_{1_{\text{fingered}}} = \frac{v}{2L_{\text{fingered}}} = \frac{v}{2(0.60)L} = \frac{1}{0.60}f_1 = \frac{180\,\text{Hz}}{0.60} = \boxed{300\,\text{Hz}}$$

29. (*a*) We assume that the speed of waves on the guitar string does not change when the string is fretted. The fundamental frequency is given by $f = \dfrac{v}{2L}$, and so the frequency is inversely proportional to the length.

$$f \propto \frac{1}{L} \;\rightarrow\; fL = \text{constant}$$

$$f_E L_E = f_A L_A \;\rightarrow\; L_A = L_E \frac{f_E}{f_A} = (0.73\ \text{m})\left(\frac{330\ \text{Hz}}{440\ \text{Hz}}\right) = 0.5475\ \text{m}$$

The string should be fretted a distance $0.73\ \text{m} - 0.5475\ \text{m} = 0.1825\ \text{m} \approx \boxed{0.18\ \text{m}}$ from the nut of the guitar.

(*b*) The string is fixed at both ends and is vibrating in its fundamental mode. Thus the wavelength is twice the length of the string (see Fig. 12-7).

$$\lambda = 2L = 2(0.5475\ \text{m}) = 1.095\ \text{m} \approx \boxed{1.1\ \text{m}}$$

(*c*) The frequency of the sound will be the same as that of the string, $\boxed{440\ \text{Hz}}$. The wavelength is given by the following.

$$\lambda = \frac{v}{f} = \frac{343\ \text{m/s}}{440\ \text{Hz}} = \boxed{0.78\ \text{m}}$$

30. (*a*) At $T = 21°\text{C}$, the speed of sound is given by $v = \big(331 + 0.60(21)\big)\,\text{m/s} = 343.6\ \text{m/s}$. For an open pipe, the fundamental frequency is given by $f = \dfrac{v}{2L}$.

$$f = \frac{v}{2L} \;\rightarrow\; L = \frac{v}{2f} = \frac{343.6\ \text{m/s}}{2(262\ \text{Hz})} = \boxed{0.656\ \text{m}}$$

(*b*) The frequency of the standing wave in the tube is $\boxed{262\ \text{Hz}}$. The wavelength is twice the length of the pipe, $\boxed{1.31\ \text{m}}$.

(*c*) The wavelength and frequency are the same in the air, because it is air that is resonating in the organ pipe. The frequency is $\boxed{262\ \text{Hz}}$ and the wavelength is $\boxed{1.31\ \text{m}}$.

31. The speed of sound will change as the temperature changes, and that will change the frequency of the organ. Assume that the length of the pipe (and thus the resonant wavelength) does not change.

$$f_{20} = \frac{v_{20}}{\lambda} \quad f_{5.0} = \frac{v_{5.0}}{\lambda} \quad \Delta f = f_{5.0} - f_{20} = \frac{v_{5.0} - v_{20}}{\lambda}$$

$$\frac{\Delta f}{f} = \frac{\dfrac{v_{5.0} - v_{20}}{\lambda}}{\dfrac{v_{20}}{\lambda}} = \frac{v_{5.0}}{v_{20}} - 1 = \frac{331 + 0.60(5.0)}{331 + 0.60(20)} - 1 = -2.6 \times 10^{-2} = \boxed{-2.6\%}$$

32. A flute is a tube that is open at both ends, and so the fundamental frequency is given by $f = \dfrac{v}{2L}$, where L is the distance from the mouthpiece (antinode) to the first open side hole in the flute tube (antinode).

$$f = \frac{v}{2L} \quad \rightarrow \quad L = \frac{v}{2f} = \frac{343\,\text{m/s}}{2(294\,\text{Hz})} = \boxed{0.583\,\text{m}}$$

33. (a) At $T = 20°\text{C}$, the speed of sound is $343\,\text{m/s}$. For an open pipe, the fundamental frequency is given by $f = \dfrac{v}{2L}$.

$$f = \frac{v}{2L} \quad \rightarrow \quad L = \frac{v}{2f} = \frac{343\,\text{m/s}}{2(294\,\text{Hz})} = \boxed{0.583\,\text{m}}$$

(b) The speed of sound in helium is 1005 m/s, from Table 12-1. Use this and the pipe's length to to find the pipe's fundamental frequency.

$$f = \frac{v}{2L} = \frac{1005\,\text{m/s}}{2(0.583\ \text{m})} = \boxed{862\,\text{Hz}}$$

34. (a) The difference between successive overtones for this pipe is 176 Hz. The difference between successive overtones for an open pipe is the fundamental frequency, and each overtone is an integer multiple of the fundamental. Since 264 Hz is not a multiple of 176 Hz, 176 Hz cannot be the fundamental, and so the pipe cannot be open. Thus it must be a $\boxed{\text{closed}}$ pipe.

(b) For a closed pipe, the successive overtones differ by twice the fundamental frequency. Thus 176 Hz must be twice the fundamental, so the fundamental is $\boxed{88.0\,\text{Hz}}$. This is verified since 264 Hz is 3 times the fundamental, 440 Hz is 5 times the fundamental, and 616 Hz is 7 times the fundamental.

35. (a) The difference between successive overtones for an open pipe is the fundamental frequency.

$$f_1 = 330\,\text{Hz} - 275\,\text{Hz} = \boxed{55\,\text{Hz}}$$

(b) The fundamental frequency is given by $f_1 = \dfrac{v}{2L}$. Solve this for the speed of sound.

$$v = 2Lf_1 = 2(1.80\ \text{m})(55\,\text{Hz}) = 198\,\text{m/s} \approx \boxed{2.0 \times 10^2\,\text{m/s}}$$

36. The difference in frequency for two successive harmonics is 40 Hz. For an open pipe, two successive harmonics differ by the fundamental, so the fundamental could be 40 Hz, with 240 Hz being the 6th harmonic and 280 Hz being the 7th harmonic. For a closed pipe, two successive harmonics differ by twice the fundamental, so the fundamental could be 20 Hz. But the overtones of a closed pipe are odd multiples of the fundamental, and both overtones are even multiples of 30 Hz. So the pipe must be an $\boxed{\text{open pipe}}$.

$$f = \frac{v}{2L} \quad \rightarrow \quad L = \frac{v}{2f} = \frac{343\,\text{m/s}}{2(40\,\text{Hz})} = \boxed{4.3\,\text{m}}$$

37. (a) The harmonics for the open pipe are $f_n = \dfrac{nv}{2L}$. To be audible, they must be below 20 kHz.

$$\frac{nv}{2L} < 2 \times 10^4\,\text{Hz} \quad \rightarrow \quad n < \frac{2(2.14\ \text{m})(2 \times 10^4\,\text{Hz})}{343\,\text{m/s}} = 249.6$$

Since there are 249 harmonics, there are $\boxed{248\ \text{overtones}}$.

(b)   The harmonics for the closed pipe are $f_n = \dfrac{nv}{4L}$, n odd. Again, they must be below 20 kHz.

$$\frac{nv}{4L} < 2 \times 10^4\,\text{Hz} \quad \rightarrow \quad n < \frac{4\left(2.14\,\text{m}\right)\left(2 \times 10^4\,\text{Hz}\right)}{343\,\text{m/s}} = 499.1$$

The values of n must be odd, so $n = 1, 3, 5, \ldots, 499$. There are 250 harmonics, and so there are $\boxed{249 \text{ overtones}}$

38. The ear canal can be modeled as a closed pipe of length 2.5 cm. The resonant frequencies are given by $f_n = \dfrac{nv}{4L}$, n odd. The first several frequencies are calculated here.

$$f_n = \frac{nv}{4L} = \frac{n\left(343\,\text{m/s}\right)}{4\left(2.5 \times 10^{-2}\,\text{m}\right)} = n\left(3430\,\text{Hz}\right),\, n\text{ odd}$$

$$\boxed{f_1 = 3430\,\text{Hz} \quad f_3 = 10300\,\text{Hz} \quad f_5 = 17200\,\text{Hz}}$$

In the graph, the most sensitive frequency is between 3000 and 4000 Hz. This corresponds to the fundamental resonant frequency of the ear canal. The sensitivity decrease above 4000 Hz, but is seen to "flatten out" around 10,000 Hz again, indicating higher sensitivity near 10,000 Hz than at surrounding frequencies. This 10,000 Hz relatively sensitive region corresponds to the first overtone resonant frequency of the ear canal.

39. The beat period is 2.0 seconds, so the beat frequency is the reciprocal of that, 0.50 Hz. Thus the other string is off in frequency by $\boxed{\pm 0.50\,\text{Hz}}$. The beating does not tell the tuner whether the second string is too high or too low.

40. The beat frequency is the difference in the two frequencies, or $277\,\text{Hz} - 262\,\text{Hz} = \boxed{15\,\text{Hz}}$. If the frequencies are both reduced by a factor of 4, then the difference between the two frequencies will also be reduced by a factor of 4, and so the beat frequency will be $\tfrac{1}{4}\left(15\,\text{Hz}\right) = 3.75\,\text{Hz} \approx \boxed{3.8\,\text{Hz}}$.

41. The 5000 Hz shrill whine is the beat frequency generated by the combination of the two sounds. This means that the brand X whistle is either 5000 Hz higher or 5000 Hz lower than the known-frequency whistle. If it were 5000 Hz lower, then it would be in the audible range for humans. Since it cannot be heard by humans, the brand X whistle must be 5000 Hz higher than the known frequency whistle. Thus the brand X frequency is $23.5\,\text{kHz} + 5\,\text{kHz} = \boxed{28.5\,\text{kHz}}$

42. Since there are 4 beats/s when sounded with the 350 Hz tuning fork, the guitar string must have a frequency of either 346 Hz or 354 Hz. Since there are 9 beats/s when sounded with the 355 Hz tuning fork, the guitar string must have a frequency of either 346 Hz or 364 Hz. The common value is $\boxed{346\,\text{Hz}}$.

43. The fundamental frequency of the violin string is given by $f = \dfrac{v}{2L} = \dfrac{1}{2L}\sqrt{\dfrac{F_T}{m/L}} = 294\,\text{Hz}$. Change the tension to find the new frequency, and then subtract the two frequencies to find the beat frequency.

$$f' = \frac{1}{2L}\sqrt{\frac{(0.98)F_T}{m/L}} = \sqrt{0.98}\frac{1}{2L}\sqrt{\frac{F_T}{m/L}} = \sqrt{0.98}\,f$$

$$\Delta f = f - f' = f\left(1 - \sqrt{0.98}\right) = (294\text{ Hz})\left(1 - \sqrt{0.98}\right) = \boxed{3.0\text{ Hz}}$$

44. Beats will be heard because the difference in the speed of sound for the two flutes will result in two different frequencies. We assume that the flute at 25.0°C will accurately play the middle C.

$$f_1 = \frac{v_1}{2L} \rightarrow L = \frac{v_1}{2f_1} = \frac{[331 + 0.6(25.0)]\text{ m/s}}{2(262\text{ Hz})} = 0.660\text{ m}$$

$$f_2 = \frac{v_2}{2L} = \frac{[331 + 0.6(5.0)]\text{ m/s}}{2(0.660\text{ m})} = 253\text{ Hz} \qquad \Delta f = 262\text{ Hz} - 253\text{ Hz} = \boxed{9\text{ beats/sec}}$$

45. Tuning fork A must have a frequency of 3 Hz either higher or lower than the 441 Hz fork B. Tuning fork C must have a frequency of 4 Hz either higher or lower than the 441 Hz fork B.

$$\boxed{f_A = 438\text{ Hz or 444 Hz} \qquad f_C = 437\text{ Hz or 445 Hz}}$$

The possible beat frequencies are found by subtracting all possible frequencies of A and C.

$$\boxed{|f_A - f_C| = 1\text{ Hz or 7 Hz}}$$

$\boxed{46.}$ (a) For destructive interference, the smallest path difference must be one-half wavelength. Thus the wavelength in this situation must be twice the path difference, or 1.00 m.

$$f = \frac{v}{\lambda} = \frac{343\text{ m/s}}{1.00\text{ m}} = \boxed{343\text{ Hz}}$$

(b) There will also be destructive interference if the path difference is 1.5 wavelengths, 2.5 wavelengths, etc.

$$\Delta L = 1.5\lambda \rightarrow \lambda = \frac{0.50\text{ m}}{1.5} = 0.333\text{ m} \rightarrow f = \frac{v}{\lambda} = \frac{343\text{ m/s}}{0.33\text{ m}} = 1029\text{ Hz} \approx \boxed{1000\text{ Hz}}$$

$$\Delta L = 2.5\lambda \rightarrow \lambda = \frac{0.50\text{ m}}{2.5} = 0.20\text{ m} \rightarrow f = \frac{v}{\lambda} = \frac{343\text{ m/s}}{0.20\text{ m}} = 1715\text{ Hz} \approx \boxed{1700\text{ Hz}}$$

47. The beat frequency is 3 beats per 2 seconds, or 1.5 Hz.

(a) The other string must be either $132\text{ Hz} - 1.5\text{ Hz} = \boxed{130.5\text{ Hz}}$ or $132\text{ Hz} + 1.5\text{ Hz} = \boxed{133.5\text{ Hz}}$.

(b) Since $f = \dfrac{v}{2L} = \dfrac{\sqrt{\dfrac{F_T}{m/L}}}{2L}$, we have $f \propto \sqrt{F_T} \rightarrow \dfrac{f}{\sqrt{F_T}} = \dfrac{f'}{\sqrt{F_T'}} \rightarrow F' = F_T\left(\dfrac{f'}{f}\right)^2$.

To change 130.5 Hz to 132 Hz: $F' = F_T\left(\dfrac{132}{130.5}\right)^2 = 1.023$, $\boxed{2.3\%\text{ increase}}$

To change 133.5 Hz to 132 Hz: $F' = F_T\left(\dfrac{132}{133.5}\right)^2 = 0.978$, $\boxed{2.2\%\text{ decrease}}$

48. To find the beat frequency, calculate the frequency of each sound, and then subtract the two frequencies.

$$f_{beat} = |f_1 - f_2| = \left|\frac{v}{\lambda_1} - \frac{v}{\lambda_2}\right| = (343\,\text{m/s})\left|\frac{1}{2.64\,\text{m}} - \frac{1}{2.76\,\text{m}}\right| = 5.649 \approx \boxed{5.6\,\text{Hz}}$$

49. (a) Observer moving towards stationary source.

$$f' = \left(1 + \frac{v_{obs}}{v_{snd}}\right)f = \left(1 + \frac{30.0\,\text{m/s}}{343\,\text{m/s}}\right)(1550\,\text{Hz}) = \boxed{1690\,\text{Hz}}$$

(b) Observer moving away from stationary source.

$$f' = \left(1 - \frac{v_{obs}}{v_{snd}}\right)f = \left(1 - \frac{30.0\,\text{m/s}}{343\,\text{m/s}}\right)(1550\,\text{Hz}) = \boxed{1410\,\text{Hz}}$$

50. (a) Source moving towards stationary observer.

$$f' = \frac{f}{\left(1 - \frac{v_{src}}{v_{snd}}\right)} = \frac{(1550\,\text{Hz})}{\left(1 - \frac{32\,\text{m/s}}{343\,\text{m/s}}\right)} = \boxed{1710\,\text{Hz}}$$

(b) Source moving away from stationary observer.

$$f' = \frac{f}{\left(1 + \frac{v_{src}}{v_{snd}}\right)} = \frac{(1550\,\text{Hz})}{\left(1 + \frac{32\,\text{m/s}}{343\,\text{m/s}}\right)} = \boxed{1420\,\text{Hz}}$$

51. (a) For the 15 m/s relative velocity:

$$f'_{\substack{source \\ moving}} = f\frac{1}{\left(1 - \frac{v_{src}}{v_{snd}}\right)} = (2000\,\text{Hz})\frac{1}{\left(1 - \frac{15\,\text{m/s}}{343\,\text{m/s}}\right)} = \boxed{2091\,\text{Hz}}$$

$$f'_{\substack{observer \\ moving}} = f\left(1 + \frac{v_{src}}{v_{snd}}\right) = (2000\,\text{Hz})\left(1 + \frac{15\,\text{m/s}}{343\,\text{m/s}}\right) = \boxed{2087\,\text{Hz}}$$

The frequency shifts are slightly different, with $f'_{\substack{source \\ moving}} > f'_{\substack{observer \\ moving}}$. The two frequencies are close, but they are not identical. To 3 significant figures they are the same.

(b) For the 150 m/s relative velocity:

$$f'_{\substack{source \\ moving}} = f\frac{1}{\left(1 - \frac{v_{src}}{v_{snd}}\right)} = (2000\,\text{Hz})\frac{1}{\left(1 - \frac{150\,\text{m/s}}{343\,\text{m/s}}\right)} = \boxed{3.55 \times 10^3\,\text{Hz}}$$

$$f'_{\substack{observer \\ moving}} = f\left(1 + \frac{v_{src}}{v_{snd}}\right) = (2000\,\text{Hz})\left(1 + \frac{150\,\text{m/s}}{343\,\text{m/s}}\right) = \boxed{2.87 \times 10^3\,\text{Hz}}$$

The difference in the frequency shifts is much larger this time, still with $f'_{\substack{source \\ moving}} > f'_{\substack{observer \\ moving}}$.

(c) For the 300 m/s relative velocity:

$$f'_{\substack{source \\ moving}} = f \frac{1}{\left(1 - \dfrac{v_{src}}{v_{snd}}\right)} = (2000\ \text{Hz}) \frac{1}{\left(1 - \dfrac{300\ \text{m/s}}{343\ \text{m/s}}\right)} = \boxed{16.0 \times 10^3\ \text{Hz}}$$

$$f'_{\substack{observer \\ moving}} = f \left(1 + \dfrac{v_{src}}{v_{snd}}\right) = (2000\ \text{Hz}) \left(1 + \dfrac{300\ \text{m/s}}{343\ \text{m/s}}\right) = \boxed{3.75 \times 10^3\ \text{Hz}}$$

The difference in the frequency shifts is quite large, still with $f'_{\substack{source \\ moving}} > f'_{\substack{observer \\ moving}}$.

.   The Doppler formulas are asymmetric, with a larger shift for the moving source than for the moving observer, when the two are getting closer to each other. As the source moves toward the observer with speeds approaching the speed of sound, the observed frequency tends towards infinity. As the observer moves toward the source with speeds approaching the speed of sound, the observed frequency tends towards twice the emitted frequency.

52. The frequency received by the stationary car is higher than the frequency emitted by the stationary car, by $\Delta f = 5.5\ \text{Hz}$.

$$f_{obs} = f_{source} + \Delta f = \frac{f_{source}}{\left(1 - \dfrac{v_{source}}{v_{snd}}\right)} \rightarrow$$

$$f_{source} = \Delta f \left(\frac{v_{snd}}{v_{source}} - 1\right) = (5.5\ \text{Hz})\left(\frac{343\ \text{m/s}}{15\ \text{m/s}} - 1\right) = \boxed{120\ \text{Hz}}$$

53. The moving object can be treated as a moving "observer" for calculating the frequency it receives and reflects. The bat (the source) is stationary.

$$f'_{object} = f_{bat}\left(1 - \frac{v_{object}}{v_{snd}}\right)$$

Then the object can be treated as a moving source emitting the frequency f'_{object}, and the bat as a stationary observer.

$$f''_{bat} = \frac{f'_{object}}{\left(1 + \dfrac{v_{object}}{v_{snd}}\right)} = f_{bat} \frac{\left(1 - \dfrac{v_{object}}{v_{snd}}\right)}{\left(1 + \dfrac{v_{object}}{v_{snd}}\right)} = f_{bat}\frac{\left(v_{snd} - v_{object}\right)}{\left(v_{snd} + v_{object}\right)}$$

$$= \left(5.00 \times 10^4\ \text{Hz}\right)\frac{343\ \text{m/s} - 25.0\ \text{m/s}}{343\ \text{m/s} + 25.0\ \text{m/s}} = \boxed{4.32 \times 10^4\ \text{Hz}}$$

54. The wall can be treated as a stationary "observer" for calculating the frequency it receives. The bat is flying toward the wall.

$$f'_{wall} = f_{bat}\frac{1}{\left(1 - \dfrac{v_{bat}}{v_{snd}}\right)}$$

Then the wall can be treated as a stationary source emitting the frequency f'_{wall}, and the bat as a moving observer, flying toward the wall.

$$f''_{bat} = f'_{wall}\left(1 + \frac{v_{bat}}{v_{snd}}\right) = f_{bat}\frac{1}{\left(1 - \frac{v_{bat}}{v_{snd}}\right)}\left(1 + \frac{v_{bat}}{v_{snd}}\right) = f_{bat}\frac{\left(v_{snd} + v_{bat}\right)}{\left(v_{snd} - v_{bat}\right)}$$

$$= \left(3.00 \times 10^4\,\text{Hz}\right)\frac{343\,\text{m/s} + 5.0\,\text{m/s}}{343\,\text{m/s} - 5.0\,\text{m/s}} = \boxed{3.09 \times 10^4\,\text{Hz}}$$

55. We assume that the comparison is to be made from the frame of reference of the stationary tuba. The stationary observers would observe a frequency from the moving tuba of

$$f_{obs} = \frac{f_{source}}{\left(1 - \frac{v_{source}}{v_{snd}}\right)} = \frac{75\,\text{Hz}}{\left(1 - \frac{10.0\,\text{m/s}}{343\,\text{m/s}}\right)} = 77\,\text{Hz} \qquad f_{beat} = 77\,\text{Hz} - 75\,\text{Hz} = \boxed{2\,\text{Hz}}.$$

56. The beats arise from the combining of the original 3.5 MHz frequency with the reflected signal which has been Doppler shifted. There are two Doppler shifts – one for the blood cells receiving the original signal (observer moving away from stationary source) and one for the detector receiving the reflected signal (source moving away from stationary observer).

$$f'_{blood} = f_{original}\left(1 - \frac{v_{blood}}{v_{snd}}\right) \qquad f''_{detector} = \frac{f'_{blood}}{\left(1 + \frac{v_{blood}}{v_{snd}}\right)} = f_{original}\frac{\left(1 - \frac{v_{blood}}{v_{snd}}\right)}{\left(1 + \frac{v_{blood}}{v_{snd}}\right)} = f_{original}\frac{\left(v_{snd} - v_{blood}\right)}{\left(v_{snd} + v_{blood}\right)}$$

$$\Delta f = f_{original} - f''_{detector} = f_{original} - f_{original}\frac{\left(v_{snd} - v_{blood}\right)}{\left(v_{snd} + v_{blood}\right)} = f_{original}\frac{2v_{blood}}{\left(v_{snd} + v_{blood}\right)}$$

$$= \left(3.5 \times 10^6\,\text{Hz}\right)\frac{2\left(2.0 \times 10^{-2}\right)}{\left(1.54 \times 10^3\,\text{m/s} + 2.0 \times 10^{-2}\right)} = \boxed{91\,\text{Hz}}$$

57. The maximum Doppler shift occurs when the heart has its maximum velocity. Assume that the heart is moving away from the original source of sound. The beats arise from the combining of the original 2.25 MHz frequency with the reflected signal which has been Doppler shifted. There are two Doppler shifts – one for the heart receiving the original signal (observer moving away from stationary source) and one for the detector receiving the reflected signal (source moving away from stationary observer).

$$f'_{heart} = f_{original}\left(1 - \frac{v_{heart}}{v_{snd}}\right) \qquad f''_{detector} = \frac{f'_{heart}}{\left(1 + \frac{v_{heart}}{v_{snd}}\right)} = f_{original}\frac{\left(1 - \frac{v_{heart}}{v_{snd}}\right)}{\left(1 + \frac{v_{heart}}{v_{snd}}\right)} = f_{original}\frac{\left(v_{snd} - v_{heart}\right)}{\left(v_{snd} + v_{heart}\right)}$$

$$\Delta f = f_{original} - f''_{detector} = f_{original} - f_{original}\frac{\left(v_{snd} - v_{blood}\right)}{\left(v_{snd} + v_{blood}\right)} = f_{original}\frac{2v_{blood}}{\left(v_{snd} + v_{blood}\right)} \quad \rightarrow$$

$$v_{blood} = v_{snd} \frac{\Delta f}{2f_{original} - \Delta f} = \left(1.54 \times 10^3 \, \text{m/s}\right) \frac{500 \, \text{Hz}}{2\left(2.25 \times 10^6 \, \text{Hz}\right) - 500 \, \text{Hz}} = \boxed{0.171 \, \text{m/s}}$$

If instead we had assumed that the heart was moving towards the original source of sound, we would

get $v_{blood} = v_{snd} \dfrac{\Delta f}{2f_{original} + \Delta f}$. Since the beat frequency is much smaller than the original frequency,

the Δf term in the denominator does not significantly affect the answer.

58. The Doppler effect occurs only when there is relative motion of the source and the observer along the line connecting them. In the first four parts of this problem, the whistle and the observer are not moving relative to each other and so there is no Doppler shift. The wind speed increases (or decreases) the velocity of the waves in the direction of the wind, and the wavelength of the waves by the same factor, while the frequency is unchanged.

(*a*), (*b*), (*c*), (*d*) $\boxed{f' = f = 570 \, \text{Hz}}$

(*e*)   The wind makes an effective speed of sound in air of 343 + 12.0 = 355 m/s, and the observer is moving towards a stationary source with a speed of 15.0 m/s.

$$f' = f\left(1 + \frac{v_{obs}}{v_{sns}}\right) = \left(570 \, \text{Hz}\right)\left(1 + \frac{15.0 \, \text{m/s}}{355 \, \text{m/s}}\right) = \boxed{594 \, \text{Hz}}$$

(*f*)   Since the wind is not changing the speed of the sound waves moving towards the cyclist, the speed of sound is 343 m/s. The observer is moving towards a stationary source with a speed of 15.0 m/s.

$$f' = f\left(1 + \frac{v_{obs}}{v_{sns}}\right) = \left(570 \, \text{Hz}\right)\left(1 + \frac{15.0 \, \text{m/s}}{343 \, \text{m/s}}\right) = \boxed{595 \, \text{Hz}}$$

59. (*a*)   We represent the Mach number by the symbol M.

$$M = \frac{v_{obj}}{v_{snd}} \quad \rightarrow \quad v_{obj} = Mv_{snd} = \left(0.33\right)\left(343 \, \text{m/s}\right) = \boxed{110 \, \text{m/s}}$$

(*b*) $M = \dfrac{v_{obj}}{v_{snd}} \quad \rightarrow \quad v_{snd} = \dfrac{v_{obj}}{M} = \dfrac{3000 \, \text{km/h}}{3.2} = 937.5 \, \text{km/h}\left(\dfrac{1 \, \text{m/s}}{3.6 \, \text{km/h}}\right) = \boxed{260 \, \text{m/s}}$

60. (*a*)   The angle of the shock wave front relative to the direction of motion is given by Eq. 12-7.

$$\sin\theta = \frac{v_{snd}}{v_{obj}} = \frac{v_{snd}}{2.3v_{snd}} = \frac{1}{2.3} \quad \rightarrow \quad \theta = \sin^{-1}\frac{1}{2.3} = 25.77° = \boxed{26°}$$

(*b*)   The displacement of the plane $\left(v_{obj}t\right)$ from the time it passes overhead to the time the shock wave reaches the observer is shown, along with the shock wave front. From the displacement and height of the plane, the time is found.

$$\tan\theta = \frac{h}{v_{obj}t} \quad \rightarrow \quad t = \frac{h}{v_{obj}\tan\theta}$$

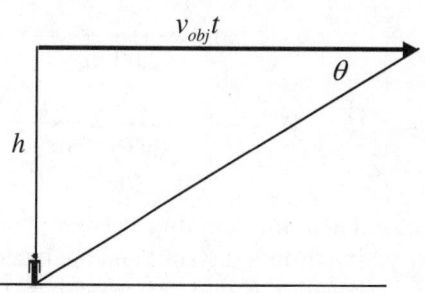

$$= \frac{7100 \, \text{m}}{\left(2.3\right)\left(310 \, \text{m/s}\right)\tan 25.77°} = 20.63 \, \text{s} \approx \boxed{21 \, \text{s}}$$

61. (*a*) The Mach number is the ratio of the object's speed to the speed of sound.

$$M = \frac{v_{obs}}{v_{sound}} = \frac{\left(1.5 \times 10^4 \, \text{km/hr}\right)\left(\dfrac{1 \, \text{m/s}}{3.6 \, \text{km/hr}}\right)}{35 \, \text{m/s}} = 119.05 \approx \boxed{120}$$

(*b*) Use Eq. 12.5 to find the angle.

$$\theta = \sin^{-1}\frac{v_{snd}}{v_{obj}} = \sin^{-1}\frac{1}{M} = \sin^{-1}\frac{1}{119.05} = \boxed{0.48°}$$

62. From Eq. 12-7, $\sin\theta = \dfrac{v_{snd}}{v_{obj}}$.

(*a*) $\theta = \sin^{-1}\dfrac{v_{snd}}{v_{obj}} = \sin^{-1}\dfrac{343 \, \text{m/s}}{8500 \, \text{m/s}} = \boxed{2.3°}$

(*b*) $\theta = \sin^{-1}\dfrac{v_{snd}}{v_{obj}} = \sin^{-1}\dfrac{1560 \, \text{m/s}}{8500 \, \text{m/s}} = \boxed{11°}$

63. Consider one particular wave as shown in the diagram, created at the location of the black dot. After a time *t* has elapsed from the creation of that wave, the supersonic source has moved a distance $v_{obj}t$, and the wave front has moved a distance $v_{snd}t$. The line from the position of the source at time *t* is tangent to all of the wave fronts, showing the location of the shock wave. A tangent to a circle at a point is perpendicular to the radius connecting that point to the center, and so a right angle is formed. From the right triangle, the angle θ can be defined.

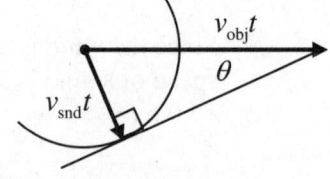

$$\boxed{\sin\theta = \frac{v_{snd}t}{v_{obj}t} = \frac{v_{snd}}{v_{obj}}}$$

64. (*a*) The displacement of the plane from the time it passes overhead to the time the shock wave reaches the listener is shown, along with the shock wave front. From the displacement and height of the plane, the angle of the shock wave front relative to the direction of motion can be found, using Eq. 12-7.

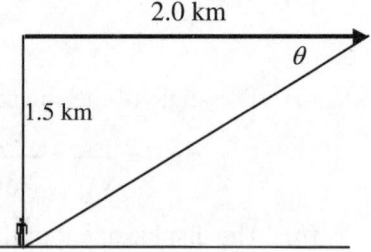

$$\tan\theta = \frac{1.5 \, \text{km}}{2.0 \, \text{km}} \quad \rightarrow \quad \theta = \tan^{-1}\frac{1.5}{2.0} = \boxed{37°}$$

(*b*) $M = \dfrac{v_{obj}}{v_{snd}} = \dfrac{1}{\sin\theta} = \dfrac{1}{\sin 37°} = \boxed{1.7}$

65. The minimum time between pulses would be the time for a pulse to travel from the boat to the maximum distance and back again. The total distance traveled by the pulse will be 400 m, at the speed of sound in fresh water, 1440 m/s.

$$d = vt \quad \rightarrow \quad t = \frac{d}{v} = \frac{400 \, \text{m}}{1440 \, \text{m/s}} = \boxed{0.28 \, \text{s}}$$

66. Each octave is a doubling of frequency. The number of octaves, n, can be found from the following.

$$20,000\ \text{Hz} = 2^n\,(20\ \text{Hz}) \quad\rightarrow\quad 1000 = 2^n \quad\rightarrow\quad \log 1000 = n\log 2 \quad\rightarrow$$

$$n = \frac{\log 1000}{\log 2} = 9.97 \approx \boxed{10\ \text{octaves}}$$

67. Assume that only the fundamental frequency is heard. The fundamental frequency of an open pipe is given by $f = \dfrac{v}{2L}$.

(a) $\quad f_{3.0} = \dfrac{v}{2L} = \dfrac{343\ \text{m/s}}{2(3.0\ \text{m})} = \boxed{57\ \text{Hz}} \qquad f_{2.5} = \dfrac{v}{2L} = \dfrac{343\ \text{m/s}}{2(2.5\ \text{m})} = \boxed{69\ \text{Hz}}$

$\quad f_{2.0} = \dfrac{v}{2L} = \dfrac{343\ \text{m/s}}{2(2.0\ \text{m})} = \boxed{86\ \text{Hz}} \qquad f_{1.5} = \dfrac{v}{2L} = \dfrac{343\ \text{m/s}}{2(1.5\ \text{m})} = 114.3\ \text{Hz} \approx \boxed{110\ \text{Hz}}$

$\quad f_{1.0} = \dfrac{v}{2L} = \dfrac{343\ \text{m/s}}{2(1.0\ \text{m})} = 171.5\ \text{Hz} \approx \boxed{170\ \text{Hz}}$

(b) On a noisy day, there are a large number of component frequencies to the sounds that are being made – more people walking, more people talking, etc. Thus it is more likely that the frequencies listed above will be a component of the overall sound, and then the resonance will be more prominent to the hearer. If the day is quiet, there might be very little sound at the desired frequencies, and then the tubes will not have any standing waves in them to detect.

68. The single mosquito creates a sound intensity of $I_0 = 1 \times 10^{-12}\ \text{W/m}^2$. Thus 1000 mosquitoes will create a sound intensity of 1000 times that of a single mosquito.

$$I = 1000 I_0 \qquad \beta = 10\log\frac{1000 I_0}{I_0} = 10\log 1000 = \boxed{30\ \text{dB}}.$$

69. The two sound level values must be converted to intensities, then the intensities added, and then converted back to sound level.

$$I_{82}:\quad 82\ \text{dB} = 10\log\frac{I_{82}}{I_0} \quad\rightarrow\quad I_{82} = 10^{8.2} I_0 = 1.585 \times 10^8 I_0$$

$$I_{87}:\quad 87\ \text{dB} = 10\log\frac{I_{87}}{I_0} \quad\rightarrow\quad I_{87} = 10^{8.7} I_0 = 5.012 \times 10^8 I_0$$

$$I_{\text{total}} = I_{82} + I_{87} = \left(6.597 \times 10^8\right) I_0 \quad\rightarrow$$

$$\beta_{\text{total}} = 10\log\frac{6.597 \times 10^8 I_0}{I_0} = 10\log 6.597 \times 10^8 = \boxed{88\ \text{dB}}$$

70. The power output is found from the intensity, which is the power radiated per unit area.

$$105\ \text{dB} = 10\log\frac{I}{I_0} \quad\rightarrow\quad I = 10^{10.5} I_0 = 10^{10.5}\left(1.0 \times 10^{-12}\ \text{W/m}^2\right) = 3.162 \times 10^{-2}\ \text{W/m}^2$$

$$I = \frac{P}{A} = \frac{P}{4\pi r^2} \quad\rightarrow\quad P = 4\pi r^2 I = 4\pi (12.0\ \text{m})^2\left(3.162 \times 10^{-2}\ \text{W/m}^2\right) = \boxed{57.2\ \text{W}}$$

71. Relative to the 1000 Hz output, the 15 kHz output is –10 dB.

$$-10\text{ dB} = 10\log\frac{P_{15\text{ kHz}}}{150\text{ W}} \rightarrow -1 = \log\frac{P_{15\text{ kHz}}}{150\text{ W}} \rightarrow 0.1 = \frac{P_{15\text{ kHz}}}{150\text{ W}} \rightarrow \boxed{P_{15\text{ kHz}} = 15\text{ W}}$$

72. The 140 dB level is used to find the intensity, and the intensity is used to find the power. It is assumed that the jet airplane engine radiates equally in all directions.

$$\beta = 140\text{ dB} = 10\log\frac{I}{I_0} \rightarrow I = 10^{14}I_0 = 10^{14}\left(1.0\times10^{-12}\text{ W/m}^2\right) = 1.0\times10^{2}\text{ W/m}^2$$

$$P = IA = I\pi r^2 = \left(1.0\times10^{2}\text{ W/m}^2\right)\pi\left(2.0\times10^{-2}\right)^2 = \boxed{0.13\text{ W}}$$

73. The gain is given by $\beta = 10\log\dfrac{P_\text{out}}{P_\text{in}} = 10\log\dfrac{100\text{ W}}{1\times10^{-3}\text{ W}} = \boxed{50\text{ dB}}$.

74. Call the frequencies of four strings of the violin f_A , f_B , f_C , f_D with f_A the lowest pitch. The mass per unit length will be named μ. All strings are the same length and have the same tension. For a string with both ends fixed, the fundamental frequency is given by $f_1 = \dfrac{v}{2L} = \dfrac{1}{2L}\sqrt{\dfrac{F_T}{\mu}}$.

$$f_B = 1.5 f_A \rightarrow \frac{1}{2L}\sqrt{\frac{F_T}{\mu_B}} = 1.5\frac{1}{2L}\sqrt{\frac{F_T}{\mu_A}} \rightarrow \mu_B = \frac{\mu_A}{(1.5)^2} = \boxed{0.44\mu_A}$$

$$f_C = 1.5 f_B = (1.5)^2 f_A \rightarrow \frac{1}{2L}\sqrt{\frac{F_T}{\mu_C}} = (1.5)^2\frac{1}{2L}\sqrt{\frac{F_T}{\mu_A}} \rightarrow \mu_C = \frac{\mu_A}{(1.5)^4} = \boxed{0.20\mu_A}$$

$$f_D = 1.5 f_C = (1.5)^4 f_A \rightarrow \frac{1}{2L}\sqrt{\frac{F_T}{\mu_D}} = (1.5)^4\frac{1}{2L}\sqrt{\frac{F_T}{\mu_A}} \rightarrow \mu_D = \frac{\mu_A}{(1.5)^8} = \boxed{0.039\mu_A}$$

75. (*a*) The wave speed on the string can be found form the length and the fundamental frequency.

$$f = \frac{v}{2L} \rightarrow v = 2Lf = 2(0.32\text{ m})(440\text{ Hz}) = 281.6 = \boxed{2.8\times10^{2}\text{ m/s}}$$

The tension is found from the wave speed and the mass per unit length.

$$v = \sqrt{\frac{F_T}{\mu}} \rightarrow F_T = \mu v^2 = \left(6.1\times10^{-4}\text{ kg/m}\right)(281.6\text{ m/s})^2 = \boxed{48\text{ N}}$$

(*b*) The length of the pipe can be found from the fundamental frequency and the speed of sound.

$$f = \frac{v}{4L} \rightarrow L = \frac{v}{4f} = \frac{343\text{ m/s}}{4(440\text{ Hz})} = \boxed{0.195\text{ m}}$$

(*c*) The first overtone for the string is twice the fundamental. $\boxed{880\text{ Hz}}$

The first overtone for the open pipe is 3 times the fundamental. $\boxed{1320\text{ Hz}}$

76. The apparatus is a closed tube. The water level is the closed end, and so is a node of air displacement. As the water level lowers, the distance from one resonance level to the next corresponds to the distance between adjacent nodes, which is one-half wavelength.

$$\Delta L = \tfrac{1}{2}\lambda \quad \rightarrow \quad \lambda = 2\Delta L = 2\left(0.395\,\text{m} - 0.125\,\text{m}\right) = 0.540\,\text{m}$$

$$f = \frac{v}{\lambda} = \frac{343\,\text{m/s}}{0.540\,\text{m}} = \boxed{635\,\text{Hz}}$$

77. The frequency of the guitar string is to be the same as the third harmonic ($n = 3$) of the closed tube.

The resonance frequencies of a closed tube are given by $f_n = \dfrac{nv}{4L}$, $n = 1, 3, 5\cdots$, and the frequency of

a stretched string is given by $f = \dfrac{1}{2L}\sqrt{\dfrac{F_T}{m/L}}$. Equate the two frequencies and solve for the tension.

$$\frac{1}{2L_{\text{string}}}\sqrt{\frac{F_T}{m/L_{\text{string}}}} = \frac{3v}{4L_{\text{tube}}} \quad \rightarrow \quad F_T = \frac{9v^2 m}{4L_{\text{string}}} = \frac{9\left(343\,\text{m/s}\right)^2\left(2.10\times10^{-3}\,\text{kg}\right)}{4\left(0.75\,\text{m}\right)} = \boxed{7.4\times10^2\,\text{N}}$$

78. By anchoring the overpass to the ground in the middle, the center of the overpass is now a node point. This forces the lowest frequency for the bridge to be twice the fundamental frequency, and so now $\boxed{\text{the resonant frequency is 8.0 Hz}}$. Since the earthquakes don't do significant shaking above 6 Hz, this modification should be effective.

79. Since the sound is loudest at points equidistant from the two sources, the two sources must be in phase. The difference in distance from the two sources must be an odd number of half-wavelengths for destructive interference.

$$0.34\,\text{m} = \lambda/2 \quad \rightarrow \quad \lambda = 0.68\,\text{m} \qquad f = v/\lambda = 343\,\text{m/s}/0.68\,\text{m} = \boxed{504\,\text{Hz}}$$

$$0.34\,\text{m} = 3\lambda/2 \quad \rightarrow \quad \lambda = 0.227\,\text{m} \qquad f = v/\lambda = 343\,\text{m/s}/0.227\,\text{m} = 1513\,\text{Hz}\ \left(\text{out of range}\right)$$

80. The Doppler shift is 3.0 Hz, and the emitted frequency from both trains is 424 Hz. Thus the frequency received by the conductor on the stationary train is 427 Hz. Use this to find the moving train's speed.

$$f' = f\frac{v_{\text{snd}}}{\left(v_{\text{snd}} - v_{\text{source}}\right)} \quad \rightarrow \quad v_{\text{source}} = \left(1 - \frac{f}{f'}\right)v_{\text{snd}} = \left(1 - \frac{424\,\text{Hz}}{427\,\text{Hz}}\right)\left(343\,\text{m/s}\right) = \boxed{2.41\,\text{m/s}}$$

81. As the train approaches, the observed frequency is given by $f'_{\text{approach}} = f\left/\left(1 - \dfrac{v_{\text{train}}}{v_{\text{snd}}}\right)\right.$. As the train

recedes, the observed frequency is given by $f'_{\text{recede}} = f\left/\left(1 + \dfrac{v_{\text{train}}}{v_{\text{snd}}}\right)\right.$. Solve each expression for f,

equate them, and then solve for v_{train}.

$$f'_{\text{approach}}\left(1 - \frac{v_{\text{train}}}{v_{\text{snd}}}\right) = f'_{\text{recede}}\left(1 + \frac{v_{\text{train}}}{v_{\text{snd}}}\right) \quad \rightarrow$$

$$v_{\text{train}} = v_{\text{snd}}\frac{\left(f'_{\text{approach}} - f'_{\text{recede}}\right)}{\left(f'_{\text{approach}} + f'_{\text{recede}}\right)} = \left(343\,\text{m/s}\right)\frac{\left(538\,\text{Hz} - 486\,\text{Hz}\right)}{\left(538\,\text{Hz} + 486\,\text{Hz}\right)} = \boxed{17\,\text{m/s}}$$

82. The sound is Doppler shifted up as the car approaches, and Doppler shifted down as it recedes. The observer is stationary in both cases. The octave shift down means that $f_{approach} = 2f_{recede}$.

$$f'_{approach} = f_{engine} \bigg/ \left(1 - \frac{v_{car}}{v_{snd}}\right) \qquad f'_{recede} = f_{engine} \bigg/ \left(1 + \frac{v_{car}}{v_{snd}}\right) \qquad f_{approach} = 2f_{recede} \quad \rightarrow$$

$$f_{engine} \bigg/ \left(1 - \frac{v_{car}}{v_{snd}}\right) = 2f_{engine} \bigg/ \left(1 + \frac{v_{car}}{v_{snd}}\right) \quad \rightarrow \quad v_{car} = \frac{v_{snd}}{3} = \frac{343 \, \text{m/s}}{3} = \boxed{114 \, \text{m/s}}$$

83. For each pipe, the fundamental frequency is given by $f = \frac{v}{2L}$. Find the frequency of the shortest pipe.

$$f = \frac{v}{2L} = \frac{343 \, \text{m/s}}{2(2.40 \, \text{m})} = 71.46 \, \text{Hz}$$

The longer pipe has a lower frequency. Since the beat frequency is 11 Hz, the frequency of the longer pipe must be 60.46 Hz. Use that frequency to find the length of the longer pipe.

$$f = \frac{v}{2L} \quad \rightarrow \quad L = \frac{v}{2f} = \frac{343 \, \text{m/s}}{2(60.46 \, \text{Hz})} = \boxed{2.84 \, \text{m}}$$

84. (a) Since both speakers are moving towards the observer at the same speed, both frequencies have the same Doppler shift, and the observer hears no beats.

(b) The observer will detect an increased frequency from the speaker moving towards him and a decreased frequency from the speaker moving away. The difference in those two frequencies will be the beat frequency that is heard.

$$f'_{towards} = f \frac{1}{\left(1 - \frac{v_{train}}{v_{snd}}\right)} \qquad f'_{away} = f \frac{1}{\left(1 + \frac{v_{train}}{v_{snd}}\right)}$$

$$f'_{towards} - f'_{away} = f \frac{1}{\left(1 - \frac{v_{train}}{v_{snd}}\right)} - f \frac{1}{\left(1 + \frac{v_{train}}{v_{snd}}\right)} = f \left[\frac{v_{snd}}{\left(v_{snd} - v_{train}\right)} - \frac{v_{snd}}{\left(v_{snd} + v_{train}\right)}\right]$$

$$(212 \, \text{Hz}) \left[\frac{343 \, \text{m/s}}{(343 \, \text{m/s} - 10.0 \, \text{m/s})} - \frac{343 \, \text{m/s}}{(343 \, \text{m/s} + 10.0 \, \text{m/s})}\right] = \boxed{12 \, \text{Hz}}$$

(c) Since both speakers are moving away from the observer at the same speed, both frequencies have the same Doppler shift, and the observer hears no beats.

85. The beats arise from the combining of the original 5.50 MHz frequency with the reflected signal which has been Doppler shifted. There are two Doppler shifts – one for the blood cells receiving the original frequency (observer moving away from stationary source) and one for the detector receiving the reflected frequency (source moving away from stationary observer).

$$f'_{blood} = f_{original} \left(1 - \frac{v_{blood}}{v_{snd}}\right) \qquad f''_{detector} = \frac{f'_{blood}}{\left(1 + \frac{v_{blood}}{v_{snd}}\right)} = f_{original} \frac{\left(1 - \frac{v_{blood}}{v_{snd}}\right)}{\left(1 + \frac{v_{blood}}{v_{snd}}\right)} = f_{original} \frac{\left(v_{snd} - v_{blood}\right)}{\left(v_{snd} + v_{blood}\right)}$$

$$\Delta f = f_{original} - f''_{detector} = f_{original} - f_{original}\frac{\left(v_{snd} - v_{blood}\right)}{\left(v_{snd} + v_{blood}\right)} = f_{original}\frac{2v_{blood}}{\left(v_{snd} + v_{blood}\right)}$$

$$= \left(5.50\times10^{6}\,\text{Hz}\right)\frac{2\left(0.32\,\text{m/s}\right)}{\left(1.54\times10^{3}\,\text{m/s} + 0.32\,\text{m/s}\right)} = \boxed{2.29\times10^{3}\,\text{Hz}}$$

86. Use Eq. 12-4, which applies when both source and observer are in motion. There will be two Doppler shifts in this problem – first for the emitted sound with the bat as the source and the moth as the observer, and then the reflected sound with the moth as the source and the bat as the observer.

$$f'_{moth} = f_{bat}\frac{\left(v_{snd} + v_{moth}\right)}{\left(v_{snd} - v_{bat}\right)}\qquad f''_{bat} = f'_{moth}\frac{\left(v_{snd} + v_{bat}\right)}{\left(v_{snd} - v_{moth}\right)} = f_{bat}\frac{\left(v_{snd} + v_{moth}\right)}{\left(v_{snd} - v_{bat}\right)}\frac{\left(v_{snd} + v_{bat}\right)}{\left(v_{snd} - v_{moth}\right)}$$

$$= \left(51.35\,\text{kHz}\right)\frac{\left(343 + 5.0\right)}{\left(343 - 6.5\right)}\frac{\left(343 + 6.5\right)}{\left(343 - 5.0\right)} = \boxed{54.9\,\text{kHz}}$$

87. It is 70.0 ms from the start of one chirp to the start of the next. Since the chirp itself is 3.0 ms long, it is 67.0 ms from the end of a chirp to the start of the next. Thus the time for the pulse to travel to the moth and back again is 67.0 ms. The distance to the moth is half the distance that the sound can travel in 67.0 ms, since the sound must reach the moth and return during the 67.0 ms.

$$d = v_{snd}t = \left(343\,\text{m/s}\right)\tfrac{1}{2}\left(67.0\times10^{-3}\,\text{s}\right) = \boxed{11.5\,\text{m}}$$

88. The Alpenhorn can be modeled as an open tube, and so the fundamental frequency is $f = \dfrac{v}{2L}$, and

the overtones are given by $f_n = \dfrac{nv}{2L},\ n = 1, 2, 3, \cdots$.

$$f_1 = \frac{v}{2L} = \frac{343\,\text{m/s}}{2\left(3.4\ \text{m}\right)} = 50.44\,\text{Hz} \approx \boxed{50\,\text{Hz}}$$

$$f_n = nf_1 = f_{F\#}\ \rightarrow\ n\left(50.44\,\text{Hz}\right) = 370\,\text{Hz}\ \rightarrow\ n = \frac{370}{50.44} = 7.34$$

Thus the 7th harmonic, which is the $\boxed{\text{6th overtone}}$, is close to F sharp.

89. The walls of the room must be air displacement nodes, and so the dimensions of the room between two parallel boundaries corresponds to a half-wavelength of sound. Fundamental frequencies are

then given by $f = \dfrac{v}{2L}$.

Length: $f = \dfrac{v}{2L} = \dfrac{343\,\text{m/s}}{2\left(5.0\ \text{m}\right)} = \boxed{34\,\text{Hz}}$ Width: $f = \dfrac{v}{2L} = \dfrac{343\,\text{m/s}}{2\left(4.0\ \text{m}\right)} = \boxed{43\,\text{Hz}}$

Height: $f = \dfrac{v}{2L} = \dfrac{343\,\text{m/s}}{2\left(2.8\ \text{m}\right)} = \boxed{61\,\text{Hz}}$

90. (*a*) The "singing" rod is manifesting standing waves. By holding the rod at its midpoint, it has a node at its midpoint, and antinodes at its ends. Thus the length of the rod is a half wavelength.

$$f = \frac{v}{\lambda} = \frac{v}{2L} = \frac{5100\,\text{m/s}}{1.80\ \text{m}} = 2833\,\text{Hz} = \boxed{2.8\times10^{3}\,\text{Hz}}$$

(b)   The wavelength of sound in the rod is twice the length of the rod, $\boxed{1.80 \text{ m}}$.

(c)   The wavelength of the sound in air is determined by the frequency and the speed of sound in air.

$$\lambda = \frac{v}{f} = \frac{343 \text{ m/s}}{2833 \text{ Hz}} = \boxed{0.12 \text{ m}}$$

91.   Eq. 11-18 gives the relationship between intensity and the displacement amplitude: $I = 2\pi^2 v \rho f^2 A^2$, where A is the displacement amplitude. Thus $I \propto A^2$, or $A \propto \sqrt{I}$. Since the intensity increased by a factor of 10^{12}, the amplitude would increase by a factor of the square root of the intensity increase, or $\boxed{10^6}$.

92.   The angle between the direction of the airplane and the shock wave front is found from Eq. 12-5.

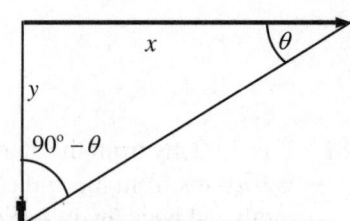

$$\sin \theta = \frac{v_{snd}}{v_{obj}} \quad \rightarrow \quad \theta = \sin^{-1} \frac{v_{snd}}{v_{obj}} = \sin^{-1} \frac{1}{2.0} = 30°$$

The distance that the plane has traveled horizontally from the observer is found from the time and the speed: $x = v_{obj} t$. The altitude is found from the angle and the horizontal distance.

$$\tan \theta = y/x \quad \rightarrow \quad y = x \tan \theta = v_{obj} t \tan 30° = 2 \left(343 \text{ m/s} \right) \left(90 \text{ s} \right) \tan 30° = \boxed{3.6 \times 10^4 \text{ m}}$$

93.   The apex angle is 15°, so the shock wave angle is 7.5°. The angle of the shock wave is also given by $\sin \theta = v_{wave}/v_{object}$.

$$\sin \theta = v_{wave}/v_{object} \quad \rightarrow \quad v_{object} = v_{wave}/\sin \theta = 2.2 \text{ km/h}/\sin 7.5° = \boxed{17 \text{ km/h}}$$

CHAPTER 13: Temperature and Kinetic Theory

Answers to Questions

1. Because the atomic mass of aluminum is smaller than that of iron, an atom of aluminum has less mass than an atom of iron. Thus 1 kg of aluminum will have more atoms than 1 kg of iron.

2. Properties of materials that can be exploited for the making of a thermometer include:
    i) Volume of a liquid (mercury thermometer)
    ii) Electrical resistance
    iii) Color (frequency) of emitted light from a heated object
    iv) Volume of a gas
    v) Expansion of a metal (bimetallic strip)

3. $1 \, C°$ is larger than $1 \, F°$. There are $100 \, C°$ between the freezing and boiling temperatures of water, while there are $180 \, F°$ between the same two temperatures.

4. The following conclusions can be drawn:
    A and B are at the same temperature
    B and C are not at the same temperature
    A and C are not at the same temperature

5. When heated, the aluminum expands more than the iron, because the expansion coefficient of aluminum is larger than that of iron. Thus the aluminum will be on the outside of the curve.

6. To be precise, L_0 is to be the initial length of the object. In practice, however, since the value of the coefficient of expansion is so small, there will be little difference in the calculation of ΔL caused by using either the initial or final length, unless the temperature change is quite large.

7. The coefficient of expansion is derived from a ratio of lengths: $\alpha = \dfrac{\Delta L}{L_0} \dfrac{1}{\Delta T}$. The length units cancel, and so the coefficient does not depend on the specific length unit used in its determination, as long as the same units are used for both ΔL and L_0.

8. The device controls the furnace by the expansion and contraction of the bimetallic strip. As the temperature increases, the strip coils more, and as the temperature decrease, the strip coils less. As the strip changes shape, it will move the liquid mercury switch. In the diagram, if the switch were tilted more to the right, the mercury would move and make contact between the heater wires, turning on the heater. By adjusting the temperature setting lever, the tilt of the mercury switch is changed, and a different amount of temperature change is needed to tilt the switch to the on (or off) position.

9. The steam pipe can have a large temperature change as the steam enters or leaves the pipe. If the pipe is fixed at both ends and the temperature changes significantly, there will be large thermal stresses which might break joints. The "U" in the pipe allows for expansion and contraction which is not possible at the fixed ends. This is similar to the joints placed in concrete roadway surfaces to allow expansion and contraction.

10. The lead floats in the mercury because $\rho_{Hg} > \rho_{Pb}$. As the substances are heated, the density of both substances will decrease due to volume expansion (see problem 17 for the derivation of this result). The density of the mercury decreases more upon heating than the density of the lead, because $\beta_{Hg} > \beta_{Pb}$. The net effect is that the densities get closer together, and so relatively more mercury will have to be displaced to hold up the lead, and the lead will float lower in the mercury.

11. The glass is the first to warm due to the hot water, and so the glass will initially expand a small amount. As the glass initially expands, the mercury level will decrease. As thermal equilibrium is reached, the mercury will expand more than the glass expands, since mercury has a larger coefficient of expansion than water, and the mercury level will rise to indicate the higher temperature.

12. If one part is heated or cooled more than another part, there will be more expansion or contraction of one part of the glass compared to an adjacent part. This causes internal stress forces which may exceed the maximum strength of the glass.

13. When Pyrex glass is heated or cooled, it will expand or contract much less than ordinary glass due to its small coefficient of linear expansion. The smaller changes in dimensions result in lower internal stresses than would be present in ordinary glass. Thus there is less of a chance of breaking the Pyrex by heating or cooling it.

14. On a hot day, the pendulum will be slightly longer than at 20°C, due to thermal expansion. Since the period of a pendulum is proportional to the square root of its length, the period will be slightly longer on the hot day, meaning that the pendulum takes more time for one oscillation. Thus the clock will run slow.

15. The soda is mostly water. As water cools below 4°C it expands. There is more expansion of the soda as it cools below 4°C and freezes than there is available room in the can, and so the freezing soda pushes against the can surfaces hard enough to push them outward. Evidently the top and bottom of the can are the weakest parts.

16. When a small mass object collides with a stationary massive object, the speed of the small mass is not changed. But when a small mass object collides with a massive object moving in the opposite direction, the speed of the small object increases. For example, a tennis ball of a given speed that is struck with a racket will rebound with a greater speed than a tennis ball of the same speed bouncing off a wall. So as the gas molecules collide with the piston that is moving toward them, their speed increases. The microscopic increase in molecular speed is manifested macroscopically as a higher temperature.

    In a similar fashion, when the molecules collide with a piston that is moving away from them, they rebound with a reduced speed compared to their initial speed. This lower speed is manifested macroscopically as a lower temperature.

17. The buoyant force on the aluminum sphere is the weight of the water displaced by the sphere, which is the volume of the sphere times the density of water times *g*. As the substances are heated, the volume of the sphere increases and the density of the water decreases. Since the volume expansion coefficient of the water is almost three times larger than that of the aluminum, the fractional decrease in the water density is larger than the fractional increase in the aluminum volume. Thus the product of the volume of the sphere times the density of water decreases, and the buoyant force gets smaller.

18. Charles's law states that the volume of a fixed mass of gas increases proportionately to the absolute temperature, when the pressure is held constant. As the temperature increases, the molecules have more kinetic energy, and the average force exerted by a gas molecule colliding with the boundaries of the container is proportional to the kinetic energy. Thus the force exerted during the collisions increases. The pressure is the force per unit area, and so for the pressure to remain constant, the surface area of the boundaries must increase, which means the volume of the container must increase.

19. Gay-Lussac's law states that at constant volume, the absolute pressure of a gas is proportional to the absolute temperature. Kinetic molecular theory has a result that the average force exerted by gas particles as they collide with the container boundaries is proportional to the kinetic energy, assuming a fixed container size. For the pressure to increase, the force on the walls must increase, which means the kinetic energy must therefore increase. But the kinetic energy of the particles is proportional to the absolute temperature, and so for the pressure to increase, the temperature must also increase.

20. Since an N_2 molecule has less mass than an O_2 molecule, at the same temperature (and thus the same kinetic energy), N_2 molecules will have a larger speed on average than O_2 molecules. If we consider "launching" molecules of both types from the Earth's surface, the faster-moving N_2 will rise higher before stopping and falling back to Earth. Thus there will be proportionally more N_2 molecules at higher altitudes than at lower altitudes.

21. Because the escape velocity is much smaller for the Moon than for the Earth, most gas molecules even at low temperatures have a speed great enough to escape the Moon's gravity. Thus the atmosphere has "evaporated" over the long time of the Moon's existence.

22. Since the alcohol evaporates more quickly, the alcohol molecules escape "easier" than the water molecules. One explanation could be that the intermolecular forces (bonds) for alcohol are smaller than those for water. Another explanation could be that the alcohol molecules are moving more rapidly than the water molecules, indicating that alcohol molecules are less massive than water molecules. However, the simplest alcohol (CH_3OH) has a molecular mass higher than that of water, so mass is probably not the explanation.

23. On a hot humid day, there is little evaporation from a human due to perspiration, because the air is already saturated with water vapor. Since perspiration is a major cooling mechanism, when it is restricted, humans will feel more uncomfortable. On a hot dry day, water molecules more easily evaporate into the air (taking their kinetic energy with them) and the body is cooled.

24. Liquids boil when their saturated vapor pressure equals the external pressure. For water, from Table 13-3, the saturated vapor pressure of water at 20°C is about 0.023 atm. So if the external pressure is lowered to that level (about 2.3% of normal air pressure), the water will boil.

25. On a day when the relative humidity is high, the percentage of air molecules that are water (as opposed to N_2 or O_2 molecules) is increased. Since the molecular mass of water is less than that of either N_2 or O_2, the average mass of air molecules in a given volume will decrease, and thus the density will be lower for the humid air.

26. The water in the radiator of an overheated automobile engine is under pressure. Similar to a pressure cooker, that high pressure keeps the water in the liquid state even though the water is quite hot – hotter than 100°C. When the cap is opened, the pressure is suddenly lowered, and the superheated water boils quickly and violently. That hot steam can cause severe burns if it contacts the skin.

Also, the violent bursting forth of steam propels some of the overheated water out of the radiator as well, which can spray onto the person opening the cap and again cause serious burns.

27. Exhaled air contains water vapor, at a relatively high percentage. Since the air inside the lungs is quite warm, the partial pressure of water in the lungs can be high without saturating the air in the lungs, and condensation does not occur. But in the cold winter air, the air can hold very little water without condensation. Thus as the warm, water-laden exhaled air cools, the partial pressure of water vapor exceeds the saturated vapor pressure in the cold air, and some of the water will condense. The white cloud seen is due to the condensed water vapor.

Solutions to Problems

In solving these problems, the authors did not always follow the rules of significant figures rigidly. We tended to take quoted temperatures as correct to the number of digits shown, especially where other values might indicate that. For example, in problem 17, values of 25°C and –40°C are used. We took both of those values to have 2 significant figures in calculating the temperature change.

1. The number of atoms is found by dividing the mass of the substance by the mass of a single atom. Take the atomic mass of carbon to be 63.

$$N_{Cu} = \frac{3.4 \times 10^{-3} \, \text{kg}}{63 \left(1.66 \times 10^{-27} \right) \text{kg/atom}} = \boxed{3.3 \times 10^{22} \, \text{atoms of Cu}}$$

2. The number of atoms in a pure substance can be found by dividing the mass of the substance by the mass of a single atom. Take the atomic mass of gold to be 197, and silver to be 108.

$$\frac{N_{Au}}{N_{Ag}} = \frac{\dfrac{2.65 \times 10^{-2} \, \text{kg}}{(197) \left(1.66 \times 10^{-27} \, \text{kg/atom} \right)}}{\dfrac{2.65 \times 10^{-2} \, \text{kg}}{(108) \left(1.66 \times 10^{-27} \, \text{kg/atom} \right)}} = \frac{108}{197} = 0.548 \quad \rightarrow \quad \boxed{N_{Au} = 0.548 N_{Ag}}$$

Because a gold atom is heavier than a silver atom, there are fewer gold atoms in the given mass.

3. (a) $T(^\circ\text{C}) = \frac{5}{9} \left[T(^\circ\text{F}) - 32 \right] = \frac{5}{9} \left[68 - 32 \right] = \boxed{20^\circ\text{C}}$

    (b) $T(^\circ\text{F}) = \frac{9}{5} T(^\circ\text{C}) + 32 = \frac{9}{5} (1800) + 32 = \boxed{3300^\circ\text{F}}$

4. High: $T(^\circ\text{C}) = \frac{5}{9} \left[T(^\circ\text{F}) - 32 \right] = \frac{5}{9} \left[136 - 32 \right] = \boxed{57.8^\circ\text{C}}$

    Low: $T(^\circ\text{C}) = \frac{5}{9} \left[T(^\circ\text{F}) - 32 \right] = \frac{5}{9} \left[-129 - 32 \right] = \boxed{-89.4^\circ\text{C}}$

5. (a) $T(^\circ\text{F}) = \frac{9}{5} T(^\circ\text{C}) + 32 = \frac{9}{5} (-15) + 32 = \boxed{5^\circ\text{F}}$

    (b) $T(^\circ\text{C}) = \frac{5}{9} \left[T(^\circ\text{F}) - 32 \right] = \frac{5}{9} \left[-15 - 32 \right] = \boxed{-26^\circ\text{C}}$

6. Assume that the temperature and the length are linearly related. The change in temperature per unit length change is as follows.

$$\frac{\Delta T}{\Delta L} = \frac{100.0°C - 0.0°C}{22.85\ \text{cm} - 11.82\ \text{cm}} = 9.066\ C°/\text{cm}$$

Then the temperature corresponding to length L is $T(L) = 0.0°C + (L - 11.82\ \text{cm})(9.066\ C°/\text{cm})$.

(a) $T(16.70\ \text{cm}) = 0.0°C + (16.70\ \text{cm} - 11.82\ \text{cm})(9.066\ C°/\text{cm}) = \boxed{44.2°C}$

(b) $T(20.50\ \text{cm}) = 0.0°C + (20.50\ \text{cm} - 11.82\ \text{cm})(9.066\ C°/\text{cm}) = \boxed{78.7°C}$

7. When the concrete cools in the winter, it will contract, and there will be no danger of buckling. Thus the low temperature in the winter is not a factor in the design of the highway. But when the concrete warms in the summer, it will expand. A crack must be left between the slabs equal to the increase in length of the concrete as it heats from 20°C to 50°C.

$$\Delta L = \alpha L_0 \Delta T = (12 \times 10^{-6}/C°)(12\ \text{m})(50°C - 20°C) = \boxed{4.3 \times 10^{-3}\ \text{m}}$$

8. The increase in length of the table is given by Equation 13-1a.

$$\Delta L = \alpha L_0 \Delta T = (0.2 \times 10^{-6}/C°)(2.0\ \text{m})(5.0C°) = \boxed{2 \times 10^{-6}\ \text{m}}$$

For steel, $\Delta L = \alpha L_0 \Delta T = (12 \times 10^{-6}/C°)(2.0\ \text{m})(5.0C°) = \boxed{1.2 \times 10^{-4}\ \text{m}}$.

The change for Super Invar is approximately only 2% of the change for steel.

9. Take the 300 m height to be the height in January. Then the increase in the height of the tower is given by Equation 13-1a.

$$\Delta L = \alpha L_0 \Delta T = (12 \times 10^{-6}/C°)(300\ \text{m})(25°C - 2°C) = \boxed{8 \times 10^{-2}\ \text{m}}$$

10. The rivet must be cooled so that its diameter becomes the same as the diameter of the hole.

$$\Delta L = \alpha L_0 \Delta T \quad \rightarrow \quad L - L_0 = \alpha L_0 (T - T_0)$$

$$T = T_0 + \frac{L - L_0}{\alpha L_0} = 20°C + \frac{1.869\ \text{cm} - 1.871\ \text{cm}}{(12 \times 10^{-6}/C°)(1.871\ \text{cm})} = \boxed{-69°C}$$

11. The density at 4°C is $\rho = \dfrac{M}{V} = \dfrac{1.00 \times 10^3\ \text{kg}}{1.00\ \text{m}^3}$. When the water is warmed, the mass will stay the same, but the volume will increase according to Equation 13-2.

$$\Delta V = \beta V_0 \Delta T = (210 \times 10^{-6}/C°)(1.00\ \text{m}^3)(94°C - 4°C) = 1.89 \times 10^{-2}\ \text{m}^3$$

The density at the higher temperature is $\rho = \dfrac{M}{V} = \dfrac{1.00 \times 10^3\ \text{kg}}{1.00\ \text{m}^3 + 1.89 \times 10^{-2}\ \text{m}^3} = \boxed{981\ \text{kg}/\text{m}^3}$

12. The change in volume of the quartz is given by the volume expansion formula, Equation 13-2.

$$\Delta V = \beta V_0 \Delta T = (1 \times 10^{-6}/C°)\left(\tfrac{4}{3}\pi\left(\frac{8.75\ \text{cm}}{2}\right)^3\right)(200°C - 30°C) = \boxed{6.0 \times 10^{-2}\ \text{cm}^3}$$

13. The amount of water that can be added to the container is the final volume of the container minus the final volume of the water. Also note that the original volumes of the water and the container are the same. We assume that the density of water is constant over the temperature change involved.

$$V_{\text{added}} = \left(V_0 + \Delta V\right)_{\text{container}} - \left(V_0 + \Delta V\right)_{H_2O} = \Delta V_{\text{container}} - \Delta V_{H_2O} = \left(\beta_{\text{container}} - \beta_{H_2O}\right)V_0\Delta T$$

$$= \left(27\times10^{-6}/C^\circ - 210\times10^{-6}/C^\circ\right)\left(350.0 \text{ mL}\right)\left(-80.0 C^\circ\right) = \boxed{5.12 \text{ mL}}$$

14. (a) The amount of water lost is the final volume of the water minus the final volume of the container. Also note that the original volumes of the water and the container are the same.

$$V_{\text{lost}} = \left(V_0 + \Delta V\right)_{H_2O} - \left(V_0 + \Delta V\right)_{\text{container}} = \Delta V_{H_2O} - \Delta V_{\text{container}} = \beta_{H_2O}V_0\Delta T - \beta_{\text{container}}V_0\Delta T$$

$$\beta_{\text{container}} = \beta_{H_2O} - \frac{V_{\text{lost}}}{V_0\Delta T} = 210\times10^{-6}/C^\circ - \frac{\left(0.35\text{g}\right)\left(\dfrac{1\,\text{mL}}{0.98324 \text{ g}}\right)}{\left(55.50 \text{ mL}\right)\left(60^\circ C - 20^\circ C\right)} = \boxed{5.0\times10^{-5}/C^\circ}$$

(b) From Table 13-1, the most likely material is $\boxed{\text{copper}}$.

15. (a) The sum of the original diameter plus the expansion must be the same for both the plug and the ring.

$$\left(L_0 + \Delta L\right)_{\text{iron}} = \left(L_0 + \Delta L\right)_{\text{brass}} \quad \rightarrow \quad L_{\text{iron}} + \alpha_{\text{iron}}L_{\text{iron}}\Delta T = L_{\text{brass}} + \alpha_{\text{brass}}L_{\text{brass}}\Delta T$$

$$\Delta T = \frac{L_{\text{brass}} - L_{\text{iron}}}{\alpha_{\text{iron}}L_{\text{iron}} - \alpha_{\text{brass}}L_{\text{brass}}} = \frac{8.753 \text{ cm} - 8.743 \text{ cm}}{\left(12\times10^{-6}/C^\circ\right)\left(8.743 \text{ cm}\right) - \left(19\times10^{-6}/C^\circ\right)\left(8.753 \text{ cm}\right)}$$

$$= -163C^\circ = T_{\text{final}} - T_{\text{initial}} = T_{\text{final}} - 20^\circ C \quad \rightarrow \quad T_{\text{final}} = -143^\circ C \approx \boxed{-140^\circ C}$$

(b) Simply switch the initial values in the above calculation.

$$\Delta T = \frac{L_{\text{brass}} - L_{\text{iron}}}{\alpha_{\text{iron}}L_{\text{iron}} - \alpha_{\text{brass}}L_{\text{brass}}} = \frac{8.743 \text{ cm} - 8.753 \text{ cm}}{\left(12\times10^{-6}/C^\circ\right)\left(8.753 \text{ cm}\right) - \left(19\times10^{-6}/C^\circ\right)\left(8.743 \text{ cm}\right)} =$$

$$= 164C^\circ = T_{\text{final}} - T_{\text{initial}} = T_{\text{final}} - 20^\circ C \quad \rightarrow \quad T_{\text{final}} = 184^\circ C \approx \boxed{180^\circ C}$$

16. We model the vessel as having a constant cross-sectional area A. Then a volume V_0 of fluid will occupy a length L_0 of the tube, given that $V_0 = AL_0$. Likewise $V = AL$.

$\Delta V = V - V_0 = AL - AL_0 = A\Delta L$ and $\Delta V = \beta V_0\Delta T = \beta AL_0\Delta T$.

Equate the two expressions for ΔV, and get $A\Delta L = \beta AL_0\Delta T \quad \rightarrow \quad \Delta L = \beta L_0\Delta T$. But $\Delta L = \alpha L_0\Delta T$,

so we see that under the conditions of the problem, $\boxed{\alpha = \beta}$

17. (a) When a substance changes temperature, its volume will change by an amount given by Equation 13-2. This causes the density to change.

$$\Delta\rho = \rho - \rho_0 = \frac{M}{V} - \frac{M}{V_0} = \frac{M}{V_0 + \Delta V} - \frac{M}{V_0} = \frac{M}{V_0 + \beta V_0\Delta T} - \frac{M}{V_0} = \frac{M}{V_0}\left(\frac{1}{1 + \beta\Delta T} - 1\right)$$

$$= \rho_0\left(\frac{1}{1 + \beta\Delta T} - \frac{1 + \beta\Delta T}{1 + \beta\Delta T}\right) = \rho_0\left(\frac{-\beta\Delta T}{1 + \beta\Delta T}\right)$$

If we assume that $\beta\Delta T \ll 1$, then the denominator is approximately 1, so $\boxed{\Delta\rho = -\rho_0\beta\Delta T}$.

(*b*) The fractional change in density is

$$\frac{\Delta\rho}{\rho_0} = \frac{-\rho_0\beta\Delta T}{\rho_0} = -\beta\Delta T = -\left(87\times10^{-6}/°C\right)\left(-40°C - 25°C\right) = 5.7\times10^{-3}$$

This is a $\boxed{0.57\% \text{ increase}}$.

18. Assume that each dimension of the plate changes according to Equation 13-1a.

$$\Delta A = A - A_0 = \left(l+\Delta l\right)\left(w+\Delta w\right) - lw = lw + l\Delta w + w\Delta l + \Delta l\Delta w - lw = l\Delta w + w\Delta l + \Delta l\Delta w$$

Neglect the very small quantity $\Delta l\Delta w$.

$$\Delta A = l\Delta w + w\Delta l = l\left(\alpha w\Delta T\right) + w\left(\alpha l\Delta T\right) = \boxed{2\alpha l\,w\Delta T}$$

19. Consider a cubic solid, where the original length of each dimension of the cube is l.

$$\Delta V = V - V_0 = \left(l+\Delta l\right)^3 - l^3 = l^3 + 3l^2\Delta l + 3l\left(\Delta l\right)^2 + \left(\Delta l\right)^3 - l^3 = 3l^2\Delta l + 3l\left(\Delta l\right)^2 + \left(\Delta l\right)^3$$

Neglect the very small quantities involving Δl squared or cubed.

$$\Delta V = 3l^2\Delta l = 3l^2\alpha l\Delta T = 3\alpha l^3\Delta T = 3\alpha V_0\Delta T$$

But Equation 13-2 states $\Delta V = \beta V_0\Delta T$. Equate the two statements for ΔV.

$$\Delta V = 3\alpha V_0\Delta T = \beta V_0\Delta T \quad\rightarrow\quad \boxed{\beta = 3\alpha}$$

20. The pendulum has a period of $\tau_0 = 2\pi\sqrt{L_0/g}$ at 17°C, and a period of $\tau = 2\pi\sqrt{L/g}$ at 25°C. Notice that $\tau > \tau_0$ since $L > L_0$. With every swing of the clock, the clock face will indicate that a time τ_0 has passed, but the actual amount of time that has passed is τ. Thus the clock face is "losing time" by an amount of $\Delta\tau = \tau - \tau_0$ every swing. The fractional loss is given by $\dfrac{\Delta\tau}{\tau_0}$, and the length at the higher temperature is given by

$$\frac{\Delta\tau}{\tau_0} = \frac{\tau-\tau_0}{\tau_0} = \frac{2\pi\sqrt{L/g} - 2\pi\sqrt{L_0/g}}{2\pi\sqrt{L_0/g}} = \frac{\sqrt{L}-\sqrt{L_0}}{\sqrt{L_0}} = \frac{\sqrt{L_0+\Delta L}-\sqrt{L_0}}{\sqrt{L_0}} = \frac{\sqrt{L_0+\alpha L_0\Delta T}-\sqrt{L_0}}{\sqrt{L_0}}$$

$$= \sqrt{1+\alpha\Delta T} - 1 = \sqrt{1+\left(19\times10^{-6}/C°\right)\left(8C°\right)} - 1 = 7.60\times10^{-5}$$

Thus the amount of time lost in any time period τ_0 is $\Delta\tau = \left(7.60\times10^{-5}\right)\tau_0$. For one year, we have the following.

$$\Delta\tau = \left(7.60\times10^{-5}\right)\left(3.16\times10^{7}\,s\right) = 2402\,s \approx \boxed{40\text{ min}}$$

21. (*a*) Consider the adjacent diagrams. The mercury expands due to the heat, as does the bulb volume. The volume of filled glass is equal to the volume of mercury at both temperatures. The value δL is the amount the thread of mercury moves. The additional length of the mercury column in the tube multiplied by the tube cross sectional area will be equal to the expansion of the volume of mercury, minus the expansion of the volume of the glass bulb. Since the tube volume is so much smaller than the bulb volume we can ignore any changes in the tube dimensions and in the mercury initially in the tube volume.

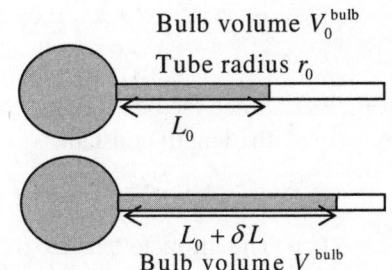

Original volume for glass bulb and Hg in bulb: V_0^{bulb}

Change in glass bulb volume: $\Delta V_{glass} = V_0^{bulb} \beta_{glass} \Delta T$

Change in Hg volume in glass bulb: $\Delta V_{Hg} = V_0^{bulb} \beta_{Hg} \Delta T$

Now find the additional volume of Hg, and use that to find the change in length of Hg in the tube.

$$(\delta L)\pi r_0^2 = \Delta V_{Hg} - \Delta V_{glass} = V_0^{bulb} \beta_{Hg} \Delta T - V_0^{bulb} \beta_{glass} \Delta T \rightarrow$$

$$\delta L = \frac{V_0^{bulb}}{\pi r_0^2}\Delta T\left(\beta_{Hg} - \beta_{glass}\right) = \frac{V_0^{bulb}}{\pi(d_0/2)^2}\Delta T\left(\beta_{Hg} - \beta_{glass}\right) = \frac{4V_0^{bulb}}{\pi d_0^2}\Delta T\left(\beta_{Hg} - \beta_{glass}\right)$$

$$= \frac{4\left(0.255\,cm^3\right)}{\pi\left(1.40\times10^{-2}\,cm\right)^2}\left(33.0°C - 11.5°C\right)\left[(180-9)\times10^{-6}/C°\right] = \boxed{6.1\,cm}$$

(b) The formula is quoted above: $\delta L = \dfrac{4V_0^{bulb}}{\pi d_0^2}\Delta T\left(\beta_{Hg} - \beta_{glass}\right)$.

22. The change in radius with heating does not cause a torque on the rotating wheel, and so the wheel's angular momentum does not change. Also recall that for a cylindrical wheel rotating about its axis, the moment of inertia is $I = \frac{1}{2}mr^2$.

$$L_0 = L_{final} \rightarrow I_0\omega_0 = I_{final}\omega_{final} \rightarrow \omega_{final} = \frac{I_0\omega_0}{I_{final}} = \frac{\frac{1}{2}mr_0^2\omega_0}{\frac{1}{2}mr^2} = \frac{r_0^2\omega_0}{r^2}$$

$$\frac{\Delta\omega}{\omega} = \frac{\omega_{final}-\omega_0}{\omega_0} = \frac{\frac{r_0^2\omega_0}{r^2}-\omega_0}{\omega_0} = \frac{r_0^2}{r^2}-1 = \frac{r_0^2}{\left(r_0+\Delta r\right)^2}-1 = \frac{r_0^2}{\left(r_0+\alpha r_0\Delta T\right)^2}-1 = \frac{r_0^2}{\left(r_0+\alpha r_0\Delta T\right)^2}-1$$

$$= \frac{1}{\left(1+\alpha\Delta T\right)^2}-1 = \frac{1-\left(1+2\alpha\Delta T+\left(\alpha\Delta T\right)^2\right)}{\left(1+\alpha\Delta T\right)^2} = \frac{-2\alpha\Delta T-\left(\alpha\Delta T\right)^2}{\left(1+\alpha\Delta T\right)^2} = -\alpha\Delta T\frac{2+\alpha\Delta T}{\left(1+\alpha\Delta T\right)^2}$$

Now assume that $\alpha\Delta T \ll 1$, and so $\dfrac{\Delta\omega}{\omega} = -\alpha\Delta T\dfrac{2+\alpha\Delta T}{\left(1+\alpha\Delta T\right)^2} \approx -2\alpha\Delta T$. Evaluate at the given values.

$$-2\alpha\Delta T = -2\left(25\times10^{-6}/C°\right)\left(55C°\right) = \boxed{-2.8\times10^{-3}}$$

23. The thermal stress must compensate for the thermal expansion. *E* is Young's modulus for the aluminum.

$$\text{Stress} = F/A = \alpha E\Delta T = \left(25\times10^{-6}/C°\right)\left(70\times10^9\,N/m^2\right)\left(35°C - 15°C\right) = \boxed{3.5\times10^7\,N/m^2}$$

24. (a) Since the beam cannot shrink while cooling, the tensile stress must compensate in order to keep the length constant.

$$\text{Stress} = F/A = \alpha E\Delta T = \left(12\times10^{-6}/C°\right)\left(200\times10^9\,N/m^2\right)\left(60C°\right) = \boxed{1.4\times10^8\,N/m^2}$$

(b) The ultimate tensile strength of steel (from chapter 9) is $5\times10^8\,N/m^2$, and so $\boxed{\text{the ultimate strength is not exceeded}}$. There would only be a safety factor of about 3.5.

(*c*) For concrete, repeat the calculation with the expansion coefficient and elastic modulus for concrete.

$$\text{Stress} = F/A = \alpha E \Delta T = \left(12\times10^{-6}/C^\circ\right)\left(20\times10^9 \; N/m^2\right)\left(60C^\circ\right) = \boxed{1.4\times10^7 \; N/m^2}$$

The ultimate tensile strength of concrete is $2\times10^6 \; N/m^2$, and so $\boxed{\text{the concrete will fracture}}$.

25. (*a*) Calculate the change in temperature needed to increase the diameter of the iron band so that it fits over the barrel. Assume that the barrel does not change in dimensions.

$$\Delta L = \alpha L_0 \Delta T \;\;\rightarrow\;\; L - L_0 = \alpha L_0 \left(T - T_0\right)$$

$$T = T_0 + \frac{L-L_0}{\alpha L_0} = 20^\circ C + \frac{134.122 \; cm - 134.110 \; cm}{\left(12\times10^{-6}/C^\circ\right)\left(134.110 \; cm\right)} = 27.457^\circ C \approx \boxed{27^\circ C}$$

(*b*) Since the band cannot shrink while cooling, the thermal stress must compensate in order to keep the length at a constant 132.122 cm. *E* is Young's modulus for the material.

$$\text{Stress} = F/A = \alpha E \Delta T \;\;\rightarrow\;\; F = AE\frac{\Delta L}{L_0} = AE\alpha\Delta T$$

$$= \left(7.4\times10^{-2} \; m\right)\left(6.5\times10^{-3} \; m\right)\left(100\times10^9 \; N/m^2\right)\left(12\times10^{-6}/C^\circ\right)\left(7.457C^\circ\right) = \boxed{4.3\times10^3 \; N}$$

26. Use the relationships $T(K) = T(^\circ C) + 273.15$ and $T(K) = \frac{5}{9}\left[T(^\circ F) - 32\right] + 273.15$.

(*a*) $T(K) = T(^\circ C) + 273.15 = 86 + 273.15 = \boxed{359 \; K}$

(*b*) $T(K) = \frac{5}{9}\left[T(^\circ F) - 32\right] + 273.15 = \frac{5}{9}\left[78 - 32\right] + 273.15 = \boxed{299 \; K}$

(*c*) $T(K) = T(^\circ C) + 273.15 = -100 + 273.15 = \boxed{173 \; K}$

(*d*) $T(K) = T(^\circ C) + 273.15 = 5500 + 273.15 = \boxed{5773 \; K}$

(*e*) $T(K) = \frac{5}{9}\left[T(^\circ F) - 32\right] + 273.15 = \frac{5}{9}\left[-459 - 32\right] + 273.15 = \boxed{0.37 \; K}$

27. Use the relationship that $T(K) = \frac{5}{9}\left[T(^\circ F) - 32\right] + 273.15$.

$$T(K) = \frac{5}{9}\left[T(^\circ F) - 32\right] + 273.15 \;\rightarrow$$

$$T(^\circ F) = \frac{9}{5}\left[T(K) - 273.15\right] + 32 = \frac{9}{5}\left[0 - 273.15\right] + 32 = \boxed{-459.67^\circ F}$$

28. Use the relationship that $T(K) = T(^\circ C) + 273.15$.

(*a*) $T(K) = T(^\circ C) + 273.15 = 4270 \; K \approx \boxed{4300 \; K}$; $T(K) = T(^\circ C) + 273.15 = \boxed{15\times10^6 \; K}$

(*b*) $\% \; \text{error} = \dfrac{\Delta T}{T(K)} \times 100 = \dfrac{273}{T(K)} \times 100$

$4000^\circ C: \;\; \dfrac{273}{4000} \times 100 \approx \boxed{7\%}$ $15\times10^6 \; ^\circ C: \;\; \dfrac{273}{15\times10^6} \times 100 \approx \boxed{2\times10^{-3}\%}$

29. Assume the gas is ideal. Since the amount of gas is constant, the value of $\dfrac{PV}{T}$ is constant.

$$\frac{P_1 V_1}{T_1} = \frac{P_2 V_2}{T_2} \;\rightarrow\; V_2 = V_1 \frac{P_1}{P_2} \frac{T_2}{T_1} = \left(3.00\,\mathrm{m}^3\right)\left(\frac{1.00\,\mathrm{atm}}{3.20\,\mathrm{atm}}\right)\frac{(273+38)\,\mathrm{K}}{273\,\mathrm{K}} = \boxed{1.07\,\mathrm{m}^3}$$

30. Assume the air is an ideal gas. Since the amount of air is constant, the value of $\dfrac{PV}{T}$ is constant.

$$\frac{P_1 V_1}{T_1} = \frac{P_2 V_2}{T_2} \;\rightarrow\; T_2 = T_1 \frac{P_2}{P_1} \frac{V_2}{V_1} = \left(293\,\mathrm{K}\right)\left(\frac{40\,\mathrm{atm}}{1\,\mathrm{atm}}\right)\left(\frac{1}{9}\right) = 1300\,\mathrm{K} = 1030^{\circ}\mathrm{C} \approx \boxed{1000^{\circ}\mathrm{C}}$$

$\boxed{31.}$ Assume the oxygen is an ideal gas. From Example 13-10, the volume of one mole of oxygen gas at STP is $22.4 \times 10^{-3}\,\mathrm{m}^3$. The mass of one mole of oxygen, with a molecular mass of 32.0 u, is 32.0 grams. Use these values to calculate the density of the oxygen gas.

$$\rho = \frac{M}{V} = \frac{32.0 \times 10^{-3}\,\mathrm{kg}}{22.4 \times 10^{-3}\,\mathrm{m}^3} = \boxed{1.43\,\mathrm{kg/m}^3}$$

32. Assume that the nitrogen and carbon dioxide are ideal gases, and that the volume and temperature are constant for the two gases. From the ideal gas law, the value of $\dfrac{P}{n} = \dfrac{RT}{V}$ is constant. Also note that concerning the ideal gas law, the identity of the gas is unimportant, as long as the number of moles is considered.

$$\frac{P_1}{n_1} = \frac{P_2}{n_2} \;\rightarrow\; P_2 = P_1 \frac{n_2}{n_1} = \left(3.65\,\mathrm{atm}\right)\left(\frac{\dfrac{21.6\,\mathrm{kg}\,CO_2}{44 \times 10^{-3}\,\mathrm{kg}\,CO_2/\mathrm{mol}}}{\dfrac{21.6\,\mathrm{kg}\,N_2}{28 \times 10^{-3}\,\mathrm{kg}\,N_2/\mathrm{mol}}}\right) = \left(3.65\,\mathrm{atm}\right)\left(\frac{28}{44}\right) = \boxed{2.32\,\mathrm{atm}}$$

33. (a) Assume the nitrogen is an ideal gas. The number of moles of nitrogen is found from the atomic weight, and then the ideal gas law is used to calculate the volume of the gas.

$$n = \left(18.5\,\mathrm{kg}\right)\frac{1\,\mathrm{mole}\,N_2}{28.0 \times 10^{-3}\,\mathrm{kg}} = 660.71\,\mathrm{mol}$$

$$PV = nRT \;\rightarrow\; V = \frac{nRT}{P} = \frac{\left(660.71\,\mathrm{mol}\right)\left(8.315\,\mathrm{J/mol \cdot K}\right)\left(273\,\mathrm{K}\right)}{1.013 \times 10^5\,\mathrm{Pa}} = 14.806\,\mathrm{m}^3$$

$$\approx \boxed{14.8\,\mathrm{m}^3}$$

   (b) Hold the volume and temperature constant, and again use the ideal gas law.

$$n = \left(18.5\,\mathrm{kg} + 15.0\,\mathrm{kg}\right)\frac{1\,\mathrm{mole}\,N_2}{28.0 \times 10^{-3}\,\mathrm{kg}} = 1196\,\mathrm{mol}$$

$$PV = nRT \;\rightarrow$$

$$P = \frac{nRT}{V} = \frac{\left(1196\,\mathrm{mol}\right)\left(8.315\,\mathrm{J/mol \cdot K}\right)\left(273\,\mathrm{K}\right)}{14.806\,\mathrm{m}^3} = \boxed{1.83 \times 10^5\,\mathrm{Pa} = 1.82\,\mathrm{atm}}$$

34. (*a*) Assume that the helium is an ideal gas, and then use the ideal gas law to calculate the volume. Absolute pressure must be used, even though gauge pressure is given.

$$PV = nRT \quad \rightarrow \quad V = \frac{nRT}{P} = \frac{(18.75\,\text{mol})(8.315\,\text{J/mol·K})(283\,\text{K})}{(1.350\,\text{atm})(1.013\times10^5\,\text{Pa/atm})} = \boxed{0.323\,\text{m}^3}$$

(*b*) Since the amount of gas is not changed, the value of PV/T is constant.

$$\frac{P_1 V_1}{T_1} = \frac{P_2 V_2}{T_2} \quad \rightarrow \quad T_2 = T_1 \frac{P_2\,V_2}{P_1\,V_1} = (283\,\text{K})\left(\frac{2.00\,\text{atm}}{1.350\,\text{atm}}\right)\left(\frac{1}{2}\right) = 210\,\text{K} = \boxed{-63°\text{C}}$$

35. Assume the argon is an ideal gas. The number of moles of argon is found from the atomic weight, and then the ideal gas law is used to find the pressure.

$$n = (105.0\,\text{kg})\frac{1\,\text{mole Ar}}{39.95\times10^{-3}\,\text{kg}} = 2628\,\text{mol}$$

$$PV = nRT \quad \rightarrow \quad P = \frac{nRT}{V} = \frac{(2628\,\text{mol})(8.315\,\text{J/mol·k})(385\,\text{K})}{(35.0\,\text{L})(1.00\times10^{-3}\,\text{m}^3/\text{L})} = \boxed{2.40\times10^8\,\text{Pa}}$$

36. Assume that the oxygen and helium are ideal gases, and that the volume and temperature are constant for the two gases. From the ideal gas law, the value of $\dfrac{P}{n} = \dfrac{RT}{V}$ is constant. Also note that concerning the ideal gas law, the identity of the gas is unimportant, as long as the number of moles is considered. Finally, gauge pressure must be changed to absolute pressure.

$$\frac{P_1}{n_1} = \frac{P_2}{n_2} \quad \rightarrow \quad n_2 = n_1\frac{P_2}{P_1} = (26.0\,\text{kg O}_2)\left(\frac{1\,\text{mole O}_2}{32\times10^{-3}\,\text{kg}}\right)\frac{(8.00\,\text{atm})}{(9.70\,\text{atm})} = 6.70\times10^2\,\text{moles}$$

$$(6.70\times10^2\,\text{moles})\left(\frac{4.0\times10^{-3}\,\text{kg}}{1\,\text{mole He}}\right) = \boxed{2.68\,\text{kg He}}$$

37. There are three forces to consider: the buoyant force upwards (which is the weight of the cold air displaced by the volume of the balloon), the downward weight of the hot air in the balloon, and the downward weight of the passengers and equipment. For the balloon to rise at constant speed, the buoyant force must equal the two weights.

$$F_{\text{buoyant}} = m_{\text{hot}}g + 2700\,\text{N} \quad \rightarrow \quad V\rho_{\text{cold}}g = V\rho_{\text{hot}}g + 2700\,\text{N}$$

The ideal gas law can be written in terms of the gas density ρ and the molecular mass M as follows.

$$PV = nRT = \frac{m}{M}RT \quad \rightarrow \quad \frac{PM}{R} = \frac{m}{V}T = \rho T$$

The gas inside and outside the balloon is air, and so M is the same for inside and outside. Also, since the balloon is open to the atmosphere, the pressure in the balloon is the same as the pressure outside the balloon. Thus the ideal gas law reduces to $\rho T = \text{constant} = (\rho T)_{\text{cold}} = (\rho T)_{\text{hot}}$.

$$V\rho_{\text{cold}}g = V\rho_{\text{hot}}g + 2700\,\text{N} = V\rho_{\text{cold}}\frac{T_{\text{cold}}}{T_{\text{hot}}}g + 2700\,\text{N} \quad \rightarrow$$

$$T_{\text{hot}} = \frac{V\rho_{\text{cold}}T_{\text{cold}}g}{(V\rho_{\text{cold}}g - 2700\,\text{N})} = \frac{(1800\,\text{m}^3)(1.29\,\text{kg/m}^3)(273\,\text{K})(9.80\,\text{m/s}^2)}{\left[(1800\,\text{m}^3)(1.29\,\text{kg/m}^3)(9.80\,\text{m/s}^2) - 2700\,\text{N}\right]}$$

$$= 309.8\,\text{K} \approx \boxed{37°\text{C}}$$

One factor limiting the maximum altitude would be that as the balloon rises, the density of the air decreases, and thus the temperature required gets higher. Eventually the air would be too hot and the balloon fabric might be damaged.

38. Assume that the air is an ideal gas. The pressure and volume are held constant. From the ideal gas law, the value of $\dfrac{PV}{R} = nT$ is held constant.

$$n_1 T_1 = n_2 T_2 \quad \rightarrow \quad \frac{n_2}{n_1} = \frac{T_1}{T_2} = \frac{(273+15)\,\text{K}}{(273+38)\,\text{K}} = \frac{288}{311} = 0.926$$

Thus $1 - 0.926 = 0.074 = \boxed{7.4\%}$ must be removed.

39. Assume the oxygen is an ideal gas. Since the amount of gas is constant, the value of PV/T is constant.

$$\frac{P_1 V_1}{T_1} = \frac{P_2 V_2}{T_2} \quad \rightarrow \quad P_2 = P_1 \frac{V_1}{V_2} \frac{T_2}{T_1} = (2.45 \text{ atm})\left(\frac{61.5 \text{ L}}{48.8 \text{ L}}\right)\frac{(273+50.0)\,\text{K}}{(273+18.0)\,\text{K}} = \boxed{3.43 \text{ atm}}$$

40. Assume the helium is an ideal gas. Since the amount of gas is constant, the value of PV/T is constant. We assume that since the outside air pressure decreases by 30%, the air pressure inside the balloon will also decrease 30%.

$$\frac{P_1 V_1}{T_1} = \frac{P_2 V_2}{T_2} \quad \rightarrow \quad \frac{V_2}{V_1} = \frac{P_1}{P_2} \frac{T_2}{T_1} = \left(\frac{1.0}{0.70}\right)\frac{(273+5.0)\,\text{K}}{(273+20.0)\,\text{K}} = \boxed{1.4 \text{ times the original volume}}$$

41. At STP, 1 mole of ideal gas occupies 22.4 L.

$$\frac{1 \text{ mole}}{22.4 \text{ L}}\left(\frac{6.02\times10^{23}\text{ molecules}}{\text{mole}}\right)\left(\frac{1 \text{ L}}{10^{-3}\text{m}^3}\right) = \boxed{2.69\times10^{25} \text{ molecules}/\text{m}^3}$$

42. We assume that the water is at 4°C so that its density is $1000 \text{ kg}/\text{m}^3$.

$$1.000 \text{ L}\left(\frac{10^{-3}\text{m}^3}{1 \text{ L}}\right)\left(\frac{1000 \text{ kg}}{1 \text{ m}^3}\right)\left(\frac{1 \text{ mol}}{(15.9994 + 2\times1.00794)\times10^{-3}\text{kg}}\right) = \boxed{55.51 \text{ mol}}$$

$$55.51 \text{ mol}\left(\frac{6.02\times10^{23}\text{ molecules}}{1 \text{ mol}}\right) = \boxed{3.34\times10^{25} \text{ molecules}}$$

43. (a) Since the average depth of the oceans is very small compared to the radius of the Earth, the ocean's volume can be calculated as that of a spherical shell with surface area $4\pi R_{\text{Earth}}^2$ and a thickness Δy. Then use the density of sea water to find the mass, and the molecular weight of water to find the number of moles.

$$\text{Volume} = 0.75\left(4\pi R_{\text{Earth}}^2\right)\Delta y = 0.75\left(4\pi\right)\left(6.38\times10^6\,\text{m}\right)^2\left(3\times10^3\,\text{m}\right) = 1.15\times10^{18}\,\text{m}^3$$

$$1.15\times10^{18}\,\text{m}^3\left(\frac{1025 \text{ kg}}{\text{m}^3}\right)\left(\frac{1 \text{ mol}}{18\times10^{-3}\text{kg}}\right) = 6.55\times10^{22} \text{ moles} \approx \boxed{7\times10^{22} \text{ moles}}$$

(b) $6.55 \times 10^{22} \text{ moles} \left(\dfrac{6.02 \times 10^{23} \text{ molecules}}{1 \text{ mol}} \right) \approx \boxed{4 \times 10^{46} \text{ molecules}}$

44. The net force on each side of the box will be the pressure difference between the inside and outside of the box, times the area of a side of the box. The outside pressure is 1 atmosphere. The ideal gas law is used to find the pressure inside the box, assuming that the mass of gas and the volume are constant.

$$\frac{P}{T} = \frac{nR}{V} = \text{constant} \quad \rightarrow \quad \frac{P_2}{T_2} = \frac{P_1}{T_1} \quad \rightarrow \quad P_2 = P_1 \frac{T_2}{T_1} = \left(1.00 \text{ atm} \right) \frac{(273 + 180) \text{ K}}{(273 + 20) \text{ K}} = 1.55 \text{ atm}$$

The area of a side of the box is given by

$$\text{Area} = L^2 = \left[\left(\text{Volume of box} \right)^{1/3} \right]^2 = \left(5.1 \times 10^{-2} \text{ m}^2 \right)^{2/3} = 1.4 \times 10^{-1} \text{ m}^2$$

The net force on a side of the box is the pressure difference times the area.

$$F = \left(\Delta \text{Pressure} \right) \left(\text{Area} \right) = \left(0.55 \text{ atm} \right) \left(1.01 \times 10^5 \text{ Pa} \right) \left(1.4 \times 10^{-1} \text{ m}^2 \right) = \boxed{7.6 \times 10^3 \text{ N}}$$

45. We assume that the last breath Galileo took has been spread uniformly throughout the atmosphere since his death. Calculate the number of molecules in Galileo's last breath, and divide it by the volume of the atmosphere, to get "Galileo molecules/m³". Multiply that factor times the size of a breath to find the number of Galileo molecules in one of our breaths.

$$PV = NkT \quad \rightarrow \quad N = \frac{PV}{kT} = \frac{\left(1.01 \times 10^5 \text{ Pa} \right) \left(2.0 \times 10^{-3} \text{ m}^3 \right)}{\left(1.38 \times 10^{-23} \text{ J/K} \right) \left(300 \text{ K} \right)} = 4.9 \times 10^{22} \text{ molecules}$$

$$\text{Atmospheric volume} = 4\pi R_{\text{Earth}}^2 h = 4\pi \left(6.38 \times 10^6 \text{ m} \right)^2 \left(1.0 \times 10^4 \text{ m} \right) = 5.1 \times 10^{18} \text{ m}^3$$

$$\frac{\text{Galileo molecules}}{\text{m}^3} = \frac{4.9 \times 10^{22} \text{ molecules}}{5.8 \times 10^{18} \text{ m}^3} = 9.6 \times 10^3 \text{ molecules/m}^3$$

$$\frac{\text{\# Galileo molecules}}{\text{breath}} = 9.6 \times 10^3 \frac{\text{molecules}}{\text{m}^3} \left(\frac{2.0 \times 10^{-3} \text{ m}^3}{1 \text{ breath}} \right) = \boxed{19 \frac{\text{molecules}}{\text{breath}}}$$

46. (a)   The average translational kinetic energy of a gas molecule is $\frac{3}{2}kT$.

$$KE_{\text{avg}} = \tfrac{3}{2}kT = \tfrac{3}{2} \left(1.38 \times 10^{-23} \text{ J/K} \right) \left(273 \text{ K} \right) = \boxed{5.65 \times 10^{-21} \text{ J}}$$

(b)   The total translational kinetic energy is the average kinetic energy per molecule, times the number of molecules.

$$KE_{\text{total}} = N \left(KE_{\text{avg}} \right) = \left(2.0 \text{ mol} \right) \left(\frac{6.02 \times 10^{23} \text{ molecules}}{1} \right) \tfrac{3}{2} \left(1.38 \times 10^{-23} \text{ J/K} \right) \left(293 \text{ K} \right)$$

$$= \boxed{7.3 \times 10^3 \text{ J}}$$

$\boxed{47.}$ The rms speed is given by Equation 13-9, $v_{\text{rms}} = \sqrt{3kT/m}$. Helium has an atomic mass of 4.0.

$$v_{\text{rms}} = \sqrt{3kT/m} = \sqrt{\frac{3 \left(1.38 \times 10^{-23} \text{ J/K} \right) \left(6000 \text{ K} \right)}{4.0 \left(1.66 \times 10^{-27} \text{ kg} \right)}} = 6116 \text{ m/s} \approx \boxed{6 \times 10^3 \text{ m/s}}$$

48. The rms speed is given by Equation 13-9, $v_{rms} = \sqrt{3kT/m}$.

$$\frac{(v_{rms})_2}{(v_{rms})_1} = \frac{\sqrt{3kT_2/m}}{\sqrt{3kT_1/m}} = \sqrt{\frac{T_2}{T_1}} = \sqrt{\frac{373\ K}{273\ K}} = \boxed{1.17}$$

49. The rms speed is given by Equation 13-9, $v_{rms} = \sqrt{3kT/m}$. Since the rms speed is proportional to the square root of the absolute temperature, to double the rms speed without changing the mass, the absolute temperature must be multiplied by a factor of 4.

$$T_{fast} = 4T_{slow} = 4(273+20)\ K = 1172\ K = \boxed{899°C}$$

50. The rms speed is the square root of the mean (average) of the squares of the speeds.

$$v_{rms} = \sqrt{\frac{6^2+2^2+4^2+6^2+0^2+4^2+1^2+8^2+5^2+3^2+7^2+8^2}{12}} = \sqrt{\frac{320}{12}} = \boxed{5.2\ km/s}$$

The average speed is $v_{avg} = \dfrac{6+2+4+6+0+4+1+8+5+3+7+8}{12} = \dfrac{54}{12} = 4.5\ km/s$.

51. The rms speed is given by Equation 13-9, $v_{rms} = \sqrt{3kT/m}$.

$$\frac{(v_{rms})_2}{(v_{rms})_1} = 1.010 = \frac{\sqrt{3kT_2/m}}{\sqrt{3kT_1/m}} = \sqrt{\frac{T_2}{T_1}} \rightarrow$$

$$T_2 = T_1(1.010)^2 = (293.2\ K)(1.010)^2 = 299.1\ K = \boxed{25.9°C}$$

52. From the ideal gas law, $PV = nRT$, if the volume and amount of gas are held constant, the temperature is proportional to the pressure, $PV = nRT \rightarrow P = \dfrac{nR}{V}T = (\text{constant})T$. Thus the temperature will be doubled . Since the rms speed is proportional to the square root of the temperature, $v_{rms} = \sqrt{3kT/m} = (\text{constant})\sqrt{T}$, the rms speed will be multiplied by a factor of $\sqrt{2} = \boxed{1.41}$.

53. The rms speed is given by Equation 13-9, $v_{rms} = \sqrt{3kT/m}$. The temperature can be found from the ideal gas law, $PV = NkT \rightarrow kT = PV/N$. The mass of the gas is the mass of a molecule times the number of molecules: $M = Nm$, and the density of the gas is the mass per unit volume, $\rho = \dfrac{M}{V}$. Combining these relationships gives the following.

$$v_{rms} = \sqrt{3kT/m} = \sqrt{\frac{3PV}{Nm}} = \sqrt{\frac{3PV}{M}} = \sqrt{\frac{3P}{\rho}}$$

54. The rms speed is given by Equation 13-9, $v_{rms} = \sqrt{3kT/m}$.

$$\frac{(v_{rms})_2}{(v_{rms})_1} = \frac{\sqrt{3kT/m_2}}{\sqrt{3kT/m_1}} \rightarrow \boxed{\frac{(v_{rms})_2}{(v_{rms})_1} = \sqrt{\frac{m_1}{m_2}}}$$

55. The temperature of the nitrogen gas is found from the ideal gas law, and then the rms speed is found from the temperature.

$$PV = nRT \rightarrow T = \frac{PV}{nR} = \frac{(2.1\,\text{atm})(1.013 \times 10^5\,\text{Pa/atm})(8.5\,\text{m}^3)}{(1300\,\text{mol})(8.315\,\text{J/mol·K})} = 167.3\,\text{K}$$

$$v_{rms} = \sqrt{\frac{3kT}{m}} = \sqrt{\frac{3(1.38 \times 10^{-23}\,\text{J/K})(167.3\,\text{K})}{28(1.66 \times 10^{-27}\,\text{kg})}} = 386.0\,\text{m/s} \approx \boxed{3.9 \times 10^2\,\text{m/s}}$$

56. (a) The rms speed is given by Equation 13-9, $v_{rms} = \sqrt{3kT/m}$.

$$v_{rms} = \sqrt{\frac{3kT}{m}} = \sqrt{\frac{3(1.38 \times 10^{-23}\,\text{J/K})(273\,\text{K})}{32(1.66 \times 10^{-27}\,\text{kg})}} = \boxed{461\,\text{m/s}}$$

(b) Assuming that the particle has no preferred direction, then we have the following:

$$v_{rms}^2 = v_x^2 + v_y^2 + v_z^2 = 3v_x^2 \rightarrow v_x = v_{rms}/\sqrt{3} .$$

The time for one crossing of the room is then given by $t = d/v_x = \sqrt{3}d/v_{rms}$, and so the time for a round trip is $2\sqrt{3}d/v_{rms}$. Thus the number of back and forth round trips per second is the reciprocal of this time, $\dfrac{v_{rms}}{2\sqrt{3}d}$.

$$\text{\# round trips per sec} = \frac{v_{rms}}{2\sqrt{3}d} = \frac{461\,\text{m/s}}{2\sqrt{3}(7.0\,\text{m})} = \boxed{19\,\text{round trips per sec}}$$

57. Assume that nitrogen is an ideal gas, and that each molecule occupies the same cubical volume of L^3 . Find the volume per molecule from the ideal gas law, and then the side length of that cubical molecular volume will be an estimate of the average distance between molecules.

$$PV = NkT \rightarrow \frac{V}{N} = \frac{kT}{P} = \frac{(1.38 \times 10^{-23}\,\text{J/K})(273\,\text{K})}{1.01 \times 10^5\,\text{Pa}} = 3.73 \times 10^{-26}\,\text{m}^3/\text{molecule}$$

$$L = \left(\frac{V}{N}\right)^{1/3} = \left(3.73 \times 10^{-26}\,\text{m}^3\right)^{1/3} = \boxed{3.34 \times 10^{-9}\,\text{m}}$$

58. It is stated in the text that the relationship $v_{rms} = \sqrt{3kT/m}$ is applicable to molecules within living cells at body temperature (37°C).

(a) For the amino acid: $v_{rms} = \sqrt{3kT/m} = \sqrt{\dfrac{3(1.38 \times 10^{-23}\,\text{J/K})(310\,\text{K})}{89(1.66 \times 10^{-27}\,\text{kg})}} = \boxed{2.9 \times 10^2\,\text{m/s}}$.

(b) For the protein: $v_{rms} = \sqrt{3kT/m} = \sqrt{\dfrac{3(1.38 \times 10^{-23}\,\text{J/K})(310\,\text{K})}{(50,000)(1.66 \times 10^{-27}\,\text{kg})}} = \boxed{12\,\text{m/s}}$

59. The pressure can be stated in terms of the ideal gas law, $P = NkT/V$. Substitute for the temperature from the expression for the rms speed, $v_{rms} = \sqrt{3kT/m} \rightarrow T = mv_{rms}^2/3k$. The mass of the gas is the mass of a molecule times the number of molecules: $M = Nm$, and the density of the gas is the mass per unit volume, $\rho = M/V$. Combining these relationships gives the following.

$$P = \frac{NkT}{V} = \frac{Nk}{V}\frac{mv_{rms}^2}{3k} = \tfrac{1}{3}\frac{Nm}{V}v_{rms}^2 = \tfrac{1}{3}\frac{M}{V}v_{rms}^2 = \tfrac{1}{3}\rho v_{rms}^2 \rightarrow \boxed{P = \tfrac{1}{3}\rho v_{rms}^2}$$

60. The rms speed is given by Equation 13-9, $v_{rms} = \sqrt{3kT/m}$.

$$\frac{\left(v_{rms}\right)_{^{235}UF_6}}{\left(v_{rms}\right)_{^{238}UF_6}} = \frac{\sqrt{3kT/m_{^{235}UF_6}}}{\sqrt{3kT/m_{^{238}UF_6}}} = \sqrt{\frac{m_{^{238}UF_6}}{m_{^{235}UF_6}}} = \sqrt{\frac{238+6(19)}{235+6(19)}} = \sqrt{\frac{352}{349}} = \boxed{1.004}$$

61. (a) From Fig. 13-21, at atmospheric pressure, CO_2 can exist as $\boxed{\text{solid or vapor}}$.

    (b) From Fig. 13-21, for CO_2 to exist as a liquid, $\boxed{5.11 \text{ atm} \le P \le 73 \text{ atm}}$ and $\boxed{-56.6°C \le T \le 31°C}$.

62. (a) From Fig. 13-20, water is $\boxed{\text{vapor}}$ when the pressure is 0.01 atm and the temperature is 90°C.

    (b) From Fig. 13-20, water is $\boxed{\text{solid}}$ when the pressure is 0.01 atm and the temperature is –20°C.

63. From Table 13-3, if the temperature is 25°C, the saturated vapor pressure is 23.8 torr. If the relative humidity is 50%, then the partial pressure of water is half the saturated vapor pressure, or 11.9 torr. The dew point is the temperature at which the saturated vapor pressure is 11.9 torr, and from Table 13-3 that is between 10°C and 15°C. Since there is no entry for 11.9 torr, the temperature can be estimated by a linear interpolation. Between 10°C and 15°C, the temperature change per torr is as follows:

$$\frac{(15-10)C°}{(12.8-9.21)\text{torr}} = 1.393 C°/\text{torr}.$$

Thus the temperature corresponding to 11.9 torr is

$$10°C + \left[(11.9-9.21)\text{torr}\right]\left(1.393 C°/\text{torr}\right) = 13.7°C \approx \boxed{14°C}.$$

64. At the boiling temperature, the external air pressure equals the saturated vapor pressure. Thus from Table 13-3, the air pressure is $\boxed{526 \text{ torr}}$ or $\boxed{7.01\times10^4 \text{ Pa}}$ or $\boxed{0.692 \text{ atm}}$.

65. At the boiling temperature, the air pressure equals the saturated vapor pressure. The pressure of 0.72 atm is equal to 7.27×10^4 Pa. From Table 13-3, the temperature is between 90°C and 100°C. Since there is no entry for 7.27×10^4 Pa, the temperature can be estimated by a linear interpolation. Between 90°C and 100°C, the temperature change per Pa is as follows:

$$\frac{(100-90)C°}{(10.1-7.01)\times10^4 \text{Pa}} = 3.236\times10^{-4} C°/\text{Pa}.$$

Thus the temperature corresponding to 7.27×10^4 Pa is

$$90°C + \left[(7.27-7.01)\times10^4 \text{Pa}\right]\left(3.236\times10^{-4} C°/\text{Pa}\right) = 90.8°C \approx \boxed{91°C}.$$

66. The relative humidity of 40% with a partial pressure of 530 Pa of water gives a saturated vapor pressure of

$$0.40 P_{\text{saturated}} = 530 \text{ Pa} \quad \rightarrow \quad P_{\text{saturated}} = \frac{530 \text{ Pa}}{0.40} = 1325 \text{ Pa}$$

From Table 13-3, the temperature at which the saturated vapor pressure is 1325 Pa is between 10°C and 15°C. Since there is no entry for 1325 Pa, the temperature can be estimated by a linear interpolation. Between 10°C and 15°C, the temperature change per Pa is as follows:

$$\frac{(15-10) \text{C}^\circ}{(1.71-1.23)\times 10^3 \text{Pa}} = 1.042\times 10^{-2} \text{ C}^\circ/\text{Pa} \;.$$

Thus the temperature corresponding to 1325 Pa is

$$10^\circ\text{C} + \left[(1325-1230) \text{Pa}\right]\left(1.042\times 10^{-2} \text{ C}^\circ/\text{Pa}\right) = 10.99^\circ\text{C} \approx \boxed{11^\circ\text{C}} \;.$$

67. From Table 13-3, the saturated vapor pressure at 25°C is 3170 Pa. Since the relative humidity is 35%, the partial pressure of water is

$$P_{\text{water}} = 0.35 P_{\text{saturated}} = 0.35(3170 \text{ Pa}) = \boxed{1.1\times 10^3 \text{Pa}}$$

68. Since the water is boiling at 120°C, the saturated vapor pressure is the same as the pressure inside the pressure cooker. From Table 13-3, the pressure is $\boxed{1.99\times 10^5 \text{Pa} = 1.97 \text{ atm}}$.

69. The total amount of water vapor that can be in the air can be found from the saturated vapor pressure in Table 13-3, using the ideal gas law. At 25°C, that pressure is $3.17\times 10^3 \text{Pa}$.

$$PV = nRT \quad \rightarrow \quad n = \frac{PV}{RT} = \frac{\left(3.17\times 10^3 \text{Pa}\right)\left(680 \text{ m}^3\right)}{\left(8.315 \text{ J/mol•K}\right)\left(273+25\right)\text{K}} = 8.70\times 10^2 \text{ moles}$$

Since the relative humidity is only 80%, only 80% of the total possible water is in the air. Thus 20% of the total possible water can still evaporate into the air.

$$m_{\text{evaporate}} = 0.20\left(8.70\times 10^2 \text{ moles}\right)\left(\frac{18\times 10^{-3} \text{kg}}{1 \text{ mole}}\right) = \boxed{3.1 \text{ kg}}$$

70. The air is saturated at the lower temperature, so the vapor pressure of water is 872 Pa. The ideal gas law gives the following result for the change in volume of the given mass of air.

$$PV = nRT \quad \rightarrow \quad \frac{P}{nR} = \frac{T}{V} = \text{constant} \quad \rightarrow \quad \frac{T_1}{V_1} = \frac{T_2}{V_2}$$

Thus the vapor pressure of a given mass of air that moves from outside to inside is as follows.

$$P_{\text{in}} = \frac{nRT_{\text{in}}}{V_{\text{in}}} = \frac{nRT_{\text{out}}}{V_{\text{out}}} = P_{\text{out}} = 872 \text{ Pa}$$

The saturated vapor pressure at the inside temperature is 3170 Pa, and so the relative humidity is as follows.

$$\text{rel. hum.} = \frac{872 \text{ Pa}}{3170 \text{ Pa}} = 0.275 = \boxed{27.5\%}$$

71. From Example 13-19, we have an expression for the time to diffuse a given distance. Divide the distance by the time to get the average speed.

$$t = \frac{\overline{C}}{\Delta C}\frac{(\Delta x)^2}{D} = \frac{\frac{1}{2}(1.00+0.40)\,\text{mol}/\text{m}^3}{(1.00-0.40)\,\text{mol}/\text{m}^3}\frac{(15\times10^{-6}\,\text{m})^2}{(95\times10^{-11}\,\text{m}^2/\text{s})} = 0.2763\,\text{s} \approx \boxed{0.28\,\text{s}}$$

$$v_{\text{diffuse}} = \frac{\Delta x}{t} = \frac{15\times10^{-6}\,\text{m}}{0.2763\,\text{s}} = \boxed{5.4\times10^{-5}\,\text{m/s}}$$

The rms thermal speed is given by Equation 13-9, $v_{\text{rms}} = \sqrt{3kT/m}$.

$$v_{\text{rms}} = \sqrt{3kT/m} = \sqrt{\frac{3(1.38\times10^{-23}\,\text{J/K})(293\,\text{K})}{75(1.66\times10^{-27}\,\text{kg})}} = \boxed{3.1\times10^2\,\text{m/s}}$$

$$\frac{v_{\text{diffuse}}}{v_{\text{rms}}} = \frac{5.4\times10^{-5}\,\text{m/s}}{3.1\times10^2\,\text{m/s}} = 1.7\times10^{-7}$$

The diffusion speed is several orders of magnitude smaller than the thermal speed.

72. (a) Use the ideal gas law to find the concentration of the oxygen. We assume that the air pressure is 1.00 atm, and so the pressure caused by the oxygen is 0.21 atm.
$$PV = nRT \rightarrow$$

$$\frac{n}{V} = \frac{P}{RT} = \frac{(0.21\,\text{atm})(1.013\times10^5\,\text{Pa/atm})}{(8.315\,\text{J/mol}\cdot\text{K})(293\,\text{K})} = 8.732\,\text{mol}/\text{m}^3 \approx \boxed{8.7\,\text{mol}/\text{m}^3}$$

(b) Use Equation 13-10 to calculate the diffusion rate.

$$J = DA\frac{C_1-C_2}{\Delta x} = (1\times10^{-5}\,\text{m}^2/\text{s})(2\times10^{-9}\,\text{m}^2)\left(\frac{8.732\,\text{mol}/\text{m}^3 - 4.366\,\text{mol}/\text{m}^3}{2\times10^{-3}\,\text{m}}\right)$$

$$= 4.366\times10^{-11}\,\text{mol/s} \approx \boxed{4\times10^{-11}\,\text{mol/s}}$$

(c) From Example 13-19, we have an expression for the time to diffuse a given distance.

$$t = \frac{\overline{C}}{\Delta C}\frac{(\Delta x)^2}{D} = \frac{\frac{1}{2}(8.732\,\text{mol}/\text{m}^3 + 4.366\,\text{mol}/\text{m}^3)}{(8.732\,\text{mol}/\text{m}^3 - 4.366\,\text{mol}/\text{m}^3)}\frac{(2\times10^{-3}\,\text{m})^2}{1\times10^{-5}\,\text{m}^2/\text{s}} = \boxed{0.6\,\text{s}}$$

73. (a) At 34°C, the tape will expand from its calibration, and so will $\boxed{\text{read low}}$.

(b) $\dfrac{\Delta L}{L_0} = \alpha\Delta T = (12\times10^{-6}/\text{°C})(34\text{°C}-20\text{°C}) = 1.68\times10^{-4} \approx \boxed{1.7\times10^{-2}\,\%}$

74. Since the glass does not expand, the measuring cup will contain 300 mL of hot water. Find the volume of water after it cools.

$$\Delta V = V_0\beta\Delta T = (300\,\text{mL})(210\times10^{-6}/\text{C°})(20\text{°C}-80\text{°C}) = -3.78\,\text{mL} \approx \boxed{-3.8\,\text{mL}}$$

The volume of cool water is 3.8 mL less than the desired volume of 300 mL.

75. Assume the helium is an ideal gas. The volume of the cylinder is constant, and we assume that the temperature of the gas is also constant in the cylinder. From the ideal gas law, $PV = nRT$, under these conditions the amount of gas is proportional to the absolute pressure.

$$PV = nRT \rightarrow \frac{P}{n} = \frac{RT}{V} = \text{constant} \rightarrow \frac{P_1}{n_1} = \frac{P_2}{n_2} \rightarrow \frac{n_2}{n_1} = \frac{P_2}{P_1} = \frac{5\,\text{atm}+1\,\text{atm}}{28\,\text{atm}+1\,\text{atm}} = \frac{6}{29}$$

Thus $\boxed{6/29 = 0.207 \approx 21\%}$ of the original gas remains in the cylinder.

76. Assume the air is an ideal gas, and that the pressure is 1.0 atm.

$$PV = NkT \quad \rightarrow$$

$$N = \frac{PV}{kT} = \frac{\left(1.013 \times 10^5 \, \text{Pa}\right)\left(6.5 \times 3.1 \times 2.5\right) \text{m}^3}{\left(1.38 \times 10^{-23} \, \text{J/K}\right)\left(273 + 22\right)\text{K}} = 1.253 \times 10^{27} \, \text{molecules} \approx \boxed{1.3 \times 10^{27} \, \text{molecules}}$$

$$1.253 \times 10^{27} \, \text{molecules} \left(\frac{1 \, \text{mole}}{6.02 \times 10^{23} \, \text{molecules}}\right) = 2082 \, \text{moles} \approx \boxed{2.1 \times 10^3 \, \text{moles}}$$

$\boxed{77.}$ The rms speed is given by Equation 13-9, $v_{rms} = \sqrt{3kT/m}$. Hydrogen atoms have a mass of 1 atomic mass unit.

$$v_{rms} = \sqrt{\frac{3kT}{m}} = \sqrt{\frac{3\left(1.38 \times 10^{-23} \, \text{J/K}\right)\left(2.7 \, \text{K}\right)}{1\left(1.66 \times 10^{-27} \, \text{kg}\right)}} = \boxed{260 \, \text{m/s}}$$

The pressure is found from the ideal gas law, $PV = NkT$.

$$PV = NkT \quad \rightarrow \quad P = \frac{NkT}{V} = \frac{(1)\left(1.38 \times 10^{-23} \, \text{J/K}\right)\left(2.7 \, \text{K}\right)}{1 \, \text{cm}^3 \left(\dfrac{1 \times 10^{-6} \, \text{m}^3}{1 \text{cm}^3}\right)} = 3.726 \times 10^{-17} \, \text{Pa} \left(\frac{1 \, \text{atm}}{1.01 \times 10^5 \, \text{Pa}}\right)$$

$$= 3.689 \times 10^{-22} \, \text{atm} \approx \boxed{4 \times 10^{-22} \, \text{atm}}$$

78. Assume the gas is ideal at those low pressures, and use the ideal gas law.

$$PV = NkT \quad \rightarrow \quad \frac{N}{V} = \frac{P}{kT} = \frac{1 \times 10^{-12} \, \text{N/m}^2}{\left(1.38 \times 10^{-23} \, \text{J/K}\right)\left(273 \, \text{K}\right)} = \left(3 \times 10^8 \, \frac{\text{molecules}}{\text{m}^3}\right)\left(\frac{10^{-6} \, \text{m}^3}{1 \, \text{cm}^3}\right)$$

$$= \boxed{3 \times 10^2 \, \frac{\text{molecules}}{\text{cm}^3}}$$

79. Assume that the air in the lungs is an ideal gas, that the amount of gas is constant, and that the temperature is constant. The ideal gas law then says that the value of PV is constant. The pressure a distance h below the surface of the water is discussed in chapter 10, and is given by $P = P_0 + \rho g h$, where P_0 is atmospheric pressure and ρ is the density of the water.

$$\left(PV\right)_{surface} = \left(PV\right)_{submerged} \quad \rightarrow \quad V_{surface} = V_{submerged} \frac{P_{submerged}}{P_{surface}} = V_{submerged} \frac{P_{atm} + \rho g h}{P_{atm}}$$

$$= \left(5.5 \, \text{L}\right) \frac{1.01 \times 10^5 \, \text{Pa} + \left(1.0 \times 10^3 \, \text{kg/m}^3\right)\left(9.8 \, \text{m/s}^2\right)\left(10 \, \text{m}\right)}{1.01 \times 10^5 \, \text{Pa}} = \boxed{11 \, \text{L}}$$

This is obviously very dangerous, to have the lungs attempt to inflate to twice their volume. Thus it is $\boxed{\text{not advisable}}$ to quickly rise to the surface.

80. The temperature can be found from the rms speed by Equation 13-9, $v_{rms} = \sqrt{3kT/m}$.

$$v_{rms} = \sqrt{3kT/m} \rightarrow$$

$$T = \frac{mv_{rms}^2}{3k} = \frac{(28)(1.66 \times 10^{-27}\,\text{kg})\left[4 \times 10^4\,\text{km/h}\left(\dfrac{1\,\text{m/s}}{3.6\,\text{km/h}}\right)\right]^2}{3(1.38 \times 10^{-23}\,\text{J/K})} = \boxed{1.4 \times 10^5\,\text{K}}$$

81. From the ideal gas law, if the volume and number of moles stay constant, then the ratio of pressure and temperature is constant.

$$PV = nRT \rightarrow \frac{P}{T} = \frac{nR}{V} = \text{constant} \rightarrow \frac{P_2}{T_2} = \frac{P_1}{T_1} \rightarrow$$

$$\frac{P_2}{P_1} = \frac{T_2}{T_1} = \frac{(273 + 360)\,\text{K}}{(273 + 110)\,\text{K}} = \frac{633\,\text{K}}{383\,\text{K}} = \boxed{1.65}$$

From the relationship $v_{rms} = \sqrt{3kT/m}$, if the mass per molecule stays constant, then the ratio of rms speed to the square root of the temperature is constant.

$$v_{rms} = \sqrt{3kT/m} \rightarrow \frac{v_{rms}}{\sqrt{T}} = \sqrt{\frac{3k}{m}} = \text{constant} \rightarrow \frac{(v_{rms})_2}{\sqrt{T_2}} = \frac{(v_{rms})_1}{\sqrt{T_1}} \rightarrow$$

$$\frac{(v_{rms})_2}{(v_{rms})_1} = \frac{\sqrt{T_2}}{\sqrt{T_1}} = \sqrt{\frac{633\,\text{K}}{383\,\text{K}}} = \boxed{1.29}$$

82. To do this problem, the "molecular weight" of air is needed. If we approximate air as 70% N_2 (molecular weight 28) and 30% O_2 (molecular weight 32), then the average molecular weight is
$$0.70(28) + 0.30(32) = 29$$

(a) Treat the air as an ideal gas. Assume that the pressure is 1.00 atm.

$$PV = nRT \rightarrow n = \frac{PV}{RT} = \frac{(1.01 \times 10^5\,\text{Pa})(770\,\text{m}^3)}{(8.315\,\text{J/mol·k})(293\,\text{K})} = 3.192 \times 10^4\,\text{moles}$$

$$m = (3.192 \times 10^4\,\text{moles})(29 \times 10^{-3}\,\text{kg/mol}) = 925.7\,\text{kg} \approx \boxed{9.3 \times 10^2\,\text{kg}}$$

(b) Find the mass of air at the lower temperature, and then subtract the mass at the higher temperature.

$$n = \frac{PV}{RT} = \frac{(1.01 \times 10^5\,\text{Pa})(770\,\text{m}^3)}{(8.315\,\text{J/mol·k})(263\,\text{K})} = 3.556 \times 10^4\,\text{moles}$$

$$m = (3.556 \times 10^4\,\text{moles})(29 \times 10^{-3}\,\text{kg/mol}) = 1031.2\,\text{kg}$$

The mass entering the house is $1031.2\,\text{kg} - 925.7\,\text{kg} = 105.5\,\text{kg} \approx \boxed{1.1 \times 10^2\,\text{kg}}$.

83. Since the pressure is force per unit area, if the pressure is multiplied by the surface area of the Earth, the force of the air is found. If we assume that the force of the air is due to its weight, then the mass of the air can be found. The number of molecules can then be found using the molecular mass of air (calculated in problem 82) and Avogadro's number.

$$P = \frac{F}{A} \rightarrow F = PA \rightarrow Mg = P4\pi R_{\text{Earth}}^2 \rightarrow$$

$$M = \frac{4\pi R_{\text{Earth}}^2 P}{g} = \frac{4\pi \left(6.38 \times 10^6 \, \text{m}\right)^2 \left(1.01 \times 10^5 \, \text{Pa}\right)}{9.80 \, \text{m/s}^2} = 5.27 \times 10^{18} \, \text{kg}$$

$$N = 5.27 \times 10^{18} \, \text{kg} \left(\frac{1 \, \text{mole}}{29 \times 10^{-3} \, \text{kg}}\right) \left(\frac{6.02 \times 10^{23} \, \text{molecules}}{1 \, \text{mole}}\right) = \boxed{1.1 \times 10^{44} \, \text{molecules}}$$

84. The temperature of the nitrogen gas is found from the ideal gas law, and then the rms speed is found from the temperature.

$$PV = nRT \quad \rightarrow \quad T = \frac{PV}{nR} = \frac{\left(4.2 \, \text{atm}\right)\left(1.013 \times 10^5 \, \text{Pa/atm}\right)\left(7.6 \, \text{m}^3\right)}{\left(1800 \, \text{mol}\right)\left(8.315 \, \text{J/mol} \cdot \text{K}\right)} = 216 \, \text{K}$$

$$v_{\text{rms}} = \sqrt{\frac{3kT}{m}} = \sqrt{\frac{3\left(1.38 \times 10^{-23} \, \text{J/K}\right)\left(216 \, \text{K}\right)}{28\left(1.66 \times 10^{-27} \, \text{kg}\right)}} = 438.7 \, \text{m/s} \approx \boxed{4.4 \times 10^2 \, \text{m/s}}$$

85. The amount of gas is the same under both sets of conditions, as is the temperature. Thus the ideal gas law gives $PV = nRT = \text{constant} \rightarrow \left(PV\right)_1 = \left(PV\right)_2$. Absolute pressure must be used instead of gauge pressure.

$$\left(PV\right)_{\substack{\text{in} \\ \text{cylinder}}} = \left(PV\right)_{\substack{\text{flowing} \\ \text{out}}} \quad \rightarrow$$

$$V_{\substack{\text{flowing} \\ \text{out}}} = \frac{\left(PV\right)_{\substack{\text{in} \\ \text{cylinder}}}}{P_{\substack{\text{flowing} \\ \text{out}}}} = \frac{\left[\left(1.38 \times 10^7 + 1.01 \times 10^5\right) \text{Pa}\right]\left(16 \, \text{L}\right)}{\left(1.01 \times 10^5 \, \text{Pa}\right)} = 2202 \, \text{L}$$

So there are 2202 L of oxygen to dispense, at a rate of 2.4 L/min.

$$t = \frac{2202 \, \text{L}}{2.4 \, \text{L/min}} = 917.5 \, \text{min} \approx \boxed{15 \, \text{hours}}$$

86. (a) The iron floats in the mercury because $\rho_{\text{Hg}} > \rho_{\text{Fe}}$. As the substances are heated, the density of both substances will decrease due to volume expansion (see problem 17 for a detailed discussion of this effect). The density of the mercury decreases more upon heating than the density of the iron, because $\beta_{\text{Hg}} > \beta_{\text{Fe}}$. The net effect is that the densities get closer together, and so relatively more mercury will have to be displaced to hold up the iron, and the iron will float $\boxed{\text{lower}}$ in the mercury.

(b) The fraction of the volume submerged is $V_{\substack{\text{Hg} \\ \text{displaced}}} \big/ V_{\text{Fe}}$. Both volumes expand as heated. The subscript "displace" is dropped for convenience.

$$\text{fractional change} = \frac{V_{\text{Hg}}/V_{\text{Fe}} - V_{0\,\text{Hg}}/V_{0\,\text{Fe}}}{V_{0\,\text{Hg}}/V_{0\,\text{Fe}}} = \frac{\dfrac{V_{0\,\text{Hg}}\left(1 + \beta_{\text{Hg}}\Delta T\right)}{V_{0\,\text{Fe}}\left(1 + \beta_{\text{Fe}}\Delta T\right)} - V_{0\,\text{Hg}}/V_{0\,\text{Fe}}}{V_{0\,\text{Hg}}/V_{0\,\text{Fe}}} = \frac{\left(1 + \beta_{\text{Hg}}\Delta T\right)}{\left(1 + \beta_{\text{Fe}}\Delta T\right)} - 1$$

$$= \frac{1 + \left(180 \times 10^{-6}/\text{C}^\circ\right)\left(25\,\text{C}^\circ\right)}{1 + \left(35 \times 10^{-6}\right)\left(25\,\text{C}^\circ\right)} - 1 = \frac{1.0045}{1.000875} - 1 = 3.6 \times 10^{-3}$$

$$\% \text{ change} = \left(3.6 \times 10^{-3}\right)\left(100\right) = \boxed{0.36\%}$$

87. (a) Assume that a mass M of gasoline with volume V_0 at $0°C$ is under consideration, and so its density is $\rho_0 = M/V_0$. At a temperature of $32°C$, the same mass has a volume $V = V_0(1 + \beta\Delta T)$.

$$\rho = \frac{M}{V} = \frac{M}{V_0(1 + \beta\Delta T)} = \frac{\rho_0}{1 + \beta\Delta T} = \frac{0.68 \times 10^3 \text{ kg/m}^3}{1 + (950 \times 10^{-6}/C°)(38C°)} = 0.6563 \times 10^3 \text{ kg/m}^3$$

$$\approx \boxed{0.66 \times 10^3 \text{ kg/m}^3}$$

(b) Calculate the percentage change in the density.

$$\% \text{ change} = \frac{(0.6563 - 0.68) \times 10^3 \text{ kg/m}^3}{0.68 \times 10^3 \text{ kg/m}^3 \ V} \times 100 = \boxed{-3.5\%}$$

88. The original length of the steel band is $L_0 = 2\pi R_{\text{Earth}}$. At the higher temperature, the length of the band is $L = L_0 + \Delta L = 2\pi R = 2\pi(R_{\text{Earth}} + \Delta R)$. The change in radius, ΔR, would be the height above the Earth.

$$\Delta L = \alpha L_0 \Delta T = 2\pi\Delta R \rightarrow$$

$$\Delta R = \frac{\alpha L_0 \Delta T}{2\pi} = \alpha R_{\text{Earth}}\Delta T = (12 \times 10^{-6}/C°)(6.38 \times 10^6 \text{ m})(45°C - 25°C) = \boxed{1.5 \times 10^3 \text{ m}}$$

89. The gap will be the radius of the lid minus the radius of the jar. Also note that the original radii of the lid and the jar are the same.

$$r_{\text{gap}} = (r_0 + \Delta r)_{\text{lid}} - (r_0 + \Delta r)_{\text{jar}} = \Delta r_{\text{lid}} - \Delta r_{\text{jar}} = (\alpha_{\text{brass}} - \alpha_{\text{glass}})r_0\Delta T$$

$$= (19 \times 10^{-6}/C° - 9 \times 10^{-6}/C°)(4.0 \text{ cm})(40C°) = \boxed{1.6 \times 10^{-3} \text{ cm}}$$

90. The change in length is to be restricted to $\Delta L < 1.0 \times 10^{-6} \text{ m}$.

$$\Delta L = \alpha L_0 \Delta T \leq 1.0 \times 10^{-6} \text{ m} \rightarrow \Delta T \leq \frac{1.0 \times 10^{-6} \text{ m}}{(9 \times 10^{-6}/C°)(1.0 \text{ m})} \leq 0.11C°$$

Thus the temperature would have to be controlled to within $\boxed{\pm 0.11 C°}$

91. (a) Treat the air as an ideal gas. Since the amount and temperature of the air are the same in both cases, the ideal gas law says $PV = nRT$ is a constant.

$$P_2 V_2 = P_1 V_1 \rightarrow V_2 = V_1 \frac{P_1}{P_2} = (11.3 \text{ L})\frac{195 \text{ atm}}{1.00 \text{ atm}} = 2203.5 \text{ L} \approx \boxed{2.20 \times 10^3 \text{ L}}$$

(b) Before entering the water, the air coming out of the tank will be at 1.00 atm pressure, and so the person will be able to breathe 2203.5 L of air.

$$t = 2203.5 \text{ L}\left(\frac{1 \text{ breath}}{2.0 \text{ L}}\right)\left(\frac{1 \text{ min}}{12 \text{ breaths}}\right) = \boxed{92 \text{ min}}$$

(c) When the person is underwater, the temperature and pressure will be different. Use the ideal gas equation to relate the original tank conditions to the underwater breathing conditions. The amount of gas will be constant, so $PV/T = nR$ will be constant. The pressure a distance h

below the surface of the water is discussed in chapter 10, and is given by $P = P_0 + \rho g h$, where P_0 is atmospheric pressure and ρ is the density of the sea water.

$$\frac{P_2 V_2}{T_2} = \frac{P_1 V_1}{T_1} \rightarrow V_2 = V_1 \frac{P_1}{P_2} \frac{T_2}{T_1}$$

$$V_2 = (11.3\,\text{L}) \left[\frac{195\,\text{atm}\left(1.01 \times 10^5\,\text{Pa/atm}\right)}{1.01 \times 10^5\,\text{Pa} + \left(1.025 \times 10^3\,\text{kg/m}^3\right)\left(9.8\,\text{m/s}^2\right)(20.0\,\text{m})} \right] \left(\frac{283\,\text{K}}{293\,\text{K}} \right)$$

$$= 7.120 \times 10^2\,\text{L} \qquad t = 7.120 \times 10^2\,\text{L} \left(\frac{1\,\text{breath}}{2.0\,\text{L}} \right) \left(\frac{1\,\text{min}}{12\,\text{breaths}} \right) = \boxed{3.0 \times 10^1\,\text{min}}$$

92. The rms speed is given by Equation 13-9, $v_{rms} = \sqrt{3kT/m}$. Using the escape velocity as v_{rms}, solve for the temperature.

    (a) For oxygen molecules: $\quad T = \dfrac{mv_{rms}^2}{3k} = \dfrac{32\left(1.66 \times 10^{-27}\,\text{kg}\right)\left(1.12 \times 10^4\,\text{m/s}\right)^2}{3\left(1.38 \times 10^{-23}\,\text{J/K}\right)} = 1.6 \times 10^5\,\text{K}$

    (b) For helium atoms: $\quad T = \dfrac{mv_{rms}^2}{3k} = \dfrac{4\left(1.66 \times 10^{-27}\,\text{kg}\right)\left(1.12 \times 10^4\,\text{m/s}\right)^2}{3\left(1.38 \times 10^{-23}\,\text{J/K}\right)} = 2.0 \times 10^4\,\text{K}$

    (c) Because the "escape temperature" is so high for oxygen, very few oxygen molecules ever escape the atmosphere. But helium, with one-eighth the mass, can escape at a much lower temperature. While the temperature of the Earth is not close to $2.0 \times 10^4\,\text{K}$ today, during the Earth's formation its temperature was possibly much hotter – presumably hot enough that helium was able to escape the atmosphere.

93. Following the development of the kinetic molecular theory in section 13-10 of the textbook, the tennis balls hitting the trash can lid are similar to the particles colliding with the walls of a container causing pressure. Quoting from the text, "the average force averaged over many collisions will be equal to the force exerted during one collision divided by the time between collisions." That average force must be the weight of the trash can lid in order to suspend it.

    $$F_{avg} = M_{lid}\,g = \frac{2m_{ball}v_{ball}}{\Delta t} \rightarrow \Delta t = \frac{2m_{ball}v_{ball}}{M_{lid}\,g}$$

    The above expression is "seconds per ball", so its reciprocal will be "balls per second".

    $$\text{balls/s} = \frac{1}{\Delta t} = \frac{M_{lid}\,g}{2m_{ball}v_{ball}} = \frac{(1.0\,\text{kg})\left(9.8\,\text{m/s}^2\right)}{2(0.060\,\text{kg})(12\,\text{m/s})} = \boxed{6.8\,\text{balls/s}}$$

94. The amount of gas and the temperature of the gas are constant. Then from the ideal gas law, the quantity $PV = nRT$ is constant. The pressure at the surface will be 1 atmosphere. The pressure a distance h below the surface of the water is discussed in chapter 10, and is given by $P = P_0 + \rho g h$, where P_0 is atmospheric pressure and ρ is the density of the water. The volume of a spherical bubble is given by $V = \frac{4}{3}\pi r^3 = \frac{1}{6}\pi d^3$.

    $$P_{surface}V_{surface} = P_{depth}V_{depth} \rightarrow P_{surface}\tfrac{1}{6}\pi d_{surface}^3 = P_{depth}\tfrac{1}{6}\pi d_{depth}^3 \rightarrow$$

$$d_{surface} = d_{depth}\left(\frac{P_{depth}}{P_{surface}}\right)^{1/3} = (3.00 \text{ cm})\left(\frac{1.01\times10^5\,\text{Pa} + (1.0\times10^3\,\text{kg/m}^3)(9.8\,\text{m/s}^2)(14.0\,\text{m})}{1.01\times10^5\,\text{Pa}}\right)^{1/3}$$

$$= \boxed{3.99 \text{ cm}}$$

95. (a) At a temperature of 30°C, the saturated vapor pressure, from Table 13-6, is $4.24\times10^3\,\text{Pa}$. If the relative humidity is 40%, then the water vapor pressure is 40% of the saturated vapor pressure.

$$0.40(4.24\times10^3\,\text{Pa}) = \boxed{1.7\times10^3\,\text{Pa}}$$

(b) At a temperature of 5°C, the saturated vapor pressure, from Table 13-6, is $8.72\times10^2\,\text{Pa}$. If the relative humidity is 80%, then the water vapor pressure is 80% of the saturated vapor pressure.

$$0.80(8.72\times10^2\,\text{Pa}) = \boxed{7.0\times10^2\,\text{Pa}}$$

96. Assume that the water is an ideal gas, and that the temperature is constant. From Table 13-3, saturated vapor pressure at 90°C is $7.01\times10^4\,\text{Pa}$, and so to have a relative humidity of 10%, the vapor pressure will be $7.01\times10^3\,\text{Pa}$. Use the ideal gas law to calculate the amount of water.
$$PV = nRT \quad \rightarrow$$

$$n = \frac{PV}{RT} = \frac{(7.01\times10^3\,\text{Pa})(7.0\,\text{m}^3)}{(8.315\,\text{J/mol·K})(273+90)\,\text{K}} = 16.26 \text{ moles}\left(\frac{18\times10^{-3}\,\text{kg}}{1 \text{ mole}}\right) = \boxed{0.29 \text{ kg}}$$

97. The density is the mass divided by the volume. Let the original volume of the mass of iron be V_0, the original density $\rho_0 = M/V_0$. The volume of that same mass deep in the Earth is $V = V_0 + \Delta V$, and so the density deep in the Earth is $\rho = M/V = M/(V_0 + \Delta V)$. The change in volume is due to two effects: the increase in volume due to a higher temperature, $\Delta V_{temp} = \beta V_0 \Delta T$, and the decrease in volume due to a higher pressure, $\Delta V_{pressure} = -V_0\Delta P/B$. So $\Delta V = \Delta V_{temp} + \Delta V_{pressure}$. The new density is then

$$\rho = M/V = \frac{M}{V_0 + \Delta V} = \frac{M}{V_0 + \Delta V_{temp} + \Delta V_{pressure}} = \frac{M}{V_0 + \beta V_0 \Delta T - V_0 \Delta P/B} = \frac{M}{V_0}\frac{1}{(1+\beta\Delta T - \Delta P/B)}$$

$$= \frac{\rho_0}{(1+\beta\Delta T - \Delta P/B)}$$

$$= \frac{\rho_0}{\left[1 + (35\times10^{-6}/\text{C}°)(2000\text{C}°) - (5000\,\text{atm})(1.01\times10^5\,\text{Pa/atm})/(90\times10^9\,\text{N/m}^2)\right]}$$

$$= \frac{\rho_0}{[1+0.07-.00561]} = 0.9395\rho_0 \quad \rightarrow \quad \boxed{6\% \text{ decrease}}$$

98. (a) Assume the pressure and amount of gas are held constant, and so $P_0V_0 = nRT_0$ and $P_0V = nRT$. From these two expressions calculate the change in volume and relate it to the change in temperature.

$$V = V_0 + \Delta V \quad \rightarrow \quad \Delta V = V - V_0 = \frac{nRT}{P_0} - \frac{nRT_0}{P_0} = \frac{nR}{P_0}(T-T_0) = \frac{V_0}{T_0}\Delta T$$

But $\Delta V = \beta V_0 \Delta T$, and so $\Delta V = \dfrac{V_0}{T_0}\Delta T = \beta V_0 \Delta T \;\rightarrow\; \beta = \dfrac{1}{T_0}$

For $T_0 = 293 \text{ K}$, $\beta = \dfrac{1}{T_0} = \dfrac{1}{293 \text{ K}} = \boxed{3.4 \times 10^{-3}/\text{K}}$, which agrees well with Table 13-1.

(b) Assume the temperature and amount of gas are held constant, and so $P_0 V_0 = nRT_0 = PV$. From these two expressions calculate change in volume and relate it to the change in pressure.

$V = V_0 + \Delta V \;\rightarrow$

$$\Delta V = V - V_0 = \frac{nRT_0}{P} - \frac{nRT_0}{P_0} = nRT_0\left(\frac{1}{P} - \frac{1}{P_0}\right) = \frac{nRT_0}{P_0}\left(\frac{P_0 - P}{P}\right) = V_0\frac{1}{P}(-\Delta P)$$

But from chapter 9, $\Delta V = -V_0 \dfrac{1}{B}\Delta P$ and so $\Delta V = V_0 \dfrac{1}{P}(-\Delta P) = -V_0 \dfrac{1}{B}\Delta P \;\rightarrow\; \boxed{B = P}$

99. Assume that the water vapor behaves like an ideal gas. At 20°C, the saturated vapor pressure is $2.33 \times 10^3 \,\text{Pa}$. Using the ideal gas law, find the number of moles of water in the air at both 95% and 30%. Subtract those mole amounts to find the amount of water that must be removed.

$PV = nRT \;\rightarrow\; n = \dfrac{PV}{RT} \;\rightarrow$

$$n_1 - n_2 = \frac{V}{RT}(P_1 - P_2) = \frac{(95 \text{ m}^2)(2.8 \text{ m})}{(8.315 \text{ J/mol}\cdot\text{k})(293 \text{ K})}(2.33 \times 10^3 \,\text{Pa})(0.95 - 0.30) = 165 \text{ mol}$$

$165 \text{ mol}\left(\dfrac{18 \times 10^{-3}\,\text{kg}}{1 \text{ mol}}\right) = \boxed{3.0 \text{ kg}}$

CHAPTER 14: Heat

Answers to Questions

1. The work goes primarily into increasing the temperature of the orange juice, by increasing the average kinetic energy of the molecules comprising the orange juice.

2. When a hot object warms a cooler object, energy is transferred from the hot object to the cold object. Temperature does NOT flow. The temperature changes of the two objects are not necessarily equal in magnitude. Under certain circumstances, they can be equal in magnitude, however. In an ideal case, the amount of heat lost by the warmer object is the same as the amount of heat gained by the cooler object.

3. (a) Internal energy depends on both the number of molecules of material and the temperature of the material. Heat will flow naturally from the object with the higher temperature to the object with the lower temperature. The object with the high temperature may or may not be the object with the higher internal energy.

   (b) The two objects may consist of one with a higher temperature and smaller number of molecules, and the other with a lower temperature and a larger number of molecules. In that case it is possible for both objects to have the same internal energy, but heat will still flow from the object with the higher temperature to the one with the lower temperature.

4. The water will coat the plants, and so the water, not the plant, is in contact with the cold air. Thus as the air cools, the water cools before the plant does – the water insulates the plant. As the water cools, it releases energy, and raises the temperature of its surroundings, which includes the plant. Particularly if the water freezes, relatively large amounts of heat are released due to the relatively large heat of fusion for water.

5. Because the specific heat of water is quite large, it can contain a relatively large amount of thermal energy per unit mass with a relatively small increase in temperature. Since the water is a liquid, it is relatively easy to transport from one location to another, and so large quantities of energy can be moved from one place to another with relative simplicity by water.

6. The mechanism of evaporation of the water from the moist cloth jacket requires energy (the latent heat of vaporization), some of which will come from the interior of the canteen. This removal of energy from the interior helps to keep the interior of the canteen cool. Also, the metal canteen is a good thermal conductor, and so heat can transfer from the water to the cloth jacket to cool the water.

7. Steam at 100°C contains more thermal energy than water at 100°C. The difference is due to the latent heat of vaporization, which for water is quite high. As the steam touches the skin and condenses, a large amount of energy is released, causing more severe burns. And the condensed water is still at 100°C , and so more burning can occur as that water cools.

8. Evaporation involves water molecules escaping the intermolecular bonds that hold the water together in the liquid state. It takes energy for the molecules to break those bonds (to overcome the bonding forces). This energy is the latent heat of vaporization. The most energetic molecules (those having the highest speed) are the ones that will be able to provide the most energy (from their kinetic energy) to be able to overcome the bonding forces. The slower moving molecules remain, lowering the average kinetic energy and thus lowering the internal energy and temperature of the liquid.

9. The potatoes will not cook faster if the water is boiling faster. The boiling water is the same temperature whether it is boiling fast or slow.

10. An ordinary fan does not cool the air directly. It actually warms the air slightly, because the motor used to power the fan will exhaust some heat into the air, and the increase in average kinetic energy of the air molecules caused by the fan blades pushing them means the air temperature increases slightly. The reason for using the fan is that it keeps air moving. The human body warms the air immediately around it, assuming the air is initially cooler than the body. If that warmed air stays in contact with the body, then the body will lose little further heat after the air is warmed. The fan, by circulating the air, removes the heated air from close to the body and replaces it with cooler air. Likewise, the body is also cooled by evaporation of water from the skin. As the relative humidity of the air close to the body increases, less water can be evaporated, and cooling by evaporation is decreased. The fan, by circulating the air, removes the humid air from close to the body and replaces it with less humid air, so that evaporation can continue.

11. Even though the temperature is high in the upper atmosphere, the density of gas particles is very low. There would be relatively very few collisions of high-temperature gas molecules with the animal to warm it. Instead, the animal would radiate heat to the rarified atmosphere. The emissivity of the animal is much greater than that of the rarified atmosphere, and so the animal will lose much more energy by radiation than it can gain from the atmosphere.

12. Snow, particularly at very low temperatures, has a low thermal conductivity because it has many tiny air pockets trapped in its structure – it might be described as "fluffy". Since this "fluffy" snow has a low thermal conductivity, the snow will not conduct much heat away from an object covered in it.

13. We assume that the wet sand has been wetted fairly recently with water that is cooler than the sand's initial temperature. Water has a higher heat capacity than sand, and so for equal masses of sand and water, the sand will cool more than the water warms as their temperatures move towards equilibrium. Thus the wet sand may actually be cooler than the dry sand. Also, if both the wet and dry sand are at a lower temperature than your feet, the sand with the water in it is a better thermal conductor and so heat will flow more rapidly from you into the wet sand than into the dry sand, giving more of a sensation of having touched something cold.

14. An object with "high heat content" does not have to have a high temperature. If a given amount of heat energy is transferred into equal-mass samples of two substances initially at the same temperature, the substance with the lower specific heat will have the higher final temperature. But both substances would have the same "heat content" relative to their original state. So an object with "high heat content" might be made of material with a very high specific heat, and therefore not necessarily be at a high temperature.

15. A hot-air furnace heats primarily by air convection. A return path (often called a "cold air return") is necessary for the convective currents to be able to completely circulate. If the flow of air is blocked, then the convective currents and the heating process will be interrupted. Heating will be less efficient and less uniform if the convective currents are prevented from circulating.

16. A ceiling fan makes more of a "breeze" when it is set to blow the air down (usually called the "forward" direction by fan manufacturers). This is the setting for the summer, when the breeze will feel cooling since it accelerates evaporation from the skin. In the winter, the fan should be set to pull air up. This forces the warmer air at the top of the room to move out towards the walls and down. The relocation of warmer air keeps the room feeling warmer, and there is less "breeze" effect on the occupants of the room.

17. When the garment is fluffed up, it will have the most air trapped in its structure. The air has a low thermal conductivity, and the more the garment can be "fluffed", the more air it will trap, making it a better insulator. The "loft" value is similar to the R value of insulation, since the thicker the insulation, the higher the R value. The rate of thermal conduction is inversely proportional to the thickness of the conductor, so a thick conductor (high loft value) means a lower thermal conduction rate, and so a lower rate of losing body heat.

18. For all mechanisms of cooling, the rate of heat transfer from the hot object to the cold one is dependent on surface area. The heat sink with fins provides much more surface area than just a solid piece of metal, and so there is more cooling of the microprocessor chip. A major mechanism for cooling the heat sink is that of convection. More air is in contact with the finned heat sink than would be in contact with a solid piece of metal. There is often a cooling fan circulating air around that heat sink as well, so that heated air can continually be replaced with cool air to promote more cooling.

19. When there is a temperature difference in air, convection currents arise. Since the temperature of the land rises more rapidly than that of the water, the air above the land will be warmer than the air above the water. The warm air above the land will rise, and that rising warm air will be replaced by cooler air from over the body of water. The result is a breeze from the water towards the land.

20. We assume that the temperature in the house is higher than that under the house. Thus heat will flow through the floor out of the house. If the house sits directly on the ground or on concrete, the heat flow will warm the ground or concrete. Dirt and concrete are relatively poor conductors of heat, and so the thermal energy that goes into them will stay for a relatively long time, allowing their temperature to rise and thus reducing the heat loss through the floor. If the floor is over a crawlspace, then the thermal energy from the floor will be heating air instead of dirt or concrete. If that warmed air gets moved away by wind currents or by convection and replaced with colder air, then the temperature difference between the inside and outside will stay large, and more energy will leave through the floor, making the inside of the house cooler.

21. Air is a poorer conductor of heat than water by roughly a factor of 20, and so the rate of heat loss from your body to the air is roughly 20 times less than the rate of heat loss from your body to the water. Thus you lose heat quickly in the water, and feel cold. Another contributing factor is that water has a high heat capacity, and so as heat leaves your body and enters the water, the temperature rise for the water close to your body is small. Air has a smaller heat capacity, and so the temperature rise for the air close to your body is larger. This reduces the temperature difference between your body and the air, which reduces the rate of heat loss to the air as well.

22. A thermometer in the direct sunlight would gain thermal energy (and thus show a higher temperature) due to receiving radiation directly from the Sun. The emissivity of air is small, and so it does not gain as much energy from the Sun as the mercury and glass do. The thermometer is to reach its equilibrium temperature by heat transfer with the air, in order to measure the air temperature.

23. Premature babies have underdeveloped skin, and they can lose a lot of moisture through their skin by evaporation. For a baby in a very warm environment, like an incubator at 37°C, there will be a large evaporative effect. A significant increase in evaporation occurs at incubator temperatures, and that evaporation of moisture from the baby will cool the baby dramatically. Thus an incubator must have not only a high temperature but also a high humidity. Other factors might include radiative energy loss, blood vessels being close to the skin surface and so there is less insulation than a more mature baby, and low food consumption to replace lost energy.

24. Shiny surfaces absorb very little of the radiation that is incident on them – they reflect it back towards the source. Thus the liner is silvered to reduce radiation energy transfer (both into and away from the substance in the thermos). The (near) vacuum between its two walls reduces the energy transfer by conduction. Vacuum is a very poor conductor of heat.

25. The overall R-value of the wall plus window is lower than R_1 and higher than R_2. The rate of heat transfer through the entire wall + window area will increase, but the total area and the temperature difference has not changed. Thus, since $\dfrac{Q}{t} = \dfrac{A}{R_{\text{effective}}}(T_1 - T_2)$, for the rate to increase means the R-value had to drop from its original value. However, the rate of heat transfer will be lower than if the wall was totally glass, and so the final R-value must be higher than that of the glass.

26. (*a*) (1) Ventilation around the edges is cooling by convection.
      (2) Cooling through the frame is cooling by conduction.
      (3) Cooling through the glass panes is cooling by conduction and radiation.
  (*b*) Heavy curtains can reduce all three heat losses. The curtains will prevent air circulation around the edges of the windows, thus reducing the convection cooling. The curtains are more opaque than the glass, preventing the electromagnetic waves responsible for radiation heat transfer from reaching the glass. And the curtains provide another layer of insulation between the outdoors and the warm interior of the room, lowering the rate of conduction.

27. The thermal conductivity of the wood is about 2000 times less than that of the aluminum. Thus it takes a long time for energy from the wood to flow into your hand. Your skin temperature rises very slowly due to contact with the wood compared to contact with the aluminum, and so the sensation of heating is much less.

28. The Earth cools primarily by radiation. The clouds act as "insulation" in that they absorb energy from the radiating Earth, and reradiate some of it back to the Earth, reducing the net amount of radiant energy loss.

29. The emergency blanket is shiny (having a low emissivity) so that it reflects a person's radiated energy back to them, keeping them warmer. Also, like any blanket, it can insulate and so reduce heat transfer by conduction.

30. Cities situated on the ocean have less temperature extremes because the oceans are a heat reservoir. Due to ocean currents, the temperature of the ocean in a locale will be fairly constant during a season. In the winter, the ocean temperature remains above freezing. Thus if the air and land near the ocean get colder than the oceans, the oceans will release thermal energy, moderating the temperature of the nearby region. Likewise, in the warm seasons, the ocean temperatures will be cooler than the surrounding land mass, which heats up more easily than the water. Then the oceans will absorb thermal energy from the surrounding areas, again moderating the temperature.

Solutions to Problems

1. The kcal is the heat needed to raise 1 kg of water by 1 C°. Use the definition to find the heat needed.

$$\left(30.0\ \text{kg}\right)\left(95^\circ\text{C} - 15^\circ\text{C}\right)\frac{1\ \text{kcal}}{\left(1\text{kg}\right)\left(1\text{C}^\circ\right)}\left(\frac{4186\ \text{J}}{1\ \text{kcal}}\right) = \boxed{1.0 \times 10^7\ \text{J}}$$

2. The kcal is the heat needed to raise 1 kg of water by 1 C°. Use that definition to find the temperature change. Then the final temperature can be found.

$$\left(\frac{7700\ \text{J}}{3.0\ \text{kg}}\right)\left(\frac{1\ \text{kcal}}{4186\ \text{J}}\right)\frac{(1\text{kg})(1\text{C}^\circ)}{1\ \text{kcal}} = 0.61\text{C}^\circ \rightarrow \text{Final Temperature} = \boxed{10.6^\circ\text{C}}$$

3. (a) $2500\ \text{Cal}\left(\dfrac{4.186\times10^3\ \text{J}}{1\ \text{Cal}}\right) = \boxed{1.0\times10^7\ \text{J}}$

   (b) $2500\ \text{Cal}\left(\dfrac{1\ \text{kWh}}{860\ \text{Cal}}\right) = \boxed{2.9\ \text{kWh}}$

   (c) At 10 cents per day, the food energy costs $\boxed{\$0.29\ \text{per day}}$. It would be practically impossible to feed yourself in the United States on this amount of money.

4. Assume that we are at the surface of the Earth so that 1 kg has a weight of 2.20 lb.

$$1\text{Btu} = (1\ \text{lb})(1^\circ\text{F})\left(\frac{0.454\ \text{kg}}{1\ \text{lb}}\right)\left(\frac{5/9^\circ\ \text{C}}{1^\circ\text{F}}\right)\frac{1\ \text{kcal}}{(1\ \text{kg})(1\text{C}^\circ)} = \boxed{0.252\ \text{kcal}}$$

$$0.252\ \text{kcal}\left(\frac{4186\ \text{J}}{1\ \text{kcal}}\right) = \boxed{1055\ \text{J}}$$

5. The energy input is causing a certain rise in temperature, expressible as a number of Joules per hour per C°. Convert that to mass using the definition of kcal.

$$\left(\frac{3.2\times10^7\ \text{J/h}}{35\ \text{C}^\circ}\right)\left(\frac{1\ \text{kcal}}{4186\ \text{J}}\right)\frac{(1\text{kg})(1\text{C}^\circ)}{1\ \text{kcal}} = \boxed{2.2\times10^2\ \text{kg/h}}$$

6. The wattage rating is Joules per second. Note that 1 L of water has a mass of 1 kg.

$$\left[(2.50\times10^{-1}\text{L})\left(\frac{1\ \text{kg}}{1\ \text{L}}\right)(40\text{C}^\circ)\right]\frac{1\ \text{kcal}}{(1\ \text{kg})(1\text{C}^\circ)}\left(\frac{4186\ \text{J}}{\text{kcal}}\right)\left(\frac{1\ \text{s}}{350\ \text{J}}\right) = \boxed{1.2\times10^2\ \text{s} = 2.0\ \text{min}}$$

7. The energy generated by using the brakes must equal the car's initial kinetic energy, since its final kinetic energy is 0.

$$Q = \tfrac{1}{2}mv_0^2 = \tfrac{1}{2}(1.2\times10^3\ \text{kg})\left[(95\ \text{km/h})\left(\frac{1\text{m/s}}{3.6\ \text{km/h}}\right)\right]^2\left(\frac{1\ \text{kcal}}{4186\ \text{J}}\right) = \boxed{1.0\times10^2\ \text{kcal}}$$

8. The heat absorbed can be calculated from Eq. 14-2. Note that 1 L of water has a mass of 1 kg.

$$Q = mc\Delta T = \left[(16\ \text{L})\left(\frac{1\times10^{-3}\ \text{m}^3}{1\ \text{L}}\right)\left(\frac{1.0\times10^3\ \text{kg}}{1\ \text{m}^3}\right)\right](4186\ \text{J/kg}\cdot\text{C}^\circ)(90^\circ\text{C}-20^\circ\text{C}) = \boxed{4.7\times10^6\ \text{J}}$$

9. The specific heat can be calculated from Eq. 14-2.

$$Q = mc\Delta T \rightarrow c = \frac{Q}{m\Delta T} = \frac{1.35\times10^5\ \text{J}}{(5.1\ \text{kg})(31.5^\circ\text{C}-18.0^\circ\text{C})} = 1961\ \text{J/kg}\cdot\text{C}^\circ \approx \boxed{2.0\times10^3\ \text{J/kg}\cdot\text{C}^\circ}$$

10. The heat absorbed by all three substances is given by Eq. 14-2, $Q = mc\Delta T$. Thus the amount of mass can be found as $m = \dfrac{Q}{c\Delta T}$. The heat and temperature change are the same for all three substances.

$$m_{\text{Cu}} : m_{\text{Al}} : m_{\text{H}_2\text{O}} = \frac{Q}{c_{\text{Cu}}\Delta T} : \frac{Q}{c_{\text{Al}}\Delta T} : \frac{Q}{c_{\text{H}_2\text{O}}\Delta T} = \frac{1}{c_{\text{Cu}}} : \frac{1}{c_{\text{Al}}} : \frac{1}{c_{\text{H}_2\text{O}}} = \frac{1}{390} : \frac{1}{900} : \frac{1}{4186}$$

$$= \frac{4186}{390} : \frac{4186}{900} : \frac{4186}{4186} = \boxed{10.7 : 4.65 : 1}$$

11. The heat gained by the glass thermometer must be equal to the heat lost by the water.

$$m_{\text{glass}}c_{\text{glass}}\left(T_{\text{eq}} - T_{i\,\text{glass}}\right) = m_{\text{H}_2\text{O}}c_{\text{H}_2\text{O}}\left(T_{i\,\text{H}_2\text{O}} - T_{\text{eq}}\right)$$

$$(35\text{ g})\left(0.20\,\text{cal}/\text{g}\cdot\text{C}°\right)\left(39.2°\text{C} - 21.6°\text{C}\right) = (135\text{ g})\left(1.00\,\text{cal}/\text{g}\cdot\text{C}°\right)\left(T_{i\,\text{H}_2\text{O}} - 39.2°\text{C}\right)$$

$$T_{i\,\text{H}_2\text{O}} = \boxed{40.1°\text{C}}$$

12. The heat lost by the copper must be equal to the heat gained by the aluminum and the water.

$$m_{\text{Cu}}c_{\text{Cu}}\left(T_{i\,\text{Cu}} - T_{\text{eq}}\right) = m_{\text{Al}}c_{\text{Al}}\left(T_{\text{eq}} - T_{i\,\text{Al}}\right) + m_{\text{H}_2\text{O}}c_{\text{H}_2\text{O}}\left(T_{\text{eq}} - T_{i\,\text{H}_2\text{O}}\right)$$

$$(0.245\text{ kg})\left(390\,\text{J}/\text{kg}\cdot\text{C}°\right)\left(285°\text{C} - T_{\text{eq}}\right) = \left[\begin{array}{c}(0.145\text{ kg})\left(900\,\text{J}/\text{kg}\cdot\text{C}°\right) \\ +(0.825\text{ kg})\left(4186\,\text{J}/\text{kg}\cdot\text{C}°\right)\end{array}\right]\left(T_{\text{eq}} - 12.0°\text{C}\right)$$

$$T_{\text{eq}} = \boxed{19.1°\text{C}}$$

13. The heat lost by the horseshoe must be equal to the heat gained by the iron pot and the water. Note that 1 L of water has a mass of 1 kg.

$$m_{\text{shoe}}c_{\text{Fe}}\left(T_{i\,\text{shoe}} - T_{\text{eq}}\right) = m_{\text{pot}}c_{\text{Fe}}\left(T_{\text{eq}} - T_{i\,\text{pot}}\right) + m_{\text{H}_2\text{O}}c_{\text{H}_2\text{O}}\left(T_{\text{eq}} - T_{i\,\text{H}_2\text{O}}\right)$$

$$(0.40\text{ kg})\left(450\,\text{J}/\text{kg}\cdot\text{C}°\right)\left(T_{i\,\text{shoe}} - 25.0°\text{C}\right) = (0.30\text{ kg})\left(450\,\text{J}/\text{kg}\cdot\text{C}°\right)\left(25.0\text{C}° - 20.0\text{C}°\right)$$

$$+ (1.35\text{ kg})\left(4186\,\text{J}/\text{kg}\cdot\text{C}°\right)\left(25.0\text{C}° - 20.0\text{C}°\right)$$

$$T_{i\,\text{shoe}} = 186°\text{C} \approx \boxed{190°\text{C}}$$

14. The heat lost by the substance must be equal to the heat gained by the aluminum, water, and glass.

$$m_x c_x\left(T_{ix} - T_{\text{eq}}\right) = m_{\text{Al}}c_{\text{Al}}\left(T_{\text{eq}} - T_{i\,\text{Al}}\right) + m_{\text{H}_2\text{O}}c_{\text{H}_2\text{O}}\left(T_{\text{eq}} - T_{i\,\text{H}_2\text{O}}\right) + m_{\text{glass}}c_{\text{glass}}\left(T_{\text{eq}} - T_{i\,\text{glass}}\right)$$

$$c_x = \frac{m_{\text{Al}}c_{\text{Al}}\left(T_{\text{eq}} - T_{i\,\text{Al}}\right) + m_{\text{H}_2\text{O}}c_{\text{H}_2\text{O}}\left(T_{\text{eq}} - T_{i\,\text{H}_2\text{O}}\right) + m_{\text{glass}}c_{\text{glass}}\left(T_{\text{eq}} - T_{i\,\text{glass}}\right)}{m_x\left(T_{ix} - T_{\text{eq}}\right)}$$

$$= \frac{\left[(0.105\text{ kg})\left(900\,\text{J}/\text{kg}\cdot\text{C}°\right) + (0.165\text{ kg})\left(4186\,\text{J}/\text{kg}\cdot\text{C}°\right) + (0.017\text{ kg})\left(840\,\text{J}/\text{kg}\cdot\text{C}°\right)\right]\left(22.5\text{C}°\right)}{(0.215\text{ kg})\left(330°\text{C} - 35.0°\text{C}\right)}$$

$$= \boxed{2.84 \times 10^2\ \text{J}/\text{kg}\cdot\text{C}°}$$

15. The heat must warm both the water and the pot to 100°C. The heat is also the power times the time.

$$Q = Pt = \left(m_{Al}c_{Al} + m_{H_2O}c_{H_2O}\right)\Delta T_{H_2O} \quad \rightarrow$$

$$t = \frac{\left(m_{Al}c_{Al} + m_{H_2O}c_{H_2O}\right)\Delta T_{H_2O}}{P} = \frac{\left[(0.36\text{ kg})\left(900\text{ J/kg}\cdot\text{C}^{\circ}\right) + (0.75\text{ kg})\left(4186\text{ J/kg}\cdot\text{C}^{\circ}\right)\right]\left(92\text{C}^{\circ}\right)}{750\text{ W}}$$

$$= \boxed{425\text{ s}} \approx 7\text{ min}$$

16. The heat released by the 15 grams of candy in the burning is equal to the heat absorbed by the bomb, calorimeter, and water.

$$Q_{15} = \left[\left(m_{bomb} + m_{cup}\right)c_{Al} + m_{H_2O}c_{H_2O}\right]\Delta T$$

$$= \left[(0.725\text{ kg} + 0.624\text{ kg})\left(0.22\text{ kcal/kg}\cdot\text{C}^{\circ}\right) + (2.00\text{ kg})\left(1.00\text{ kcal/kg}\cdot\text{C}^{\circ}\right)\right]\left(53.5^{\circ}\text{C} - 15.0^{\circ}\text{C}\right)$$

$$= 88.43\text{ kcal}$$

The heat released by 75 grams of the candy would be 5 times that released by the 15 grams.

$$Q_{75} = 5Q_{15} = 5\left(88.43\text{ kcal}\right) = 440\text{ kcal} = \boxed{440\text{ Cal}}$$

$\boxed{17.}$ The heat lost by the iron must be the heat gained by the aluminum and the glycerin.

$$m_{Fe}c_{Fe}\left(T_{iFe} - T_{eq}\right) = m_{Al}c_{Al}\left(T_{eq} - T_{iAl}\right) + m_{gly}c_{gly}\left(T_{eq} - T_{igly}\right)$$

$$(0.290\text{ kg})\left(450\text{ J/kg}\cdot\text{C}^{\circ}\right)\left(142\text{C}^{\circ}\right) = (0.095\text{ kg})\left(900\text{ J/kg}\cdot\text{C}^{\circ}\right)\left(28\text{C}^{\circ}\right) + (0.250\text{ kg})c_{gly}\left(28\text{C}^{\circ}\right)$$

$$c_{gly} = \boxed{2.3\times10^{3}\text{ J/kg}\cdot\text{C}^{\circ}}$$

18. We assume that all of the kinetic energy of the hammer goes into heating the nail.

$$KE = Q \quad \rightarrow \quad 10\left(\tfrac{1}{2}m_{hammer}v_{hammer}^{2}\right) = m_{nail}c_{Fe}\Delta T \quad \rightarrow$$

$$\Delta T = \frac{10\left(\tfrac{1}{2}m_{hammer}v_{hammer}^{2}\right)}{m_{nail}c_{Fe}} = \frac{5(1.20\text{ kg})(6.5\text{ m/s})^{2}}{(0.014\text{ kg})\left(450\text{ J/kg}\cdot\text{C}^{\circ}\right)} = 40.24\text{ C}^{\circ} \approx \boxed{4.0\times10^{1}\text{ C}^{\circ}}$$

19. 65% of the original potential energy of the aluminum goes to heating the aluminum.

$$0.65PE = Q \quad \rightarrow \quad 0.65m_{Al}gh = m_{Al}c_{Al}\Delta T \quad \rightarrow$$

$$\Delta T = \frac{0.65gh}{c_{Al}} = \frac{0.65\left(9.80\text{ m/s}^{2}\right)(45\text{ m})}{\left(900\text{ J/kg}\cdot\text{C}^{\circ}\right)} = \boxed{0.32\text{ C}^{\circ}}$$

20. (a) Since $Q = mc\Delta T$ and $Q = C\Delta T$, equate these two expressions for Q and solve for C.

$$Q = mc\Delta T = C\Delta T \quad \rightarrow \quad \boxed{C = mc}$$

(b) For 1.0 kg of water: $\quad C = mc = (1.0\text{ kg})\left(4186\text{ J/kg}\cdot\text{C}^{\circ}\right) = \boxed{4.2\times10^{3}\text{ J/C}^{\circ}}$

(c) For 25 kg of water: $\quad C = mc = (25\text{ kg})\left(4186\text{ J/kg}\cdot\text{C}^{\circ}\right) = \boxed{1.0\times10^{5}\text{ J/C}^{\circ}}$

21. The silver must be heated to the melting temperature and then melted.

$$Q = Q_{heat} + Q_{melt} = mc\Delta T + mL_{fusion}$$

$$= (16.50\text{ kg})\left(230\text{ J/kg}\cdot\text{C}^{\circ}\right)\left(961^{\circ}\text{C} - 20^{\circ}\text{C}\right) + (16.50\text{ kg})\left(0.88\times10^{5}\text{ J/kg}\right) = \boxed{5.0\times10^{6}\text{ J}}$$

22. Assume that the heat from the person is only used to evaporate the water. Also, we use the heat of vaporization at room temperature (585 kcal/kg), since the person's temperature is closer to room temperature than 100°C.

$$Q = mL_{vap} \rightarrow m = \frac{Q}{L_{vap}} = \frac{180 \text{ kcal}}{585 \text{ kcal/kg}} = 0.308 \text{ kg} \approx \boxed{0.31 \text{ kg}} = 310 \text{ mL}$$

23. The oxygen is all at the boiling point, so any heat added will cause oxygen to evaporate (as opposed to raising its temperature). We assume that all the heat goes to the oxygen, and none to the flask.

$$Q = mL_{vap} \rightarrow m = \frac{Q}{L_{vap}} = \frac{2.80 \times 10^5 \text{ J}}{2.1 \times 10^5 \text{ J/kg}} = \boxed{1.3 \text{ kg}}$$

24. Assume that all of the heat lost by the ice cube in cooling to the temperature of the liquid nitrogen is used to boil the nitrogen, and so none is used to raise the temperature of the nitrogen. The boiling point of the nitrogen is $77 \text{ K} = -196°\text{C}$.

$$m_{ice} c_{ice} \left(T_{i \ ice} - T_{f \ ice} \right) = m_{nitrogen} L_{vap} \rightarrow$$

$$m_{nitrogen} = \frac{m_{ice} c_{ice} \left(T_{i \ ice} - T_{f \ ice} \right)}{L_{vap}} = \frac{\left(3.0 \times 10^{-2} \text{ kg} \right)\left(2100 \text{ J/kg} \cdot \text{C}° \right)\left(0°\text{C} - -196°\text{C} \right)}{200 \times 10^3 \text{ J/kg}} = \boxed{6.2 \times 10^{-2} \text{ kg}}$$

25. The heat lost by the aluminum and 310 g of liquid water must be equal to the heat gained by the ice in warming in the solid state, melting, and warming in the liquid state.

$$m_{Al} c_{Al} \left(T_{i \ Al} - T_{eq} \right) + m_{H_2O} c_{H_2O} \left(T_{i H_2O} - T_{eq} \right) = m_{ice} \left[c_{ice} \left(T_{melt} - T_{i \ ice} \right) + L_{fusion} + c_{H_2O} \left(T_{eq} - T_{melt} \right) \right]$$

$$m_{ice} = \frac{\left(0.095 \text{ kg} \right)\left(900 \text{ J/kg} \cdot \text{C}° \right)\left(3.0 \text{ C}° \right) + \left(0.31 \text{ kg} \right)\left(4186 \text{ J/kg} \cdot \text{C}° \right)\left(3.0 \text{ C}° \right)}{\left[\left(2100 \text{ J/kg} \cdot \text{C}° \right)\left(8.5 \text{ C}° \right) + 3.3 \times 10^5 \text{ J/kg} + \left(4186 \text{ J/kg} \cdot \text{C}° \right)\left(17 \text{ C}° \right) \right]} = \boxed{9.90 \times 10^{-3} \text{ kg}}$$

$\boxed{26.}$ (a) The heater must heat both the boiler and the water at the same time.

$$Q_1 = Pt_1 = \left(m_{Fe} c_{Fe} + m_{H_2O} c_{H_2O} \right) \Delta T \rightarrow$$

$$t_1 = \frac{\left(m_{Fe} c_{Fe} + m_{H_2O} c_{H_2O} \right) \Delta T}{P} = \frac{\left[\left(230 \text{ kg} \right)\left(450 \text{ J/kg} \cdot \text{C}° \right) + \left(830 \text{ kg} \right)\left(4186 \text{ J/kg} \cdot \text{C}° \right) \right]\left(82 \text{ C}° \right)}{5.2 \times 10^7 \text{ J/h}}$$

$$= 5.642 \text{ h} \approx \boxed{5.6 \text{ h}}$$

(b) Assume that after the water starts to boil, all the heat energy goes into boiling the water, and none goes to raising the temperature of the iron or the steam.

$$Q_2 = Pt_2 = m_{H_2O} L_{vap} \rightarrow t_2 = \frac{m_{H_2O} L_{vap}}{P} = \frac{\left(830 \text{ kg} \right)\left(22.6 \times 10^5 \text{ J/kg} \right)}{5.2 \times 10^7 \text{ J/h}} = 36.073 \text{ h}$$

Thus the total time is $t_1 + t_2 = 5.642 \text{ h} + 36.073 \text{ h} = 41.72 \text{ h} \approx \boxed{42 \text{ h}}$

27. We assume that the cyclist's energy is only going to evaporation, not any heating. Then the energy needed is equal to the mass of the water times the latent heat of vaporization for water. Note that 1 L of water has a mass of 1 kg. Also, we use the heat of vaporization at room temperature (585 kcal/kg), since the cyclist's temperature is closer to room temperature than 100°C.

$$Q = m_{H_2O} L_{vap} = \left(8.0 \text{ kg} \right)\left(585 \text{ kcal/kg} \right) = \boxed{4.7 \times 10^3 \text{ kcal}}$$

28. The heat lost by the steam condensing and then cooling to 20°C must be equal to the heat gained by the ice melting and then warming to 20°C.

$$m_{steam}\left[L_{vap}+c_{H_2O}\left(T_{i\,steam}-T_{eq}\right)\right]=m_{ice}\left[L_{fus}+c_{H_2O}\left(T_{eq}-T_{i\,ice}\right)\right]$$

$$m_{steam}=m_{ice}\frac{\left[L_{fus}+c_{H_2O}\left(T_{eq}-T_{i\,ice}\right)\right]}{\left[L_{vap}+c_{H_2O}\left(T_{i\,steam}-T_{eq}\right)\right]}=\left(1.00\text{ kg}\right)\frac{\left[3.33\times10^5\text{ J/kg}+\left(4186\text{ J/kg}\cdot\text{C}°\right)\left(20\text{C}°\right)\right]}{\left[22.6\times10^5\text{ J/kg}+\left(4186\text{ J/kg}\cdot\text{C}°\right)\left(80\text{C}°\right)\right]}$$

$$=\boxed{1.61\times10^{-1}\text{ kg}}$$

29. The heat lost by the aluminum and the water must equal the heat needed to melt the mercury and to warm the mercury to the equilibrium temperature.

$$m_{Al}c_{Al}\left(T_{i\,Al}-T_{eq}\right)+m_{H_2O}c_{H_2O}\left(T_{i\,H_2O}-T_{eq}\right)=m_{Hg}\left[L_{fusion}+c_{Hg}\left(T_{eq}-T_{melt}\right)\right]$$

$$L_{fusion}=\frac{m_{Al}c_{Al}\left(T_{i\,Al}-T_{eq}\right)+m_{H_2O}c_{H_2O}\left(T_{i\,H_2O}-T_{eq}\right)}{m_{Hg}}-c_{Hg}\left(T_{eq}-T_{melt}\right)$$

$$=\frac{\left[\left(0.620\text{ kg}\right)\left(900\text{ J/kg}\cdot\text{C}°\right)+\left(0.400\text{ kg}\right)\left(4186\text{ J/kg}\cdot\text{C}°\right)\right]\left(12.80°\text{C}-5.06°\text{C}\right)}{1.00\text{ kg}}$$

$$-\left(138\text{ J/kg}\cdot\text{C}°\right)\left[5.06°\text{C}-\left(-39.0°\text{C}\right)\right]$$

$$=\boxed{1.12\times10^4\text{ J/kg}}$$

30. Assume that the kinetic energy of the bullet was all converted into heat which melted the ice.

$$\tfrac{1}{2}m_{bullet}v^2=Q=m_{ice}L_{fusion}\quad\rightarrow$$

$$m_{ice}=\frac{\tfrac{1}{2}m_{bullet}v^2}{L_{fusion}}=\frac{\tfrac{1}{2}\left(7.0\times10^{-2}\text{ kg}\right)\left(250\text{ m/s}\right)^2}{3.33\times10^5\text{ J/kg}}=\boxed{6.6\times10^{-3}\text{ kg}}=6.6\text{ g}$$

31. Assume that all of the melted ice stays at 0°C, so that all the heat is used in melting ice, and none in warming water. The available heat is half of the original kinetic energy

$$\tfrac{1}{2}\left(\tfrac{1}{2}m_{skater}v^2\right)=Q=m_{ice}L_{fusion}\quad\rightarrow$$

$$m_{ice}=\frac{\tfrac{1}{4}m_{skater}v^2}{L_{fusion}}=\frac{\tfrac{1}{4}\left(54.0\text{ kg}\right)\left(6.4\text{ m/s}\right)^2}{3.33\times10^5\text{ J/kg}}=\boxed{1.7\times10^{-3}\text{ kg}}=1.7\text{ g}$$

32. The kinetic energy of the bullet is assumed to warm the bullet and melt it.

$$\tfrac{1}{2}mv^2=Q=mc_{Pb}\left(T_{melt}-T_i\right)+mL_{fusion}\quad\rightarrow$$

$$v=\sqrt{2\left[c_{Pb}\left(T_{melt}-T_i\right)+L_{fusion}\right]}=\sqrt{2\left[\left(130\text{ J/kg}\cdot\text{C}°\right)\left(327°\text{C}-20°\text{C}\right)+\left(0.25\times10^5\text{ J/kg}\right)\right]}$$

$$=\boxed{3.6\times10^2\text{ m/s}}$$

33. The heat conduction rate is given by Eq. 14-4.

$$\frac{Q}{t}=kA\frac{T_1-T_2}{l}=\left(200\text{ J/s}\cdot\text{m}\cdot\text{C}°\right)\pi\left(1.0\times10^{-2}\text{ m}\right)^2\frac{\left(460°\text{C}-22°\text{C}\right)}{0.33\text{ m}}=\boxed{83\text{ W}}$$

34. The heat conduction rate is given by Eq. 14-4.

$$\frac{Q}{t} = kA\frac{T_1 - T_2}{l} = \left(0.84\,\mathrm{J/s \cdot m \cdot C^\circ}\right)\left(3.0\,\mathrm{m}^2\right)\frac{\left[15.0^\circ C - \left(-5^\circ C\right)\right]}{3.2 \times 10^{-3}\,\mathrm{m}} = \boxed{1.6 \times 10^4\,\mathrm{W}}$$

35. (a) The power radiated is given by Eq. 14-5. The temperature of the tungsten is $273\,\mathrm{K} + 25\,\mathrm{K} = 298\,\mathrm{K}$.

$$\frac{\Delta Q}{\Delta t} = e\sigma A T^4 = \left(0.35\right)\left(5.67 \times 10^{-8}\,\mathrm{W/m^2 \cdot K^4}\right)4\pi\left(0.22\,\mathrm{m}\right)^2\left(298\,\mathrm{K}\right)^4 = \boxed{95\,\mathrm{W}}$$

(b) The net flow rate of energy is given by Eq. 14-6. The temperature of the surroundings is 268 K.

$$\frac{\Delta Q}{\Delta t} = e\sigma A\left(T_1^4 - T_1^4\right) = \left(0.35\right)\left(5.67 \times 10^{-8}\,\mathrm{W/m^2 \cdot K^4}\right)4\pi\left(0.22\,\mathrm{m}\right)^2\left[\left(298\,\mathrm{K}\right)^4 - \left(268\,\mathrm{K}\right)^4\right]$$

$$= \boxed{33\,\mathrm{W}}$$

36. The distance can be calculated from the heat conduction rate, given by Eq. 14-4. The rate is given as a power (200 W = 200 J/s).

$$\frac{Q}{t} = P = kA\frac{T_1 - T_2}{l} \;\rightarrow\; l = kA\frac{T_1 - T_2}{P} = \left(0.2\,\mathrm{J/s \cdot m \cdot C^\circ}\right)\left(1.5\,\mathrm{m}^2\right)\frac{0.50\,\mathrm{C^\circ}}{200\,\mathrm{W}} = \boxed{8 \times 10^{-4}\,\mathrm{m}}$$

$\boxed{37.}$ This is a heat transfer by conduction, and so Eq. 14-4 is applicable.

$$\frac{Q}{t} = P = kA\frac{T_1 - T_2}{l} = \left(0.84\,\mathrm{J/s \cdot m \cdot C^\circ}\right)\left(16\,\mathrm{m}^2\right)\frac{30^\circ C - 10^\circ C}{0.12\,\mathrm{m}} = 2.24 \times 10^3\,\mathrm{W}$$

If we assume that all of the energy from the light bulbs goes into this conduction, then:

$$2.24 \times 10^3\,\mathrm{W}\left(\frac{1\,\mathrm{bulb}}{100\,\mathrm{W}}\right) = 22.4\,\mathrm{bulbs} \;\;\text{and so}\;\; \boxed{23\,\mathrm{bulbs}} \;\;\text{are needed.}$$

38. Eq. 14-7 gives the heat absorption rate for an object facing the Sun. The heat required to melt the ice is the mass of the ice times the latent heat of fusion for the ice. The mass is found by multiplying the volume of ice times its density.

$$\Delta Q = mL_f = \rho V L_f = \rho A\left(\Delta x\right)L_f \qquad \frac{\Delta Q}{\Delta t} = \left(1000\,\mathrm{W/m^2}\right)eA\cos\theta \;\rightarrow$$

$$\Delta t = \frac{\rho A\left(\Delta x\right)L_f}{\left(1000\,\mathrm{W/m^2}\right)eA\cos\theta} = \frac{\rho\left(\Delta x\right)L_f}{\left(1000\,\mathrm{W/m^2}\right)e\cos\theta}$$

$$= \frac{\left(9.17 \times 10^2\,\mathrm{kg/m^3}\right)\left(1.0 \times 10^{-2}\,\mathrm{m}\right)\left(3.33 \times 10^5\,\mathrm{J/kg}\right)}{\left(1000\,\mathrm{W/m^2}\right)\left(0.050\right)\cos 30^\circ} = \boxed{7.1 \times 10^4\,\mathrm{s}} = 20\,\mathrm{h}$$

39. For the temperature at the joint to remain constant, the heat flow in both rods must be the same. Note that the cross-sectional areas and lengths are the same. Use Eq. 14-4 for heat conduction.

$$\left(\frac{Q}{t}\right)_{Cu} = \left(\frac{Q}{t}\right)_{Al} \;\rightarrow\; k_{Cu}A\frac{T_{hot} - T_{middle}}{l} = k_{Al}A\frac{T_{middle} - T_{cool}}{l} \;\rightarrow$$

$$T_{middle} = \frac{k_{Cu}T_{hot} + k_{Al}T_{cool}}{k_{Cu} + k_{Al}} = \frac{\left(380\,\mathrm{J/s \cdot m \cdot C^\circ}\right)\left(250^\circ C\right) + \left(200\,\mathrm{J/s \cdot m \cdot C^\circ}\right)\left(0.0^\circ C\right)}{380\,\mathrm{J/s \cdot m \cdot C^\circ} + 200\,\mathrm{J/s \cdot m \cdot C^\circ}} = \boxed{1.6 \times 10^2\,^\circ C}$$

40. (a) The cross-sectional area of the Earth, perpendicular to the Sun, is a circle of radius R_{Earth}, and so has an area of πR_{Earth}^2. Multiply this area times the solar constant to get the rate at which the Earth is receiving solar energy.

$$\frac{Q}{t} = \pi R_{Earth}^2 \left(\text{solar constant}\right) = \pi \left(6.38 \times 10^6\, m\right)^2 \left(1350\, W/m^2\right) = \boxed{1.73 \times 10^{17}\, W}$$

(b) Use Eq. 14-5 to calculate the rate of heat output by radiation.

$$\frac{Q}{t} = e\sigma A T^4 \quad \rightarrow$$

$$T = \left(\frac{Q}{t}\frac{1}{\varepsilon \sigma A}\right)^{1/4} = \left[\left(1.7 \times 10^{17}\, J/s\right)\frac{1}{(1.0)\left(5.67 \times 10^{-8}\, W/m^2 \cdot K^4\right) 4\pi \left(6.38 \times 10^6\, m\right)^2}\right]^{1/4}$$

$$= \boxed{278\, K = 5°C}$$

41. This is an example of heat conduction, and the temperature difference can be calculated by Eq. 14-4.

$$\frac{Q}{t} = P = kA\frac{T_1 - T_2}{l} \quad \rightarrow \quad \Delta T = \frac{Pl}{kA} = \frac{(95\, W)\left(1.0 \times 10^{-3}\, m\right)}{\left(0.84\, J/s \cdot m \cdot C°\right) 4\pi \left(3.0 \times 10^{-2}\, m\right)^2} = \boxed{10C°}$$

42. The conduction rates through the two materials must be equal. If they were not, the temperatures in the materials would be changing. Call the temperature at the boundary between the materials T_x.

$$\frac{Q}{t} = k_1 A\frac{T_1 - T_x}{l_1} = k_2 A\frac{T_x - T_2}{l_2} \quad \rightarrow \quad \frac{Q}{t}\frac{l_1}{k_1 A} = T_1 - T_x \ ; \ \frac{Q}{t}\frac{l_2}{k_2 A} = T_x - T_2$$

Add these two equations together, and solve for the heat conduction rate.

$$\frac{Q}{t}\frac{l_1}{k_1 A} + \frac{Q}{t}\frac{l_2}{k_2 A} = T_1 - T_x + T_x - T_2 \quad \rightarrow \quad \frac{Q}{t}\left(\frac{l_1}{k_1} + \frac{l_2}{k_2}\right)\frac{1}{A} = T_1 - T_2 \quad \rightarrow$$

$$\frac{Q}{t} = A\frac{\left(T_1 - T_2\right)}{\left(\frac{l_1}{k_1} + \frac{l_2}{k_2}\right)} = A\frac{\left(T_1 - T_2\right)}{\left(R_1 + R_2\right)} = \left(240\, ft^2\right)\frac{\left(12F°\right)}{(1 + 19)\, ft^2 \cdot h \cdot F°/Btu} = 144\, Btu/h \approx \boxed{1.4 \times 10^2\, Btu/h}$$

This is about 42 Watts.

43. (a) We assume that $T_2 > T_1$. The conduction rates through the three materials must be equal. If they were not, the temperatures in the materials would be changing. Call the temperature at the boundary between the air and the left-most piece of glass, T_x, and the temperature at the boundary between the air and the right-most piece of glass, T_y. Write the conduction rate for each material separately, and solve for the temperature differences.

$$\frac{Q}{t} = k_1 A\frac{T_x - T_1}{l_1} = k_2 A\frac{T_y - T_x}{l_2} = k_3 A\frac{T_2 - T_y}{l_3} \quad \rightarrow$$

$$\frac{Q}{t}\frac{l_1}{k_1 A} = T_x - T_1 \ ; \ \frac{Q}{t}\frac{l_2}{k_2 A} = T_y - T_x \ ; \ \frac{Q}{t}\frac{l_3}{k_3 A} = T_2 - T_y$$

Add these three equations together, and solve for the heat conduction rate.

$$\frac{Q}{t}\frac{l_1}{k_1 A}+\frac{Q}{t}\frac{l_2}{k_2 A}+\frac{Q}{t}\frac{l_3}{k_3 A}=T_x-T_1+T_y-T_x+T_2-T_y \ \rightarrow \ \frac{Q}{t}\left(\frac{l_1}{k_1}+\frac{l_2}{k_2}+\frac{l_3}{k_3}\right)\frac{1}{A}=T_2-T_1 \ \rightarrow$$

$$\boxed{\frac{Q}{t}=A\frac{\left(T_2-T_1\right)}{\left(l_1/k_1+l_2/k_2+l_3/k_3\right)}}$$

(b) For *n* materials placed next to one another, the expression would be

$$\frac{Q}{t}=A\frac{\left(T_2-T_1\right)}{\displaystyle\sum_{i=1}^{n}l_i/k_i}= \ \rightarrow \ \boxed{\frac{Q}{t}=A\frac{\left(T_2-T_1\right)}{\displaystyle\sum_{i=1}^{n}R_i}}$$

44. This is an example of heat conduction. The heat conducted is the heat released by the melting ice, $Q=m_{ice}L_{fusion}$. The area through which the heat is conducted is the total area of the six surfaces of the box, and the length of the conducting material is the thickness of the styrofoam. We assume that all of the heat conducted into the box goes into melting the ice, and none into raising the temperature inside the box. The time can then be calculated by Eq. 14-4.

$$\frac{Q}{t}=kA\frac{T_1-T_2}{l} \ \rightarrow \ t=\frac{m_{ice}L_{fusion}l}{kA\Delta T}$$

$$=\frac{\left(11.0\,\text{kg}\right)\left(3.33\times10^5\,\text{J/kg}\right)\left(1.5\times10^{-2}\,\text{m}\right)}{2\left(0.023\,\text{J/s}\cdot\text{m}\cdot\text{C}^\circ\right)\left[2\left(0.25\,\text{m}\right)\left(0.35\,\text{m}\right)+2\left(0.25\,\text{m}\right)\left(0.55\,\text{m}\right)+2\left(0.35\,\text{m}\right)\left(0.55\,\text{m}\right)\right]\left(32\,\text{C}^\circ\right)}$$

$$=\boxed{4.5\times10^4\,\text{s}}\approx12\,\text{h}$$

45. The heat needed to warm the liquid can be calculated by Eq. 14-2.

$$Q=mc\Delta T=\left(0.20\,\text{kg}\right)\left(1.00\,\text{kcal}/\text{kg}\cdot\text{C}^\circ\right)\left(37^\circ\text{C}-5^\circ\text{C}\right)=6.4\,\text{kcal}=\boxed{6.4\,\text{C}}$$

46. Since 30% of the heat generated is lost up the chimney, the heat required to heat the house is 70% of the heat provided by the coal.

$$2.0\times10^5\,\text{MJ}=0.70\left(30\times10^6\,\text{MJ/kg}\right)\left(m\,\text{kg}\right) \ \rightarrow \ m=\frac{2.0\times10^5\,\text{MJ}}{0.70\left(30\,\text{MJ/kg}\right)}=\boxed{9.5\times10^3\,\text{kg}}$$

47. The heat released can be calculated by Eq. 14-2. To find the mass of the water, use the density (of pure water).

$$Q=mc\Delta T=\rho Vc\Delta T=\left(1.0\times10^3\,\text{kg}/\text{m}^3\right)\left(1.0\times10^3\,\text{m}\right)^3\left(4186\,\text{J/kg}\cdot\text{C}^\circ\right)\left(1\text{C}^\circ\right)=\boxed{4\times10^{15}\,\text{J}}$$

48. We assume that the initial kinetic energy of the bullet all goes into heating the wood and the bullet.

$$\tfrac{1}{2}m_{bullet}v_i^2=Q=m_{bullet}c_{lead}\Delta T_{lead}+m_{wood}c_{wood}\Delta T_{wood} \ \rightarrow$$

$$v_i=\sqrt{\frac{\left(m_{bullet}c_{lead}+m_{wood}c_{wood}\right)\Delta T}{\tfrac{1}{2}m_{bullet}}}$$

$$=\sqrt{\frac{\left[\left(0.015\,\text{kg}\right)\left(130\,\text{J/kg}\cdot\text{C}^\circ\right)+\left(1.05\,\text{kg}\right)\left(1700\,\text{J/kg}\cdot\text{C}^\circ\right)\right]\left(0.020\,\text{C}^\circ\right)}{\tfrac{1}{2}\left(0.015\,\text{kg}\right)}}=\boxed{69\,\text{m/s}}$$

49. (a) Use Eq. 14-5 for total power radiated.

$$\frac{Q}{t} = e\sigma A T^4 = e\sigma 4\pi R_{Sun}^2 T^4 = (1.0)(5.67\times10^{-8}\ \text{W/m}^2\cdot\text{K}^4)4\pi(7.0\times10^8\ \text{m})^2(5500\ \text{K})^4$$

$$= 3.195\times10^{26}\ \text{W} \approx \boxed{3.2\times10^{26}\ \text{W}}$$

(b) Assume that the energy from the Sun is distributed symmetrically over a spherical surface with the Sun at the center.

$$\frac{P}{A} = \frac{Q/t}{4\pi R_{Sun\text{-}Earth}^2} = \frac{3.195\times10^{26}\ \text{W}}{4\pi(1.5\times10^{11}\ \text{m})^2} = 1.130\times10^3\ \text{W/m}^2 \approx \boxed{1.1\times10^3\ \text{W/m}^2}$$

50. The temperature rise can be calculated from Eq. 14-2.

$$Q = mc\Delta T \quad\rightarrow\quad \Delta T = \frac{Q}{mc} = \frac{(0.80)(200\,\text{kcal/h})(1.00\ \text{h})}{(70\ \text{kg})(0.83\,\text{kcal/kg}\cdot\text{C}^\circ)} = \boxed{2.8\,\text{C}^\circ}$$

51. We assume that the starting speed of the boulder is zero, and that 50% of the original potential energy of the boulder goes to heating the boulder.

$$\tfrac{1}{2}PE = Q \quad\rightarrow\quad \tfrac{1}{2}(mgh) = mc_{marble}\Delta T \quad\rightarrow\quad \Delta T = \frac{\tfrac{1}{2}gh}{c_{marble}} = \frac{0.50(9.8\ \text{m/s}^2)(140\ \text{m})}{860\,\text{J/kg}\cdot\text{C}^\circ} = \boxed{0.80\,\text{C}^\circ}$$

52. The heat lost by the lead must be equal to the heat gained by the water. Note that 1 L of water has a mass of 1 kg.

$$m_{Pb}c_{Pb}\left(T_{iPb} - T_{eq}\right) = m_{H_2O}c_{H_2O}\left(T_{eq} - T_{iH_2O}\right)$$

$$(2.3\ \text{kg})(130\,\text{J/kg}\cdot\text{C}^\circ)(T_{iPb} - 28.0^\circ\text{C}) = (2.5\ \text{kg})(4186\,\text{J/kg}\cdot\text{C}^\circ)(8.0\,\text{C}^\circ) \quad\rightarrow$$

$$T_{iPb} = 308^\circ\text{C} \approx \boxed{310^\circ\text{C}}$$

$\boxed{53.}$ Use the heat conduction rate equation, Eq. 14-4.

(a) $$\frac{Q}{t} = kA\frac{T_1 - T_2}{l} = (0.025\,\text{J/s}\cdot\text{m}\cdot\text{C}^\circ)(1.2\ \text{m}^2)\frac{\left[34^\circ\text{C} - (-20^\circ\text{C})\right]}{3.5\times10^{-2}\ \text{m}} = \boxed{46\ \text{W}}$$

(b) $$\frac{Q}{t} = kA\frac{T_1 - T_2}{l} = (0.56\,\text{J/s}\cdot\text{m}\cdot\text{C}^\circ)(1.2\ \text{m}^2)\frac{\left[34^\circ\text{C} - (-20^\circ\text{C})\right]}{5.0\times10^{-3}\ \text{m}} = \boxed{7.3\times10^3\ \text{W}}$$

54. We assume that all of the heat provided by metabolism goes into evaporating the water. For the energy required for the evaporation of water, we use the heat of vaporization at room temperature (585 kcal/kg), since the runner's temperature is closer to room temperature than 100°C.

$$2.5\ \text{h}\left(\frac{950\ \text{kcal}}{1\ \text{h}}\right)\left(\frac{\text{kg}\ \text{H}_2\text{O}}{585\ \text{kcal}}\right) = \boxed{4.1\ \text{kg}}$$

55. For an estimate of the heat conduction rate, use Eq. 14-4.

$$\frac{Q}{t} = kA\frac{T_1 - T_2}{l} = (0.2\,\text{J/s}\cdot\text{m}\cdot\text{C}^\circ)(1.5\ \text{m}^2)\frac{(37^\circ\text{C} - 34^\circ\text{C})}{4.0\times10^{-2}\ \text{m}} = 22.5\ \text{W} \approx \boxed{20\ \text{W}}$$

This is only about 10% of the cooling capacity that is needed for the body. Thus convection cooling is clearly necessary.

56. (*a*) To calculate heat transfer by conduction, use Eq. 14-4 for all three areas – walls, roof, and windows. Each area has the same temperature difference.

$$\frac{Q_{conduction}}{t} = \left[\left(\frac{kA}{l}\right)_{walls} + \left(\frac{kA}{l}\right)_{roof} + \left(\frac{kA}{l}\right)_{windows}\right](T_1 - T_2)$$

$$= \left[\frac{(0.023\,\text{J/s}\cdot\text{m}\cdot\text{C}^\circ)(410\,\text{m}^2)}{1.75\times10^{-1}\,\text{m}} + \frac{(0.12\,\text{J/s}\cdot\text{m}\cdot\text{C}^\circ)(280\,\text{m}^2)}{6.5\times10^{-2}\,\text{cm}}\right.$$
$$\left.+ \frac{(0.84\,\text{J/s}\cdot\text{m}\cdot\text{C}^\circ)(33\,\text{m}^2)}{6.5\times10^{-3}\,\text{m}}\right](33\,\text{C}^\circ)$$

$$= 1.596\times10^5\,\text{W} \approx \boxed{1.6\times10^5\,\text{W}}$$

(*b*) The energy being added must both heat the air and replace the energy lost by conduction, as considered above. The heat required to raise the temperature is given by Eq. 14-2, $Q_{raise\;temp} = m_{air}c_{air}(\Delta T)_{warming}$. The mass of the air can be found from the density of the air times its volume. The conduction heat loss is proportional to the temperature difference between the inside and outside, which varies from 20C° to 33C°. We will estimate the average temperature difference as 26.5°C and scale the answer from part (a) accordingly.

$$Q_{added} = Q_{raise\;temp} + Q_{conduction} = \rho_{air}Vc_{air}(\Delta T)_{warming} + \left(\frac{Q_{conduction}}{t}\right)(1800\,\text{s})$$

$$= \left(1.29\,\frac{\text{kg}}{\text{m}^3}\right)(750\,\text{m}^3)\left(0.24\,\frac{\text{kcal}}{\text{kg}\cdot\text{C}^\circ}\right)\left(\frac{4186\,\text{J}}{\text{kcal}}\right)(13^\circ\text{C})$$

$$+ \left(1.596\times10^5\,\frac{\text{J}}{\text{s}}\right)\left(\frac{26.5^\circ\text{C}}{33^\circ\text{C}}\right)(1800\,\text{s}) = \boxed{2.4\times10^8\,\text{J}}$$

(*c*) We assume a month is 30 days.

$$0.9Q_{gas} = \left(\frac{Q}{t}\right)_{conduction}t_{month} \rightarrow$$

$$Q_{gas} = \frac{1}{0.9}\left(\frac{Q}{t}\right)_{conduction}t_{month} = \frac{1}{0.9}(1.596\times10^5\,\text{J/s})(30\,\text{d})\left(\frac{24\,\text{h}}{1\,\text{d}}\right)\left(\frac{3600\,\text{s}}{1\,\text{h}}\right) = 4.596\times10^{11}\,\text{J}$$

$$4.6\times10^{11}\,\text{J}\left(\frac{1\,\text{kg}}{5.4\times10^7\,\text{J}}\right)\left(\frac{\$0.080}{\text{kg}}\right) = \boxed{\$680}$$

57. (*a*) The bullet will gain an amount of heat equal to 50% of its loss of kinetic energy. Initially assume that the phase of the bullet does not change, so that all of the heat causes a temperature increase.

$$\frac{1}{2}\left[\frac{1}{2}m\left(v_i^2 - v_f^2\right)\right] = Q = mc_{Pb}\Delta T \rightarrow \Delta T = \frac{\frac{1}{4}\left(v_i^2 - v_f^2\right)}{c_{Pb}} = \frac{(220\,\text{m/s})^2 - (160\,\text{m/s})^2}{4(130\,\text{J/kg}\cdot\text{C}^\circ)} = \boxed{44\,\text{C}^\circ}$$

(*b*) The final temperature of the bullet would be about 64°C, which is not above the melting temperature of lead, which is 327°C. Thus none of the bullet will melt.

58. (*a*) The rate of absorbing heat for an object facing the Sun is given by Eq. 14-7. The rise in temperature is related to the absorbed heat by Eq. 14-2. We assume that all absorbed heat raises the temperature of the leaf.

$$\Delta Q = mc\Delta T \qquad \frac{\Delta Q}{\Delta t} = \left(1000\,\text{W}/\text{m}^2\right)eA\cos\theta \;\rightarrow$$

$$\frac{\Delta T}{\Delta t} = \frac{\left(1000\,\text{W}/\text{m}^2\right)eA\cos\theta}{mc} = \frac{\left(1000\,\text{W}/\text{m}^2\right)(0.85)\left(40\,\text{cm}^2\right)\left(\dfrac{1\,\text{m}^2}{1\times10^4\,\text{cm}^2}\right)(1)}{\left(4.5\times10^{-4}\,\text{kg}\right)\left(0.80\,\text{kcal}/\text{kg}\cdot\text{C}^\circ\right)\left(\dfrac{4186\,\text{J}}{1\,\text{kcal}}\right)} = \boxed{2.3\,\text{C}^\circ/\text{s}}$$

(*b*) We assume that the rate of heat loss by radiation must equal the rate of heat absorption of solar energy. Note that the area of the leaf that radiates is twice the area that absorbs heat energy.

$$\left(\frac{\Delta Q}{\Delta t}\right)_{\substack{\text{Solar}\\\text{heating}}} = \left(\frac{\Delta Q}{\Delta t}\right)_{\text{radiation}} \;\rightarrow\; \left(1000\,\text{W}/\text{m}^2\right)eA_{\text{absorb}}\cos\theta = e\sigma A_{\text{radiate}}\left(T_1^4 - T_2^4\right) \;\rightarrow$$

$$T_1 = \left[\frac{\left(1000\,\text{W}/\text{m}^2\right)\cos\theta}{2\sigma} + T_2^4\right]^{1/4} = \left[\frac{\left(1000\,\text{W}/\text{m}^2\right)(1)}{2\left(5.67\times10^{-8}\,\text{W}/\text{m}^2\cdot\text{K}^4\right)} + \left(293\,\text{K}\right)^4\right]^{1/4}$$

$$= 357\,\text{K} = \boxed{84^\circ\text{C}}$$

This is very hot, which indicates that the leaf must lose energy by other means than just radiation.

(*c*) The leaf can also lose heat by $\boxed{\text{conduction}}$ to the cooler air around it; by $\boxed{\text{convection}}$, as the wind continually moves cooler air over the surface of the leaf; and $\boxed{\text{evaporation}}$ of water.

59. The rate of energy absorption from the Sun must be equal to the rate of losing energy by radiation plus the rate of losing energy by evaporation if the leaf is to maintain a steady temperature. The latent heat of evaporation is taken be the value at 20°C, which is 2450 kJ/kg. Also note that the area of the leaf that radiates is twice the area that absorbs heat energy.

$$\left(\frac{\Delta Q}{\Delta t}\right)_{\substack{\text{Solar}\\\text{heating}}} = \left(\frac{\Delta Q}{\Delta t}\right)_{\text{radiation}} + \left(\frac{\Delta Q}{\Delta t}\right)_{\text{evaporation}} \;\rightarrow$$

$$\left(1000\,\text{W}/\text{m}^2\right)eA_{\text{absorb}}\cos\theta = e\sigma A_{\text{radiate}}\left(T_1^4 - T_2^4\right) + \frac{m_{\text{H}_2\text{O}}L_{\text{evaporation}}}{\Delta t} \;\rightarrow$$

$$\frac{m_{\text{H}_2\text{O}}}{\Delta t} = eA_{\text{absorb}}\frac{\left(1000\,\text{W}/\text{m}^2\right)\cos\theta - 2\sigma\left(T_1^4 - T_2^4\right)}{L_{\text{evaporation}}}$$

$$= (0.85)\left(40\times10^{-4}\,\text{m}^2\right)\frac{\left(1000\,\text{W}/\text{m}^2\right)(1) - 2\left(5.67\times10^{-8}\,\text{W}/\text{m}^2\cdot\text{K}^4\right)\left[\left(308\,\text{K}\right)^4 - \left(293\,\text{K}\right)^4\right]}{\left(2.45\times10^6\,\text{J}/\text{kg}\right)}$$

$$= 1.1\times10^{-6}\,\text{kg}/\text{s} = \boxed{4.1\,\text{g}/\text{h}}$$

60. Assume that the final speed of the meteorite, as it completely melts, is 0, and that all of its initial kinetic energy was used in heating the iron to the melting point and then melting the iron.

$$\tfrac{1}{2}mv_i^2 = mc_{\text{Fe}}\left(T_{\text{melt}} - T_i\right) + mL_{\text{fusion}} \;\rightarrow$$

$$v_i = \sqrt{2\left[c_{\text{Fe}}\left(T_{\text{melt}} - T_i\right) + L_{\text{fusion}}\right]} = \sqrt{2\left[\left(450\,\text{J}/\text{kg}\cdot\text{C}^\circ\right)\left(1808^\circ\text{C} - -125^\circ\text{C}\right) + 2.89\times10^5\,\text{J}/\text{kg}\right]}$$

$$= \boxed{1.52\times10^3\,\text{m}/\text{s}}$$

61. (*a*) We consider just the 30 m of crust immediately below the surface of the Earth, assuming that all the heat from the interior gets transferred to the surface, and so it all passes through this 30 m layer. This is a heat conduction problem, and so Eq. 14-4 is appropriate. The radius of the Earth is about 6.38×10^{6} m.

$$\frac{Q}{t} = kA\frac{T_1 - T_2}{l} \rightarrow$$

$$Q_{\text{interior}} = kA\frac{T_1 - T_2}{l}t = \left(0.80\,\text{J}/\text{s} \cdot \text{m} \cdot \text{C}^\circ\right)4\pi R_{\text{Earth}}^2\frac{1.0\,\text{C}^\circ}{30\,\text{m}}\left[1\,\text{day}\left(\frac{86,400\,\text{s}}{\text{day}}\right)\right]$$

$$= 1.179 \times 10^{18}\,\text{J} \approx \boxed{1.2 \times 10^{18}\,\text{J}}$$

(*b*) The cross-sectional area of the Earth, perpendicular to the Sun, is a circle of radius R_{Earth}, and so has an area of πR_{Earth}^2. Multiply this area times the solar constant of $1350\,\text{W}/\text{m}^2$ to get the amount of energy incident on the Earth from the Sun per second, and then convert to energy per day.

$$Q_{\text{Sun}} = \pi R_{\text{Earth}}^2\left(1350\,\text{W}/\text{m}^2\right)\left[1\,\text{day}\left(\frac{86,400\,\text{s}}{\text{day}}\right)\right] = 1.492 \times 10^{22}\,\text{J}$$

Thus $\dfrac{Q_{\text{interior}}}{Q_{\text{Sun}}} = \dfrac{1.179 \times 10^{18}\,\text{J}}{1.492 \times 10^{22}\,\text{J}} = 7.902 \times 10^{-5}$, or $\boxed{Q_{\text{Sun}} = 1.3 \times 10^{4}\,Q_{\text{interior}}}$.

62. Assume that the loss of kinetic energy is all turned into heat which changes the temperature of the squash ball.

$$KE_{\text{lost}} = Q \rightarrow \tfrac{1}{2}m\left(v_i^2 - v_f^2\right) = mc\Delta T \rightarrow \Delta T = \frac{v_i^2 - v_f^2}{2c} = \frac{\left(22\,\text{m}/\text{s}\right)^2 - \left(12\,\text{m}/\text{s}\right)^2}{2\left(1200\,\text{J}/\text{kg} \cdot \text{C}^\circ\right)} = \boxed{0.14\,\text{C}^\circ}$$

63. The heat gained by the ice (to melt it and warm it) must be equal to the heat lost by the steam (in condensing and cooling).

$$mL_{\text{F}} + mc_{\text{H}_2\text{O}}\left(T_{\text{eq}} - 0\right) = mL_{\text{V}} + mc_{\text{H}_2\text{O}}\left(100^\circ\text{C} - T_{\text{eq}}\right)$$

$$T_{\text{eq}} = \frac{L_{\text{V}} - L_{\text{F}}}{2c_{\text{H}_2\text{O}}} + 50^\circ\text{C} = \frac{2260\,\text{kJ}/\text{kg} - 333\,\text{kJ}/\text{kg}}{2\left(4.186\,\text{kJ}/\text{kg} \cdot \text{C}^\circ\right)} + 50^\circ\text{C} = 280^\circ\text{C}$$

This answer is not possible. Because this answer is too high, the steam must not all condense, and none of it must cool below 100°C. Calculate the energy need to melt a kilogram of ice and warm it to 100°C.

$$Q = mL_{\text{F}} + mc_{\text{H}_2\text{O}}\left(T_{\text{eq}} - 0\right) = \left(1\,\text{kg}\right)\left[333\,\text{kJ}/\text{kg} + \left(4.186\,\text{kJ}/\text{kg} \cdot \text{C}^\circ\right)\left(100\,\text{C}^\circ\right)\right] = 751.6\,\text{kJ}$$

Calculate the mass of steam that needs to condense in order to provide this much energy.

$$Q = mL_{\text{V}} \rightarrow m = \frac{Q}{L_{\text{V}}} = \frac{751.6\,\text{kJ}}{2260\,\text{kJ}/\text{kg}} = 0.333\,\text{kg}$$

Thus one-third of the original steam mass must condense to liquid at 100°C in order to melt the ice and warm the melted ice to 100°C. The final mixture will be at 100°C, with 1/3 of the total mass as steam, and 2/3 of the total mass as water.

64. The body's metabolism (blood circulation in particular) provides cooling by convection. If the metabolism has stopped, then heat loss will be by conduction and radiation, at a rate of 200 W, as given. The change in temperature is related to the body's heat loss by Eq. 14-2, $Q = mc\Delta T$.

$$\frac{Q}{t} = P = \frac{mc\Delta T}{t} \rightarrow$$

$$t = \frac{mc\Delta T}{P} = \frac{(70 \text{ kg})(3470 \text{ J/kg}\cdot\text{C}°)(36.6°\text{C} - 35.6°\text{C})}{200 \text{ W}} = \boxed{1200 \text{ s}} = 20 \text{ min}$$

65. (a) The amount of heat energy required is given by Eq. 14-2. 1 L of water has a mass of 1 kg.

$$Q = mc\Delta T = (185 \text{ kg})(4186 \text{ J/kg}\cdot\text{C}°)(50°\text{C} - 10°\text{C}) = 3.098 \times 10^7 \text{ J} \approx \boxed{3.1 \times 10^7 \text{ J}}$$

(b) The heat energy is the power input times the time.

$$Q = Pt \rightarrow t = \frac{Q}{P} = \frac{3.098 \times 10^7 \text{ J}}{9.5 \times 10^3 \text{ W}} = 3260 \text{ s} \approx \boxed{3.3 \times 10^3 \text{ s}} = 54 \text{ min}$$

66. We assume that the light bulb emits energy by radiation, and so Eq. 14-6 applies. Use the data for the 60-W bulb to calculate the product $e\sigma A$ for the bulb, and then calculate the temperature of the 150-W bulb.

$$(Q/t)_{60 \text{ W}} = e\sigma A \left(T_{60 \text{ W}}^4 - T_{room}^4 \right) \rightarrow$$

$$e\sigma A = \frac{(Q/t)_{60 \text{ W}}}{\left(T_{60 \text{ W}}^4 - T_{room}^4 \right)} = \frac{(0.90)(60 \text{ W})}{\left[(273 + 65) \text{ K} \right]^4 - \left[(273 + 18) \text{ K} \right]^4} = 9.182 \times 10^{-9} \text{ W/K}^4$$

$$(Q/t)_{150 \text{ W}} = e\sigma A \left(T_{150 \text{ W}}^4 - T_{room}^4 \right) \rightarrow$$

$$T_{150 \text{ W}} = \left[\frac{(Q/t)_{150 \text{ W}}}{e\sigma A} + T_{room}^4 \right]^{1/4} = \left[\frac{(0.90)(150 \text{ W})}{\left(9.182 \times 10^{-9} \text{ W/K}^4 \right)} + (291 \text{ K})^4 \right]^{1/4}$$

$$= 385 \text{ K} = 112°\text{C} \approx \boxed{110°\text{C}}$$

CHAPTER 15: The Laws of Thermodynamics

Answers to Questions

1. If water vapor condenses on the outside of a cold glass of water, the internal energy of the water vapor has decreased, by an amount equal to the heat of vaporization of the water vapor. Heat energy has left the water vapor, causing it to condense, and heat energy has entered the glass of water, and the air, causing them to get slightly warmer. No work is done, but heat is exchanged.

2. During compression, work is done on the gas. Assuming that there is no heat flow to or from the gas (since the process is quick), by conservation of energy (the first law of thermodynamics) the work done on the gas becomes internal energy of the gas, and so the temperature of the gas is increased. During expansion, work is done by the gas on its surroundings. Again assuming that there is no heat flow to or from the gas, by conservation of energy, the work is done by the gas at the expense of the internal energy of the gas, and so the temperature of the gas is decreased.

3. Since the process is isothermal, there is no change in the internal energy of the gas. Thus $\Delta U = Q - W = 0 \;\rightarrow\; Q = W$, and so the heat absorbed by the gas is equal to the work done by the gas. Thus 3700 J of heat was added to the gas.

4. It is possible for temperature (and thus internal energy) to remain constant in a system even though there is heat flow into or out of the system. By the first law of thermodynamics, there must be an equal amount of work done on or by the system, so that $\Delta U = Q - W = 0 \;\rightarrow\; Q = W$. The isothermal expansion or compression of a gas would be an example of this situation.

5. If the gas is compressed adiabatically, no heat enters or leaves from the gas. The compression means that work was done ON the gas. By the first law of thermodynamics, $\Delta U = Q - W$, since $Q = 0$, then $\Delta U = -W$. The change in internal energy is equal to the opposite of the work done by the gas, or is equal to the work done on the gas. Since positive work was done on the gas, the internal energy of the gas increased, and that corresponds to an increase in temperature. This is conservation of energy – the work done on the gas becomes internal energy of the gas particles, and the temperature increases accordingly.

6. Mechanical energy can be transformed completely into heat. As a moving object slides across a rough level floor and eventually stops, the mechanical energy of the moving object has been transformed completely into heat. Also, if a moving object were to be used to compress a frictionless piston containing an insulated gas, the kinetic energy of the object would become internal energy of the gas. A gas that expands adiabatically (without heat transfer) transforms internal energy into mechanical energy, by doing work on its surroundings at the expense of its internal energy. Of course, that is an ideal (reversible) process.

7. It is possible to warm the kitchen in the winter by having the oven door open. The oven heating elements radiate heat energy into the oven cavity, and if the oven door is open, the oven is just heating a bigger volume than usual. However, you cannot cool the kitchen by having the refrigerator door open. The refrigerator exhausts more heat than it removes from the refrigerated volume, so the room actually gets warmer with the refrigerator door open. If you could have the refrigerator exhaust into some other room, then the refrigerator would be similar to an air conditioner, and it could cool the kitchen, while heating up some other space.

8. This definition of efficiency is not useful, because with this definition, if the exhaust heat Q_L is less than the work done W (which is possible), the "efficiency" would exceed unity. Efficiency should be comparing to the heat input, not the heat output.

9. (*a*) In an internal combustion engine, the high temperature reservoir is the ignited gas-air mixture. The low temperature reservoir is the gases exhausted from the cylinder into the atmosphere.
   (*b*) In a steam engine, the high temperature reservoir is the heated, high-pressure steam from the boiler. The low temperature reservoir is the low-pressure steam from the exhaust.

10. The efficiency of a Carnot engine is given by Eq. 15-5, $e = 1 - \dfrac{T_L}{T_H}$. Both a decrease in T_L and an increase in T_H would cause the value of T_L / T_H to decrease, increasing the efficiency. Since $T_L < T_H$, the 10C° change is a larger percentage of change for T_L, and so will change the fraction more than the same numeric increase in the denominator. Note $e_1 = 1 - \dfrac{T_L - 10}{T_H} = \dfrac{T_H - T_L + 10}{T_H}$ and

    $e_2 = 1 - \dfrac{T_L}{T_H + 10} = \dfrac{T_H - T_L + 10}{T_H + 10}$. Both efficiencies have the same numerator, but e_2 has a larger

    denominator, and so $e_1 > e_2$.

11. To utilize the thermal energy in the ocean waters, a heat engine would need to be developed that operated between two different temperatures. If surface temperature water was to be both the source and the exhaust, then no work could be extracted. If the temperature difference between surface and deep ocean waters were to be used, there would be considerable engineering obstacles, high expense, and potential environmental difficulties involved in having a heat engine that connected surface water and deep ocean water. Likewise, if the difference in temperature between tropical water and arctic or Antarctic water were to be used, the same type of major difficulties would be involved because of the large distances involved.

12. (*a*) If a gas expands adiabatically, there is no heat transfer, and therefore $\Delta S = 0$ by Eq. 15-8, $\Delta S = Q/T$.
   (*b*) If a gas expands isothermally, there is no change in its internal energy, and the gas does work on its surroundings. Thus by the first law of thermodynamics, there must be heat flow into the gas, and so $\Delta S > 0$ – the entropy of the gas increases.

13. The adiabatic expansion results in no change in entropy, since there is no heat transfer. The isothermal expansion requires heat flow into the gas to compensate for the work that the gas does, and so the entropy of the gas $\left(\Delta S = Q/T\right)$ increases more for the isothermal expansion.

14. (*a*) The erosion of soil due to water flow over the ground.
   (*b*) The oxidation of various metals (copper, zinc, iron, etc.) when left exposed to the air.
   (*c*) The conversion of mechanical energy to heat energy by friction; i.e., a sliding object decreasing in speed and eventually stopping, and the surfaces of contact getting warmer.
   (*d*) A pile of compost decomposing.
   The reverse of these processes is not observed.

15. 1 kg of liquid iron has more entropy, because the atoms in liquid iron are less "ordered" than those in solid iron. Also, heat had to be added to solid iron in order to melt it, and $\Delta S = Q/T$.

16. (a) If the lid is removed from a bottle of chlorine gas, the gas molecules will diffuse out of the mouth of the bottle, and eventually spread out uniformly in whatever volume to which they are confined.

    (b) The reverse process, that of individual chlorine gas molecules in a closed volume spontaneously entering a small volume, never happens. The probability of the gas molecules all entering the bottle is infinitesimal compared to the probability of the gas molecules being uniformly spread throughout the room. The reverse process would require a spontaneous decrease in entropy.

    (c) Some other examples of irreversibility: the shuffling of an ordered deck of cards; the diffusion of dye in a liquid; the toppling of buildings during an earthquake.

17. Any air conditioner-type heat engine will remove heat from the room (Q_L – the low temperature input). Work (W) is input to the device to enable it to remove heat from the low temperature region. By the 2nd law of thermodynamics (conservation of energy), there must be a high-temperature exhaust heat Q_H which is larger than Q_L. Perhaps the inventor has some clever method of having that exhaust heat move into a well-insulated heat "sink", like a container of water. But eventually the addition of that heat into the device will cause the device to heat up warmer than the room, and then heat will be transferred to the room. One very simple device that could do what is described in the problem would be a fan blowing over a large block of ice. Heat from the room will enter the ice; cool air from near the surface of the ice can be blown out of the box by a fan. But after the ice melts, the only end result is that the fan motor would heat the air.

18. (a) An empty perfume bottle is placed in a room containing perfume molecules, and all of the perfume molecules move into the bottle from various directions at the same time.

    (b) Water on the sidewalk coalesces into droplets, are propelled upward, and rise into the air.

    (c) Popcorn is placed in the refrigerator, and it "unpops", changing backed into uncooked kernels.

    (d) A house got warmer in the winter while the outdoors got colder, due to heat moving from the outdoors to inside the house.

19. While the state of the papers has gone from disorder to order, they did not do so spontaneously. An outside source (you) caused the increase in order. You had to provide energy to do this (through your metabolic processes), and in doing so, your entropy increased more than the entropy of the papers decreased. The overall effect is that the entropy of the universe increased, satisfying the second law of thermodynamics.

20. The first statement, "You can't get something for nothing," is a whimsical way of saying that energy is conserved. For instance, one way to write the 1st law is $W = Q - \Delta U$. This says that work done by a system must have a source – either heat is input to the system or the internal energy of the system is lowered. It "costs" energy – either heat energy or internal energy – to get work done. Another way to say this is that no heat engine can be built which puts out more energy in the form of work than it extracts in the form of heat or internal energy.

The second statement, "You can't even break even," reflects the fact that a consequence of the 2nd law is that there is no heat engine that is 100% efficient. Even though the 1st law is satisfied by an engine that takes in 100 J of heat and outputs 100 J of work, the 2nd law says that is impossible. If 100 J of heat were taken in, less than 100 J of work can be output from the heat engine, even if it is an ideal heat engine. Some energy will be "lost" as exhaust energy.

21. In an action movie, seeing a building or car go from an exploded state to an un-exploded state. In a movie with vehicle crashes, seeing two collided vehicles separate from each other, becoming un-wrecked as they separate. Watching someone "un-write" something on a piece of paper – moving a pen over paper, taking away written marks as the pen moves.

22. The synthesis of complex molecules from simple molecules does involve a decrease in entropy of the constituent molecules, since they have become more "structured" or "ordered". However, the molecules are not a closed system. This process does not occur spontaneously or in isolation. The living organism in which the synthesis process occurs is part of the environment that must be considered for the overall change in entropy. The living organism will have an increase in entropy that is larger than the decrease in entropy of the molecules, and so overall, the second law is still satisfied, and the entropy of the entire system will increase.

Solutions to Problems

1. Use the first law of thermodynamics, Eq. 15-1, and the definition of internal energy, Eq. 14-1. Since the work is done by the gas, it is positive.

    (a) Since the temperature does not change, $\boxed{\Delta U = 0}$

    (b) $\Delta U = Q - W \rightarrow Q = \Delta U + W = 0 + 3.40 \times 10^3 \, \text{J} = \boxed{3.40 \times 10^3 \, \text{J}}$

2. (a) The work done by a gas at constant pressure is found from Eq. 15-3.

    $$W = P\Delta V = \left(1 \, \text{atm}\right)\left(\frac{1.01 \times 10^5 \, \text{Pa}}{1 \, \text{atm}}\right)\left(18.2 \, \text{m}^3 - 12.0 \, \text{m}^3\right) = 6.262 \times 10^5 \, \text{J} \approx \boxed{6.3 \times 10^5 \, \text{J}}$$

    (b) The change in internal energy is calculated from the first law of thermodynamics

    $$\Delta U = Q - W = \left(1400 \, \text{kcal}\right)\left(\frac{4186 \, \text{J}}{1 \, \text{kcal}}\right) - 6.262 \times 10^5 \, \text{J} = \boxed{5.2 \times 10^6 \, \text{J}}$$

3. For the drawing of the graph, the pressure is given relative to the starting pressure, which is taken to be P_0.

    Segment A is the cooling at constant pressure.

    Segment B is the isothermal expansion.

    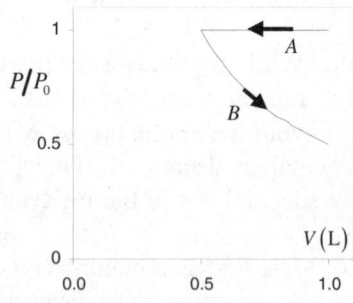

4. Segment A is the compression at constant pressure.

    Segment B is the isothermal expansion.

    Segment C is the pressure increase at constant volume.

    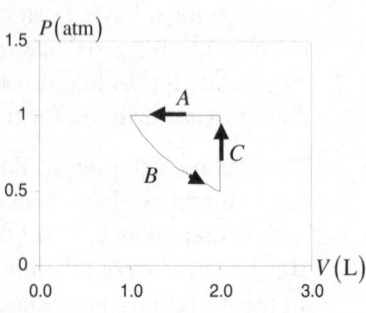

5. Segment *A* is the isothermal expansion. Since the temperature and the amount of gas are constant, the quantity $PV = nRT$ is constant. Since the pressure is reduced by a factor of 4.5, the volume will increase by a factor of 4.5, to a final volume of 4.5 L.

    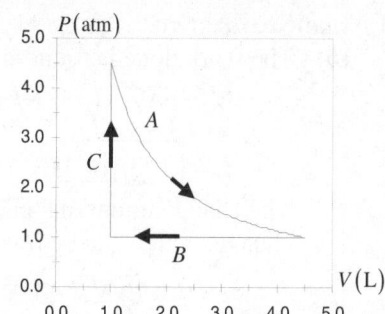

    Segment *B* is the compression at constant pressure.

    Segment *C* is the pressure increase at constant volume.

6. (*a*) Since the container has rigid walls, there is no change in volume.
    $$W = P\Delta V = \boxed{0\ \text{J}}$$
    (*b*) Use the first law of thermodynamics to find the change in internal energy.
    $$\Delta U = Q - W = (-265\ \text{kJ}) - 0 = \boxed{-265\ \text{kJ}}$$

7. (*a*) Since the process is adiabatic, $Q = \boxed{0\ \text{J}}$
    (*b*) Use the first law of thermodynamics to find the change in internal energy.
    $$\Delta U = Q - W = 0 - (-1850\ \text{J}) = \boxed{1850\ \text{J}}$$
    (*c*) Since the internal energy is proportional to the temperature, a rise in internal energy means a $\boxed{\text{rise}}$ in temperature.

8. (*a*) Work is only done in the expansion at constant pressure, since there must be a volume change to have work done.
    $$W = P\Delta V = (3.0\ \text{atm})\left(\frac{1.01\times10^{5}\,\text{Pa}}{1\ \text{atm}}\right)\left(660\times10^{-3}\,\text{L} - 400\times10^{-3}\,\text{L}\right)\frac{1\times10^{-3}\,\text{m}^{3}}{1\ \text{L}} = \boxed{79\ \text{J}}$$
    (*b*) Use the first law of thermodynamics to find the heat flow. Notice that the temperature change over the entire process is 0, so there is no change in internal energy.
    $$\Delta U = Q - W = 0 \quad\rightarrow\quad Q = W = \boxed{79\ \text{J}}$$

9. Since the expansion is adiabatic, there is no heat flow into or out of the gas. Use the first law of thermodynamics to calculate the temperature change.
    $$\Delta U = Q - W \quad\rightarrow\quad \tfrac{3}{2}nR\Delta T = 0 - W \quad\rightarrow$$
    $$\Delta T = -\tfrac{2}{3}\frac{W}{nR} = -\frac{2(7500\ \text{J})}{3(1.5\ \text{mol})(8.315\,\text{J/mol}\cdot\text{K})} = -401\,\text{K} = \boxed{-4.0\times10^{2}\,\text{K}}$$

10. (*a*) No work is done during the first step, since the volume is constant. The work in the second step is given by $W = P\Delta V$.
    $$W = P\Delta V = (1.4\ \text{atm})\left(\frac{1.01\times10^{5}\,\text{Pa}}{1\ \text{atm}}\right)(9.3\,\text{L} - 6.8\,\text{L})\frac{1\times10^{-3}\,\text{m}^{3}}{1\ \text{L}} = \boxed{3.5\times10^{2}\,\text{J}}$$
    (*b*) Since there is no overall change in temperature, $\Delta U = \boxed{0\ \text{J}}$
    (*c*) The heat flow can be found from the first law of thermodynamics.
    $$\Delta U = Q - W \quad\rightarrow\quad Q = \Delta U + W = 0 + 3.5\times10^{2}\,\text{J} = \boxed{3.5\times10^{2}\,\text{J}\ (\text{into the gas})}$$

11. (*a,c*) See diagram.

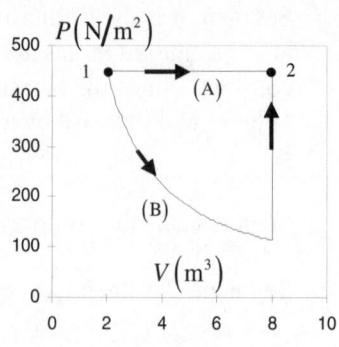

(*b*) The work done is found from Eq. 15-3.

$$W = P\Delta V = \left(455\,\text{N/m}^2\right)\left(8.00\,\text{m}^3 - 2.00\,\text{m}^3\right)$$

$$= \boxed{2.73\times10^3\,\text{J}}$$

The change in internal energy depends on the temperature change, which can be related to the ideal gas law, $PV = nRT$.

$$\Delta U = \tfrac{3}{2}nR\Delta T = \tfrac{3}{2}\left(nRT_2 - nRT_1\right) = \tfrac{3}{2}\left[\left(PV\right)_2 - \left(PV\right)_1\right]$$

$$= \tfrac{3}{2}P\Delta V = \tfrac{3}{2}W = \tfrac{3}{2}\left(2.73\times10^3\,\text{J}\right) = \boxed{4.10\times10^3\,\text{J}}$$

(*d*) The change in internal energy only depends on the initial and final temperatures. Since those temperatures are the same for process (B) as they are for process (A), the internal energy change is the same for process (B) as for process (A), $\boxed{4.10\times10^3\,\text{J}}$.

12. For the path ac, use the first law of thermodynamics to find the change in internal energy.

$$\Delta U_{ac} = Q_{ac} - W_{ac} = -63\,\text{J} - \left(-35\,\text{J}\right) = -28\,\text{J}$$

Since internal energy only depends on the initial and final temperatures, this ΔU applies to any path that starts at a and ends at c. And for any path that starts at c and ends at a, $\Delta U_{ca} = -\Delta U_{ac} = 28\,\text{J}$

(*a*) Use the first law of thermodynamics to find Q_{abc}.

$$\Delta U_{abc} = Q_{abc} - W_{abc} \;\rightarrow\; Q_{abc} = \Delta U_{abc} + W_{abc} = -28\,\text{J} + \left(-48\,\text{J}\right) = \boxed{-76\,\text{J}}$$

(*b*) Since the work along path bc is 0, $W_{abc} = W_{ab} = P_b\Delta V_{ab} = P_b\left(V_b - V_a\right)$. Also note that the work along path da is 0.

$$W_{cda} = W_{cd} = P_c\Delta V_{cd} = P_c\left(V_d - V_c\right) = \tfrac{1}{2}P_b\left(V_a - V_b\right) = -\tfrac{1}{2}W_{abc} = -\tfrac{1}{2}\left(-48\,\text{J}\right) = \boxed{24\,\text{J}}$$

(*c*) Use the first law of thermodynamics to find Q_{abc}.

$$\Delta U_{cda} = Q_{cda} - W_{cda} \;\rightarrow\; Q_{cda} = \Delta U_{cda} + W_{cda} = 28\,\text{J} + 24\,\text{J} = \boxed{52\,\text{J}}$$

(*d*) As found above, $U_c - U_a = \Delta U_{ca} = -\Delta U_{ac} = \boxed{28\,\text{J}}$

(*e*) Since $U_d - U_c = 5\,\text{J} \;\rightarrow\; U_d = U_c + 5\,\text{J} \;\rightarrow\; \Delta U_{da} = U_a - U_d = U_a - U_c - 5\,\text{J} = \Delta U_{ca} - 5\,\text{J} = 23\,\text{J}$. Use the first law of thermodynamics to find Q_{da}.

$$\Delta U_{da} = Q_{da} - W_{da} \;\rightarrow\; Q_{da} = \Delta U_{da} + W_{da} = 23\,\text{J} + 0 = \boxed{23\,\text{J}}$$

13. We are given that $Q_{ac} = -80\,\text{J}$ and $W_{ac} = -55\,\text{J}$.

(*a*) Use the first law of thermodynamics to find $U_a - U_c = \Delta U_{ca}$

$$\Delta U_{ca} = -\Delta U_{ac} = -\left(Q_{ac} - W_{ac}\right) = -\left(-80\,\text{J} - -55\,\text{J}\right) = \boxed{25\,\text{J}}$$

(*b*) Use the first law of thermodynamics to find Q_{cda}.

$$\Delta U_{cda} = Q_{cda} - W_{cda} \;\rightarrow\; Q_{cda} = \Delta U_{cda} + W_{cda} = \Delta U_{ca} + W_{cda} = 25\,\text{J} + 38\,\text{J} = \boxed{63\,\text{J}}$$

(*c*) Since the work along path bc is 0, $W_{abc} = W_{ab} = P_a\Delta V_{ab} = P_a\left(V_b - V_a\right)$.

$$W_{abc} = W_{ab} = P_a\Delta V_{ab} = P_a\left(V_b - V_a\right) = 2.5P_d\left(V_c - V_d\right) = -2.5W_{cda} = -2.5\left(38\,\text{J}\right) = \boxed{-95\,\text{J}}$$

(*d*) Use the first law of thermodynamics to find Q_{abc}

$$\Delta U_{abc} = Q_{abc} - W_{abc} \;\rightarrow\; Q_{abc} = \Delta U_{abc} + W_{abc} = -25\,\text{J} - 95\,\text{J} = \boxed{-120\,\text{J}}$$

(*e*) Since $U_a - U_b = 10\text{ J} \rightarrow U_b = U_a - 10\text{ J}$, we have the following.

$$\Delta U_{bc} = U_c - U_b = U_c - (U_a - 10\text{ J}) = \Delta U_{ac} + 10\text{ J} = -25\text{ J} + 10\text{ J} = -15\text{ J}.$$

Use the first law of thermodynamics to find Q_{bc}.

$$\Delta U_{bc} = Q_{bc} - W_{bc} \rightarrow Q_{bc} = \Delta U_{bc} + W_{bc} = -15\text{ J} + 0 = \boxed{-15\text{ J}}$$

14. In Example 15-8, the total energy transformed was $1.15 \times 10^7\text{ J}$. We will subtract away the energy for 1 hour of desk work and add in the energy for 1 hour of running.

$$\text{Energy} = 1.15 \times 10^7\text{ J} + [-115\text{ J/s} + 1150\text{ J/s}](3600\text{ s/h}) = \boxed{1.52 \times 10^7\text{ J}} \approx 3600\text{ Cal}$$

15. Follow the pattern set in Example 15-8. Find the average rate by dividing the total energy for the day by 24 hours.

$$\text{Avg. Energy} = \left[\begin{array}{l}(8.0\text{ h})(70\text{ J/s}) + (8.0\text{ h})(115\text{ J/s}) + (4.0\text{ h})(230\text{ J/s}) \\ + (2.0\text{ h})(115\text{ J/s}) + (1.5\text{ h})(460\text{ J/s}) + (0.5\text{ h})(1150\text{ J/s})\end{array}\right] \Big/ 24\text{ h} = \boxed{1.62 \times 10^2\text{ W}}$$

16. From Table 15-2, the change in metabolic rate if one hour of sleeping is exchanged for light activity is an addition of 230 watts – 70 watts = 160 watts. Note that this increased rate is only applicable for one hour per day.

$$\left(160\frac{\text{J}}{\text{s}}\right)\left(\frac{3600\text{ s}}{1\text{ h}}\right)\left(\frac{1\text{ h}}{\text{day}}\right)\left(\frac{365\text{ day}}{1\text{ y}}\right)\left(\frac{1\text{ kg fat}}{4 \times 10^7\text{ J}}\right) = 5.256\text{ kg} \approx \boxed{5.3\text{ kg}}\left(\frac{2.20\text{ lb}}{1\text{ kg}}\right) = \boxed{12\text{ lbs}}$$

17. The efficiency of a heat engine is given by Eq. 15-4.

$$e = \frac{W}{Q_\text{H}} = \frac{W}{W + Q_\text{L}} = \frac{3200\text{ J}}{3200\text{ J} + 8200\text{ J}} = 0.28 = \boxed{28\%}$$

18. The efficiency of a heat engine is given by Eq. 15-4.

$$e = \frac{W}{Q_\text{H}} = \frac{9200\text{ J}}{(22.0\text{ kcal})(4186\text{ J/kcal})} = 0.10 = \boxed{10\%}$$

19. The maximum (or Carnot) efficiency is given by Eq. 15-5, with temperatures in Kelvins.

$$e = 1 - \frac{T_\text{L}}{T_\text{H}} = 1 - \frac{(380 + 273)\text{ K}}{(580 + 273)\text{ K}} = 0.23 = \boxed{23\%}$$

20. The Carnot efficiency is given by Eq. 15-5, with temperatures in Kelvins.

$$e = 1 - \frac{T_\text{L}}{T_\text{H}} \rightarrow T_\text{H} = \frac{T_\text{L}}{1 - e} = \frac{(230 + 273)\text{ K}}{1 - 0.28} = 699\text{ K} = 426°\text{C} \approx \boxed{430°\text{C}}$$

21. The maximum (or Carnot) efficiency is given by Eq. 15-5, with temperatures in Kelvins.

$$e = 1 - \frac{T_\text{L}}{T_\text{H}} = 1 - \frac{(350 + 273)\text{ K}}{(625 + 273)\text{ K}} = 0.306$$

Thus the total power generated can be found as follows.

$$\text{Actual Power} = (\text{Total Power})(\text{max. eff.})(\text{operating eff.}) \rightarrow$$

$$\text{Total Power} = \frac{\text{Actual Power}}{(\text{max. eff.})(\text{operating eff.})} = \frac{1.3\,\text{GW}}{(0.306)(0.75)} = 5.664\,\text{GW}$$

$$\text{Exhaust Power} = \text{Total Power} - \text{Actual Power} = 5.664\,\text{GW} - 1.3\,\text{GW} = 4.364\,\text{GW}$$

$$= (4.364 \times 10^9\,\text{J/s})(3600\,\text{s/h}) = \boxed{1.6 \times 10^{13}\,\text{J/h}}$$

22. Calculate the Carnot efficiency for the given temperatures.

$$e_{\text{ideal}} = 1 - \frac{T_L}{T_H} = 1 - \frac{77\,\text{K}}{293\,\text{K}} = 0.7372 \approx \boxed{74\%}$$

23. This is a perfect Carnot engine, and so its efficiency is given by Eqs. 15-4 and 15-5. Equate these two expressions for the efficiency.

$$e = 1 - \frac{T_L}{T_H} = \frac{W}{Q_H} \quad \rightarrow$$

$$T_L = T_H\left(1 - \frac{W}{Q_H}\right) = T_H\left(1 - \frac{W/t}{Q_H/t}\right) = \left[(570 + 273)\,\text{K}\right]\left(1 - \frac{4.4 \times 10^5\,\text{J/s}}{(680\,\text{kcal/s})(4186\,\text{J/kcal})}\right)$$

$$= 713\,\text{K} = \boxed{440°\text{C}}$$

24. This is a perfect Carnot engine, and so its efficiency is given by Eqs. 15-4 and 15-5. Use these two expressions to solve for the rate of heat output.

$$e = 1 - \frac{T_L}{T_H} = 1 - \frac{(45 + 273)\,\text{K}}{(210 + 273)\,\text{K}} = 0.3416 \qquad e = \frac{W}{Q_H} = \frac{W}{W + Q_L} \quad \rightarrow \quad Q_L = W(1/e - 1)$$

$$Q_L/t = W/t(1/e - 1) = (950\,\text{W})(1/0.3416 - 1) = \boxed{1.83 \times 10^3\,\text{W}}$$

25. The efficiency of a heat engine is given by Eq. 15-4.

$$e = \frac{W}{Q_H} = \frac{W}{W + Q_L} \quad \rightarrow \quad Q_L = W(1/e - 1) \quad \rightarrow$$

$$Q_L/t = W/t(1/e - 1) = (550\,\text{MW})(1/0.38 - 1) = \boxed{9.0 \times 10^2\,\text{MW}}$$

26. Find the exhaust temperature from the original Carnot efficiency, and then recalculate the intake temperature for the new Carnot efficiency, using the same exhaust temperature.

$$e_1 = 1 - \frac{T_L}{T_{H1}} \quad \rightarrow \quad T_L = T_{H1}(1 - e) = (550 + 273)\,\text{K}(1 - 0.28) = 592.6\,\text{K}$$

$$e_2 = 1 - \frac{T_L}{T_{H2}} \quad \rightarrow \quad T_{H2} = \frac{T_L}{1 - e_2} = \frac{592.6\,\text{K}}{1 - 0.35} = 912\,\text{K} = 639°\text{C} \approx \boxed{640°\text{C}}$$

27. Find the intake temperature from the original Carnot efficiency, and then recalculate the exhaust temperature for the new Carnot efficiency, using the same intake temperature.

$$e_1 = 1 - \frac{T_{L1}}{T_H} \quad \rightarrow \quad T_H = \frac{T_{L1}}{1 - e_1} = \frac{(350 + 273)\,\text{K}}{1 - 0.39} = 1021\,\text{K}$$

$$e_2 = 1 - \frac{T_{L2}}{T_H} \rightarrow T_{L2} = T_H(1-e_2) = (1021\text{ K})(1-0.49) = 521\text{ K} = 248°\text{C} \approx \boxed{250°\text{C}}$$

28. For each engine, the efficiency is given by $e = 0.60e_{Carnot}$. Thus

$$e_1 = 0.6e_{C-1} = 0.60\left(1 - \frac{T_{L1}}{T_{H1}}\right) = 0.60\left[1 - \frac{(440+273)\text{K}}{(670+273)\text{K}}\right] = 0.146$$

$$e_2 = 0.6e_{C-2} = 0.60\left(1 - \frac{T_{L2}}{T_{H2}}\right) = 0.60\left[1 - \frac{(290+273)\text{K}}{(430+273)\text{K}}\right] = 0.119$$

For the first engine, the input heat is from the coal.

$$W_1 = e_1 Q_{H1} = e_1 Q_{coal} \text{ and } Q_{L1} = Q_{H1} - W_1 = (1-e_1)Q_{coal}.$$

For the second energy, the input heat is the output heat from the first engine.

$$W_2 = e_2 Q_{H2} = e_2 Q_{L1} = e_2(1-e_1)Q_{coal}$$

Add the two work expressions together, and solve for Q_{coal}.

$$W_1 + W_2 = e_1 Q_{coal} + e_2(1-e_1)Q_{coal} = (e_1 + e_2 - e_1 e_2)Q_{coal}$$

$$Q_{coal} = \frac{W_1 + W_2}{e_1 + e_2 - e_1 e_2} \rightarrow Q_{coal}/t = \frac{(W_1 + W_2)/t}{e_1 + e_2 - e_1 e_2}$$

Calculate the rate of coal use from the required rate of input energy, Q_{coal}/t.

$$Q_{coal}/t = \frac{1100 \times 10^6\text{ W}}{0.146 + 0.119 - (0.146)(0.119)} = 4.442 \times 10^9\text{ J/s}$$

$$(4.442 \times 10^9\text{ J/s})\left(\frac{1\text{ kg}}{2.8 \times 10^7\text{ J}}\right) = 158.6\text{ kg/s} \approx \boxed{1.6 \times 10^2\text{ kg/s}}$$

29. The coefficient of performance for a refrigerator is given by Eq. 15-6c, with temperatures in Kelvins.

$$\text{COP} = \frac{T_L}{T_H - T_L} = \frac{(-15+273)\text{K}}{(30+273)\text{K} - (-15+273)\text{K}} = \boxed{5.7}$$

30. The coefficient of performance for a refrigerator is given by Eq. 15-6c, with temperatures in Kelvins.

$$\text{COP} = \frac{T_L}{T_H - T_L} \rightarrow T_L = T_H\left(\frac{\text{COP}}{1+\text{COP}}\right) = [(24+273)\text{K}]\left(\frac{7.0}{8.0}\right) = 259.9\text{K} \approx \boxed{-13°\text{C}}$$

31. The coefficient of performance for a refrigerator is given by Eq. 15-6c, with temperatures in Kelvins. Use that expression to find the temperature inside the refrigerator.

$$\text{COP} = \frac{T_L}{T_H - T_L} \rightarrow T_L = T_H\frac{\text{COP}}{1+\text{COP}} = [(29+273)\text{K}]\frac{5.0}{6.0} = 252\text{ K} = \boxed{-21°\text{C}}$$

$\boxed{32.}$ The efficiency of a perfect Carnot engine is given by Eqs. 15-4 and 15-5. Equate these two expressions to solve for the work required.

$$e = 1 - \frac{T_L}{T_H} = \text{ ; } e = \frac{W}{Q_H} \rightarrow 1 - \frac{T_L}{T_H} = \frac{W}{Q_H} \rightarrow W = Q_H\left(1 - \frac{T_L}{T_H}\right)$$

(*a*) $\quad W = Q_H \left(1 - \dfrac{T_L}{T_H} \right) = 2800 \text{ J} \left(1 - \dfrac{0+273}{22+273} \right) = \boxed{210 \text{ J}}$

(*b*) $\quad W = Q_H \left(1 - \dfrac{T_L}{T_H} \right) = 2800 \text{ J} \left(1 - \dfrac{-15+273}{22+273} \right) = \boxed{350 \text{ J}}$

33. The heat to be removed, Q_L, is the latent heat of fusion for the ice, so $Q_L = mL_{\text{fusion}} = V_{H2O}\rho_{H2O}L_{\text{fusion}}$.

    The work done in one hour is 1.0 kilowatt-hour. The COP for a refrigerator is $\text{COP} = \dfrac{Q_L}{W}$, and so

    $Q_L = (\text{COP})W$. Equate the two expressions for Q_L and solve for the volume.

    $(\text{COP})W = V_{H_2O}\rho_{H_2O}L_{\text{fusion}} \quad \rightarrow$

$$m = \frac{(\text{COP})W}{\rho_{H_2O}L_{\text{fusion}}} = \frac{(7.0)\left(1.0\times10^3\,\text{watt}-\text{hour}\right)\left(\dfrac{3600\text{ s}}{1\text{ hour}}\right)}{\left(1.00\times10^3\text{ kg/m}^3\right)\left(3.33\times10^5\text{ J/kg}\right)}\left(\frac{1\text{ L}}{1.0\times10^{-3}\text{ m}^3}\right) = \boxed{76\text{ L}}$$

34. The COP for a heat pump is $\text{COP} = \dfrac{Q_H}{W}$ and the efficiency is $e = \dfrac{W}{Q_H}$. Thus they are reciprocals of each other. So if the efficiency is 0.35, the COP is $\dfrac{1}{0.35} = \boxed{2.9}$.

35. Heat energy is taken away from the water, so the change in entropy will be negative. The heat transfer is the mass of the steam times the latent heat of vaporization.

$$\Delta S = \frac{Q}{T} = -\frac{mL_{\text{vap}}}{T} = -\frac{(0.25\text{ kg})\left(22.6\times10^5\text{ J/kg}\right)}{(273+100)\text{ K}} = \boxed{-1.5\times10^3\text{ J/K}}$$

36. The heat added to the water is found from $\Delta Q = mc\Delta T$. Use the average temperature of $50°\text{C}$ in the approximate entropy calculation.

$$\Delta S = \frac{Q}{T} = \frac{mc\Delta T}{T} = \frac{(1.00\text{ kg})\left(4186\text{ J/kg}\cdot\text{C}°\right)\left(100\text{C}°\right)}{(273+50)\text{ K}} = \boxed{1.30\times10^3\text{ J/K}}$$

37. Heat energy is taken away from the water, so the change in entropy will be negative. The heat taken away from the water is found from $\Delta Q = mL_{\text{fusion}}$. Note that 1.00 m^3 of water has a mass of $1.00\times10^3\text{ kg}$.

$$\Delta S = \frac{Q}{T} = -\frac{mL_{\text{fusion}}}{T} = -\frac{\left(1.00\times10^3\text{ kg}\right)\left(3.33\times10^5\text{ J/kg}\right)}{273\text{ K}} = \boxed{-1.22\times10^6\text{ J/K}}$$

38. There are three terms of entropy to consider. First, there is a loss of entropy from the water for the freezing process, ΔS_1. Second, there is a loss of entropy from that newly-formed ice as it cools to $-10°\text{C}$, ΔS_2. That process has an "average" temperature of $-5°\text{C}$. Finally, there is a gain of entropy by the "great deal of ice", ΔS_3, as the heat lost from the original mass of water in steps 1 and 2 goes

into that great deal of ice. Since it is a large quantity of ice, we assume that its temperature does not change during the processes.

$$\Delta S_1 = \frac{Q_1}{T_1} = -\frac{mL_{\text{fusion}}}{T_1} = -\frac{\left(1.00\times10^3\,\text{kg}\right)\left(3.33\times10^5\,\text{J/kg}\right)}{273\,\text{K}} = -1.2198\times10^6\,\text{J/K}$$

$$\Delta S_2 = \frac{Q_2}{T_2} = -\frac{mc_{ice}\Delta T_2}{T_2} = -\frac{\left(1.00\times10^3\,\text{kg}\right)\left(2100\,\text{J/kg}\cdot\text{C}^\circ\right)\left(10\text{C}^\circ\right)}{\left(-5+273\right)\text{K}} = -7.8358\times10^4\,\text{J/K}$$

$$\Delta S_3 = \frac{Q_3}{T_3} = \frac{-Q_1 - Q_2}{T_3} = \frac{mL_{\text{fusion}} + mc_{ice}\Delta T_2}{T_3}$$

$$= \frac{\left(1.00\times10^3\,\text{kg}\right)\left[\left(3.33\times10^5\,\text{J/kg}\right) + \left(2100\,\text{J/kg}\cdot\text{C}^\circ\right)\left(10\text{C}^\circ\right)\right]}{\left(-10+273\right)\text{K}} = 1.3460\times10^6\,\text{J/K}$$

$$\Delta S = \Delta S_1 + \Delta S_2 + \Delta S_3 = -1.2198\times10^6\,\text{J/K} - 7.8358\times10^4\,\text{J/K} + 1.3460\times10^6\,\text{J/K}$$

$$= 4.784\times10^4\,\text{J/K} \approx \boxed{5\times10^4\,\text{J/K}}$$

39. Energy has been made "unavailable" in the frictional stopping of the sliding box. We take that "lost" kinetic energy as the heat term of the entropy calculation.

$$\Delta S = Q/T = \tfrac{1}{2}mv_i^2/T = \tfrac{1}{2}\left(10.0\,\text{kg}\right)\left(3.0\,\text{m/s}\right)^2/293\,\text{K} = \boxed{0.15\,\text{J/K}}$$

Since this is a decrease in "availability", the entropy of the universe has increased.

40. Take the energy transfer to use as the initial kinetic energy of the rock, because this energy becomes "unusable" after the collision – it is transferred to the environment. We assume that the rock and the environment are both at temperature T_0.

$$\Delta S = Q/T \quad \rightarrow \quad \boxed{\Delta S = KE/T_0}$$

41. The same amount of heat that leaves the high temperature heat source enters the low temperature body of water.

$$\Delta S = \Delta S_1 + \Delta S_2 = -\frac{Q}{T_{\text{high}}} + \frac{Q}{T_{\text{low}}} = Q\left(\frac{1}{T_{\text{low}}} - \frac{1}{T_{\text{high}}}\right) \quad \rightarrow$$

$$\frac{\Delta S}{t} = \frac{Q}{t}\left(\frac{1}{T_{\text{low}}} - \frac{1}{T_{\text{high}}}\right) = \left(7.50\,\text{cal/s}\right)\left(\frac{4.186\,\text{J}}{1\text{cal}}\right)\left(\frac{1}{\left(27+273\right)\text{K}} - \frac{1}{\left(240+273\right)\,\text{K}}\right)$$

$$= \boxed{4.35\times10^{-2}\,\frac{\text{J/K}}{\text{s}}}$$

42. The same amount of heat that leaves the high temperature water will enter the low temperature water. Since the two masses of water are the same, the equilibrium temperature will be the midpoint between the two initial temperatures, 45°C. The cool water average temperature is $\left(30^\circ\text{C} + 45^\circ\text{C}\right)/2 = 37.5^\circ\text{C}$, and the warm water average temperature is $\left(60^\circ\text{C} + 45^\circ\text{C}\right)/2 = 52.5^\circ\text{C}$.

$$\Delta S = \Delta S_1 + \Delta S_2 = -\frac{Q}{T_{\text{high}}} + \frac{Q}{T_{\text{low}}} = mc\Delta T\left(\frac{1}{T_{\text{low}}} - \frac{1}{T_{\text{high}}}\right)$$

$$= (1.0 \text{ kg})(4186 \text{ J/kg·C}^\circ)(15\text{C}^\circ)\left(\frac{1}{(37.5+273)\text{ K}} - \frac{1}{(52.5+273)\text{ K}}\right) = \boxed{9.3 \text{ J/K}}$$

43. The equilibrium temperature is found using calorimetry, from chapter 14. The heat lost by the aluminum is equal to the heat gained by the water.

$$m_{Al}c_{Al}\left(T_{iAl} - T_f\right) = m_{H_2O}c_{H_2O}\left(T_f - T_{iH_2O}\right) \quad \rightarrow$$

$$T_f = \frac{m_{Al}c_{Al}T_{iAl} + m_{H_2O}c_{H_2O}T_{iH_2O}}{m_{Al}c_{Al} + m_{H_2O}c_{H_2O}}$$

$$= \frac{(3.8 \text{ kg})(900 \text{ J/kg·C}^\circ)(30.0^\circ\text{C}) + (1.0 \text{ kg})(4186 \text{ J/kg·C}^\circ)(20^\circ\text{C})}{(3.8 \text{ kg})(900 \text{ J/kg·C}^\circ) + (1.0 \text{ kg})(4186 \text{ J/kg·C}^\circ)} = 24.5^\circ\text{C}$$

The amount of heat lost by the aluminum, and gained by the water, is

$$Q = m_{H_2O}c_{H_2O}\left(T_f - T_{iH_2O}\right) = (1.0 \text{ kg})(4186 \text{ J/kg·C}^\circ)(24.5^\circ\text{C} - 20^\circ\text{C}) = 1.9 \times 10^4 \text{ J}$$

In calculating the entropy change, we will need to use estimates for the temperatures of the water and the aluminum since their temperatures are not constant. We will use their average temperatures.

$$T_{H_2O}_{\text{avg}} = (20^\circ\text{C} + 24.5^\circ\text{C})/2 = 22.25^\circ\text{C} \qquad T_{Al}_{\text{avg}} = (30^\circ\text{C} + 24.5^\circ\text{C})/2 = 27.25^\circ\text{C}$$

$$\Delta S = \Delta S_{Al} + \Delta S_{H_2O} = -\frac{Q}{T_{Al}_{\text{avg}}} + \frac{Q}{T_{H_2O}_{\text{avg}}} = (1.9 \times 10^4 \text{ J})\left(\frac{1}{(22.25+273)\text{ K}} - \frac{1}{(27.25+273)\text{ K}}\right) = \boxed{1.1 \text{ J/K}}$$

44. (a) $e_{\text{actual}} = W/Q_H = 550 \text{ J}/2200 \text{ J} = 0.250 \qquad e_{\text{ideal}} = 1 - T_L/T_H = 1 - 650 \text{ K}/970 \text{ K} = 0.330$

Thus $e_{\text{actual}}/e_{\text{ideal}} = 0.250/0.330 = 0.758 \approx \boxed{76\% \text{ of ideal}}$

(b) The heat reservoirs do not change temperature during the operation of the engine. There is an entropy loss from the input reservoir, because it loses heat, and an entropy gain for the output reservoir, because it gains heat. Note that $Q_L = Q_H - W = 2200 \text{ J} - 550 \text{ J} = 1650 \text{ J}$.

$$\Delta S = \Delta S_{\text{input}} + \Delta S_{\text{output}} = -\frac{Q_H}{T_H} + \frac{Q_L}{T_L} = -\frac{2200 \text{ J}}{970 \text{ K}} + \frac{1650 \text{ J}}{650 \text{ K}} = \boxed{0.27 \text{ J/K}}$$

(c) For the Carnot engine, the exhaust energy will be $Q_L = Q_H\left(1 - e_{\text{Carnot}}\right) = Q_H T_L/T_H$.

$$\Delta S = \Delta S_{\text{input}} + \Delta S_{\text{output}} = -\frac{Q_H}{T_H} + \frac{Q_L}{T_L} = -\frac{Q_H}{T_H} + \frac{Q_H T_L/T_H}{T_L} = -\frac{Q_H}{T_H} + \frac{Q_H}{T_H} = \boxed{0}$$

A numeric calculation might give a very small number due to not keeping all digits in the calculation.

45. When throwing two dice, there are 36 possible microstates.

(a) The possible microstates that give a total of 5 are: (1)(4), (2)(3), (3)(2), and (4)(1). Thus the probability of getting a 5 is $4/36 = \boxed{1/9}$.

(b) The possible microstates that give a total of 11 are: (5)(6) and (6)(5). Thus the probability of getting an 11 is $2/36 = \boxed{1/18}$.

46. A macrostate is a set of 5 cards from the deck, as given in the problem. For example, four aces and a king is a macrostate. Two jacks, two queens, and an ace is a macrostate. A microstate is a specific set of cards that meets the criterion of a certain macrostate. For example, the set (ace of spades, ace of clubs, ace of hearts, ace of diamonds, king of spades) is a microstate of the macrostate of 4 aces and a king. The problem then is asking for the relative number of microstates for the 4 given macrostates.

   (*a*) There are only 4 microstates for this macrostate, corresponding to the particular suit to which the king belongs.

   (*b*) Since every card is specified, there is only 1 microstate for this macrostate.

   (*c*) There are 6 possible jack pairs, (spade/club, spade/heart, spade/diamond, club/heart, club/diamond, and heart/diamond), 6 possible queen pairs, and 4 possible aces, so there are 6 x 6 x 4 = 144 card combinations or 144 microstates for this macrostate.

   (*d*) There are 52 possibilities for the first card, 48 possibilities for the second card, and so on. It is apparent that there are many more microstates for this macrostate than for any of the other listed macrostates.

Thus in order of increasing probability, we have (b), (a), (c), (d).

47. From the table below, we see that there are a total of $2^6 = 64$ microstates.

Macrostate	Possible Microstates (H = heads, T = tails)						Number of microstates
6 heads, 0 tails	H H H H H						1
5 heads, 1 tails	H H H H T	H H H H T H	H H H T H H	H H T H H H	H T H H H H	T H H H H H	6
4 heads, 2 tails	H H H H T T	H H H T H T	H H T H H T	H T H H H T	T H H H H T		15
	H H H T T H	H H T H T H	H T H H T H	T H H H T H	H H T T H H		
	H T H T H H	T H H T H H	H T T H H H	T H T H H H	T T H H H H		
3 heads, 3 tails	H H H T T T	H H T H T T	H T H H T T	T H H H T T	H H T T H T		20
	H T H T H T	T H H T H T	H T T H H T	T H T H H T	T T H H H T		
	T T T H H H	T T H T H H	T H T T H H	H T T T H H	T T H H T H		
	T H T H T H	H T T H T H	T H H T T H	H T H T T H	H H T T T H		
2 heads, 4 tails	T T T T H H	T T T H T H	T T H T T H	T H T T T H	H T T T T H		15
	T H T H T T	H T T H T T	T H H T T T	H T H T T T	H H T T T T		
1 heads, 5 tails	T T T T T H	T T T T H T	T T T H T T	T T H T T T	T H T T T T	H T T T T T	6
0 heads, 6 tails	T T T T T T						1

   (*a*) The probability of obtaining three heads and three tails is 20/64 .

   (*b*) The probability of obtaining six heads is 1/64 .

48. The required area is $\left(22\dfrac{10^3\,\text{W}\cdot\text{h}}{\text{day}}\right)\left(\dfrac{1\,\text{day}}{9\,\text{h Sun}}\right)\left(\dfrac{1\,\text{m}^2}{40\,\text{W}}\right) = \boxed{61\,\text{m}^2}$. A small house with 1000 ft^2 of floor

space, and a roof tilted at 30°, would have a roof area of $\left(1000\,\text{ft}^2\right)\left(\dfrac{1}{\cos 30^\circ}\right)\left(\dfrac{1\,\text{m}}{3.28\,\text{ft}}\right)^2 = 110\,\text{m}^2$,

which is about twice the area needed, and so the cells would fit on the house . But not all parts of the roof would have 9 hours of sunlight, so more than the minimum number of cells would be needed.

49. (*a*) Assume that there are no dissipative forces present, and so the energy required to pump the
    water to the lake is just the gravitational potential energy of the water.

    $$U_{\text{grav}} = mgh = \left(1.00 \times 10^5 \text{ kg/s}\right)\left(10.0 \text{ h}\right)\left(9.80 \text{ m/s}^2\right)\left(135 \text{ m}\right) = 1.323 \times 10^9 \text{ W} \cdot \text{h}$$

    $$\approx \boxed{1.32 \times 10^6 \text{ kWh}}$$

    (*b*) $$\frac{\left(1.323 \times 10^6 \text{ kW} \cdot \text{h}\right)\left(0.75\right)}{14 \text{ h}} = \boxed{7.1 \times 10^4 \text{ kW}}$$

50. We assume that the electrical energy comes from the 100% effective conversion of the gravitational
     potential energy of the water.

    $$W = mgh \quad \rightarrow$$

    $$P = \frac{W}{t} = \frac{m}{t} gh = \rho \frac{V}{t} gh = \left(1.00 \times 10^3 \text{ kg/m}^3\right)\left(35 \text{ m}^3/\text{s}\right)\left(9.8 \text{ m/s}^2\right)\left(45 \text{ m}\right) = \boxed{1.5 \times 10^7 \text{ W}}$$

51. According to the heat figures provided by the inventor, the engine is 50% efficient:

    $$e = \frac{W}{Q_{\text{H}}} = \frac{W/t}{Q_{\text{H}}/t} = \frac{1.50 \text{ MW}}{3.00 \text{ MW}} = 0.500$$

    The ideal engine efficiency at the operating temperatures is given by Eq. 15-5.

    $$e_{\text{ideal}} = 1 - \frac{T_{\text{L}}}{T_{\text{H}}} = 1 - \frac{215 \text{ K}}{425 \text{ K}} = 0.494$$

    Thus his engine is not possible, even if it were ideal. So $\boxed{\text{yes}}$, there is something "fishy" about his
    claim. His engine is better than ideal.

52. (*a*) The work done at constant pressure is $W = P\Delta V$.

    $$W = P\Delta V$$

    $$= \left(1.00 \text{ atm}\right)\left(1.01 \times 10^5 \text{ Pa/atm}\right)\left(4.1 \text{ m}^3 - 1.9 \text{ m}^3\right)$$

    $$= 2.22 \times 10^5 \text{ J} \approx \boxed{2.2 \times 10^5 \text{ J}}$$

    (*b*) Use the first law of thermodynamics.

    $$\Delta U = Q - W = 5.30 \times 10^5 \text{ J} - 2.22 \times 10^5 \text{ J} = \boxed{3.1 \times 10^5 \text{ J}}$$

    (*c*) See the adjacent graph.

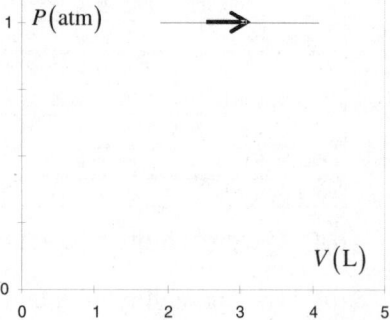

53. (*a*) $\text{Work/s} = \left(\dfrac{220 \text{ J}}{\text{cycle} \cdot \text{cylinder}}\right)\left(\dfrac{45 \text{ cycles}}{\text{s}}\right)\left(4 \text{ cylinders}\right) = 3.96 \times 10^4 \text{ J/s} \approx \boxed{4.0 \times 10^4 \text{ J/s}}$

    (*b*) $e = \dfrac{W}{Q_{\text{H}}} \rightarrow Q_{\text{H}} = \dfrac{W}{e} \rightarrow Q_{\text{H}}/t = \dfrac{W/t}{e} = \dfrac{3.96 \times 10^4 \text{ J/s}}{0.25} = 1.584 \times 10^5 \text{ J/s} \approx \boxed{1.6 \times 10^5 \text{ J/s}}$

    (*c*) $\left(1.0 \text{ L}\right)\left(\dfrac{35 \times 10^6 \text{ J}}{1 \text{ L}}\right)\left(\dfrac{1 \text{ s}}{1.584 \times 10^5 \text{ J}}\right) = \boxed{220 \text{ s}} = 3.7 \text{ min}$

54. (*a*) The heat that must be removed from the water $\left(Q_{\text{L}}\right)$ is found in three parts – cooling the liquid
    water to the freezing point, freezing the liquid water, and then cooling the ice to the final
    temperatures.

$$Q_L = m\left(c_{liquid}\Delta T_{liquid} + L_{fusion} + c_{ice}\Delta T_{ice}\right)$$

$$= \left(0.50\,\text{kg}\right)\left[\begin{array}{c}\left(4186\,\text{J/kg}\cdot\text{C}^\circ\right)\left(25\text{C}^\circ\right)+\left(3.33\times10^5\,\text{J/kg}\right)\\ +\left(2100\,\text{J/kg}\cdot\text{C}^\circ\right)\left(17\text{C}^\circ\right)\end{array}\right] = 2.367\times10^5\,\text{J}$$

The Carnot efficiency can be used to find the work done by the refrigerator.

$$e = 1 - \frac{T_L}{T_H} = \frac{W}{Q_H} = \frac{W}{W + Q_L} \quad\rightarrow$$

$$W = Q_L\left(\frac{T_H}{T_L}-1\right) = \left(2.367\times10^5\,\text{J}\right)\left(\frac{(25+273)\,\text{K}}{(-17+273)\,\text{K}}-1\right) = 3.883\times10^4\,\text{J} \approx \boxed{3.9\times10^4\,\text{J}}$$

(b)   Use the compressor wattage to calculate the time.

$$P = W/t \quad\rightarrow\quad t = W/P = 3.883\times10^4\,\text{J}/210\,\text{W} = 184.9\,\text{s} \approx \boxed{3.1\,\text{min}}$$

55. (a)   Calculate the Carnot efficiency for an engine operated between the given temperatures.

$$e_{ideal} = 1 - \frac{T_L}{T_H} = 1 - \frac{(273+4)\,\text{K}}{(273+27)\,\text{K}} = 0.077 = \boxed{7.7\%}$$

(b)   Such an engine might be feasible in spite of the low efficiency because of the large volume of "fuel" (ocean water) available. Ocean water would appear to be an "inexhaustible" source of heat energy.

(c)   The pumping of water between radically different depths would probably move smaller sea-dwelling creatures from their natural location, perhaps killing them in the transport process. Mixing the water at different temperatures will also disturb the environment of sea-dwelling creatures. There is a significant dynamic of energy exchange between the ocean and the atmosphere, and so any changing of surface temperature water might affect at least the local climate, and perhaps also cause larger-scale climate changes.

56. Take the energy transfer to use as the initial kinetic energy of the cars, because this energy becomes "unusable" after the collision – it is transferred to the environment.

$$\Delta S = \frac{Q}{T} = \frac{2\left(\tfrac{1}{2}mv_i^2\right)}{T} = \frac{\left(1.1\times10^3\,\text{kg}\right)\left[\left(95\,\text{km/h}\right)\left(\frac{1\,\text{m/s}}{3.6\,\text{km/h}}\right)\right]^2}{(20+273)\,\text{K}} = \boxed{2.6\times10^3\,\text{J/K}}$$

57. (a)   The equilibrium temperature is found using calorimetry, from chapter 14. The heat lost by the water is equal to the heat gained by the aluminum.

$$m_{H_2O}c_{H_2O}\left(T_{iH_2O}-T_f\right) = m_{Al}c_{Al}\left(T_f-T_{iAl}\right) \quad\rightarrow$$

$$T_f = \frac{m_{Al}c_{Al}T_{iAl} + m_{H_2O}c_{H_2O}T_{iH_2O}}{m_{Al}c_{Al} + m_{H_2O}c_{H_2O}}$$

$$= \frac{\left(0.12\,\text{kg}\right)\left(900\,\text{J/kg}\cdot\text{C}^\circ\right)\left(15^\circ\text{C}\right)+\left(0.14\,\text{kg}\right)\left(4186\,\text{J/kg}\cdot\text{C}^\circ\right)\left(50^\circ\text{C}\right)}{\left(0.12\,\text{kg}\right)\left(900\,\text{J/kg}\cdot\text{C}^\circ\right)+\left(0.14\,\text{kg}\right)\left(4186\,\text{J/kg}\cdot\text{C}^\circ\right)} = 44.55^\circ\text{C} \approx \boxed{45^\circ\text{C}}$$

(b)   The amount of heat lost by the aluminum, and gained by the water, is

$$Q = m_{H_2O}c_{H_2O}\left(T_{iH_2O}-T_f\right) = \left(0.14\,\text{kg}\right)\left(4186\,\text{J/kg}\cdot\text{C}^\circ\right)\left(50^\circ\text{C}-44.55^\circ\text{C}\right) = 3.194\times10^3\,\text{J}$$

In calculating the entropy change, we need to use estimates for the temperatures of the water and the aluminum since their temperatures are not constant. We will use their average temperatures.

$$T_{H_2O\,avg} = \left(50°C + 44.55°C\right)/2 = 47.26°C \quad T_{Al\,avg} = \left(15°C + 44.55°C\right)/2 = 29.78°C$$

$$\Delta S = \Delta S_{Al} + \Delta S_{H_2O} = -\frac{Q}{T_{H_2O\,avg}} + \frac{Q}{T_{Al\,avg}} = \left(3.194\times10^3\,J\right)\left(\frac{1}{(29.78+273)\,K} - \frac{1}{(47.26+273)\,K}\right)$$

$$= 0.5758\,J/K \approx \boxed{0.58\,J/K}$$

58. The COP for an ideal heat pump is given by Eq. 15-7.

(a) $\text{COP} = \dfrac{Q_H}{W} = \dfrac{Q_H}{Q_H - Q_L} = \dfrac{T_H}{T_H - T_L} = \dfrac{(24+273)\,K}{18\,K} = 16.5 \approx \boxed{17}$

(b) $\text{COP} = \dfrac{Q_H}{W} \rightarrow Q_H = (W/t)(t)(\text{COP}) = (1200\,W)(3600\,s)(16.5) = 7.128\times10^7\,J \approx \boxed{7.1\times10^7\,J}$

59. The efficiency is given by $e = W/Q_H = \dfrac{W/t}{Q_H/t}$, and so the input power and the useful power are needed.

$$W/t = (25\,hp)(746\,W/hp) = 1.9\times10^4\,J/s$$

$$Q_H/t = \left(\frac{3.0\times10^4\,kcal}{1\,gal}\right)\left(\frac{1\,gal}{41\,km}\right)\left(\frac{90\,km}{1\,h}\right)\left(\frac{4186\,J}{1\,kcal}\right)\left(\frac{1\,h}{3600\,s}\right) = 7.7\times10^4\,J/s$$

$$e = \frac{W/t}{Q_H/t} = \frac{1.9\times10^4\,J/s}{7.7\times10^4\,J/s} = 0.24 = \boxed{24\%}$$

60. Find the original intake temperature T_{H1} from the original Carnot efficiency, and then recalculate the intake temperature for the new Carnot efficiency, T_{H2}, using the same exhaust temperature.

$$e_1 = 1 - \frac{T_L}{T_{H1}} \rightarrow T_{H1} = \frac{T_L}{1-e_1} \quad e_2 = 1 - \frac{T_L}{T_{H2}} \rightarrow T_{H2} = \frac{T_L}{1-e_2}$$

$$T_{H2} - T_{H1} = T_L\left(\frac{1}{1-e_2} - \frac{1}{1-e_2}\right) = (273\,K + 20\,K)\left(\frac{1}{0.60} - \frac{1}{0.70}\right) = \boxed{70\,K}$$

61. Note that there is NO work done as the gas goes from state A to state B or state D to state C, because there is no volume change. In general, the work done can be found from the "area" under the PV curve representing the process under consideration.

(a) $W_{ADC} = \boxed{P_A\left(V_C - V_A\right)}$

(b) $W_{ABC} = \boxed{P_C\left(V_C - V_A\right)}$

(c) $W_{AC} = \boxed{\tfrac{1}{2}\left(P_C + P_A\right)\left(V_C - V_A\right)}$

62. (*a*)   The exhaust heating rate is found from the delivered power and the efficiency. Use the output energy with the relationship $Q = mc\Delta T = \rho V c\Delta T$ to calculate the volume of air that is heated.

$$e = W/Q_H = W/(Q_L + W) \quad \rightarrow \quad Q_L = W(1/e - 1) \quad \rightarrow$$

$$Q_L/t = W/t(1/e - 1) = (8.5 \times 10^8 \text{ W})(1/0.33 - 1) = 1.726 \times 10^9 \text{ W}$$

$$Q_L = mc\Delta T \quad \rightarrow \quad Q_L/t = \frac{mc\Delta T}{t} = \frac{\rho V c\Delta T}{t} \quad \rightarrow \quad V/t = \frac{(Q_L/t)}{\rho c\Delta T}$$

The change in air temperature is $7.0\text{C}°$. The heated air is at a constant pressure of 1 atm.

$$V/t = \frac{(Q_L/t)t}{\rho c\Delta T} = \frac{(1.726 \times 10^9 \text{ W})(8.64 \times 10^4 \text{ s/day})}{(1.2 \text{ kg/m}^3)(1.0 \times 10^3 \text{ J/kg} \cdot \text{C}°)(7.0\text{C}°)}$$

$$= 1.775 \times 10^{10} \text{ m}^3/\text{day} \left(\frac{10^{-9}\text{km}^3}{1 \text{ m}^3} \right) \approx \boxed{18 \text{ km}^3/\text{day}}$$

(*b*)   If the air is 200 m thick, find the area by dividing the volume by the thickness.

$$A = \frac{\text{Volume}}{\text{thickness}} = \frac{18 \text{ km}^3}{0.2 \text{ km}} = \boxed{90 \text{ km}^2}$$

This would be a square of approximately 6 miles to a side. Thus the local climate for a few miles around the power plant might be heated significantly.

63. (*a*)   The exhaust heating rate can be found from the delivered power P and the Carnot efficiency. Then use the relationship between energy and temperature change, $Q = mc\Delta T$, to calculate the temperature change of the cooling water.

$$e = 1 - \frac{T_L}{T_H} = \frac{W}{Q_H} = \frac{W}{Q_L + W} \quad \rightarrow \quad Q_L = W\frac{T_L}{T_H - T_L} \quad \rightarrow \quad Q_L/t = W/t\frac{T_L}{T_H - T_L} = P\frac{T_L}{T_H - T_L}$$

$$Q_L = mc\Delta T \quad \rightarrow \quad Q_L/t = \frac{m}{t}c\Delta T = \rho\frac{V}{t}c\Delta T$$

Equate the two expressions for Q_L/t, and solve for ΔT.

$$P\frac{T_L}{T_H - T_L} = \rho\frac{V}{t}c\Delta T \quad \rightarrow \quad \Delta T = \frac{P}{\rho\frac{V}{t}c}\frac{T_L}{T_H - T_L}$$

$$= \frac{9.8 \times 10^8 \text{ W}}{(1.0 \times 10^3 \text{ kg/m}^3)(37 \text{ m}^3/\text{s})(4186 \text{ J/kg} \cdot \text{C}°)}\frac{285 \text{ K}}{(625 \text{ K} - 285 \text{ K})} = 5.303 \text{ K} = \boxed{5.3\text{C}°}$$

(*b*)   The addition of heat per kilogram for the downstream water is $Q_L/t = c\Delta T$. We use the "average" temperature of the river water for the calculation: $T = T_0 + \frac{1}{2}\Delta T$. Now the entropy increase can be calculated.

$$\Delta S = \frac{\Delta Q}{T} = \frac{c\Delta T}{T_0 + \frac{1}{2}\Delta T} = \frac{(4186 \text{ J/kg} \cdot \text{C}°)(5.303 \text{ K})}{\left[285 + \frac{1}{2}(5.303)\right]\text{K}} = \boxed{77 \text{ J/kg} \cdot \text{K}}$$

64. (*a*)   Calculate the Carnot efficiency by $e = 1 - T_L/T_H$ and compare it to the 15% actual efficiency.

$$e_{\text{Carnot}} = 1 - T_L/T_H = 1 - (85 + 273) \text{ K}/(495 + 273) \text{ K} = 0.534 = 53.4\%$$

Thus the engine's relative efficiency is $e_{\text{actual}}/e_{\text{Carnot}} = 0.15/0.534 = 0.281 = \boxed{28\%}$

(b) Take the stated 100 hp as the useful power obtained from the engine. Use the efficiency to calculate the exhaust heat.

$$P = \frac{W}{t} = (100\,\text{hp})\left(\frac{746\,\text{W}}{1\,\text{hp}}\right) = \boxed{7.46 \times 10^4\,\text{W}}$$

$$e = \frac{W}{Q_H} = \frac{W}{Q_L + W} \rightarrow$$

$$Q_L = W\left(\frac{1}{e} - 1\right) = Pt\left(\frac{1}{e} - 1\right) = (7.46 \times 10^4\,\text{J/s})(1\,\text{h})\left(\frac{3600\,\text{s}}{1\,\text{h}}\right)\left(\frac{1}{0.15} - 1\right)$$

$$= \boxed{1.5 \times 10^9\,\text{J}} = (1.5 \times 10^9\,\text{J})\left(\frac{1\,\text{kcal}}{4186\,\text{J}}\right) = \boxed{3.6 \times 10^5\,\text{kcal}}$$

65. The net force on the piston must be 0, and so the weight of the piston must be equal to the net force exerted by the gas pressures on both sides of the piston. See the free-body diagram.

$$\sum F = F_{\substack{\text{inside}\\\text{air}}} - F_{\substack{\text{outside}\\\text{air}}} - mg = 0 = P_{\text{inside}}A - P_{\text{outside}}A - mg = 0$$

$$P_{\text{inside}} = P_{\text{outside}} + \frac{mg}{A} = (1.0\,\text{atm})\left(1.01 \times 10^5\,\frac{\text{Pa}}{\text{atm}}\right) + \frac{(0.10\,\text{kg})(9.8\,\text{m/s}^2)}{0.080\,\text{m}^2}$$

$$= 1.0101 \times 10^5\,\text{Pa} \approx 1\,\text{atm}$$

We see that the weight of the piston is negligible compared to the pressure forces.

When the gas is heated, we assume that the inside pressure does not change. Since the weight of the piston does not change, and the outside air pressure does not change, the inside air pressure cannot change. Thus the expansion is at a constant pressure, and so the work done can be calculated. Use this with the first law of thermodynamics to find the heat required for the process.

$$U = \tfrac{3}{2}nRT = \tfrac{3}{2}PV \rightarrow \Delta U = \tfrac{3}{2}P\Delta V = Q - W$$

$$Q = \Delta U + W = \tfrac{3}{2}P\Delta V + P\Delta V = \tfrac{5}{2}P\Delta V = \tfrac{5}{2}PA\Delta y = 2.5(1.0 \times 10^5\,\text{Pa})(0.080\,\text{m}^2)(1.0 \times 10^{-2}\,\text{m})$$

$$= \boxed{200\,\text{J}}$$

66. (a) Multiply the power times the time times the mass per Joule relationship for the fat.

$$(95\,\text{J/s})(3600\,\text{s/h})(24\,\text{h/d})(1.0\,\text{kg fat}/3.7 \times 10^7\,\text{J}) = 0.2218\,\text{kg/d} \approx \boxed{0.22\,\text{kg/d}}$$

(b) $1.0\,\text{kg}(1\text{d}/0.2218\,\text{kg}) = \boxed{4.5\,\text{d}}$

67. The radiant energy is the heat to be removed at the low temperature. It can be related to the work necessary through the efficiency.

$$e = 1 - \frac{T_L}{T_H} = \frac{W}{Q_H} = \frac{W}{W + Q_L} \rightarrow W = Q_L\left(\frac{T_H}{T_L} - 1\right) \rightarrow W/t = Q_L/t\left(\frac{T_H}{T_L} - 1\right)$$

$$(W/t)_{5300} = (5300\,\text{W})\left(\frac{T_H}{T_L} - 1\right) \quad (W/t)_{500} = (500\,\text{W})\left(\frac{T_H}{T_L} - 1\right)$$

$$\left(W/t\right)_{\text{savings}} = \left(W/t\right)_{5300} - \left(W/t\right)_{500} = \left(5300\ \text{W} - 500\ \text{W}\right)\left(\frac{\left(273+32\right)\text{K}}{\left(273+21\right)\text{K}} - 1\right) = \boxed{180\ \text{W}}$$

68. To find the mass of water removed, find the energy that is removed from the low temperature reservoir from the work input and the Carnot efficiency. Then use the latent heat of vaporization to determine the mass of water from the energy required for the condensation. Note that the heat of vaporization used is that given in chapter 14 for evaporation at 20°C.

$$e = 1 - \frac{T_{\text{L}}}{T_{\text{H}}} = \frac{W}{Q_{\text{H}}} = \frac{W}{W + Q_{\text{L}}} \quad \rightarrow \quad Q_{\text{L}} = W\frac{T_{\text{L}}}{\left(T_{\text{H}} - T_{\text{L}}\right)} = mL_{\text{vapor}}$$

$$m = \frac{W}{L_{\text{vapor}}}\frac{T_{\text{L}}}{\left(T_{\text{H}} - T_{\text{L}}\right)} = \frac{\left(600\ \text{W}\right)\left(3600\ \text{s}\right)}{\left(2.45 \times 10^{6}\ \text{J/kg}\right)}\frac{\left(273+8\right)\text{K}}{17\ \text{K}} = \boxed{14.6\ \text{kg}}$$

PHYSICS

Principles with Applications
6th edition

Douglas C. Giancoli

**End of Chapter
Questions and Problems
6th Edition – 5th Edition
Comparison/Correlation Grid**

Douglas C. Giancoli *Physics: Principles with Applications, 6th edition*
End of Chapter Questions and Problems Comparison Grid

N = New to the 6th edition
M = 5th edition Question/Problem modified for the 6th edition

CHAPTER 1: Introduction, Measurement, Estimating

Questions		Problems		Problems	
6/e	5/e	6/e	5/e	6/e	5/e
1	1,2	1	1M	37N	
2	3	2	4M	38N	
3N		3	3M	39N	
4	5M	4	2M	40	36
5N		5	6M	41	37
6	8	6	5M	42	38
7	9	7	7M	43	39
8N		8	9M	44	40M
9N		9	8M	45	41
10	6	10	10M	46	43M
		11	11M	47	44M
		12	13M	48N	
		13	12M	49N	
		14	15M	50N	
		15	16	51N	
		16N		52	32
		17N		53N	
		18	17	54N	
		19	18M		
		20	19		
		21	20		
		22	21		
		23	22M		
		24	23M		
		25N			
		26	24M		
		27	30M		
		28N			
		29	27		
		30	25		
		31	31		
		32N			
		33N			
		34N			
		35	35		
		36	33		

Douglas C. Giancoli *Physics: Principles with Applications, 6ᵗʰ edition*
End of Chapter Questions and Problems Comparison Grid

N = New to the 6ᵗʰ edition
M = 5ᵗʰ edition Question/Problem modified for the 6ᵗʰ edition

CHAPTER 2: Describing Motion: Kinematics in One Dimension

Questions		Problems		Problems		Problems	
6/e	5/e	6/e	5/e	6/e	5/e	6/e	5/e
1	1	1	1M	37	38M	73N	
2	3	2	2	38	39	74N	
3	4	3	3	39	41M	75N	
4	5	4	4M	40	42	76N	
5	6	5N		41	43	77	67M
6	7	6N		42	44M	78	65M
7	9	7	5M	43	45	79N	
8	10	8	6	44	46M	80N	
9	11	9	7	45	47M	81N	
10	13	10	8M	46	48	82N	
11	14	11	9	47	49M	83N	
12N		12N		48	50M	84N	
13	15	13	10M	49	53	85N	
14	16	14	11M	50	51		
15N		15	12	51	52		
16N		16	13	52	54		
17N		17	15	53	55		
18	17	18	14	54	56		
19N		19N		55	57		
20N		20	17	56	59		
21	18	21	19M	57	60		
22	19	22	20M	58	61		
		23	21M	59	62		
		24	22	60	73M		
		25	23M	61	64M		
		26	24M	62N			
		27	26M	63	66M		
		28	27M	64N			
		29	28	65	68M		
		30	71	66	69		
		31	31	67	70		
		32	30M	68N			
		33	34M	69	72		
		34	33M	70	63M		
		35	35	71N			
		36	36M	72N			

Douglas C. Giancoli *Physics: Principles with Applications, 6th edition*
End of Chapter Questions and Problems Comparison Grid

N = New to the 6th edition
M = 5th edition Question/Problem modified for the 6th edition

CHAPTER 3: Kinematics in Two Dimensions; Vectors

Questions		Problems		Problems		Problems	
6/e	5/e	6/e	5/e	6/e	5/e	6/e	5/e
1	10M	1	1M	37	41M	73N	
2N		2	2M	38	42	74N	
3	3	3N		39	43	75N	
4	4	4	4M	40	44M		
5	5	5	5M	41	45M		
6	6	6	10M	42	46M		
7	7	7	6M	43	47		
8	8	8	8M	44	48		
9N		9	9M	45	49M		
10	13	10	11M	46	50M		
11N		11	12M	47	51M		
12N		12	13M	48	52M		
13	14	13	14M	49	53M		
14N		14	15M	50	56M		
15N		15	17M	51	57M		
16	15	16	18M	52	55M		
17N		17	19M	53	58		
18N		18	20M	54	60M		
19N		19	21M	55	61M		
20N		20	22M	56	62		
		21	24M	57	63		
		22	26M	58	64		
		23	27	59	65		
		24	30M	60	66		
		25	29	61	67M		
		26	32M	62	68M		
		27	31M	63	69		
		28	25	64	70		
		29	23M	65	71M		
		30	35M	66	72		
		31	36M	67	73		
		32	28M	68	16M		
		33N		69N			
		34	37	70N			
		35	38	71N			
		36	40M	72N			

381

Douglas C. Giancoli *Physics: Principles with Applications, 6th edition*
End of Chapter Questions and Problems Comparison Grid

N = New to the 6th edition
M = 5th edition Question/Problem modified for the 6th edition

CHAPTER 4: Dynamics: Newton's Laws of Motion

Questions		Problems		Problems		Problems	
6/e	5/e	6/e	5/e	6/e	5/e	6/e	5/e
1	1	1	1M	37	39M	73	76M
2N		2	2M	38N		74	77
3	3	3	4M	39N		75	79
4	5M	4	5M	40N		76	81M
5	6	5	6	41	56M	77	57M
6N		6	7M	42N		78	80
7	8	7	8M	43	40	79N	
8	9	8	9M	44	42M	80N	
9	10	9	10M	45N		81	31M
10	11	10	12	46	43	82N	
11N		11N		47	44	83N	
12N		12	13M	48	45M	84N	
13N		13	14M	49	47	85	71M
14	12	14	15	50	48	86	72M
15	16	15	16	51	49	87	73
16	14	16	17M	52	52M	88	74M
17	15	17	18M	53	53	89N	
18	13	18	21M	54	55M		
19	21	19	23M	55	56		
20	20	20	25	56N			
21N		21	26	57N			
		22	24M	58	46M		
		23N		59	50M		
		24	27	60	75M		
		25	30M	61	60M		
		26	28M	62N			
		27N		63	61		
		28	33M	64	62M,63M		
		29	32M	65	64		
		30	29M	66	65		
		31N		67	66M		
		32	34M	68	67		
		33	35	69	68M		
		34	36	70	69M		
		35	37M	71	70M		
		36	38	72N			

Douglas C. Giancoli *Physics: Principles with Applications, 6th edition*
End of Chapter Questions and Problems Comparison Grid

N = New to the 6th edition
M = 5th edition Question/Problem modified for the 6th edition

CHAPTER 5: Circular Motion; Gravitation

Questions		Problems		Problems		Problems	
6/e	5/e	6/e	5/e	6/e	5/e	6/e	5/e
1	1M	1	2M	37	33	73	70M
2	2	2	1M	38	30M	74	71
3	3	3	3	39	35M	75	72M
4	4	4	4M	40	36M	76	73M
5	5	5N		41	37	77	74
6	14	6N		42	38	78	75
7	15	7	8M	43	39	79	76M
8N		8	6M	44N		80	77
9N		9	7M	45	41M	81	78
10N		10	9	46	42	82N	
11	6	11	10M	47N		83N	
12	7	12	11	48	43	84N	
13	13	13	12M	49	45M	85N	
14N		14	13M	50	46M	86N	
15N		15	14	51	47M	87N	
16N		16N		52	49M	88	56
17N		17N		53	44M	89N	
18N		18	18M	54	40	90N	
19	9	19	5	55	50M	91N	
20	16	20	19M	56	51	92N	
21	12	21	20M	57	52	93N	
22	17	22	17M	58	53	94N	
23	18M	23	16	59	55		
24N		24	21	60N			
		25	22M	61	57		
		26	23M	62	54		
		27	24M	63	58		
		28	25M	64	59		
		29	29M	65	61		
		30	26	66	63M		
		31	27M	67	62		
		32	28M	68	65M		
		33N		69	66		
		34	34	70	67		
		35	32	71	69M		
		36	31	72	68M		

Douglas C. Giancoli *Physics: Principles with Applications, 6th edition*
End of Chapter Questions and Problems Comparison Grid

N = New to the 6th edition
M = 5th edition Question/Problem modified for the 6th edition

CHAPTER 6: Work and Energy

Questions		Problems		Problems		Problems	
6/e	5/e	6/e	5/e	6/e	5/e	6/e	5/e
1	1M	1N		37	39M	73	73M
2	2	2	1M	38	41	74	74
3	3	3	2M	39	43M	75	79
4	4	4	3M	40	44	76	71M
5	5	5N		41	45M	77	76
6	6	6	9M	42	42M	78	77M
7	7	7N		43	40M	79	80M
8	9	8	10M	44N		80	69
9	10	9	11	45	46	81	81M
10	12	10	7M	46	48M	82	83
11	13	11	12	47	49M	83N	
12	14	12	13	48	50M	84N	
13	15	13	14	49	51M	85	84M
14	16	14	15M	50N		86	85M
15	17	15	17	51N		87	86M
16	18	16	18	52	52M	88N	
17	19	17	19	53	53M	89N	
18	20	18	20M	54	54	90N	
19	22	19	22M	55	55M	91N	
20	23	20	23M	56	56M	92N	
21	24	21	24	57	57M	93N	
22	25	22	25	58	58M	94N	
23	26	23	26	59	59M		
24	27	24N		60N			
25	28	25	28M	61	60M		
		26	29	62	61M		
		27	30M	63	62M		
		28	31	64	63		
		29N		65	64M		
		30	32	66	65M		
		31	33M	67	66M		
		32N		68	67M		
		33	35M	69	68M		
		34	36M	70N			
		35	37M	71	70		
		36	38	72	72M		

Douglas C. Giancoli *Physics: Principles with Applications, 6th edition*
End of Chapter Questions and Problems Comparison Grid

N = New to the 6th edition
M = 5th edition Question/Problem modified for the 6th edition

CHAPTER 7: Linear Momentum

Questions		Problems		Problems		Problems	
6/e	**5/e**	**6/e**	**5/e**	**6/e**	**5/e**	**6/e**	**5/e**
1	1	1	1M	37	34	73	71
2	2	2N		38	35	74	72
3	3	3	15M	39	36M	75	73
4	4	4	2M	40	37	76N	
5	5	5	3M	41	38	77N	
6	6	6	4	42	39	78	76M
7	7	7	5M	43	41	79	74
8	8M	8	6M	44	44	80	75
9	10M	9	61	45N		81	77
10	11M	10	62M	46N			
11N		11	10	47	46		
12	13	12	11M	48	47		
13N		13	12	49	49M		
14	14	14	13	50	48		
15	15	15	16M	51	50		
16	16	16N		52	51		
17	17	17	17	53	52		
18	20	18N		54	53		
19	19	19	18M	55	54		
		20	19	56	55		
		21	20	57	56		
		22	21M	58	57M		
		23	22	59	58		
		24	23	60	59		
		25	24M	61	60		
		26	25M	62	63M		
		27	26	63	64		
		28	27	64	65		
		29	28	65	66M		
		30	29	66N			
		31N		67	68		
		32	30M	68	69M		
		33	31	69	67M		
		34	32	70N			
		35	33M	71N			
		36N		72	70M		

Douglas C. Giancoli *Physics: Principles with Applications, 6th edition*
End of Chapter Questions and Problems Comparison Grid

N = New to the 6th edition
M = 5th edition Question/Problem modified for the 6th edition

CHAPTER 8: Rotational Motion

Questions		Problems		Problems		Problems	
6/e	5/e	6/e	5/e	6/e	5/e	6/e	5/e
1	2	1	1	37	43M	73	76
2	3	2	3	38	44M	74	77M
3N		3	5M	39	45M	75	78M
4	5	4	10M	40	46	76N	
5	6M	5	11M	41	48	77	79M
6	7	6	12M	42	49	78	80
7	9	7	6M	43	51M	79	81
8	10	8N		44N		80	82
9	11	9	14	45	50M	81N	
10	12	10	15	46	52	82N	
11	14	11	16	47	53M	83N	
12	15	12	17M	48	54M	84	83
13	16	13	18	49	55	85	84
14	18	14	19M	50	56M	86N	
15	19	15	21	51	57		
16	20	16	22M	52N			
17N		17	23	53	58		
18N		18	24M	54	59		
19N		19N		55	60		
20	21	20	26	56N			
21	22	21	27M	57	62		
22	24	22	29M	58	63		
23	25	23	30M	59	64		
24	27	24	31M	60	65M		
		25N		61	66M		
		26	33M	62	68		
		27	34M	63	69		
		28	35	64	61		
		29	38M	65	67		
		30N		66	71		
		31	36	67	70		
		32	37	68	72		
		33	39M	69	73		
		34	40	70	74		
		35	41	71N			
		36	42M	72	75		

Douglas C. Giancoli *Physics: Principles with Applications, 6th edition*
End of Chapter Questions and Problems Comparison Grid

N = New to the 6th edition
M = 5th edition Question/Problem modified for the 6th edition

CHAPTER 9: Static Equilibrium; Elasticity and Fracture

Questions		Problems		Problems		Problems	
6/e	5/e	6/e	5/e	6/e	5/e	6/e	5/e
1	1	1	1M	37	43	73N	
2	2	2	3M	38	44M	74N	
3	3	3	6	39	45M	75N	
4	4	4	4M	40	46M	76N	
5	8	5	5M	41	47M	77	69
6	7	6	19M, 20M	42	49	78	70M
7	6	7	8M	43	50	79N	
8	10	8	7M	44	51	80	78
9N		9	10M	45	52		
10	9	10	15	46	53		
11	11	11	12M	47	54		
12	13	12	13M	48	55		
13	14	13N		49	56		
14	15	14	16	50	57M		
15	16	15	22M	51	58		
16	12	16	18	52	59		
17N		17N		53	60		
18	17	18	23M	54	61		
19	18M	19	25M	55	62		
		20	26M	56	63M		
		21	27M	57	64M		
		22N		58	66M		
		23	30M	59	67		
		24	24M	60	73M		
		25	17	61N			
		26	28	62	65		
		27	31M	63	68		
		28	32M	64	71		
		29	33	65N			
		30	34M	66N			
		31	35	67	74		
		32	36M, 38M	68	72M		
		33	37	69	80		
		34	39M	70	82		
		35	40M	71N			
		36	42	72	81M		

Douglas C. Giancoli *Physics: Principles with Applications, 6th edition*
End of Chapter Questions and Problems Comparison Grid

N = New to the 6th edition
M = 5th edition Question/Problem modified for the 6th edition

CHAPTER 10: Fluids

Questions 6/e	Questions 5/e	Problems 6/e	Problems 5/e	Problems 6/e	Problems 5/e	Problems 6/e	Problems 5/e
1	1	1	1	37N		73	69
2	2	2	2M	38N		74	70
3	3	3	3M	39	36M	75	71
4	4	4	4M	40	37M	76	73
5	6	5	5	41N		77N	
6	17	6	6	42	38M	78	74M
7	8M	7	8M	43	39M	79	75
8	9	8	7	44	40M	80	76M
9N		9	9M	45	41	81	72M
10N		10	10M	46	43M	82	78
11	7	11	11M	47	44	83N	
12	10	12	12M	48N		84	80M
13	12	13	13	49N		85N	
14	15	14	14M	50	45	86N	
15	14	15	15M	51	46	87	48
16	16M	16	16	52N		88N	
17	19	17	17M	53	47		
18	20	18	18M	54	49M		
19	18	19N		55	51		
20	21	20	19M	56	50		
21	23	21	20	57	52M		
22	25	22	22M	58	54		
23	27	23	23	59	55		
24N		24N		60	56		
		25	24M	61	57M		
		26	25	62	58M		
		27	26M	63	61M		
		28N		64	62		
		29N		65	63		
		30N		66	65M		
		31	27	67	64M		
		32	29M	68N			
		33	30	69	66		
		34	32M	70	67M		
		35	34	71N			
		36	35M	72N			

Douglas C. Giancoli *Physics: Principles with Applications, 6th edition*
End of Chapter Questions and Problems Comparison Grid

N = New to the 6th edition
M = 5th edition Question/Problem modified for the 6th edition

CHAPTER 11: Vibrations and Waves

Questions		Problems		Problems		Problems	
6/e	5/e	6/e	5/e	6/e	5/e	6/e	5/e
1	1	1	3M	37	35M	73	74M
2	2	2	2M	38	36	74N	
3	3M	3	1M	39	37	75	72
4	4M	4	4M	40	38	76	73M
5	5	5	8	41	39M	77	75
6N		6	5	42N		78	77
7	8	7	6M	43	41	79N	
8	9	8	10M	44	42	80	78M
9	10	9	9M	45	43	81N	
10	12	10	23M	46	44M	82N	
11	13	11	16M	47	45M	83N	
12	15	12	12M	48	47	84N	
13	16	13N		49	48	85N	
14	17	14	13M	50	49	86N	
15	18	15	15	51	50	87	69M
16	19	16	17M	52	51	88	71
17	20	17	23M	53	52		
18	21M	18	22M	54	53		
19	22	19	20M	55	55		
20	25	20	11	56	56		
21	26	21	18M	57	57M		
22	23	22N		58	58		
		23	14M	59	60M		
		24	19M	60	61M		
		25	27M	61N			
		26	21M	62	63M		
		27	26M	63	64		
		28	28M	64N			
		29N		65	65M		
		30N		66N			
		31	30M	67N			
		32	31M	68	70M		
		33N		69	68M		
		34	32	70	80M		
		35	33M	71	76M		
		36	34M	72	67		

Douglas C. Giancoli *Physics: Principles with Applications, 6th edition*
End of Chapter Questions and Problems Comparison Grid

N = New to the 6th edition
M = 5th edition Question/Problem modified for the 6th edition

CHAPTER 12: Sound

Questions		Problems		Problems		Problems	
6/e	5/e	6/e	5/e	6/e	5/e	6/e	5/e
1	1	1	1M	37	39M	73	76
2	2	2	2M	38	40M	74	72
3	3	3	3	39	42	75	73M
4	4	4	6	40	43	76	75
5	5	5	68	41	44	77	79M
6	6	6	5M	42	45	78	33
7	10	7N		43	47M	79	83M
8	9	8	9	44N		80	55M
9	12	9	10	45N		81	78M
10N		10N		46	48M	82	70
11	13	11	12	47	46	83N	
12	14	12	13M	48	49M	84	77M
13	15	13	14	49	51M	85	80
14N		14	15	50N		86	86M
15N		15	16M	51	56M	87	85
16	18	16	17M	52	54	88N	
17	17	17	11	53	52	89N	
		18	18	54N		90N	
		19	20	55	53	91N	
		20	21M	56	57M	92N	
		21	23	57	58M	93	60M
		22	24	58	82M		
		23	25	59	61		
		24	26	60	63		
		25	31	61	64		
		26	29M	62	65M		
		27	30	63	62		
		28N		64	66		
		29	27M	65N			
		30	28M	66	67		
		31	34	67N			
		32	32	68	69		
		33	35M	69N			
		34	36	70N			
		35	37M	71	74M		
		36	38	72N			

N = New to the 6th edition
M = 5th edition Question/Problem modified for the 6th edition

CHAPTER 13: Temperature and Kinetic Theory

Questions 6/e	Questions 5/e	Problems 6/e	Problems 5/e	Problems 6/e	Problems 5/e	Problems 6/e	Problems 5/e
1	1	1	2	37N		73	74
2	2	2	1M	38	37	74	75
3	3	3	3	39	38M	75	76M
4N		4	5	40	40	76	78M
5	6M	5	4	41	42	77	80
6	7M	6	6M	42	43	78	79
7	9M	7	9M	43	44	79	81
8	5M	8	10M	44	45M	80	83
9	8	9N		45	46	81	84M
10	10M	10	12	46	48M	82	85
11	13	11N		47	47	83	87
12	12	12	17M	48N		84	88
13	14	13	15	49	50M	85N	
14	15M	14	16M	50	49	86	92
15	16	15	18M	51	51M	87N	
16	18	16	19	52	52	88	93M
17N		17	20	53	55M	89N	
18	19	18	13	54	53	90N	
19	20	19	21	55N		91N	
20	21	20	22	56N		92N	
21	22M	21	89M	57	90M	93N	
22	25	22	23M	58	54	94N	
23	26	23	25	59	55	95N	
24	27	24	26M	60	56	96N	
25N		25	27M	61	57	97	14M
26N		26	28M	62	59	98	86
27N		27	29	63	60	99	66
		28	30	64	61		
		29	31M	65	62M		
		30N		66	63		
		31	32	67N			
		32	33	68	64		
		33	34	69	65		
		34	35M	70	68		
		35	36M	71	71		
		36N		72	72		

Douglas C. Giancoli *Physics: Principles with Applications, 6th edition*
End of Chapter Questions and Problems Comparison Grid

N = New to the 6th edition
M = 5th edition Question/Problem modified for the 6th edition

CHAPTER 14: Heat

Questions		Problems		Problems	
6/e	5/e	6/e	5/e	6/e	5/e
1	1	1	1M	37	37
2	2	2	3	38	38
3	3	3	4	39	39
4	4	4	5	40	40M
5	5	5	7M	41	41
6	6	6	6M	42	43M
7	7	7	8M	43	44
8	8	8	10M	44	45M
9	9	9	9M	45N	
10	10	10	11	46	47M
11	11	11	14M	47N	
12	12	12	16M	48	48
13	13	13	18M	49	49
14N		14	20M	50	50
15	15	15	21M	51	51
16	16	16N		52N	
17	17	17	19M	53	54M
18	18	18	15M	54	55M
19	19	19N		55	56
20	20	20	52M	56	58
21N		21	22	57	59
22	23	22	23	58	60
23	24	23N		59	61
24	22	24	24	60	62
25N		25	25M	61N	
26	26	26	26M	62N	
27	27	27	27	63N	
28	21	28	28	64N	
29N		29	29	65N	
30N		30N		66N	
		31	30		
		32	31		
		33N			
		34	32		
		35	33		
		36	34		